NEW TENDENCIES IN ART

ALDO PELLEGRINI

NEW TENDENCIES IN ART

TRANSLATED BY ROBIN CARSON

Book design by Paola Mazzetti

CROWN PUBLISHERS, INC. / NEW YORK

Contents

Contents

Introduction

The directions of modern art

What, to begin with, is art? Charles Morris has said, with exemplary lucidity, that « art is the language of the communication of values. » This definition is fundamental: there can be no art if in the first place there does not exist in the work a value, and if in the second place the value is not communicable. Yet « value » and « communication » in our dramatic age are not what they have been in the past; they have changed, in art as well as in other human activities, as radically as have approaches to reality.

Science, for instance, has opened innumerable new paths for the artist. Nature herself has been amplified through the world of the microscope. Anatomical tissues (especially the microscopic view of the nervous system), the microbe world, and the structure of metals and alloys revealed by metallography have brought to light new aspects of reality. Electronic photography reproduces ultramicroscopic states of matter that bring to mind certain tachist visions. Modern life itself offers hitherto unperceived landscapes: those seen from an airplane or on space flights or observed at great speed. Many of these aspects have without doubt inspired certain pictorial structures that are considered abstract.

And parallel with the prodigious advance of science and technology, art in this century has pursued an accelerated rhythm of exploration. The artist, by investigating new materials, has penetrated the secrets of the very elements that form the basis of his art. For color he sometimes uses the new industrial paints, latex and acrylic, which not only offer new qualities and new shades of color but also induce new forms through a different view of painting. Such new materials alone represent for the artist a revolution no less significant than the introduction of oil in painting during the Renaissance. But the modern artist also investigates the movement of form, the most subtle visual and psychological effects of color, the nature of large spaces or masses, and the visual idiosyncrasies of matter.

Furthermore, the plastic arts have been subject to the impact of the evolution of the concept of reality in science: the old concept of reality being matter is replaced by the concept of reality being energy, and the artist seeks each time to express further this reality of energy.

The artist, like the scientist, is dedicated to the task of apprehending the ultimate reality, and this reality is not something that man receives passively from the outside; it is something that he acquires in his attempts to understand, to use, and to transform, and that ultimately he employs to express himself. It has always been thus, in the art of all times and in all cultures. For this reason art is mobile, in spite of those who want it to remain static.

The development of abstract art

During World War II, the evolution of modern art suffered an apparent setback in that its outward signs were suspended. But surely the artists continued their interior development, for at the outset of the postwar period the art world witnessed, not a mere continuation of the situation before the war, but a definite change. The fundamental change was the enormous development of abstract art.

For the artists who resumed their work in this postwar era, and even more for those first starting out, there can be no doubt that the directions had been laid down in the first quarter of the century. Futurism, cubism, fauvism, and expressionism had created new conditions of expression on a foundation of rupture with the principle of imitation in art. This break was accentuated in dadaism, which swept away all artistic principles in existence up to that date, and unfurled the banner of anti-art. Symbols of this rupture with tradition are to be found in the figure of Marcel Duchamp's Gioconda with a moustache and in Francis Picabia's blotch of ink entitled *Immaculate Conception.* Surrealism signified an advance by proclaiming the supremacy of the subconscious and the absolute values of spontaneity, of the first impulse, and by denying all control by reason; but it also signaled a regression by its support of such academic painters as Salvador Dalí and René Magritte.

But even the years between the wars had witnessed a violent reaction against the anti-imitative principles of these schools and movements, in the form of a return to the certain and solid principles of the art of the past. In Germany this reaction took the name of « Die Neue Sachlichkeit » (The New Objectivity), and in Italy it centered around a movement called « Valori Plastici » (Plastic Values), a reaction that the German critic Franz Roh called « magic realism. » This critic furthermore proclaimed the definitive death of abstract art in a book of that title, published in 1924. The critics' total lack of a prophetic gift and their disorganization are shown by the fact that in the period after the Second World War Roh was converted into an enthusiastic defender of abstract art.

In any event, the period between the wars saw the acceptance of surrealism and of the artists who emerged from cubism, such as Braque, Picasso, and Léger, or from the fauves, such as Matisse, dedicated to the systematization of the plastic freedoms that had been won. But the real advance was proclaimed in the steady evolution of two great masters of abstract art – Kandinsky and Mondrian – who maintained their positions, the first in the Bauhaus in Germany (until its closing by the Nazis in 1933), the second in Paris. Around these two fundamental figures a quiet but growing movement, having its center in Paris, was created, first through the review *Cercle et Carré,* begun in 1930, and in the movement of concrete art, created in the same year by Theo Van Doesburg, and later by the « Abstraction-Création » association of Paris, which was founded in 1933 and existed until 1938. The activities of this association,

with its international character, bore fruit in the immediate postwar period.

At the outset of the Second World War an event came to pass that was to have wide repercussions and to awaken the new American painting, one of the crucial phenomena of the postwar period: the wave of artists and writers, thrown out by the Nazi invasion, who went to the United States. The two fundamental influences can be divided as follows: constructivism, stimulated by the arrival of Mondrian, but which already counted with the activity of Laszlo Moholy-Nagy and Josef Albers, who had fled from Germany with the closing of the Bauhaus; and surrealism, enriched by the presence, at first of André Breton, and later by artists of such importance as Max Ernst, André Masson, Matta, Yves Tanguy, and the influence of Wolfang Paalen from Mexico.

The emergence of new forms

Before every new transformation of direction there is talk of the decadence of art. But what obtains is not decadence but change, and change always indicates the vitality of art, because every style has within itself the germ of its own negation. And it is this negation that houses the change and the promise that art cannot die. This necessity for change has been implicitly enunciated by Heinrich Wölfflin in his *Principles of Art History,* when he refers to the « exhaustion of forms. »

The death of art has been spoken of since Hegel, and it was precisely in this period, with its romanticism, that an accelerated process of transformation was begun. In the plastic arts this transformation became a revolution with impressionism, which initiated the true modern period. Today the process of transformation proceeds in a constantly accelerated rhythm. Therefore the well-known art historian and theorist Georges Duthuit was able to say during an interview given in

1962, to *Arts* magazine, « Art as it was known in the past is finished. »

One of the fundamental characteristics of today's art is that it became a movement of international character. The reasons for this are obvious: gigantic and accelerated mass media of information and the speed of international communications. This internationalization of art is undeniable, notwithstanding the nearsightedness of those of every country who speak of the need for a national art.

In any event, the situation is intensely complicated by the diversification of tendencies, though in reality they all flow together toward two basic philosophies: one that considers art in relation to life, and the other that considers it in relation to intellect. These two demarcations of strength are not new; more correctly, they are as old as the world, and it could be said that to consider art as a manifestation of life will result in an art of expression, and to consider it as depending on intellect is to understand it as a formal art, or, to put it more clearly, purely visual, in which color, as well as form, enters.

The postwar period began with an astonishing upsurge of abstract art (a designation that roughly includes all painting renouncing representation), with a predominance of the geometric or formalist line, that is, with the triumph of calculation and reason. At the same time, expressive, antiformalist, and irrational tendencies made themselves felt, and soon were to be the dominant element, reducing to a minimum for a few years the geometric or pure formal tendency. But again the exhaustion was felt, and informalism gave way to two apparently opposite tendencies: on the one hand, neodadaism with its derivation, pop art, and on the other hand the currents of pure visuality, with the variations called « neoconstructivism, » « new abstraction, » « hard-edge, » « op art, » « new tendency, » and « programmed art. » Both currents oppose the academization of informalism which had evolved into an empty

formula of indeterminism - to achieve a colder expression, free from emotional content based on apparent reality that would permit a direct visual communication. Some sought, as Umbro Apollonio said in referring to programmed art, « the esthetic coefficient which can be obtained by technique. » Others, like the pop artists, sought to utilize familiar images of the mass media, reproduced without artifice, sometimes using such popular techniques as imitating the processes and colors of the billboards or employing mechanical reproduction techniques such as silk prints. Through a slight distortion of the image, by enlargement or serial reproduction, they gave a mythical quality to the object reproduced, well accessible to all and for the enjoyment of all. The two last currents, in spite of the apparent distance that separates them, strive for the same impersonality of art and for the elimination of the instinctive and the vital and all traces of the author's individuality. Art thus acquires characteristics of anonymity appropriate to mass consumption.

Two distinct attitudes are thus present in modern art. In one, the artist *expresses* himself; this is lyrical abstraction or abstract expressionism (called informalism), to which now is added the new trend of figural art, which is nothing other than a neoexpressionism. In the other the artist *constructs* a constructivist or purely visual tendency. In the first, the instinctual is indisputably charged with emotion and the individual is present.

In the second, the procedure is purely rational, emotion is excluded, the individual as a concrete personality is absent, and the result relies on the exclusively visual. Related to this last tendency (although with indisputable echoes of the first, by its content of humor) is a third one, which pretends to nothing more than « display. » To this last category belong certain forms of pop art, which limit themselves to enlarging or reproducing images, as exemplified by Roy Lichtenstein, Andy Warhol, and Claes Oldenburg.

None of the attitudes can really be considered as pure, particularly when they are the result of creative effort (it could almost be said that impurity is the stamp of the true creators); consequently, a constructivist work can impart a high poetic sense contained in its visual qualities, while a determinedly spontaneous or instinctive work may reveal an underlying constructive element.

Every work of art has a structure, or, at least, a shape, and the shape permits it to be labeled a species. And it is well to categorize it as such, for it is indeed a thing alive, a living thing presuming to vanquish inexorable time. To construct and to express are qualities contained in each man; one represents security, the norm, the law; the other, adventure, the unknown ... risk. A man must choose between these two destinies. At times he may doubt and float in an intermediate zone between both; at other times he chooses and soon changes because he realizes that it is not a suitable destiny. In some cases this change reveals a true inner necessity, but in the majority of cases the change is only in answer to a maneuver in search of success. In the overwhelming and dizzying succession of tendencies, how many are quick to follow any new fashion, which, however, never suits them? And so the pastiches come about, immense quantities of pastiches.

Art is not a phenomenon isolated from the surrounding reality. When art is free and authentic it is always an expression of its ambient and epoch, of the dominating characteristics of the society in which the individual is creating. No authentic art is an art purely of the individual, although it may pretend to be so; conversely, no authentic art can totally exclude the individual, although it may pretend to do so. The artist is always present in his work as a concrete being, and it is this quality that represents man in his surroundings at a given moment of time.

Artists are very sensitive to the contingencies of the milieu in which they live, not only to the mental climate but also to philosophical, political, and scientific theories. The artists' pictorial principles are impregnated with all these influences. No one as much as the artist senses the « winds of change. » The artist is a man of his times, and participates in the mental universe, whether technical or formal.

All works of art have a *purpose*. First is the need to express the self with vigor, intensity, and dimension. This expression need not be sentimental; it can reflect, simply, the position of the artist before the world, but basically it expresses his own sphere of interest. The artist wants to be present in his work. The work should be an extension of himself, and through the work he endeavors to establish a bond with his surroundings.

In this fashion a true artist shows in his work at one and the same time the following: what he is as an individual, what the milieu is in which he lives, and what man is generally. Thus he conveys both the particular and the universal, the transitory and the permanent, but all seen through the eyes of a concrete individual. Inevitably, then, all authentic works of art assume a position, and by so doing express an attitude. It will be shown that the extreme exaggeration of this position has led to one of the most recent manifestations of the *avant-garde*, the one designated as activist art.

To make life visible

As with science, which has ceased to be descriptive and does not speak of the aspect but of the constitution of matter, art has ceased to be descriptive for the sake of delving into reality considered in itself. But it also goes deeply into the reality of man, who is by definition the fundamental protagonist of all reality, on the premise that all reality exists only in relation to man and, conversely, that a man who is not a function of the reality about him does not exist. It is this interaction between man and the world that the artist endeavors to express through the eloquence of art in its absolute integrity, without discounting, as does science, any of its parts. In any event, art and science are not opposed, as we have seen, but complement each other. Conrad Fiedler says, « Without art the view of the world would be incomplete. »

One new way of presenting reality is to incorporate actual materials and objects in the painting, thus outlining their plastic qualities. Alberto Burri belongs to the group of artists who exploit the materiality of burlap and other textiles, as well as wood and metals, emphasizing this materiality through various procedures that range from tearing through charring. Things in such instances are not an aid in modifying or concealing what is meant to represent something else; things begin to represent themselves.

In what measure do artists show us an aspect of reality, and to what degree do they become our guides to this reality? The Renaissance constituted a contact with one face of reality; informalism brings us into contact with another aspect of the same reality, closer, perhaps, to the telescopic or microscopic view, the nuclear investigation, the world of the infinitesimally small and of the infinitely large from which present man has evolved.

Paul Klee, in his essay on engravings, published in 1918, uttered a very revealing phrase: « Art does not reproduce the visible, but makes visible. » And with this the problem of creation inevitably arises, which in the end is: to make visible. But the artist does not wish to make form visible, but to make life visible; this is to be understood as a continuous search.

Truth and meaning in art

Truth in art resides in its totality. However, totality and unity are not synonymous. Though a modern picture can be composed of apparently incoherent elements, the artist may succeed in eliciting from them an intense capacity for integration; this can be observed in certain surrealist works and in the collages by Kurt Schwitters or in those of the American neodadaist Robert Rauschenberg. The more dynamic term « integration » replaces the relatively static term « unity. » In integration what is looked for is not harmony or equilibrium but only cohesion between the parts. The structure of a picture consists in the association of elements directed in a plastic sense.

The so-called unity of a picture may be obtained by the emphasis on form (visual unity) or by the emphasis on context (poetic unity or meaning). The theme, be it plastic or anecdotal, confers only an apparent unity (unity of intention), and the picture may disintegrate in all other respects. There exists a more substantial unity, which the artist achieves by an adequate interplay of the plastic elements. The artist arrives at this unity upon discovering the secret affinity between elements by themselves apparently dissimilar. The picture then becomes coherent. Coherence does not consist solely in a plastic fusion (cohesion) but in an affinity of sense. This relates the elements of the picture in such a way that the apparent antinomy disappears. Coherence opposes the incoherence of certain mystifiers of the modern, who try to unite things whose antipathetic relation is manifest. An artist can for this reason strive for composition, with a totally incoherent result. Conversely, a picture can wholly lack actual composition and still be profoundly coherent, such as those of the new geometricians Ellsworth Kelly and Kenneth Noland and of Jules Olitski and Piero Dorazio. A painting can even lack structure and be coherent, as occurs with many informalist artists (aside from the work of Pollock, Tàpies, and so on).

But the term « unity » may still lose validity in certain modern works in which the artist intentionally breaks this unity that imposes on him a too confining limit. Yet even then, the work, when completed, is not chaotic: it has acquired a direction toward an objective, or it may be that it has recovered its coherence. From this it appears that in some works of art the term « direction, » which is a more fluid term, should be substituted for « unity. »

All pictorial works have a content, and this content implies a meaning. The meaning does not of necessity have to be of an emotional type; it can have a plastic significance. It must be understood that there is no purely plastic significance, because in the last analysis it always carries a poetic connotation. But the poetic in its turn does not necessarily mean the literary. The poetic constitutes the essential value of a work of art of whatever category, and represents the impetus that sends man to the conquest of archetypes. It was thus understood by Picasso, who, referring to painting, said, « There is no other key than that of poetry; the lines and forms rhyme in the manner of a poem. » *

Many painters have known of this relation of their art with poetry. Joan Miró, for example, said, « I make no distinction between painting and poetry »; Roger Bissière stated, « The important element is the poetry contained in painting »; and Pierre Soulages speaks insistently of the poetry found in the canvas.

Art signifies the poetic as opposed to the utilitarian focus. This does not gratuitously imply something like « art for art's sake. » Art is in a unique and definite manner essentially committed to man: in everything else it should be free. It cannot be committed to dogmas of any sort, for dogma is a prison that would make it lose this essential quality of its nature, that of being free; liberty is the foundation of the creative process.

It devolves on art to set in motion the free potentialities of man's spirit in an active manner. In contrast to religion or the law, which demand from man a passive deportment, that is, subordination to a norm, art opens the perspective on a free development; and it is in modern art that this call for free development of man's potentialities is most intense, when it is an art that does not subject itself to any norm. Yet to be free from dogma does not mean that the art should not reflect an ideology; undoubtedly it does, for the simple reason that it reflects the man who created it, and no authentic man lives without an ideology.

In being committed to man, art cannot but be whole and essentially human. But such is the absurd deformation that man has suffered through the works of the deformers of all types, by the most diverse agents (religious, economic, political), using means of pressure that range from hypnotic persuasion (such as those of mass publicity) to compulsion by terror (such as that resorted to by various political regimes), that it becomes almost impossible to discover what in reality is the truly human. This continues to be the difficult mission of art: always to keep the flame of authentic humanity lit.

Esthetic value

At one time it was understood that in art the beautiful was what was useful; with this idea functional esthetics was baptized. « Useful to whom? » the artist asks. Supposedly it is not useful for the spirit of man, nor for his thirst for liberty and full selfrealization. In the field of art the term « utility » has no sense. It may be said that the accent of art is on the antifunctional. A machine is artistic only when it is absolutely useless, which does not deny the beauty and elegance

* In *Arts de France* (September, 1946).

of a streamlined automobile; but this beauty has nothing to do with art. The artist declares his absolute scorn for utilitarian conventions.

There is, in fact, a functional aspect in art, and this is the one in which the task is to represent man in his wholeness. Art is functionally the image of integrated man.

Because of the particular conditions of urban life, people in large cities are submerged in surroundings divorced from nature, surroundings created totally by man, where he is subject to enticements, to visual commands, as well as to limitations of his freedom of movement; this creates a mentality and a type of reaction totally characteristic of our epoch. It is worth asking, then: If beauty is in the function of man, should not then a work of art develop in accord with the new conditions of life? Should not the artist transmit the optic pleasure in accord with these conditions? Should not a new esthetic emerge from all this? Recent tendencies, particularly in the United States, appear to give an affirmative answer to these questions.

Anyway, esthetic value is far from being universal and immovable: the various cultural circles, the different races, esteemed and still do esteem esthetic values that are apparently different. But this difference is only apparent; it treats of the inevitable variability of a fluid value, which always revolves about an immovable axis consisting of a search for the archetype situated in the meeting of man with the world.

Bound to this variability of esthetic values, our epoch has not only raised the question of the fundamentals of art but has also demanded that a new table of values be constructed. All through the history of painting artists have been reevaluated; some formerly neglected have been upgraded, and others held in high esteem have been downgraded. This table of values applied to our contemporaries is also subject to rapid changes; fame and sometimes even glory last no longer than from one day to the next. There have been similar occurrences in the past, and the proof of time has been necessary for anything to be incorporated in the group of durable values. But the confusion created in our times has no precedents. Undoubtedly there are artists whose names are assured, and it would be too obvious to enumerate them, but how many, after an ephemeral glory, are forgotten while they are still alive. In recent years reappraisals have occurred that are useful to note, because in them lies the key to the fluctuating criteria of our times.

To begin with, the fundamental importance of expressionism, formerly considered as a phenomenon existing almost exclusively in the Germanic countries, has been demonstrated. There has been a reevaluation of futurism, not so much for its doctrine as for what its components anticipated. The importance of surrealism has been acknowledged and is found to be the primordial influence in the genesis of various modern movements such as « Cobra, » action painting, informalism, assemblages, and the artistic object. The dada movement has reassumed significance, with the neodadaist groups and pop, with the new European realists (the Restany group), and with the « O » group in Germany and the Netherlands. In all the new movements the experiences from the end of the last century to the present have served to prepare the ground.

The important contribution of the fauves was to liberate color not only from the imitation of the real but also from its dependence on form. The importance of cubism was that it provoked a rupture from the figure as it appears in empirical representation, and this rupture in greater part determined the later abstract exercises based on the geometric interplay of analytical cubism; expressionism instigated a degree of deformation of the figure that led to the same result. All the disquisitions of synthetic cubism on the reconstruction of planes or the composition of plural vision of the object signify a step backward, and have only contributed by their essential artificial-ity to the worst pictorial modern academism. This justifies the preponderance in the postwar era of abstraction, be it geometric or constructive abstraction deriving from analytical cubism, or free abstraction deriving from expressionism. The destruction of the taboo surrounding the object was a slow process begun by the impressionists. But this result was unavoidable.

Cubism and geometric abstraction follow classical canons, and at their best amplify and enlarge them. In the postwar period a rupture with these canons was produced for the first time. The old terms of traditional esthetics (harmony, equilibrium) lost their meaning. The new designation proposed by Michel Tapié of *un art autre* (another art) for the art that emerged in the last few years, appears right. A breakaway from all esthetic conventions developed. This upheaval was evidenced almost simultaneously in the United States and in Europe, and was given many names: informalism, action painting, tachism, lyrical abstraction, and spatialism. The picture begins to interest not only as surface but also as substance and material quality. Informalism (a designation that, being the most general, can be used to embrace all these tendencies) acquires a fundamental importance in contemporary plastics in liberating art from any prejudice, even that of form, and leaves open every direction, including the one leading to its own destruction. Because of this, the latest manifestations (neodadaism, chromatic abstraction) apparently oppose it, but nevertheless do not escape its influence.

Tradition and originality

There is no spontaneous generation in art, any more than there is in life, and art is a form of life. Each generation bases its development on the postulates left by the preceding generation; or they reject them, and by this rejection absorb them, and furthermore blend in some manner with an even older generation. This derivation from one or the other does not signify a lack of originality, but on the contrary is the only way in which to be truly original. Lack of originality consists in docilely copying those who went before, in being imitators. This explains how in the postwar period concrete art departs from Mondrian, who in his turn had departed from geometricized cubism, which had reached the peak of its development. Informalism in its negation of geometry and negation of forms went further back, to the Kandinsky of the abstract expressionism and of the improvisations. So pop art signals a negation of informalism (its previous incarnation) and a fusion with dadaism, particularly in the key figure of Marcel Duchamp. But in each of these steps art is enriched. All tendencies ultimately strive to widen the field of perception as well as to construct approaches to new zones of the spirit, and await their followers or opponents.

Communication and the ethical content of art

Communication is not an easy matter, nor is it passive. No directly popular art exists, nor has it existed at any time in any part of the globe. Certain forms of folklore or primitive art or art of the past were not popular as art but as a form of reportage, as a document, as a symbol (religious or not), or as a game. In the Orient, a painter of the Sung epoch, Mi Fei (1051-1107), averred that « painting ought not to be shown to everybody, » and added that « to understand a work of art is as difficult as creating it. » This last phrase defines the fundamental importance of the spectator, whose function is not in any way a passive one. The work is only potentially a work of art until the spectator confronts it. He « re-creates » the work in his mind, and from that moment the work ceases to be potential and becomes real. Some of this communion between a work of art and the beholder was suggested in the conception of *Einfühlung*, but this idea of affective empathy is insufficient; in reality the beholder, in « recreating » the work, reproduces in his own mind the process of creation that the artist went through. Each spectator is thus potentially a creator, and being a creator is not an easy matter; it demands, beside natural aptness, a determined preparation, an effort. Art does not yield itself without this effort: hence the apparent unpopularity of art.

How does the modern artist conceive of art? Any imaginable answer is possible. For Dubuffet it is total inebriation. The Dutch group Reflex, of which Appel was a member, proclaimed in a manifesto of 1948: « A picture is now not merely a construction of colors and lines, but an animal, a night, a cry, a human being, or all of these together. » Other artists are interested only in the technical aspect of the work, and undoubtedly do not see in it any transcendental overtone. In this respect the fundamental pursuit for an artist can be one of many different things, through a constantly varying spectrum: color, form, light, movement, vibration, rhythm, gesture, symbol, space, meaning, the medium or the immaterial (as with Yves Klein). Such a diverse collection of aims is bound to give a chaotic aspect to the panorama of today's art.

The line between different sections of plastic art becomes even more imprecise; so is it between painting and sculpture. In deciding whether an artist belongs in this book, we have borne in mind, not the traditional techniques, but the direct impression of his work; in this, following in part D. H. Kahnweiler, who in 1920 held that « relief is bound to painting, even though it is executed with the tools of sculpture, because it creates a fictitious space, while true sculpture lives in the space common to all of us. » Without fully sharing this criterion, the pictorial quality of many works in relief is evident: those by Jesús Soto, Jean Arp, Jacob Agam, Luis Tomasello, and Zoltán Kemény; the wire reliefs of Walter Bodmer; and works by numerous modern constructivists such as Victor Pasmore and Anthony Hill. Those apparatuses that produce luminous projections either in color or not (for example, by Frank Malina, Nicolas Schöffer, and Julio Le Parc) must be considered as paintings, as well as certain mobiles that function frontally (some constructions of Jean Tinguely, Pol Bury, and so on).

A work of art is born in a secret and mysterious manner. Once created, it separates from the artist and emerges with an autonomous life, ready to receive its nourishment from the admiration of the spectator. The work then exists and acquires power to create around itself this spiritual atmosphere, the function of which is to improve man. And in this lies, in the final analysis, the whole secret of art, a secret of ethical content. Thus art does not exist only as a means of communicating or imparting information, as it is supposed today; it continues being, as it has always been, a path that endeavors to lead to the spiritual betterment of man.

Chapter one

The avant-garde at the end of the Second World War

In 1930 the activity of the abstract painters began to be concentrated in Paris; wholly unnoticed, its repercussions among the general public were at first nil. In that year the three most important members of the De Stijl group, exponents of neoplasticism, Mondrian, Van Doesburg, and Georges Vantongerloo, were in Paris; and soon afterward Gabo and Pevsner, exponents of Russian constructivism, arrived. Arp had lived there since 1926, painting simultaneously in abstract and surrealist styles; and Kandinsky installed himself in the city in 1933. These artists, who represent the most important currents of abstract art, came in contact with the groups already working in Paris: Delaunay and his wife, Kupka, Gleizes, Auguste Herbin, and the newcomers Hélion and Jean Gorin, who had come under the influence of neoplasticism. The nucleus of these artists decided to found an association of international character aimed at projecting and spreading abstract work. It would thus appear that abstract art was the result of the experiments of a minority.

The « Abstraction-Création » association was founded on February 15, 1931; it lasted until 1937. Contemporaneous with the activity of this association was a reaction in the opposite direction, also in Paris, distinguished by an attempt to return to traditional, preimpressionistic painting, a reaction that fused with what had been produced around 1924 in Europe and that was called the « Neue Sachlichkeit » in Germany and « Valori Plastici » in Italy. The presence of such a contrary reaction is a constant phenomenon in vigorous movements, and corresponds to what S. Lupasco designates « the dialectics of contradiction. »

Some of the artists who participated in «Abstraction-Création» emigrated during the war, especially to the United States, where they in turn stimulated the abstract movement. It devolved on those who remained in Europe and on the young artists who followed the « Abstraction-Création » manner to explain the impressive development of abstraction as a dominant style after the end of the Second World War.

In 1930 the artist Theo Van Doesburg, of the De Stijl group, founded the concrete art group in Paris. This event, which at the time passed almost unnoticed, came to be of fundamental importance in the development of geometric tendencies immediately after the war, particularly in the Swiss school, whose most outstanding representative and champion was Max Bill.

In 1930 the concrete art group published the only number of a review-manifesto edited by Van Doesburg. It summarized some of the ideas circulating among the artists inclined toward geometric rigor and which were the result of a fusion of the principles of neoplasticism and Russian constructivism. In addition to Van Doesburg, the group was composed of Otto Gustaf Carlsund, Jean Hélion, Tutundjian, and Wantz. The group was dissolved after Van Doesburg's death in March, 1931. Tutundjian exhibited in the first « Abstraction-Création » show, but afterward disappeared from the painting scene, as did Wantz, without leaving any traces. Carlsund abandoned painting for many years. Hélion emigrated to the United States during the war, where he returned to figural painting. But the fundamental ideas of this group were to constitute the basis of concrete art in the postwar period. They are summarized in six fundamental precepts:

1. The predominance of individualism, as well as the predominance of a local spirit, has always been the greatest obstacle to the appearance of a universal art. The object of art is to create a universal language.

2. A work of art must be spiritually conceived before its execution. It must not receive any of the formal elements of nature or of the senses or of emotion.

3. The picture must be constructed entirely with purely plastic elements. A pictorial element

has no significance other than being pictorial.

4. The construction of the picture, as well as its elements, must be visually simple and controllable.

5. The technique must be mechanical, that is, exact, anti-impressionistic.

6. The clarity of the work must be absolute.

In addition to these premises the following commentaries were added:

1. In their search for purity, the artists who preceded us abstracted the natural forms concealed in the plastic elements, destroying the nature form and replacing it with art form. Today art form has fallen into disuse, as has nature form; we inaugurate the period of pure painting, constructing the spirit form. Painting is the concretion of the creative spirit.

2. Emotion, sentiment, and feeling have not advanced art toward its perfection. Thought alone (the intellect), with a velocity undoubtedly superior to that of light, *creates*. Lyricism, dramatism, symbolism, the unconscious, dreams, and inspiration are all ersatz to creative thought. Of all human activity, the most important is intellectuality. Outside what is created through thought, there remains nothing but the baroque, fauvism, animalism, sentimentalism, and the hyperbaroque confession of weakness: fantasy. On the contrary, the era that is commencing is one of certainty, or it could be of perfection. Everything is measurable, even the spirit with its 199 dimensions. We are painters who measure and think.

3. Painting is the medium by which thought is visually realized. Each picture is a color-thought.

4. Construction differs entirely from arrangement (decoration) and from composition according to taste. The majority of artists work like pastrycooks and dressmakers. We work with the data of mathematics (Euclidean and non-Euclidean) and of science, that is, with intellectual elements.

JEAN BAZAINE. *The sea port.* 1948.

5. Before a work materializes, it exists fully completed in the spirit. Its realization must demonstrate a technical perfection equal to the perfection of the concept. It must not reveal any trace of human weakness: no uncertainty, no imprecision, no vacillation, no unfinished parts. If one is not able to draw a straight line freehand, one employs a ruler. The writing from a typewriter is more beautiful, clearer, and more legible than what is written by hand. If one is not capable of drawing a circle freehand, one takes a compass. All instruments intellectually devised as an aid to perfection are to be recommended.

6. The work of art thus conceived realizes the clarity that will be the basis for a new culture.

It is very important to examine the principles propounded by Van Doesburg, because they will be repeated in the recent works of optical art. In reading the maxims advanced by Vasarely, the essential analogy with those just outlined can be noted.

ALFRED MANESSIER. *Resurrection.* 1961.

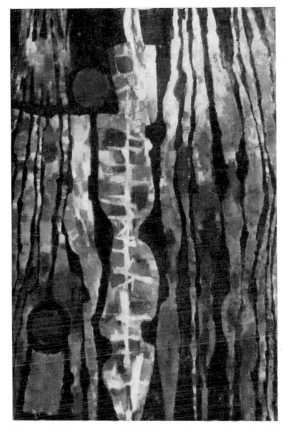

ALFRED MANESSIER. *Offering to the earth.* 1961/62.

The movement founded on these principles had to be developed by various artists who definitively adopted the designation « concrete artists, » rejecting outright the label « abstraction, » which among other disadvantages presupposed that the work was separated from reality. The term « concrete, » advanced by Van Doesburg, appeared not to have had much success for some years, until Max Bill appropriated it in 1936, explaining its significance in the following way: « Concrete creation is creation springing forth by its own means and following its own laws, without having derived these from the appearance of natural phenomena. Color, form, space, light, and movement supply the constituent elements of optical figuration. Creation is transported from its spiritual state to reality, transforming itself into an object of use for the eyes and the spirit. » *

In a later essay, Bill reiterates the point: « Concrete painting eliminates all naturalistic representation; it avails itself exclusively of the funda-

mental elements of painting, the color and form of the surface. Its essence is, then, the complete emancipation of every natural model: pure creation. » [+]

The definitions by Bill are evidently more extensive than those of Van Doesburg, and in a certain sense justify the inclusion of painters of the informal school, an inclusion sanctioned by Max Bill himself in an exhibition of concrete art he organized in Switzerland in 1960, where artists such as Mathieu and Tobey were represented.

The label « concrete art » was adopted by Arp to

* In the catalog of the exhibition in the Kunsthaus in Zurich in 1936 « Zeit Probleme in der Schweizer Malerei und Plastik. »
[+] In *Domus* (February, 1946), p. 37.

define his work, and in 1938 Kandinsky decided to employ the same nomenclature to designate his own. This name was rapidly diffused in the post-war era, groups of concrete art were founded in various countries, and isolated artists adopted the designation, so that concrete art appears as the dominant manifestation in the avant-garde art in the days following World War II. In 1944 an exhibition under the name « Konkrete Kunst » took place in the Kunsthalle in Basel, inspired by Bill. In June, 1945, the Drouin Gallery mounted an exhibition in Paris with the title of « Art Concret. » In 1946 an antiquarian, Frédo Sidès, founded the Salon des Réalités Nouvelles, which included a great number of concrete and abstract artists; the salon revealed the predominance of the concrete artists. And in 1949 the first number of the French review *Art d'aujourd'hui* appeared, edited by the architect and plastic artist André Bloc; it came to be the tribunal for the defense of concrete art.

Contemporaneous with the dominant evolution of concrete art, a type of abstraction was developed in Paris that proposed to blend with the sources of a pictorial sentiment of national character. In May, 1941, in the very midst of the German occupation, an exhibition with the name « Young Painters of the French Tradition » opened in the Braun Gallery, home of the famous art publication of the same name. This exhibition was in defiance of the categorization of degenerate art that the Nazis gave to various manifestations of new art, and was characterized, in spite of the individual differences among the exhibiting painters, by its accentuated modernity. The dominant element in the show was a group of abstract paintings that intended to give an impression of reality, concentrating their colors and essential forms, returning to an earlier stage of abstraction that departed from naturalness. This group was made up of Jean Bazaine, Alfred Manessier, Lapicque, Jean Le Moal, and Gustave Singier; for the most part they had received their training in the former Ranson Academy under the direction of Roger Bissière. In 1944 the paintings exhibited by this group in the Salon d'Automne in Paris showed that the abstract tendencies had increased.

Bissière, the teacher of this group of artists, must be included among these « Abstractionists in the French Tradition.» Bissière was born in Villeréal, France, in 1888. From 1925 to 1938 he taught in the Ranson Academy, through which many painters who later would command attention passed. In 1939 he was afflicted with an eye disease that lasted for five years and that prevented him from painting. In 1945, in the Salon de Mai, an exhibition entitled « Homage to Bissière » was arranged, and another big show of his pictures and tapestries took place in 1947 in the Drouin Gallery in Paris.

Bissière covered the entire surface of the canvas with small signs and vaguely geometrical forms, regularly distributed but in a free manner within compartments obtained by an unequal division of the field. The whole structure was achieved by utilizing color in the manner of the impressionists, searching for the interplay of values heightened by vibrant touches. Of the members of this group, Bissière and Singier have reached the highest degree of purity in abstraction.

Jean Bazaine was born in Paris in 1904. In his pictures, within the general style of this tendency, which are inspired by natural motifs, the structure is freer and more dynamic, as if dashed off with large nervous strokes. He also became known as a brilliant theorist after the publication of his *Notes on Painting of Today.*

Alfred Manessier was born in 1911 in Saint–Ouen of the Somme Department. His painting consists of clean, overlapping, intercrossed forms, glittering with exquisitely shaded colors and transparencies, which give the effect of sumptu-

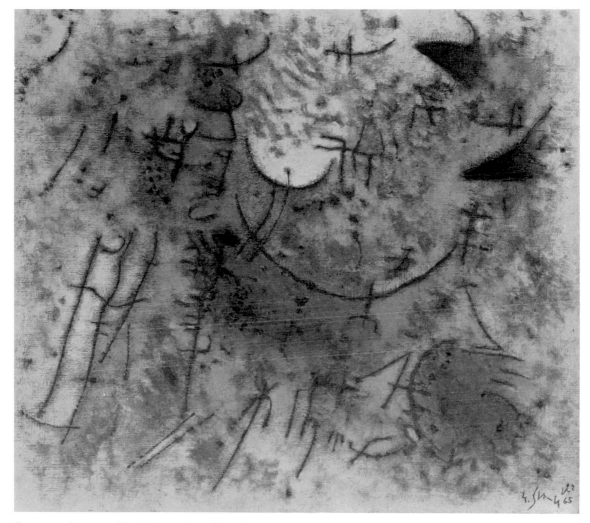

GUSTAVE SINGIER. *Meridian and sands.* 1965.

ous stained glass. His work puts him in the fore-
front of this kind of abstraction. In 1962 he won
first prize in painting at the Venice Biennale. On
the subject of his purpose as a painter, Manessier
says: « The object is to put the spiritual equivalences of the exterior and the interior world into
the open, by authentically plastic means, and to
make these equivalences intelligible by transposition and transmutation. »

Jean Le Moal was born in Athon-du-Perche in
1909. In his abstractions of elements of reality
he achieves a fine, sensitive line and vibrant equivalence.

Gustave Singier was born in Warneton, Belgium,
in 1909. He uses spare and precise forms in
which the line is emphasized, in a free internal
organization, but leaving the space active, an ele-

ment that plays a much larger role for this artist than for any other artist of this school.

All these painters transpose nature into its purely plastic values (lines and color), endeavoring to transmit to us the essential plastic emotion of the natural phenomenon. In a certain sense they can be considered as representing a new form of impressionism; all of them are, in fact, characterized by their search for a vibrant, chromatic atmosphere, which brings their work close to the impressionistic tradition and which justifies the designation « abstract impressionists » for the majority of the members of this group. Many of them retained elements of visible reality in their pictures for a long time. In fact, Manessier and Bazaine declared that they had nothing to do with abstract art.

To summarize: when plastic activity was renewed at the end of the Second World War, Paris – which had always shown a strong resistance to abstract art – found itself faced with the phenomenon of an overwhelming influx of painters of this tendency. This indifference to abstract art is not so surprising when one considers that Mondrian had resided in Paris since 1930 and Kandinsky since 1933, both passing practically unnoticed.

Hartung and Magnelli

The work of two abstract painters, Hans Hartung and Alberto Magnelli, who made their debut in the immediate postwar period, was a revelation and was instrumental in contributing to the new heights that abstraction reached in those years. They signaled a change in orientation of the then dominant neoplastic and constructivist school. The tendencies of this group had appeared a short time before the war in Holland, Switzerland, and the United States. It was to America that the outstanding geometric artists Mondrian, Moholy-Nagy, and Albers went; each of them was the center of a powerful influence that even-

Alberto Magnelli. *Composition.* 1940.

tually led to the association that united the abstract Americans: the « American Abstract Artists » association.

The work of Hartung and Magnelli is characterized by its emphasis on fantasy and the intuitive element as against the purely rational. Both had begun painting long before the outbreak of the Second World War, but the dislocation created by this event prevented their work from being widely known. Both of them had departed from the principles of rigorous and rational plasticity, but with different objectives: Magnelli to have free play in plastic fantasy, which, however, he kept severe and disciplined; Hartung to express interior emotional impulses arranged within a coherent plastic vision. Magnelli followed the organic plasticity practiced by Arp, but went beyond his simplicity toward a baroque complexity of

ALBERTO MAGNELLI. *Contrasted aspects.* 1941.

forms. Hartung was influenced by the early Kandinsky and the automatic graphics of the surrealists. These two painters did not theorize and speculate about the principles of abstract art. This elimination of all preoccupation with theories left them free to proceed with pure creation. At this moment in the evolution of abstract art, the painter, firmly grounded in a conceptual horizon previously established, could freely develop in his task as a creator.

Magnelli was born in Florence in 1888, a year after Arp. When he was seventeen years old he began painting figural canvases distinguished by a great simplification of form and the use of pure colors. In 1915 he executed his first nonfigural picture. For the duration of the First World War he produced no paintings, and did not resume his work before 1921, when he again began producing figural canvases. After an interval of painting blocks of stone (1931 to 1933, his stone period) inspired by a visit to the Carrara marble quarries, Magnelli returned to nonfigural art. In

1932 he settled permanently in Paris, counting himself a painter of the « School of Paris, » and after 1935 he began his present cycle of abstractionism.

To an inquiry about his role as a painter, Magnelli answered: « I follow no theories, nor do I bother having any. As to what concerns me, I paint abstract pictures – as they are called – because it is the language which affords me the greatest liberty to create forms and colors which are absolutely necessary for the construction of my canvases. » He is not, however, indifferent to purely plastic problems. On this subject he offers simple, concrete statements: « It is necessary to bring to the picture the greatest possible density of composition. The value of a work does not lie in its subject matter but in the power of its realization. » On the content of plastic works, he says: « It is easy to draw curved or parallel lines, natural or imaginary forms; what is difficult is to turn them into expression, infuse them with fire. »

With Magnelli the fundamental question is the interplay of forms. These constitute a conglomerate; they are interconnected to themselves and form a unity with the space. It is a strange conglomeration that at first glance gives the forms the appearance of precise figures marking the space clearly, but when closely observed they are found to be so intricately enlaced that form and space constitute an inseparable whole. Analyzed separately, fragments of this continuity of forms appear to be separate volumes in the space, an illusion obtained by the thickness and accentuation of some of the outlines or by a modeling by means of tonal gradations; then suddenly and brusquely they are crossed by another form and are transformed into planes, into surfaces without volume, and into actual emptiness. All together, the forms appear, most of the time, sharp, precise, and semigeometric, with free borders, well outlined and accentuated. This technique of at the same time accentuating and effacing the forms and the space resembles somewhat the technique with which Albers creates and annuls perspective. With Magnelli this results in a form that is at one and the same time solid and airy, heavy and floatingly light.

For this reason his pictures do not gravitate toward a horizontal base, and so suffer less through a change of position. The forms are free, not subordinated to gravity or to the human empirical concept of space and perspective; hence their degree of abstraction is total.

His colors are also « abstract, » not because, like Mondrian's, they are primary colors, but because he deliberately eliminates all luminosity, choosing mat and at times sharp colors that are usually not found in nature. He distributes them according to a harmonious principle and with an eye to contributing to this uncertainty of forms, as has already been mentioned.

From all that has been said, it seems evident that for Magnelli the important thing is a strictly abstract plastic interplay, and that his work is totally and purely a mental creation. In Arp there are still traces of a latent organicism that can suggest elemental biological organisms. In Magnelli there is nothing of this: his forms, without being purely geometric, neutralize one another; the spaces that for a moment give the impression of the profundity of real space become, if attentively observed, deleted and incorporated into the mechanism of the forms. His colors shun all similarity to natural colors; they are absolutely imaginary.

Magnelli makes the forms perform in all their possibilities. The result is an almost baroque manner of deletion of a fixed style, for the path it has opened for the free play of imagination has exercised a considerable influence over the French and young Italian (especially the school of Rome) abstract painting. Taking a different route from Mondrian, he also established a continuous space-form based on a multiplication of forms in juxtaposition and in the intricacy of their enlacement with space.

HANS HARTUNG. *436-11.*

HANS HARTUNG. *Painting.* 1950.
Louis Carré Gallery.

As regards content, his art is not intimate, but objective and direct, with certain tendencies toward the monumental, as the German critic Naef has pointed out. Regardless of this, his pictures

RICHARD MORTENSEN. *Suite à Ominanda I.* 1963.
Denise René Gallery.

emanate a depersonalized poetry, at times dry and
cold, springing not from the individual existence
of the artist but from the very universe of plastic
forms. Magnelli, in the manner of Klee and Arp,
gives his pictures names that reflect a poetic
equivalence.

Magnelli was considered to be the most important
exponent of this free plasticity in which the form,
surging spontaneously from the imagination, ar-
ranges itself into an expressive and concrete
whole. It signifies, conclusively, the synthesis of
the intellectual and organic currents of abstraction. It seeks the organic through the path of free
imagination controlled by an intuitive and sensitive intellect. In a sentence about Sophie Taeuber-
Arp (1889-1943) which could well be applied to

himself, Magnelli said: « Fantasy, evasion, is permitted only to those who possess an intensive
sense of balance and measure. »

The work of Magnelli, within the concrete and
constructive current, by utilizing precise, definite
forms, geometric or semigeometric, abandons the
puristic and rigorously geometric line (to which
Max Bill was converted, becoming one of its most
active exponents), for fantasy and an intuitive,
mobile construction. This last quality makes clear
why Magnelli was the only concrete artist who
interested Breton, and also explains the disdain
in which he was held by Max Bill.

Hans Hartung is an artist who has not forgotten
his humane mission in society. For this reason
his work has been interrupted at times because
his concern as a man whose duty it is to take
part in the struggle has made him momentarily
abandon his task as an artist. But perhaps his
intense living through the conflicts of his epoch
has made his work mature more rapidly and with
exceptional strength and sincerity.

Hartung is of German origin (born in 1904 in
Leipzig). He studied painting at the academies
of Dresden and Leipzig, and during this time came
under the influence of the expressionist period of
Kandinsky and the expressionists of the « Blaue
Reiter » (Blue Rider) group. He lived in Spain for
two years, then returned to Germany in 1934.
Pursued by the Gestapo, he managed to escape
into France, then enlisted as a volunteer in the
Gaullist forces of the Foreign Legion, and went
through the war to its end. At the disembarka-
tion of the Legion in France, he lost a leg. His
art began to be known after the termination of
the war.

Hartung's abstract work began in 1922. His ac-
quaintance with Kandinsky dates from 1925, and
he was also profoundly impressed by the works
of Kandinsky's lyrical or expressionist period.
Hartung's first group show took place in 1947
in the Lidia Conti Gallery, where he revealed him-

Max Bill. *Accentuation of a spiral.* 1947.

self as one of the foremost abstract painters of that epoch.

Hartung is the artist who more than anyone achieves an expressiveness of line, an objective toward which Klee had striven. He searches for the dynamism of line, which for him is a humanized dynamism, a revealer of vital expression. His style is characterized by a kind of drawing that appears to respond to a spontaneous and uncontrolled impulse. This drawing circulates within the picture, seemingly without relation to the background and the spots of color distributed over it. Drawing and background appear to present two superimposed themes, that of color and that of line, themes plastically united, like the melody and accompaniment in a musical composition.

There exists, furthermore, a contrast of content between the two plastic themes: the theme of the line is the theme of man, dramatic or sweet, lyrical or tortured; the theme of the background and the planes of color are the expression of the cosmic universe, of its serenity or impassive force. In the drawing, Hartung generally employs black

MAX BILL. *Rhythm divided in eight parts.* 1942.

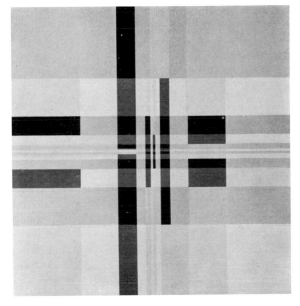

R. PAUL LOHSE. *16 progressive assymetric color groups within a symmetric system.* 1956/60/3.

which for him has more strength and power of dramatic contrast than all other colors, and which expresses the anguish with which he plunges into plastic calligraphy.

This anguish, lyrical in tone, which much of his work reveals, is tied to the great German romantic tradition that includes Novalis and Hölderlin. The will to expression is for Hartung the most important element in art, and in it lies the greatest possibility for communication among men. As Hartung says: « The expression of our art is the more valid the deeper it can penetrate our soul. »

He employs colors in various manners: he begins with a tenuous, airy coat of color, which forms the background; afterward come the amorphous spots of color, clean and of even outline, distributed in a balanced fashion over the picture; finally he places the lines, for which he sometimes uses colors instead of the customary black. The illusion of space is obtained by the contrast between the light, luminous coat of the background and the black lines that stand out, creating a feeling of depth.

Hartung's compositions are conscientious and reflective. First he makes sketches that provide the basis for the linear element of the picture. Then he makes the background, representing the cosmic element to which the human-spiritual element represented by the lines will be united. Finally he organizes both elements according to a basically plastic and expressive order. That is, first he draws and then he composes.

Although his characteristic style in a large sense has remained unchanged, the content of the work has followed the different epochs of the painter's life. Around 1932 it is marked by a predominantly nervous and tormented linear design, as if expressing an interior distress; at other times the tone is dramatic and almost solemn. In his later works he inclines more to clarity and serenity; the lines are less tortuous and violent and adapt themselves more to the plastic function of the picture, expressing an extraordinary lyrical vigor of mind. In this last phase he has proceeded toward an extraordinary simplification of elements; at times the linear scheme is reduced to a single lead line upon a uniform background.

Because Hartung has faith in the clarity of his plastic message, his pictures have no titles, only the year and number corresponding to each. Hartung's painting, which makes use of automatic and irrational elements, proved to be the actual forerunner of surrealist painting, a form of painting charged with irrational elements, but which nevertheless in order to be a communicable language has to submit to plastic coherence. In this he is in accord with Breton, who in later years altered the definition of the first Manifesto—which had eliminated all concern with esthetics in expression—admitting that the automatic elements should be disposed so as to become transformed into a poem or a work of art.

Hartung's importance in the evolution of abstract art – apart from his extraordinary quality as an artist – lies in his having resumed the line of Kandinsky's first period, the line of expressive abstraction, carrying it to is utmost development and demonstrating the wide scale of possibilities

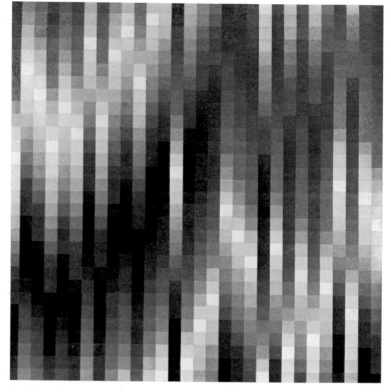

R. PAUL LOHSE. *30 systematic series of color tones.* 1955/63.

inherent in it. The path he has opened has proved very fertile for modern painting.

The Denise René Gallery

An event of great importance for the history of concrete art came with the opening of the Denise René Gallery in Paris in 1944, inaugurated with an exhibition of Vasarely's work. The gallery, dedicated from the beginning to abstract art, rapidly oriented itself toward the concretists; and because of the support it lent all manifestations of this persuasion, wherever it existed, it became their spokesman and outlet, not only in Paris but in all the rest of Europe. The gallery passed sev-

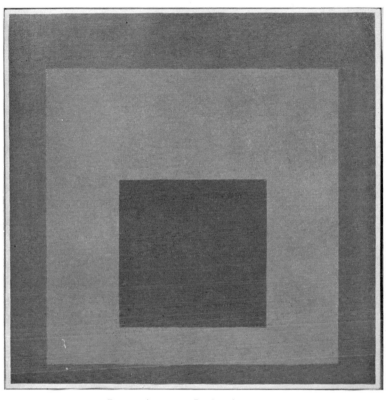

JOSEF ALBERS. *Light slate.* 1961.
Sidney Janis Gallery.

Art, which had a very brief existence but which motivated attacks by the critic Charles Estienne, who took its name as a pretext for an article entitled « Is Abstractism an Academism? »
Dewasne had begun under the influence of Magnelli, but soon went on to a personal style, characterized by a sort of concrete baroqueism in which he fused free imagination in inventing forms with the most severe geometric rigor. His work is original and unique within the various manifestations of concrete art.

Richard Mortensen was born in 1910 in Copenhagen, Denmark. Forming part of a group of Danish abstract-surrealist artists, he soon turned to a type of geometric abstraction that he has maintained, with few variations, up to the present. In spite of an apparent rigidity in the planes and economy of the medium, Mortensen obtains a dynamic quality in his pictures, not only from an efficacious juxtaposition of planes of differing orientation, but also, and particularly, from the use of color, which he prefers highly saturated, taking advantage of its spatial potency. There is no doubt that Mortensen is not only a precursor but actually the outstanding exponent of the hard-edge school.

Max Bill, Josef Albers, Paul Lohse

Two great artists are at the head of the evolution of concrete art in the period that began after the last war: they are Max Bill and Josef Albers.

Max Bill was born in 1908 in Winterthur, Switzerland. He studied at the Bauhaus in Dessau from 1927 to 1929, and thereafter developed a multiple activity as painter, sculptor, architect, graphic artist, industrial designer, and theorist. After 1930 he resided for a time in Zurich, and between 1932 and 1936 he took part in the activities of the « Abstraction-Création » association in

eral difficult years during the epoch of the rise of informalism, without losing its faith in the art it defended. The present upsurge of the trend called « optics » has consolidated its position, and the presence of its artists in any movement of this type, in any place in the world, is indispensable. At the outset the gallery chiefly promoted three painters: Vasarely, Dewasne, and Mortensen. (Vasarely later gravitated toward kinetics, and will be discussed further on in this chapter.)

Jean Dewasne was born in Hellemmes-Lille in 1921. His abstract period began in 1943, and in 1946 he won the Kandinsky prize. Together with Pillet he founded a famous Academy of Abstract

Paris. In 1937 he entered the « Allianz » group in Switzerland, which united concrete and surrealist artists. In 1945 he was responsible for the Konkrete Kunst exhibition in Basel. He won the Kandinsky prize for painting in 1949, and in 1951 he was awarded the first prize for sculpture in the Biennale of São Paulo. Bill founded the Hochschule für Gestaltung in Ulm in 1952, a university for visual arts that was created to continue the Bauhaus tradition, but in 1956 he left the directorship. In 1960 he organized the important Konkrete Kunst exhibition in Zurich (Züricher Kunstgesellschaft, Helmhaus), which summarized the activity of the concrete artists up to that time. Bill began his career by departing from the style of Klee, his teacher at the Bauhaus, but he was always concerned with the problem of rigor in form and in composition, which impelled a search for a mathematical basis for his art. Together with his painting he began spatial constructions, following the lines of the constructivists. Later he was to liberate himself from these influences to begin experiments with the problem of « good form » (or, perhaps, ideal form), which led to his series developed on a given plastic theme, and to constructions in space in accordance with forms that correspond to the principle of finite-infinite that he had studied, a principle introduced by the theory of relativity and that appears to have inspired his constructions on the order of space-continuum.

Bill holds that his visit to the Poincaré Museum, where he became acquainted with plastic construction based on mathematical formulae, was as significant to him as the discovery of Negro art was to the fauves and the cubists. He is, as we have said, one of the supporters of the principle of a mathematical basis for art, but he also states that mathematical reasoning in art does not mean measures and calculations applied to the creation of the work. All works of art – whether consciously or subconsciously – have always had a mathematical foundation based on geometric

STUART DAVIS. *Pochade.* 1958.
The Downtown Gallery.

structures and distribution, a basis that exists even in the primitives. The strong tie between mathematics and art, says Bill, owes its existence to the fact that mathematics is a science of relations, and art expresses itself through relations. In modern art, mathematics in the role of objective regulator assures the work of its harmony and equilibrium; this holds today just as it did in the times of Dürer and Leonardo da Vinci. Kandinsky, in his book *The Spiritual in Art*, also affirmed the importance of mathematical reasoning for the artist.

Max Bill realizes that today's art poses problems that enter not only into the field of mathematics but also into philosophy, and this he explains by the fact that art has gradually risen from hierarchism: from anecdotal reproduction of natural appearances in the service of religious or other

POLK SMITH. *Correspondence Red Black*. 1962.
Galerie Chalette.

RICE PERLIRA. *The diagonal*. 1938.
Galerie Internationale.

iconography or from documentation, art has risen to the most intimate penetration of the phenomenon of reality and of life. « Art, » says Max Bill, « has thus become a branch of philosophy, the one part of the representation of existence. »

It must be added that the same evolution is to be observed in music and poetry as well as in the plastic arts. In all these can be seen a liberation as much from the old norms as from a subjection to an exterior theme, so that creation now is guided only by inner spiritual necessities.

For Bill the fundamental norms of concrete art are simplicity, clarity, and harmony. Like Mondrian, he sees in the new art an ethical content. For him, concrete art brings a message of pure harmony and universality, a constructive order, an optimism opposed to the anguish of the man of our times and the pessimistic and disintegrating forces enveloping him.

Josef Albers was born in 1888 in Bottrop, Germany. He attended courses at the Art Academy in Munich in 1919 and 1920, and later, from 1920 to 1923, at the Bauhaus. In 1924 he was named professor of this institute, and continued in this capacity until its close in 1933. From Germany he went to the United States, where he was head of the Art Department at Black Mountain College in North Carolina until 1949. From 1934 to 1937 he took part in the annual exhibitions of the « Abstraction-Création » group in Paris, and also became a member of the « American Abstract Artists » association. From 1950 to 1959 he was Chairman of the Department of Design at Yale University.

He has had more than one hundred exhibitions in the United States and abroad, and his work appears in many museums, institution and buildings in the Americas and throughout the world. At present he lives in New Haven, Connecticut.

Albers's specialty in the beginning was painting on transparent or opaque glass, but he also dedicated himself to woodcuts, linoleum, engraving, and photography.

During his stay at the Bauhaus he began a series of experiments in planimetric painting. Albers can be considered as the actual originator of the experiments in serial forms, produced in 1926. Later he studied the presentation of geometric volumes and perspective on a plane, creating works on a principle that could be defined as « intricacies of perspectives. » For this he used two simultaneous geometric perspectives based on the optical illusion of the stair. These perspectives neutralized each other, and alternated, giving a curious mobility to the forms. Motivated by Gestalt research, Albers conducted important experiments on the phenomena of optical illusion. The importance of Albers has grown with time, as he penetrated deeper into the problems of plastics, but the work by which he gained international renown is the one that developed in his later years during his American period and that corresponds to his experiments on the activity of color. His famous *Homage to the Square* shows how he utilized a single theme: three or four squares inserted one into another, developing on this theme all the possibilities of the color in its interaction. This activity of Albers was to exercise a considerable influence over the new generation of American painters, who were oriented toward explorations into the field of pure visuality in color.

Another artist of importance in the present concrete art movement is the Swiss Richard Paul Lohse, born in 1902 in Zurich. He is self-taught, and is a painter and engraver. Beginning with neoplasticism, he launched into wider investigations in this line. Like Bill, he accepts a mathe-

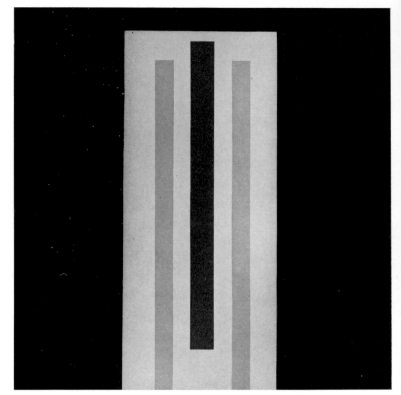

Burgoyne Diller. *First theme.* 1964.
Galerie Chalette.

matical basis for art, and declares that geometry is his work tool.

Lohse considered that the passage from abstraction (that is, the point of departure in nature) to concrete form (that is, the point of departure in mind) has established possibilities for art that are not easy to foresee. The aspect that for the present is evident from this change is the ever-greater simplification of forms and compositions. In contrast with the multiplication of geometric forms of abstractions, there appears a tendency to the formation of types (resulting from the simplification and purification of forms). These types tend to unite in groups that constitute actual formal complexes in which the variety of form is

found. To understand this process it is necessary to imagine the form reduced, so to speak, to its atomic component: the line, and later the formation, by the combination of lines, give the « formtype, » as in chemistry one obtains new substances by a combination of atoms. The advantage of this group of types lies in creating open structures that tend to expand and multiply into infinity, in a given order, in opposition to the customary closed structure in which everything is thought out so that the plastic activity does not extend beyond the limits of the picture.

Further along, when examining the new constructivist tendencies, we shall see that the idea of an open structure is dominant among a large group of the new artists.

The utilization of types in serial form permits Lohse to obtain an objective rhythm, with which he has had special success, and which can be considered as one of the fundamental factors in his plastic arrangements. Through this objective rhythm Lohse transmits to us — with an intensity not often equaled — the visual sensation of time. The lines utilized, in accordance with neoplastic ideas, are straight in their vertical and horizontal positions, outlining orthogonal forms that generally are the result of the sum of squares. These forms have a logical development in accordance with his conception of groups, but the handling of these permits the forms, in themselves unalterable and rigid, to compose figures of unsuspected flexibility.

The dynamics of the forms is supplied by the color. They are plain and uniform and limited to no more than five colors for each picture, but often using the oppositions of cold and warm colors and the variations of intensity among them. The colors are also allocated according to a logical development and in groups, in such a manner that the color acts as a counterpoint to the forms, giving the whole a singular mobility and variability. In this way, by always subordinating the development of the plastic theme to unchanging prin-

ciples, he obtains, through the interplay of forms and colors, the most extensive variability within the strictest regularity.

As a follower of Mondrian, Lohse has developed orthogonalism in an exceptionally fecund and variable way and with an apparently severe and unspoiled art. Through rigorously calculated structures, he obtains a visual richness that at times reaches a true poetic quality. This evidently is the poetry of geometry of which Novalis speaks.

Lohse's works — which, with those of Bill, Albers, and the last works of Vantongerloo, constitute the most important contribution of concrete art in the postwar period — make him a true pioneer of serial conception, a conception later taken up by Vasarely.

Many Swiss artists also worked in the concrete idiom. Among those who deserve to be mentioned are Camille Graeser, Leo Leuppi, and Walter Bodmer. The work of Graeser, who was born in Geneva in 1892, developed along neoplastic lines. Leuppi, born in 1893 in Zurich, works in a freer geometric abstraction style; he was founder and president of the « Allianz » group, which united the modern Swiss artists of abstract as well as surrealist tendencies. Bodmer was born in Basel in 1903; he is the creator of original constructions in wire reliefs supported on boards.

The evolution of abstract art in the United States

Around 1945 the United States proved to be the country where the abstract movement was most widely diffused. Artists of this tendency are very numerous throughout the various states, with the most active centers in New York, Chicago, and the state of California.

The abstract evolution in America was not a post-

Madí group. Salon des Realités Nouvelles. 1953.

war phenomenon but had started simultaneously with the European movements. The process, however, was slower and in the beginning was oriented toward the French teachers, and in its development sponsoring bodies and amateurs were particularly influential, succeeding by their enthusiasm and by their education of the public and artists in bringing it to its present state.

The vanguard

To explain this exceptional development, a brief history of the vanguard in the United States is necessary. It began with the solitary and tenacious work of the notable pioneer, the photographer Alfred Stieglitz, who died in July, 1946. In his New York gallery at 291 Fifth Avenue, in the

ATANASIO SOLDATI. *Last stars*. Galleria Nazionale d'Arte Moderna.

years preceding the First World War, Stieglitz introduced the vanguard movement from Paris, particularly the fauves, the cubist, and the *douanier* Rousseau. He defended this work through publications, articles, lectures, and especially in his own controversial review *291* (the street number of the gallery), founded in 1915, in whose honor Picabia published his review, *391*, in Barcelona. Stieglitz vigorously took the part of the first abstractionists. Arthur G. Dove, in particular, owes it to Stieglitz that he was able to continue in his work.

But the great event that marked a historic phase in painting in America was the Armory Show in 1913, where the works of some cubists were shown, and the star exhibit was Marcel Duchamp's *Nude Descending a Stairway*. In the same show were works by the first American abstractionists living in Paris: Stanton Macdonald-Wright, Morgan Russell, and Patrick Henry Bruce (1881-1937).

Macdonald-Wright returned to the United States in 1916. In Paris he had founded a movement called synchromism, a form of abstraction based on the pure action of color similar to the simultaneism of Delaunay. Though his influence on the American scene was almost nonexistent, he has exhibited both nationally and internationally, and is the author of *Treatise on Color*, *A History of Mosaics*, and a work in Japanese, *Beyond Esthetics*.

Of great importance after Stieglitz were the collectors and galleries that were oriented toward the art of the extreme vanguard. Let us enumerate the facts chronologically. In 1920 the Société Anonyme, which began by bringing together the works of the most important painters of the 20th century, was founded by Duchamp and Katherine S. Dreier. This collection was presented to Yale University in 1941, and may be seen there. Somewhat later, about 1927, A. E. Gallatin founded the Gallery of Living Art, which later came to be the museum of the same name. Today, incorporated with the museum in Philadelphia, it has a large collection of modern painting, especially in the abstract field.

The foundation of the Museum of Modern Art in New York in 1929 by a large group of modern art enthusiasts constitutes the most important event in the evolution of art in the United States. In 1936 the director, Alfred Barr, organized a famous exhibition called « Cubism and Abstract Art, » accompanied by the publication of an important book of the same title. Although this museum displayed only slight interest in abstract art for some time, it contributed to the knowledge of the previous vanguard schools.

The Solomon R. Guggenheim Foundation created a museum that at first was called the Museum of Nonobjective Art, and it undertook the difficult task of spreading the idea of abstract art. Notwithstanding the particular predilection for artists of secondary merit by the museum's first director, Hilla Rebay, herself a painter, the museum soon possessed an important collection of Kandinsky's work. In its later evolution, the museum became the showplace of the vanguard in all its phases. It changed direction and name (it is now called the Solomon R. Guggenheim Museum), and is one of the focal points of information concerning contemporary international art. At present under the directorship of Thomas M. Messer, it enjoys, at the time of writing, the inestimable collaboration of the noted English critic Lawrence Alloway.

Another important event was the founding of the « American Abstract Artists » association in 1936, stimulated by the painter George L. K. Morris. The highest point of activity of this group was achieved during the war when some of the most important artists who had emigrated from Europe – Mondrian, Moholy-Nagy, Léger, and Albers – joined it. The association represented only a limited number of American artists, and chiefly those with an orientation toward pure plasticity.

SERGE POLIAKOFF. Dotremont Collection, Brussels.

It could be said that all the European currents had their counterparts within this organization. The oldest is the one derived from cubism; following in importance is neoplasticism, stimulated by the presence of Mondrian in New York. Moholy-Nagy also made his influence felt, and Kandinsky did so through the Museum of Nonobjective Art.

Another, and different, influence came with

Hans Hofmann and his academy, who inspired an expressionistic abstraction. But there are also many less classifiable tendencies. The oldest American abstractionists figure in the current that sprang from cubism. Stanton Macdonald-Wright and Morgan Russell, trained in Paris, had no appreciable effect on American circles; both abandoned abstraction in 1919. The work of Stuart Davis has been influential. Born in Philadelphia in 1894, he exhibited at the Armory Show in 1913, and since then has worked in the cubist style. He has completed several murals, among them those at Radio City. His abstractions bear the typical cubist stamp but tend to reflect daily life in the spirit that animated some of the work of Léger, and it seems certain that Davis's work influenced some of the new pop artists.

Early American abstractionists

Among the abstractionists of the first epoch it is necessary to mention Arthur G. Dove (1880-1945). His abstractionism derived rather from fauvism and always sprang from a natural motif handled with great economy of the medium.

Karl Knaths, who was born in Eau Claire, Wisconsin, in 1891, united the cubism of Braque with the color of fauvism. His is a predominantly chromatic abstraction. He has exhibited in many U. S. museums and abroad, and has won the Carnegie Institute and Altman prizes.

A. E. Gallatin was born in Pennsylvania in 1882 and died in 1952; he began his abstraction in 1936. Beside being a painter, he was a writer and essayist.

George L. K. Morris, born in New York in 1906, began to practice abstraction in 1932. He was the founder of the « American Abstract Artists » association. His work appears in many American universities. He was U. S. painting delegate to the 1952 UNESCO Conference in Venice, Italy, and is Artist-in-Residence, St. John's College, Annapolis, Maryland.

Burgoyne Diller was born in New York in 1906. A pupil of Mondrian and also of Hofmann, his work was oriented toward neoplasticism. Later he painted in a more rhythmic style, in a manner similar to that of the Swiss painter Lohse.

Fritz Glarner was born in Zurich, Switzerland, in 1899. Until his thirty-seventh year he lived in Paris, but now is an American citizen. He was a close friend of Mondrian's whose influence is seen in his work. He has exhibited both nationally and internationally, and has had three one-man shows.

Harry Holtzman was born in New York in 1912. He knew Mondrian in Paris, promoted his move to New York, and was the executor of Mondrian's estate. Holtzman's painting falls within the neoplastic idiom.

Ilya Bolotowsky was born in St. Petersburg, Russia, in 1907. He began his abstractions in 1932. He was one of the founders of the « American Abstract Artists » in 1936, was head of the Art Department at Black Mountain College from 1946 to 1948, associate professor of art at the University of Wyoming from 1948 to 1957, and professor of art at the New York State University at New Paltz. He compiled a Russian-English art dictionary in 1962.

Leon Polk Smith was born in Chickasha, Oklahoma, in 1906; his work is close to neoplasticism. He has had one-man exhibitions in New York, and has exhibited nationally and internationally.

Giorgio Cavallon was born in Sorio, Italy, in 1904. Though he was a pupil of Hans Hofmann, he turned toward neoplasticism; he uses varying and resplendent colors. He is Artist-in-Residence, University of North Carolina, at Greensboro.

Harry Bertoia, sculptor, was born in Italy in 1915. He was active in California and now works in Pennsylvania. Bertoia employs a technique of rhythmic tension through groups of lines. His work appears at MGM Technical Center, St. Louis, and Dulles International Airport.

Karel J. Biederman was born in 1906 in Cleveland, Ohio. He works in reliefs of neoplastic tendency. Biederman is the author of several books, one of the best known being *Art as the Evolution of Visual Knowledge*, which was extremely influential, chiefly on Victor Pasmore, in the resurgence of plastic concretism in England. He has exhibited nationally and internationally.

Adolf Richard Fleischmann was born in 1902 in Esslingen, Germany. He has been active in the United States since 1952. His work is along neoplastic lines, and appears in institutes and museums in the U. S. and abroad.

Irene Rice Pereira was born in 1907 in Boston. In 1937 she exhibited her first abstract work. She departed from neoplasticism, but vitalized the planes through overlapping orthogonal forms and the toning of surfaces. She has worked in spatial paintings on glass with two panes of glass in which part of the form is seen in the transparency. She is the author of five books.

Carl Holty was born in Freiburg, Germany, in 1900 but was brought to the United States in the year of his birth. His work is in the neoplastic idiom. He is an instructor and lecturer.

Many of these artists ceased working or disappeared during the formidable upswing of abstract expressionism, but returned on the scene with the recent upsurge of optical currents in the United States. This has happened with Leon Polk Smith and Lorser Feitelson, who became outstanding members of the hard-edge school.

Concrete art in Argentina

The beginning of geometric art in Argentina was heralded in 1944 by the appearance of the single number of the review *Arturo* in Buenos Aires, which embraced the plastic artists and poets. Arden Quin, Kosice, and Maldonado collaborated on this review; later they independently promoted various manifestations of Argentinian concrete art. These artists resolutely turned their backs on the country's traditional painting, and instead took as their precursor, justifiably and with foresight, the notable Uruguayan artist Torres García, one of the most original and creative artists that the American continent has produced.

The artists of the « Arturo » group, for the first time in Argentina, cultivated a nonfigural art without any geometric base. Though this group was soon dissolved, Arden Quin, Gyula Kosice, and Martín Blaszko were the central figures in a new group formed in 1945, which in 1946 became the Madí movement. Also founded in 1945 was the « Arte Concreto - Invención » association (which later turned into the « Arte Concreto » group), headed by Maldonado, and in which Raul Lozza, Hlito, Manuel Espinosa, Ennio Iommi, Claudio Girola, Lidy Prati, and Sousa; some time later, also Gregorio Vardánega and Virgilio Villalba were active. This concrete art group had a tremendous influence on the development of present-day Argentinian art. The Madí group split in 1947; on one side were Arden Quin and Blaszko, on the other Kosice, who launched the Madinensor movement. Lozza broke away from the « Arte Concreto - Invención » association, and in 1948 founded perceptism. The « Arte Concreto » group, whose teachings came directly from the Swiss Max Bill, soon dwindled to only the painters Hlito and Prati and the sculptors Iommi and Girola. The rest worked as independent artists.

The artists before the « Arturo » group, in spite of

JEAN ATLAN. *Oil.* 1945.

the formal differences that separated them, united in proclaiming a scientific esthetic, stemming from a materialist ideology, eliminating all emotionalism of the romantic type, everything instinctive, and especially the metaphysical and fantastic. Instead of the irrational, they named the rational as the creative source, and substituted the word « creation, » which appeared to have occult origins, for the word « invention, » which related to faculties obviously intellectual. They proposed an objective art against the subjective of whatever persuasion; their chief enemy appeared to be surrealism. The text of the catalog of the first Madí exhibition in 1946 speaks of « founding an art of mathematical spirit, cold, dynamic, cerebral, dialectic. » And the Inventionist-Concrete Manifesto, in the same year, 1946, proclaims that « scientific esthetics will replace the thousand-year-old speculative and idealist esthetics, » and goes on to quarrel with « the existentialist and romantic weevil. »

The two movements attempted to depart completely from all emotional content, and for this reason they resorted to geometric images. The concretists were interested in the ideal form (the « good form » as Max Bill defined it), and used fundamental geometric figures – straight lines, rectangles, circles – with utmost rigor, elimi-

WILLI BAUMEISTER. *Am Orontes.* 1954.

nating all traces of the brushwork from the surface, all marks of the individual work of the artist to achieve a maximum of impersonality. The Madí artists, although respecting the central idea of geometrics, proceeded to a greater imagination and freedom of organization, and began to break with the traditional orthogonal conception of the picture by introducing a frame that was irregular and even jagged. The perceptism of Lozza brought the opposition to the traditional concept of the picture to the extreme limit, freeing and separating the formal geometric elements that act independently in space in direct relation with the wall.

In Buenos Aires almost at the same time, 1948, the sculptor Lucio Fontana launched his first manifesto of spatialism, a teaching the artist was to develop in Italy where he produced all his works in this idiom, identifying himself with the Italian school. He did not leave any followers in Buenos Aires.

In 1948 Arden Quin departed for Paris, remaining there until 1953. There the Madí group was revived with artists who were working in the French capital, among them the Venezuelan Guevara, the Argentinian Wolf Roitman, and the Frenchman Georges Sallaz. They exhibited in a group in the Salon des Réalités Nouvelles of 1953. In the same year Arden Quin returned to Buenos Aires, and the group in Paris dissolved.

Concrete art in Italy

The abstract movement in Italy sprang from the transformation of futurism, and in that sense two of the foremost plastic artists, Umberto Boccioni and Giacomo Balla, acquired importance as precursors of this movement.

Futurism could be considered to have oriented toward abstraction in 1929 through the work of two of its exponents, Enrico Prampolini and Munari, who exhibited abstract works in the Venice Biennale in that year.

In Milan in 1933 the first abstract showing of another futurist, Atanasio Soldati, took place in the Galleria del Milione. This gallery, directed by the abstract painter Virginio Ghiringhelli, must be considered as the first center of diffusion of abstractism in Italy, aided also by the publication of a bulletin.

The outstanding names of this first period are Oswald Licini, Soldati, Veronesi, Fausto Melotti, Mario Radice, Bruno Munari, Ghiringhelli, and Mauro Reggiani.

After the war, the first movement directed toward abstraction was the New Front of the Arts, which in 1946 gathered abstract and semiabstract (neocubist) artists together: Renato Birolli, Renato Guttuso (who later became the leader of social realism), Armando Pizzinato, Giuseppe Santomaso, and Emilio Vedova, and the abstract Venetian sculptor Alberto Viani. Joining later were the Roman abstractionists Antonio Corpora and Turcato.

In 1948, through the initiative of Atanasio Soldati, the Movement of Concrete Art (MAC) was founded in Milan; it soon became the most active in all Italy. In a short time there was not a single Italian city of any importance from Naples to Como that did not have a local abstract group or exponent. As it would be impossible to mention them all, we are confining our remarks to only a few of the places where the activity was most important.

In Rome the movement was intense, and this city became one of the most active centers of modern art. Of the artists working there before the war, the most important was Prampolini, who was attached to the futuristic movement. He was one of the first to turn to abstraction, and executed some notable works in abstract mosaics. Later the sculptor Consagra, and afterward the painters Turcato, Corpora, and Corrado Cagli, increased the number.

Carla Accardi, Piero Dorazio, Achille Perilli, Pietro Consagra, Turcato, and Antonio Sanfilippo, a group of young artists in Rome, founded the movement called « Forma I, » in 1947. This movement was instituted to rectify the problematic neocubism of the Italian vanguards; all its artists felt the influence of Magnelli, and later evolved toward freer and more divergent ventures. Three of them, Dorazio, Perilli, and Lorenzo Guerrini, founded the gallery and group called « L'Age d'Or. » A young painter of great promise belonging to the « L'Age d'Or » group, and who exhibited there, was Rotella (who later became a pioneer of the torn poster).

A younger group made their appearance in Florence, formed by six painters, one of whom, Bozzolini, went to France to become part of the School of Paris. The remaining five were Gualterio Nativi, Vinicio Berti, Mario Nuti, Alvaro Monnini, and Bruno Brunetti. They gave their group the name « Classical Abstraction, » for, as they affirmed, they came from the formalist tradition of Renaissance Florence.

In Venice the most interesting abstractionist was Emilio Vedova, at this moment one of the most important in Italy. His paintings then were vehement, even within the spirit of a certain geometric accommodation.

Milan became the center of activity for the abstractionists, where the veteran Soldati figured in the front rank. Most of the Milanese artists took the name of concretists. In particular Munari commanded much interest by his inventiveness and exceptional quality, in which traces of dadaist humor were to be found; he created useless machines, illegible books (enchanting works in which all the drama is conveyed by pure colors), mobiles (influenced by Calder), and sculptures made with metal nets. Another artist, Lucio Veronesi, produced abstract films, woodcuts, abstract photographs, and graphic arts. Also belonging to the Milanese group are Dova, Gianni Monnet, Galliano Mazzon, Gillo Dorfles (better known as a critic and commentator), and, in the direction of mathematical concretism, Bombelli and Huber. In Naples, Guido Tatafiore and De Fusco were outstanding among the group working there; in Turin a group was active whose most important members were Moreni and Mario Davico; and in Como the old abstract artists Radice and Manlio Rho worked.

The appearance in Rome of the « Origine » group began as a turning away from geometric abstraction in favor of instinctivist and vitalist abstractionism. The members of this group were the Roman artists Burri, Capogrossi, and Ettore Colla, and the Milanese painter Ballocco, who spread their ideas through the review *AZ*, which Ballocco published.

Free abstraction

The name « free abstraction » is a name I arbitrarily give to a type of painting that developed along the general lines of prewar painting outside the geometric tendency, freely following the impulses from the School of Paris or from artists such as Klee. The most important among the first to appear in this field in the postwar period were, in France, three Russian artists of the School of Paris, De Staël, Poliakoff, and Lanskoi, and the Algerian Atlan; and, in Germany, Willi Baumeister and Julius Bissier, who in spite of having studied and worked before the war, produced their major works in the postwar era. These artists, although not strictly formalists, did not provoke the rupture the first informalists had intended, but their work nevertheless contributed to opening new perspectives in present-day painting. If a clean distinction were to be made between geometric and lyrical abstraction, these painters would fall into an intermediate zone between the two.

Since 1945 there have been many artists of abstract painting who occupy this intermediate zone between informalism and formal abstraction, particularly among the School of Paris (Pierre Tal Coat, Zao-Wu-Ki, Benard Saby, Key Sato, Raoul Ubac, Maria Elena Vieira da Silva, Jean Piaubert, and others), but also in Italy (Afro, Santomaso, and others), Germany (Ernest Wilhelm Nay, Fritz Winter, Heinz Trökes, Georg Meistermann), England (Keith Vaughan, Roger Hilton, William Scott, Peter Lanyon, Adrian Heath), the United States (Corrado Marca-Relli, Richard Pousette Dart, and many more), Belgium (Van Lint, Bram van Velde), and Greece (Jannis Spyropoulos). Many are excellent artists and bring an original view. Some of them will be dealt with in

JULIUS BISSIER. *Ascona III.* 1958. Anne Abels Gallery.

this work, but an analysis of all of them would transcend the extent of a volume dedicated to the new tendencies.

Nicolas de Staël was born in St. Petersburg (now Leningrad), Russia, in 1914. After the Russian Revolution he was brought first to Poland and then, in 1922, to Brussels. In 1932 he attended the Academy of Fine Arts in Brussels, and from 1933 onward he traveled about Europe, spending a long time in Spain. In 1935 he returned to Belgium, but soon thereafter undertook another long journey to Morocco and Algiers. At the outbreak of the war he enlisted in the Foreign Legion. Discharged, he lived in Nice from 1940, and in 1943 he was in Paris. De Staël appeared to be pursued by a tragic fate. For many years his pictures attracted only a small circle of cognoscenti, and he lived in misery; when economic success finally arrived, he was consumed by melancholy, and committed suicide in Antibes in 1955. De Staël's abstract period began in 1942, but in the last part of his life he returned to figural painting maintaining the same structure and quality. He used to say: « I need to feel life before me, and to take it all in so that it penetrates through the eyes and the skin. » His painting therefore has a vital quality, something tactile and vibrant, achieved without vehemence. His impasto is heavy but without aggressiveness, modeled in such a manner that the surface can play with the lights; the color is exquisitely musical; the space conveys an intense expressive force. De Staël is one of the painters of the highest order to appear in the postwar era.

Serge Poliakoff was born in Moscow in 1906. In 1919 he left Russia, traveling between Constantinople, Belgrade, and Berlin, earning his livelihood by playing the guitar. In 1923 he came to Paris, and in 1930 he began to attend the academy of painting of the Grande Chaumière. From 1935 to 1937 he was in London, studying at the Slade School, but 1937 saw him again in Paris, where he knew Kandinsky. After 1938 he became an abstract painter, and in 1947 he won the Kandinsky prize.

Poliakoff's painting can be classed as neocubist. He organizes the surface freely in a continuation of precise planes, of sharp, rectilinear contours, but without falling into a rigorous geometricality. His colors are sober, severe, of low gamma, and the surfaces are toned in such a manner as to achieve an intense vibration of the planes.

André Lanskoi was born in Moscow in 1902, and arrived in Paris in 1921. His painting, fun-

damentally chromatic, is achieved by short brush-strokes of intense color juxtaposed on the all-over principle, which creates a vibrant, mobile surface.

Jean Atlan was born in Constantine, Algeria, in 1913, of Judeo-Berber parents, and died in Paris in 1960. Atlan installed himself in Paris and began painting in 1942. His painting slowly acquired the mastery and personality that were to characterize it in the last years of his career. The canvas is structured by means of arabesques of heavy, uniform black tracery, that contort and cross the space, dividing it into sections, and giving a sense of severe rhythm to the picture. He used canvases of coarse weave, the texture of which he preserved in the picture, thus obtaining background effects of great expressive intensity.
Atlan's work, hovering between lyrical and formal abstraction, has not failed to influence the new generations by its originality and strength. The followers of the « Cobra » group consider Atlan and Dubuffet as the precursors of their search. Atlan said of painting: « Valid forms partake of the cosmic potencies of the metamorphosis, where the true adventure lies. »

Willi Baumeister was born in Stuttgart in 1889. After the First World War he produced a figural painting very close to that of Léger, but after the Second World War he recognized the attraction that surrealism had for him, and also, probably, Miró. He changed his painting completely, producing a poetic abstraction owing as much to Miró as to Klee, but with a very personal tone, on a base of free and fluid forms in a pictorial space of very subtle texture, with which he obtained an expressive vibration of the surface. In 1952 he won first prize at the Biennale in São Paulo. He died in 1955.

Julius Bissier was born in Freiburg, Germany, in 1893. Although his first exhibitions date from 1920, his work attained full maturity in the postwar era, and he became known after being given the Jubiläum award in São Paulo. He was a friend of Baumeister and Schlemmer, and his first work up to 1930 (which was destroyed) belonged to the « Neue Sachlichkeit » (New Objectivity) school. Bissier's latest painting consists of small compositions, generally tempera or gouache, hovering between color sketch and calligraphy. Uncertain, trembling figures, almost splashes, that vaguely contain forms of objects – vases, bottles, amphorae – are exquisitely illuminated by tenuous and diluted colors, distributed over the surface in rhythmic and mobile units. His forms are fragile, transparent, and floating, as it were, in an unreal space. Bissier's art is one of extreme, muted purity, with the intense lyricism of a short poem.

Chapter two

Reaction against concrete art

Dubuffet, Fautrier, Wols, Mathieu

The most important phenomenon of the postwar period, for its consequences, was the appearance of two French painters who were to revolutionize profoundly the ideas and concepts of what was then the vanguard. They were Dubuffet and Fautrier. These two painters were in many ways similar; they did not indulge in the polemics about abstract and figural art, but both, although they practiced figural painting, proved more negative to the cause of figural painting (whether traditional, cubist, or fauve) than to geometric abstraction itself. They proved more negative because they questioned the very essence of what was understood by painting, founded still, even among the vanguard, on lines, forms, and color on an even surface.

There were certain differences between their work: Fautrier was more strictly plastic; Dubuffet more aggressive and polemical. In Fautrier's work there is nothing of the grotesque, which Dubuffet delights in. But they have in common their determined break with the whole esthetic tradition.

Jean Dubuffet was born in Le Havre in 1901. In 1918 he went to Paris to study painting, and for a short time attended courses at the Julian Academy. Later he avidly studied ethnology, literature, philosophy, and music, and painted a little. In 1924 he abandoned everything for business. He traveled to Buenos Aires as an industrial designer, but after six months returned to France. In 1930, after trying various enterprises, he established himself as a wine merchant. Once more, in 1933, he tried his hand at painting, again abandoning it for business, until in 1942, in his forty-first year, he returned definitely to painting, with landscapes and still lifes of intense fauve colors. Then he embarked on an expressionism with distortion of figures, until in 1944 he began work based on graffiti. He held his first exhibition in the Drouin Gallery on October 20, 1944 – a historic date. Georges Limbour, originally a surrealist, but separated from the trend after its first purge, who became an early Dubuffet enthusiast (he wrote one of the first books about the painter), introduced him to Drouin. The exhibition of Dubuffet's now famous « heavy impastations » with the title of « Mirobulus, Macadam and Company » was held in 1946. The pictures were produced by a mixture of white lead, putty, coal dust, pebbles, pieces of glass, and rubble. In this paste he drew with a stick, knife, spoon, and even with his fingers the furrows that constituted the drawing. His colors were ochers, gray, and black as he searched for the natural color of the material. In 1945 the Pierre Matisse Gallery in New York showed works by Dubuffet that had wide repercussions, and their influence on the American vanguard cannot be ignored. In 1947 he also held an exhibition at Drouin of his portraits of various literary personages, which differ from caricatures by their violence and awesomeness. Dubuffet himself explains: « For a portrait to fulfill its function it first must almost cease to be a portrait. I like things brought to their extreme limit. Thus a painting must be at the very limit of not being a painting. » This utterance contains the key to his art, the principle of his total break with tradition.

In 1950 he exhibited his *Bodies of Ladies* – coarse, monstrous bodies, drawn with a refined heaviness guided by humor, and showing a kind of geological surface. In 1952 he abruptly gave up his painting in relief, and exhibited his « landscapes » (mental landscapes, philosophical stones). In 1953 he began his « assemblages » (a term Dubuffet preferred to collages), produced in the following manner: first he paints textures on paper or canvas; then he cuts these into pieces and uses the fragments of different pictures in the manner of collages. In that way he obtained the *Sols et Terrains*, a work of serene abstraction, removed from the violent expressionism of the « Mirobolus » or his portraits and his *Bodies of Ladies*.

In the same year he also showed his first series of assemblages with butterfly wings, which he was to repeat in 1955 and 1957. His « Texturologies » were exhibited in 1957, and in 1959 and 1960 his « Matériologies, » a series in which the material again emerges in relief. In 1964 he introduced his « Hourloupe » (a word invented by Dubuffet) series, of forms cut and spread over the plane in the all-over style.

Dubuffet works in successive series, thematically and structurally distinct, to avoid fossilization of a formula. Thus the smooth medium of his mental landscapes follow on the heaviness of his first works, and the heavy « Matériologies » follow the smooth « Texturologies. » In the « Hourloupes » he returns to a smooth medium. For him the visual texture in the smooth paintings has the same effects as the reliefs of the material.

To understand fully Dubuffet's principles one cannot exclude his ideas on *art brut*. According to this, a legitimate sense of art exists instinctively in simple and uncultured natures, or even in the mad or children. He organized in 1947 an exhibition of *art brut*, which had as subtitle « *art brut* as opposed to cultural arts. » This exhibition comprised works by artists who later were slated for distinction: the schizophrenic Wölfli (who already figured in Prinzhorn's book on art and madness), the Canadian Scottie Wilson, the shoemaker Gaston Chaissac (who later was to make a career in art and figure among the « stars » of the Iris Clert Gallery). The sum of the exhibited works constituted a notable collection that Dubuffet delivered to the Philippine millionaire and collector Alfonso Ossorio, who brought it to the United States. Recently Dubuffet has revived the idea of *art brut*, promoting the publication of a series of books on these primitive artists.

Although they may at certain points become confused, it is necessary to differentiate between the *art brut* artists and the primitive artists in the manner of the *douanier* Rousseau. In the *art brut* artist only one concern exists: to express himself; there are absolutely no esthetic pretensions. In the primitive artist the esthetic intention is always prevalent.

Dubuffet classifies his own art as *art brut*, and his friend Limbour's book, the first on the artist, has the title *The Art Brut of Dubuffet*. In his work Dubuffet derives inspiration from the pictorial expressions of children and of very simple and unsophisticated natures; he uses the elements of what is heavy, trivial, or grotesque to search for the original essence of things, the natural expression undistorted by culture. But the real rupture Dubuffet provoked in Western art emerges from his attacks on the traditional notion of beauty that had remained inviolate through cubism and abstract art.

Dubuffet declared himself an enemy of the idea in painting; only the spontaneous or, better still, the instinctive has value. In 1947 the publishing house Gallimard released a book with the title *Prospectus aux Amateurs de tout Genre*, containing Dubuffet's reflections. In it he says: « It is necessary to take nourishment from the inscriptions, from the instinctive tracings, to respect impulses, the ancestral spontaneity of the human hand in its desire to trace its signs. It is necessary to make men feel the weakness and clumsiness of man in every detail of the picture, as well as the inherent hazards of the material employed, the hazards of the hand (its fickleness, tics, its peculiar reactions). » And in another part he says: « I want to reveal things that were thought to be ugly, which men have forgotten to look at; they also are great marvels. I want to avoid all misconception: this is not humor or satire; my effort is to rehabilitate deprecated objects. My work is always an act of celebration. » And, completing the idea, he adds: « The function of the artist is to enlarge the conquest and annexation of worlds which appeared hostile to man; and if it is possible to transform into beauty a thing that formerly horrified us, the battle is won. » He thus proposes a theory of actual restoration of the

RICHARD PAUL LOHSE. *Pure elements concentrated in rhythmic groups.* 1949/56/1.

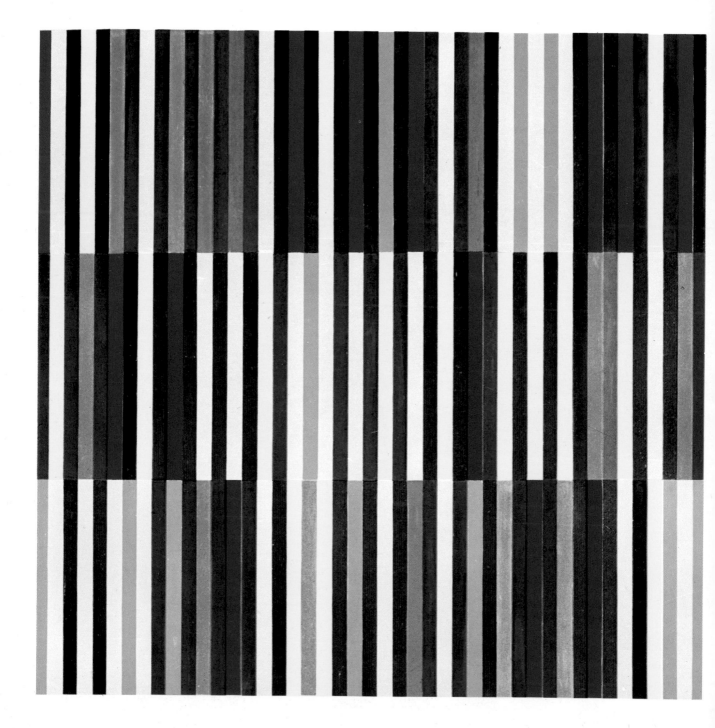

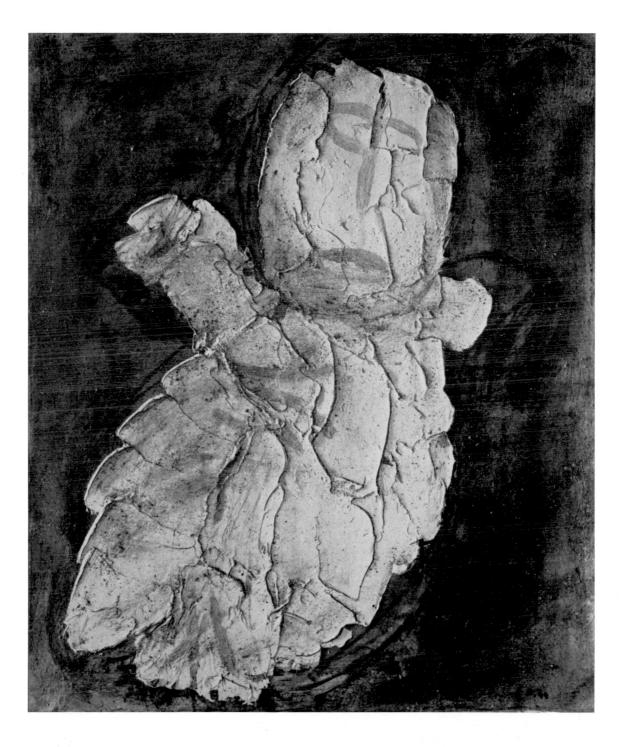

WOLS. *Oil.* 1947. Iolas Gallery.

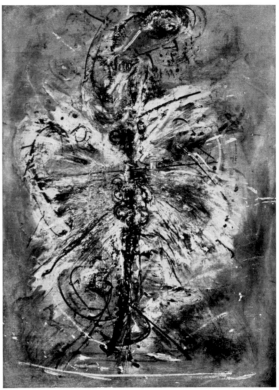

WOLS. *Oil.* 1949. Iolas Gallery.

world through the medium of art: the total restoration of things.

In the first text mentioned, Dubuffet speaks of hazard. This is a very important factor in his work. « The artist is tied to chance, » he says, « a hazard peculiar to the nature of the material he employs. » Dubuffet met this hazard, and placed it at the service of his quest for expressiveness. He has taken advantage of all expediencies of texture and of the quality of the material in order to construct, as he expresses it, « a keyboard of a new kind that permits the exploitation of resources heretofore unknown in painting. » Michel Tapié, who greatly admired him and who owes a large part of his impetus toward explorations in new esthetics to him, says on this matter: « Dubuffet gives to chance the role of " divo " formerly usurped by the science of composition and other concepts dear to these false prophets who are the esthetes. » Another of Dubuffet's concepts, ambiguously interpreted, is his idea of art as a *plaisanterie*, a joke. There is no doubt that this idea of art as a joke or diversion has spread to the most modern tendencies. But it must be explained that for Dubuffet it is a jest that provokes both laughter and fear at the same time. That is to say, what in the end he actually brings forth is a desperate, diabolical humor. « There is no art without inebriation, » he says, « but in that case a mad inebriety. To make reason totter! The highest degree of delirium! Immersion in burning madness! Art is the most impassioned orgy within reach of man! » This is the *plaisanterie* of Dubuffet. It is the great adventure,

Georges Mathieu. *Composition.* 1957.

with all the risks that this implies. Dubuffet is in the tradition of the French dramatist Alfred Jarry, the great pataphysical tradition.

The works of Dubuffet constitute the most violent attempt against the good taste and refinement of the French bourgeoisie, and, as always, perpetrated by one of its own class; Dubuffet was a prosperous wine merchant. Yet it is not solely against bourgeois good taste, but – and most particularly – against the good taste and refinement into which the vanguard had fallen, namely, geometric abstraction on the one hand, and on the other surrealism, which had lost its initial violent anti-artistic force and now entered into the period of the review *Minotaur*, which can be called the beginning of its artistic era.

For these reasons Dubuffet in the beginning was violently attacked by the critics, and denounced by Gaston Diehl, director of the Salon de Mai, by Waldemar George, and by René Huyghe (chief curator of the Louvre). But the poets and writers – Jean Paulhan, Ponge, Paul Eluard, Marcel Arland, and Limbour – upheld him. It must be added that Dubuffet is a solitary; he has never wanted to play the traditional part of a painter and has always refused to compete in the salons. In spite of his leaning on the instinctive and his search for original innocence, Dubuffet's art is not popular art. It is much more subtle and refined than the academic or esthetizing arts he opposes. It is so because it is rich in questions, in content, filled with effects of texture and material. His art gives due credit and significance to the totality of the existing, it poetizes the unpoetical, and offers an example of maximum freedom in creation. His example has opened the path for many who follow him, some of whom think that they owe nothing to him.

Jean Fautrier was born in Paris on May 16, 1898. Educated in England, he attended courses at the Royal Academy of Arts and the Slade School of London until his mobilization in 1917. After the war he established himself in Paris. He began painting in the expressionist manner, and in 1925 he exhibited with success in Paris. His palette turned somber and became uninteresting for the art dealers, until in 1945 he mounted his famous exhibition with the series « *Les Otages* » (The Hostages) in the Drouin Gallery, with an introduction by Malraux. In spite of his success among the intellectuals (Malraux and Paulhan upheld him), in order to make a living in the years between 1949 and 1953, he undertook to make reproductions of modern masters by a method of his own. In 1951 he exhibited in the show mounted in the Facchetti Gallery by Michel Tapié, with the title « *Signifiants de l'informel.* » In 1960 he shared the first prize of the Venice Biennale with Hans Hartung. He died in Paris on July 21, 1964.

Like Dubuffet, Fautrier exhibited thematic series at each showing, such as those of « boxes, » « objects, » « nudes, » « landscapes, » and so forth.

After his exhibition of « *Les Otages* » series in 1945, Fautrier became the most important forerunner of informal painting (the practically contemporary exhibit of Dubuffet's « *Hautes Pâtes* » must be mentioned, held only a few months later). In this exhibition, figuration (heads, torsoes) was reduced to a mere sign, but what attracted attention was the extremely heavy impasto, with conformations resembling hardened lava, which created an ample central relief on the canvas. This « matter painting, » which was then totally strange, was soon to enjoy a wide diffusion and to create a new style within a few years.

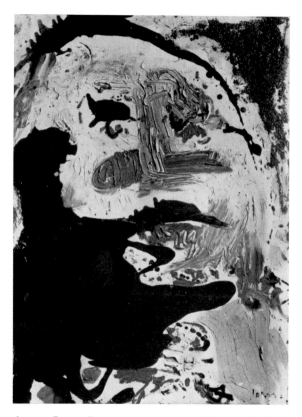

ASGER JORN. *Personage.* 1956. La Medusa Gallery.

In contrast to Dubuffet, Fautrier's work is neither aggressive nor polemical. On the contrary, a sort of calmness seems to flow from it. The surface of the impasto reveals very sober impressions of ample and regular spatula work. What is surprising is the contrast between the strong, almost aggressive quality of the relief of the impasto and the delicately tenuous traces of color with which they are covered. They are blue, ocher, and rose, very soft, almost transparent. But this apparent contrast helps Fautrier to give the medium a floating aspect of lightness, and more than anything it serves to create a sense of ambiguity in the work, something to which the artist was particularly given.

ASGER JORN. *The stubborn bird.* 1957.

Wols (the pseudonym for Alfred Otto Wolfgang Schulze) was born in Berlin on May 27, 1913. For a short time he frequented the Bauhaus, and after 1933 settled in Paris. There he had contact with the surrealists, particularly Max Ernst. He made his living as a photographer, and in 1937 he had an exhibition of photographs in the Pléiades Gallery. In 1939, at the outbreak of the Second World War, he was interned for fourteen months because he was a German subject. Later he was freed, and spent the rest of the war in Cassis, which belonged to the free zone of France. There his painting acquired the personality that came to characterize it. « In Cassis, » he said, « the rocks seen through a lens have made me look at human importance. »

Wols is the last of the great *peintres maudits*. Sartre gives a moving portrait of him in « Wols in Person, » which is included in his book *Sit-*

uations IV. Poisoned by alcohol, indifferent to things of the world, and filled with Oriental philosophy (he had a thorough knowledge of the Tao Teh Ching and the Bhagavad Gita), he was wont to say: « In every moment, in every thing is eternity. » He died, destroyed by alcohol after what appeared to have been a case of food poisoning, on September 1, 1951.

Wols's first exhibition at the Drouin Gallery was in 1945, and his exhibition in the same gallery in 1947 established him decisively and had far-reaching effects. Settled in Cassis, Wols began producing a great number of gouaches and drawings in small format, in which a fascination with the microscopic is evident. He continued this series on his return to Paris, but in his later years he began producing large canvases with vermiculate patterns, striated and splattered, an abstraction that was the first example of tachism, and in which in reality he merely wanted to fix « the supradimensional and transoptic bases of things. » At the end of his life he returned to figuration in fine, calligraphic sketches of ships, cities, and landscapes.

Wols's painting is fundamentally automatic and hallucinatory, and marks the extreme limit that the plasticism of the imaginary can reach. There is a mixture of sketched signs, spots, tracings, crosshatchings, all without apparent order in a kind of cobwebby reticule, at times resembling flowering algae with organic elements, all of it frequently developing from a center, ramifying starlike into a complex space. It suggests a dynamism similar to what certain growing organisms may exhibit. It is a manner of painting in which Wols endeavored to assimilate the unassimilable. Ultimately, his work is the unsurpassed source of a large part of informal painting that came afterward.

Georges Mathieu was born in Boulogne-sur-Mer, France, in 1921. He studied law and philosophy, and in 1942 he began painting. After the war he

KAREL APPEL. *Oil.* 1962. La Medusa Gallery.

CORNEILLE. *Night falls on a garden.* 1964.

appears to have been impressed by the heavy black graphism of Hartung. In 1947 he began painting directly from the tube, and the same year he held the first show of lyrical abstraction, with the title « *L'Imaginaire*, » which had an introduction by the critic J. J. Marchand. After this he became the sponsor for this movement. In 1950 he held his first exhibition at the Drouin Gallery, with pictures of violent, aggressive strokes that sprang from a dense central amorphous zone. He differed from Hartung in the heaviness of his medium, rough and of an exalted vehemence. In his later works he progressed toward the calligraphic style characteristic of him.

Mathieu upholds and practices a completely spontaneous painting, and its degree of spontaneity is determined by the rapidity of the execution. In May, 1956, for example, in front of an audience that filled the Sarah Bernhardt Theater in Paris, he painted, for the International Festival of Dramatic Art, a canvas 8 meters by 4 meters, entitled *Homage to Louis XIV*, in twenty minutes. Mathieu is a lover of this kind of painting-spectacle, and he has performed it in Japan, Europe, and America. According to him it is in the speed of execution that the possibility to express the *élan vital* resides. For this painter a work of art must represent a trilogy of « *jeu, fête, sacré* » (game, feast, and sacrament). The game contains the spontaneity, the possible discovery, but also the risk. The feast is an artificial but artistic exaltation of life, and the painting must emerge as a visual feast. The sacrament is ceremonial, and a conjuration of the immensity of the universe and the infinity of memory. Many of the titles of his pictures are taken from the history of feudal France, as a homage to this memory.

PIERRE ALECHINSKY. *Thrown into water.* 1965. La Medusa Gallery.

This whole conception is founded on a reactionary ideology of the purest kind (among other things, Mathieu is a monarchist), and it is accompanied by an exhibitionistic activity very similar to that of Dali's (with whom he shares a similarly reactionary ideology), although lacking the imagination and ingeniousness of the Catalan painter. In support of his ideas, he is fond of quoting T. S. Eliot: « Nothing that is not fundamentally traditional can be really new. »

His pictures consist of a central motif in an empty space. This central motif is no more than a calligraphic tracing lengthened very frequently with the character of a heading, and can be crossed or adorned by other, shorter, tracings. The mechanism of this tracing is always very similar, which explains the rapidity of execution: it consists of an integrated and more or less extended zigzag. The execution of this large sign is not automatic, but mechanical; thus this pictorial gesture is similar to a kind of tic, in which the freedom of the truly spontaneous is annulled.

Graphisms in their total inexpressiveness are widely separated from Oriental calligraphy, and justify the scorn with which the calligraphers of Japan have received the suggestion of any similarity.

« Cobra »

The « Cobra » movement sprang up as a result of the artistic activities of three small countries of northern Europe and as somewhat of an uprising against the School of Paris; in the end, that movement absorbed the « Cobra » group. The name « Cobra, » which was also the name of the review that was the organ of expression of the group, was formed by the first letters of the names of the three cities united in this group, COpenhagen, BRussels, and Amsterdam. In Copenhagen the nucleus consisted of the old Danish abstract-surrealist group in which Ejler Bille, Egill Jacobsen, and Asger Jorn figured. To these it is also necessary to add Karl-Heining Pedersen who, after the war, worked in a sort of elementarism with magic elements of surrealist origin. The Dutch part consisted of the Dutch experimental group, which published the review *Reflex*, and was formed by Karel Appel, Corneille, and George Constant. (Constant abandoned painting for many years but returned to it later, painting in a type of constructivism). In Belgium the principal impetus came from the poet Christian Dotremont, who had started in surrealism but then separated from the orthodox group to support a movement called « Revolutionary Surrealism, » which published one issue of a review of the same name. Dotremont, in collaboration with the young Belgian painter and poet Pierre Alechinsky, succeeded in uniting the three groups, and they published the review *Cobra.*

The group considered themselves as representing an International of Experimental Art. In 1949 they were joined by the German painter Karl-Otto Götz, who published the review *Méta*, the Icelander Gudnaçon, and the Frenchman Doucet, and they received the support and sympathy of Atlan. « Cobra » launched itself into the struggle against geometric painting, against pretty painting, and against hack painting, to « fuse the surrealist dream with concrete life into a romantic realism. » Two big exhibitions were held for the painters of « Cobra, » the first in the Stedelijk Museum in Amsterdam, in November, 1949, the second in the Palace of Fine Arts in Liége, in October, 1951. Soon after this second exhibition the group

was dissolved. The majority of its more active members live in Paris, and have been integrated in its school. Jorn had already exhibited in the Breteau Gallery in Paris in 1948. The Dutch group (Appel, Corneille, and Constant) exhibited in the Colette Allendy Gallery in 1949.

The surrealist origin of practically all the « Cobra » members is indisputable. The painter Constant said in *Cobra*, « Our desire is what makes revolution. » They search for absolute spontaneity, something that breaks with limits and shackles. All this contributed to a yearning for freedom, which resulted in a vehemence that is highly characteristic of a large number of the painters in the group. In the manifesto published in *Reflex* in 1948, the Dutch painters said, « A picture is no longer merely a construction of colors and lines, but an animal, a night, a scream, a human being, or all together. » The members of « Cobra » searched for their inspiration in folk art, in sketches by children, and in prehistoric art, as well as in the old Viking art and that of the Eskimos, and they showed an aversion for the cultural arts. In this they agreed with Dubuffet, for whom they felt the highest esteem. The same manifesto in the 1948 *Reflex* spoke of a liberty « that permits a man to express himself in accord with the exigencies of the instinct. »

The « Cobra » group lasted three years, and during this time ten issues of the review appeared. Simultaneously, a series of monographs were published with the title *Library of Cobra*, dedicated to the painters and sculptors of the group: Alechinsky, Appel, Atlan, Else Alfelt, Corneille, Doucet, Jorn, Henry Heerup, Ejler Bille, Karl-Heining Pedersen, Egill Jacobsen, Gilbert, Sonja Ferlov, Constant, and Gudnaçon.

The « Cobra » group, together with Dubuffet and Fautrier, constituted the great deviation from the painting of the postwar period: the idea of total liberty, the conquest of the antinomy between figuration and abstraction, and a tumultuous vitality, so uncontrolled that it created an apparent

LATASTER. *Come Liberty*. 1963/65. Paul Facchetti Gallery.

chaos, but curbed by an evident dynamic coherence. Exuberance prevailed in all of them, as did spontaneity of design and humor. In Alechinsky and Corneille there is more order in the headlong rush; in Jorn and Appel, all the vehemence possible, in such a manner that form and color are confounded one with the other, color becoming form and form color.

The « Cobra » group has exercised a healthy influence on contemporary European painting. Even today the fundamental principles that gave birth to the group may be seen in some of their followers. An example of this influence is evident in the « Spur » group of Munich (Heimrad Prem, Zimmer, and Sturm), which undoubtedly stemmed from Asger Jorn.

Asger Jorn was born in Vejrum, Jutland, Denmark, in 1914. In 1936 he went to Paris, where he studied with Léger. Léger introduced him to Le Corbusier, and thereafter Jorn and Le Corbusier collaborated in preparing the Pavilion of *L'Esprit Nouveau* in the Universal Exposition in Paris in 1937. Possibly the interest that Jorn showed in the problems of town planning dates from this time, an interest that later led to the creation of the International Situationist. In Denmark he belonged to the « Host » and « Spiralen » groups, and from the year 1948 to 1951 he was a member of « Cobra » and was one of its foremost proponents. In 1948 he had a one-man show in Paris in the Breteau Gallery, while in 1953, in collaboration with Baj, he formed the Bauhaus Imaginist in opposition to the Hochschule für Gestaltung founded by Max Bill. It was after this that he founded the International Situationist, with headquarters in Paris but with other branches, particularly in Italy and England. He settled in Paris in 1958. In 1962 he showed his « Disfigurations », which were paintings of landscapes and pompous figures that he had purchased in the Paris Flea Market and had changed by means of brushstrokes full of humor.

Jorn figures among the most restless and impassioned personalities of modern art. Constantly on the go, his avid curiosity always stimulated by his steely sense of humor, he penetrates into all possible fields of man's endeavor, without his paintings in any way being resented.

Jorn's work is profoundly instinctive, almost brutal, and of an intense vitality. He avails himself of the possibilities of violence in color, making it poetically shout in his pictures through vigorous brushstrokes that respond to large gestures, using intense contrasts. He uses a rudimentary figuration that seems to want to crumble under the overriding demonic rhythm of his impulsive, vehement brushstrokes. The whole gives an impression of wanting to turn all living forms back to their original state of pure organic matter, where the very principle of life begins, the life that it is necessary for each man to recover. In these impassioned pictures, sparkling with color, a deep irony is submerged, an irony that is the weapon with which the highest quality of what is vital is conquered.

Karel Appel was born in Amsterdam in 1921. In 1946 he was a member of the Dutch experimental group who expressed themselves through the *Reflex* review and who opposed the theories of Mondrian, the search for a style, formal purity, and all reasonable and harmonious construction. Appel was a cofounder of « Cobra » in 1948. Since 1950, when he exhibited in the Colette Allendy Gallery, he has resided in Paris. In 1952 he took part in an exhibition organized by Michel Tapié called « *Un art autre.* »

Appel begins with figurations having their inspiration in infantile scratchings and in folk imagery, achieved through violently traced images of complete spontaneity. He prefers primary colors, and uses them undiluted to delineate cross-hatchings inside the images. About 1958 he incorporated the vigorous brushstrokes that characterize action painting, and the picture is turned into matter in movement agitated by a particular frenzy, in a manner similar to that of Jorn. The art of Appel is fundamentally energetic; in the picture, form and space disappear to form a sort of graphic development of pure energy, apparently directed by chance.

In his more recent works Appel appears to return to a less disintegrating concept. His figures, expressionistic in quality, of schematic outlines but of explosive color, are defined with more precision and appear to be stabilized in a pictorial space that is more traditional. Lately he has also assiduously used collages of objects or various elements in the picture.

Corneille, a pseudonym for Cornelis van Beverloo, was born in 1922 in Liége, of Dutch parentage.

He was cofounder of the Dutch « Reflex » group in 1947 and cofounder of « Cobra » in 1948. In 1950 he settled in Paris.

Corneille is a lyricist of painting. His characteristics are organization of forms, serenity of narrative, and generous use of color, but with emphasis on their quality of seduction and not on their violence. Groups of visions, organic forms, symbols, vague stories of an unreal world spread over his picture in a controlled baroqueness of great plasticity. His themes are original and inimitable, and his work is among the best in the contemporary plastic arts.

Pierre Alechinsky was born in 1927 in Brussels. In 1947 he participated in the *La Jeune Peinture Belge* movement, and was a member of « Cobra » in 1948. In 1955 he took a long voyage to the Far East, and in Japan he studied Japanese calligraphy, producing a film on the subject. In 1957 he settled in Paris.

Alechinsky's work is characterized by the use of the all-over technique in almost all cases. This means that his canvases are completely covered with organic forms that interpenetrate and repeat themselves with slight variations. Frequently he includes figural elements that are scattered over the picture, usually eyes, fragments of bodies, sketches of grimacing visages blending with abstract biomorphic elements, creating an organic universe that might be as much in the process of forming as of disintegrating. The picture acquires a particular mobility, as if trembling with minute life or moving, tentacular forms, and at the same time it has an air of burlesque. His color does not approach the violence that is Jorn's or Appel's; many of his pictures are, actually, monochrome. He uses reds, greens, blues, and whites, but without any of them dominating the picture.

Karl-Heining Pedersen, a self-taught painter and a cofounder of the « Cobra » group, was born in Copenhagen in 1913. He is married to Else Alfelt, another « Cobra » painter.

Pedersen's motifs, as is often the case with the painters of the « Cobra » group, are inspired by folklore, and in his technique he follows an elementary design, a crude and spontaneous image, sketched in a manner of the primitives. In his canvases, figures, masks, birds, and fantasmal beings appear, transmitting a nightmarish atmosphere.

Lucebert, whose real name is Van Swaanswijk, was born in Amsterdam in 1924. He is a leader of experimental Dutch poetry, and a self-taught painter. He exhibited with the « Cobra » group in the Stedelijk Museum in 1949. His paintings, less violent in execution, utilize images of a sarcastic expression.

Related to the « Cobra » group because of his affinity of style is Ger Lataster. Born in Schaesberg, Netherlands, in 1920, Lataster studied at the Academy of Fine Arts in Amsterdam. He is a gesture painter, and his works have great impetuosity and use explosive colors; his painting, although completely abstract, is close to the work of Appel and Jorn.

Chapter three

Informalism as the dominant international tendency

We have said that at the end of the war two tendencies manifested themselves: one appeared to be dominant, and brought with it the constructive spirit that generally follows upon a period of destruction; the other was charged with impulses of protest, romantic vehemence, and a hunger for vitality, which were also the consequences of a catastrophe, on the one hand because it was concerned with the purely vital; on the other, because it was a protest against a world ruled by reason which gave evidence of insensitivity. This second tendency began with an almost complete rejection by the critics, who were particularly irritated by two pioneers, Dubuffet and Jackson Pollock (the latter was nicknamed Jack the Dripper in the United States), and with the indifference of the public; nevertheless it rapidly gained acceptance owing to a general satiation with the uncompromisingly geometric exercises into which the so-called constructivist or concrete tendencies had fallen.

In part, the new tendency evolved from the abstract expressionism that Kandinsky practiced before the First World War, which two Germans in Paris, Wols and Hartung, introduced with a new twist added; and in part it was sustained by the new contributions of the two French figural artists, Fautrier and Dubuffet. A parallel movement was developing in the United States, following on the determined experiments and automatic techniques brought by surrealism.

In Paris all these preparations suddenly took on the character of an organized movement, and the first evidence of it was given at the Luxembourg Gallery with an exhibition organized by Mathieu under the name of « The Imaginary »: the catalog carried an introduction by the critic J. J. Marchand, with the title « Toward a Lyrical Abstraction. » This last designation was the name by which the new trend became known.

It is also necessary to recognize the influence of the surrealist ideology (more, possibly, than that of the pictorial works) which hailed automatism and pure chance as valid techniques in creation at the same time that it glorified the mechanics of irrationality and vitality. With this, the surrealist ideas transcend the activities of a closed group to become sustaining principles that, almost without revealing their origin, serve as nourishment for the new revolutionary generations in art.

Mathieu, who had become an active promoter of the new tendencies, organized two new exhibitions in 1948: one with the enigmatic title « HWPSMTB, » formed by the first initial of each participant (Hartung, Wols, Picabia, François Stahly, Mathieu, Michel Tapié, and Camille Bryen), and another, with almost the same participants, which was called « Black and White. » Lyrical abstraction, which at this time was represented by Wols, Hartung, Mathieu, and Bryen, was in the first place a reaction against the formalism of the constructivist tendencies and against the rationalism that held sway. This new tendency placed everything under the heading of the irrational, and against reflective they put spontaneous painting, created from impulse or by improvisation. High value was put on pure chance, ambiguity, and imprecision. Figure and form were replaced by signs or dashes without special significance, simply as expressions of vital activity.

New designations appeared, on the one hand enriching the nomenclature and on the other introducing confusion in it. The term « Informalism » began to be used in 1952, following the exhibition entitled « *Signifiants de l'informel* » in the Studio Facchetti, organized by Michel Tapié with the artists of the new idiom. The year before, Tapié had organized an exhibition with the title « *Vehemences confrontées* » in the Nina Dausset Gallery, a show of the artists whom he considered were characterized by vehemence. Soon thereafter appeared the term « tachism » (from the French word for « spot » or « blot »), proposed by Charles Estienne – a critic who years

GÉRARD SCHNEIDER. *The hanged.* 1944.

FRANÇOIS ARNAL. *The blue boy.* 1954.

earlier had conducted a violent campaign against the academism of the geometric painters – in a famous article in *Combat*, where he used in a serious way the ironic designation that Pierre Guéguen had applied to the then new painters some time back. At the same time, other designations were being used in the United States for artists who were painting in the same style as those in France: first, « abstract expressionism » and, later, « action painting. » The American « action painting » is analogous to the European term « gesture painting. »

Michel Tapié, the inspired inventor of the name « informalism, » propounded his concept of an *art autre*, explaining that in the case of the new tendencies it was not a question of an anti-art but of a truly *other* art, a different art, which starts out from zero and runs an entirely distinct road with a distinctive esthetic. He reaches the conclusion that it is not enough to decide to use free forms instead of geometry in painting. It is necessary to break with the theories and prejudices of the plastic problems; the only thing of importance is purely and simply to *do*, the creation in its primary state without control, and what is important is the result: a work that, instead of saying and expressing, just lives. Taking part in the first exhibition of *art autre* were Appel, Camille Bryen (the painter-poet), Burri, Dubuffet, Domoto, de Kooning, Fautrier, Ruth Francken, René Guiette, Hosiasson, Imai, Jenkins, Mathieu, Riopelle, Tobey, and Wols.

Of the various terms, used by some as synonyms and by others in a more restricted sense, we chose « informalism » for its rather more general and

JEAN PAUL RIOPELLE. *Painting.* 1951.
Paul Facchetti Gallery.

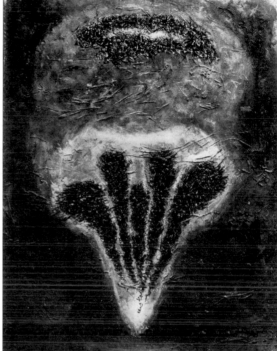

JAROSLAV SERPAN. *Hereuns N. 695.* 1963.
Stadler Gallery.

ambiguous implication, to designate all those tenddencies that not only eliminate form as the central element of the painting but that also consider in the creative process only the factor of total spontaneity. The term « lyrical abstraction » is too defining, and supposes the existence of a poetic element that can exist, and undoubtedly does exist, in other forms of abstraction. Tachism should be reduced to a part of informalism in which an adynamic element, the spot – that is, the irregular form in which the element of pure chance enters – constitutes the fundamental element, whether it be achieved by dripping, pouring, or rapid, instinctive brushstrokes. For American painting we shall retain the designation « abstract expressionism » in order to include the whole of this new painting (keeping in mind, however, the lack of precision and difficulty in embracing certain manifestations of this painting), and we shall use « action painting » (called

« gesture painting » in Europe) as a subdivision of one of its sections, and « quietistic » or « invisible » painting as another, as will be shown later.

From the foregoing, one gathers that informalism comprises various currents that demand definite subdivisions. Tachism and gesture painting have been mentioned; remaining are painting based on the predominant action of the matter (matter painting), painting that takes the form of a kind of script (calligraphic painting), and painting that employs signs (considering as signs what does not correspond to gesture calligraphy). It must be explained that, as with all classifications, these serve only as a useful guide in tracing a less confused itinerary through the various trends,

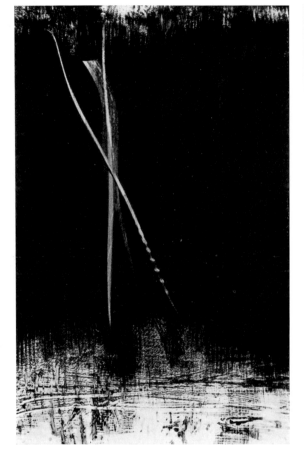

PHILIPPE HOSIASSON. *Oil.* 1962.
Karl Flinker Gallery.

JEAN DEGOTTEX. *Pink and black suite.* 1964.
Paul Facchetti Gallery.

but do not in any way pretend to reduce the artists to strict schematizations (something impossible in any event). In fact, many artists employ a combination of techniques, and would thus fall within more than one of the categories mentioned; and in other cases it is difficult to determine whether one kind of sign-dashes is straight gesture calligraphy or whether, for example, it has the characteristics of symbols.

We must insist that informal painting does not imply a total lack of form, because certain struc-

tures do exist that are neither spontaneous nor irrational, as would be the case, for instance, with the painting of Dorazio, and furthermore this would exclude the spots or blots, which after all do constitute a form, however irregular. As Herbert Read explains, the informal is « irregular form » that does not present the regularity of the geometric or of the organic. Informalism not only opposes painting based on the construction with forms but also every type of precise structure or composition, holding up against it indetermination and the advantage of chance. Indetermination permits the color to be at the same time matter, and vice versa, and the line can be color.

It is true that formalist painters such as Vasarely (and some Americans of the new abstraction)

NICOLAS DE STAËL. *Oil*. 1952. Anne Abels Gallery.

FRÉDÉRIC BENRATH. *Lace, interlace – what interlaces Infinity is serpent.* 1963. Karl Flinker Gallery.

JEAN MESSAGIER. *Louis XIV.* 1966.

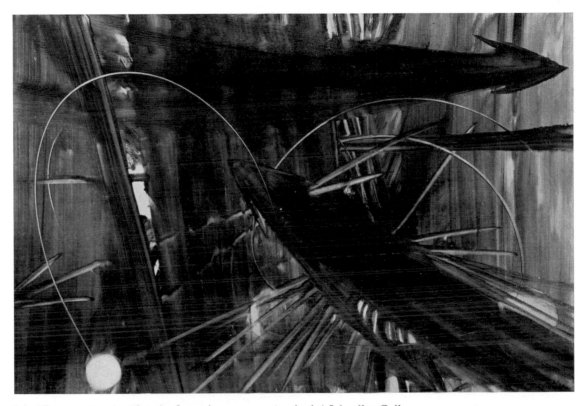

RÉNÉ DUVILLIER. *Aerial cycle. Saturn's moons.* 1964. André Schoeller Gallery.

speak of form-color, but in any event this means a precise and well-defined form (although it may be significant only as a support for the color), and it upholds a precise structure.

After this explanation we can attempt a classification of the painters in accordance with the divisions we are presenting.

Gesture painting, so called from the movement in which it originates, has the expressive value of imitative art, and as it is a direct product of myokinetic activity its essence is biological – that is, it is an expression of pure vitality. It corresponds to automatic writing – rapid, immediate, proceeding from a previous state of vacuity, that is, without a premeditated plan, and would fit

what Breton defines as automatism. As the product of this movement is the outline, this may at times assume a calligraphic aspect, suggesting writing. For the Japanese, the expressive tracing of the brush is a natural and traditional means of communication; this tracing, at the same time that it has significance, speaks. For this reason their writing is at the same time calligraphy and picture, and this explains why calligraphy constitutes the germ of the great traditional painting of Japan.

In the calligraphy of the informal painters, the tracing speaks but does not embody significance. This tracing is automatic, is rooted in the subconscious. At other times this tracing is mechan-

HENRI MICHAUX. *Composition B. 337.* 1959. Blu Gallery.

ical, that is, it obeys a mechanism of repetition, something like what happens in the case of a tic; such is the case with Mathieu.

The most important action painters are Pollock, de Kooning, and Kline, who will be discussed as abstract expressionists; then Soulages (although his action is directed and organized), Schneider, Mattia Moreni, Saura, the French « nuagists » (Benrath, Messagier, and Duvillier), Degottex, Karl-Otto Götz, Peter Brüning (bordering on calligraphy), and Lataster. There is an element of action in many painters' work, for example, Hartung (his heavy linear strokes), Alan Davie, Appel, and Jorn; the calligraphic action impulse is found in Sønderborg, Noël, and Twombly; and the pure nonaction calligraphy is represented by Tobey's work.

In matter painting, the material as a fundamental element of the painting imposes its own visual laws, totally opposed to the traditional sense of perception of a picture. The action of the medium is determined primarily by the heaviness of the impasto, with or without the addition of powders or solidifying substances. The precursors or pioneers of matter painting were Dubuffet and Fautrier; later came Tàpies, Schumacher Hosiasson,

EMIL SCHUMACHER. *Darkness.* 1961. La Medusa Gallery.

Dahmen, Horia Damian, Feito, and Donati. The action of the medium can also be got directly from an aplastic material, as is the case in the work of Burri, Millares, and others.

The material has subtle visual qualities that may be compared to the harmonies that give the timbre to musical sounds. Through the effects of dispersion, refraction, and diffraction of the luminous waves, the visual knowledge of the intimate structure of the material is transmitted to us.

In tachist painting the chromatic spot is the dominant element, but this also obeys gesture, whether spattered, dripped, or extended; the imprecise contour gives color the possibility of an expansion, of a breakthrough of the limits. It could be defined as a static form of the gesture, and in this sense, the limits of the term, in the original concept of its creator, Estienne, it came to include the informal in its entirety, and so included gesture painting. The pioneers of tachism were Wols (in whose work graphic and action elements are also present), and later Still, Sam Francis, and Jenkins. This list reveals the

American influence on European tachism, and it could be said that the predominant cause of its spread was the dripping technique of Pollock. Unfortunately, the seductive easiness of the method has contributed to an increase in the number of tachists and attracted painters who had nothing to say and who have turned informalism into another academy, contributing to its decline. In painting using lines and symbols, form is substituted by the signs that dominate the structure of the picture. This can be a free calligraphic sign (Mathieu and Sønderborg would be included under this category), but actually it belongs more directly to those who employ linear patterns of no special content – of meaning, not gesture – for example, Capogrossi, Carla Accardi, Jaroslav Serpan, and Tomlin. Tobey could also be included in this category.

In a special category are those artists concerned with spatial problems, such as Fontana, who endeavor to introduce space into the material solidity of the canvas by means of slits and perforations. These lacerations then acquire the quality of signs and symbols. Among those who concern themselves with the spatial, Rothko and Newman should be mentioned.

Informalism, spreading from its centers of radiation, the School of Paris and the New York School, soon was diffused all over the world, and from South America to Japan there were innumerable artists who turned to the new tendency. With this it fell into mannerism, into a facile formula, which caused its decline, and produced, as is always the case, a reaction of opposing tendencies, on one side by the heirs of constructivism, which at one time it had replaced, but who now returned rejuvenated, and on the other side by a movement proceeding from dadaism and which had its greatest development in the United States. For a study of the more outstanding informalist artists, a division according to countries is the best way of proceeding, beginning with the School of Paris. We are already familiar with the

K. R. H. Sønderborg. *Gouache.* 1958.

originators: Fautrier, Dubuffet, Hartung, Wols, and Mathieu. The number of painters in this movement is so large that our examination must be limited to those whose contributions are more original or to those who are most orthodox in character.

Informalism in the school of Paris

Pierre Soulages was born in Rodez in 1919. In 1946 he settled in Paris, and in the following year exhibited in the *Salon des Surindépendents.* His pictures have a vigorous graphic design, and

K. R. H. SØNDERBORG. *Nautisch*. 1952.

he uses black brushstrokes done in single outline but which follow a direction and give a constructive sense to the picture. There is an order obtained by the straight lines, generally vertical, although some arc horizontal (the verticality gives the curious ascending force of a Gothic cathedral). The succession of lines creates a sense of rhythm to which is added a dynamic tension, sometimes heightened by the calculated and sober use of directional diagonals. But, as Soulages himself says, his pictures reject the description of the movement: « The figuration of the movement is equal to the figuration of objects in traditional painting. » He nevertheless achieves a graphic rhythm, a dynamism that is, as he says, « potential energy, not movement, » all within a perfect equilibrium. This sense of equilibrium, this constructive base, separates his painting from that of the American Franz Kline, with whom he may be compared in his use of the large black outline, although it has to be made clear that Soulages is earlier than Kline inasmuch as his first exhibition of this kind of painting dates from 1947. This calligraphic architecture rests on a background that is generally gray; but the great final touch lies in the application of color. This appears as a lateral illumination, an accent heightening the solemnity of the black. He uses some of the primary colors very soberly, generally yellow or red, but also employs blues and ochers in the right measure so that they will signify just this: a reference to the world of light, which does not combat but sustains the profound mystery of the black. From all this emanates a powerful lyrical force, a kind of chant, almost religious. « Art is a humanization of the world, » he says, « but in abstract painting the world is not beheld, but lived. » And he adds: « Painting in the degree that it is a poetic experience transforms the universe; the picture is merely a metaphor. » This shows a painter who is fully conscious in his work. When once the confused panorama of art in which the man of today is submerged is clarified, there is no doubt that Soulages will appear as one of the truest talents of the painting of the present.

Gérard Schneider was born in Vaud, Switzerland, in 1896, was educated at Neuchâtel, and is a naturalized French citizen. Though his first paintings reveal the influence of cubism, by 1944 he changed to what would be his definitive style. His first exhibition was held in the Denise René Gallery in 1946. Schneider's painting is based on a violence and spontaneity of outline in black or in color, and is loose in its pictorial space. The black outlines prevail in Schneider's painting, but contrary to Soulages's they are not structured in dominant directions (vertical, horizontal, and diagonal), but disseminate freely, crossing and intermingling, lending great dynamism and violence and at the same time a particular drama to the picture. In addition to black he uses white in great abundance, as well as pure colors, but not with the intent of creating a luminous medium to heighten the function of the black, as Soulages does, but to seek the dynamic function in the opposition and juxtaposition of colors.

Jean Paul Riopelle was born in Montreal, in 1923. In 1946 he exhibited with the Canadian automatists, a group formed by Paul-Emile Borduas,

PETER BRÜNING. *Oil.* 1960.

HANS PLATSCHEK. *Job bonvivant.* 1961.

Karl Fred Dahmen. *Composition.*

Bernard Schultze. *Table du Migof.* 1963.

and in 1948 he and Borduas signed the *Refus Global* Manifesto. After settling in Paris, Rio pelle attached himself to the surrealists and exhibited with them. In 1947 he figured in the great International Exhibition of Surrealism held in the Maeght Gallery. In 1949 he held his first one-man show at Nina Dausset's. In 1948 he took part in *L'Imaginaire* exhibition organized by Mathieu in the Luxembourg Gallery. In 1951 he exhibited in « *Véhémences confrontées,* » a group of works gathered by Michel Tapié. He is married to the American painter Joan Mitchell.

Deriving first from Pollock, Riopelle arrived at a personal style of great musicality of color. His painting does not fall within the action group, and he has declared himself against automatism and in favor of controlled chance, understood in the sense of Nietzsche, who said: « What you

Alberto Burri. *Big wood.* 1959.
Galleria Nazionale d'Arte Moderna, Roma.

ALBERTO BURRI. *Sack.*

call chance is your true being revealed in what happens and in what is inflicted on you. » Riopelle constructs his pictures with small outlines in juxtaposed color of changing orientation according to the all-over principle, sometimes shot through by fine linear traces of color in a manner that gives the surface a sense of mobility, heightened by the succulent quality of the material. Toward 1956 his outlines became larger and more simplified. From 1963 onward he began emphasizing the importance of the whites, and created areas of monochrome color, but he retained his technique of working the medium with the spatula.

Paul-Emile Borduas (1905-1960) was born in Saint-Hilaire, Canada. From 1928 to 1930 he was in Paris, and then settled in Montreal in 1932, remaining there until 1948. There he created the literary-artistic movement, the suprarational automatists, which was associated with surrealism. After 1955 he lived in Paris.
Borduas came under the influence of the New York school in 1958, especially that of Kline, and began producing pictures that were almost monochrome with large black networks determined by the crossing of horizontal-vertical lines.

Jaroslav Serpan was born in Prague in 1922. He was brought to Paris in 1928, where he later stud-

LUCIO FONTANA. *Spatial concept.* 1957. La Salita Gallery.

ied mathematics and biology at the Sorbonne. He exhibited in the International Exposition of Surrealism in the Maeght Gallery in 1947, and collaborated with Edouard Jaguer in publishing the *Rixes* review, a forerunner of *Phases*. Later he came to form part of Michel Tapié's *art autre* group, of which he became one of the staunchest supporters.

Serpan constructs his pictures with signs and symbols of calligraphic character, often resembling small commas. The surface of the canvas is densely covered with these small lines, or microforms, generally black, in the all-over manner, at regular intervals. Sometimes the signs form groups or borders and occasionally orthogonal configurations. This multitude of irregular microforms appears to make the surface bubble and vibrate in a very distinct manner.

François Arnal was born in La Valette, Var, in 1924. After studying administration, he turned to painting. He was a member of the « Phases » group and of Tapié's *art autre*. Arnal began with figural painting, later changing to informal abstraction with very dense colors. At present he practices a kind of matter painting on a base of juxtaposed themes and signs that are impressed into the picture, without any particular regularity. The impressions are in black and white and then supplemented with moderate colors. In spite of their complexity, the canvases show great cohesion and, so to speak, a true vivacity and eloquence.

Jean Degottex, a self-taught painter, was born in Sathonay, l'Ain, in 1918. He was awarded the Kandinsky first prize in 1951, and had his first one-man show in 1955 in the L'Etoile Scellée, the gallery of the surrealists. His painting style falls between action painting and the sign-and-symbol manner. It consists of a few isolated lines, symbols lost in an amplitude of space, giving the picture a fundamentally individual quality.

Philippe Hosiasson was born in Odessa in 1898. In 1922 he was in Berlin, and in 1924 in Paris. His nonfigural period began in 1948, and in 1955 he exhibited for the first time in Paris. He belongs to the *art autre* group of Michel Tapié. Hosiasson works on a premise of relations between matter and space, with rich, smooth material, achieved through a slow process of stratification, of intense color, and with tachist elements that seem to come from the dripping method.

One aspect of the gesture painting of the School of Paris is nuagism. The action here produces cursive lines or circular rhythms, revealing a tendency toward arabesques or vortices, somewhat of an adaptation to natural forms, perhaps spirals of smoke or rolling waves of water. There is also a certain resemblance to cloud landscapes (more emphasized in Frédéric Benrath, less so in Duvillier), which is the reason for the name of this

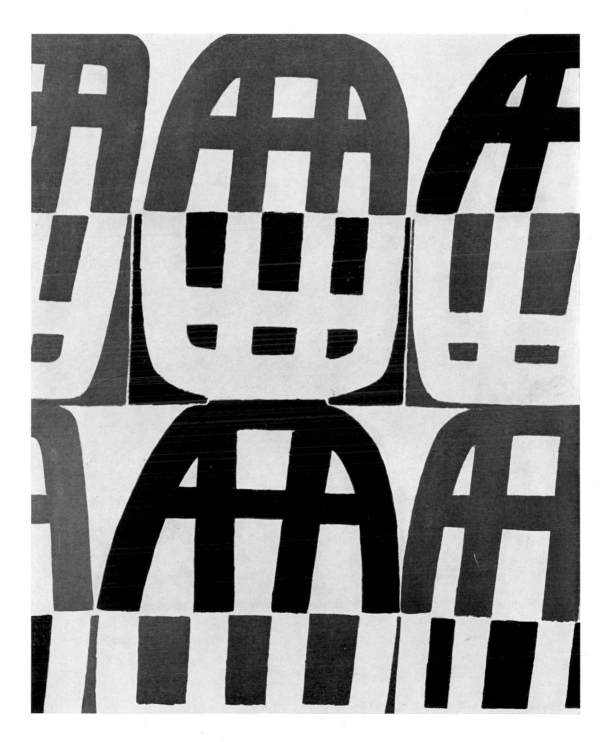

GIUSEPPE CAPOGROSSI. *Painting.* 1966.
Galleria Bonino.

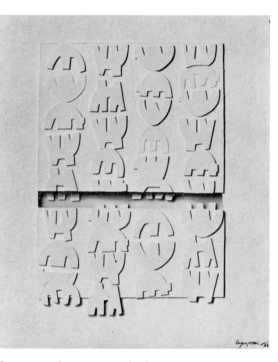

GIUSEPPE CAPOGROSSI. *Surface 577.* 1966.
Del Cavallino Gallery.

style. The tendency embraces artists such as Benrath, Messagier, and Duvillier. The last two were
presented by Estienne as representative of surrealist tachism in 1953.

Frédéric Benrath was born in Chanton, France,
in 1930. His first phase was characterized by
violent action and color, with sweeping, circular
rhythms, sometimes with a sort of web of straight
lines. His latest works are mellower, the essential action reduced to a central, cottony zone,
which creates an ample sense of luminous space,
of fine chromatism, which justifies the designation of « luminous Parisian space, » a designation
sometimes given this whole style.

Jean Messagier was born in Paris in 1920. From
1946 to 1948 he lived in Italy and in Algiers.
In his work he searches for a spatial rhythm by

means of large undulating brushstrokes, and he
endeavors to convey a feeling of states of nature
in its climatic or seasonal aspect.

René Duvillier was born in Dijon, Aix, in 1919.
His pictures, frequently of very large dimensions,
represent a development of wide spirals or large
swirls in a vortex, almost monochrome, which
succeed in transmitting a vertiginous sense of
space.

There is a poet who has been closely connected
with the pioneers of informal art and who has
exhibited at the same time, continuing their plastic experiments up to the present. This is Henri
Michaux, one of the great poets and figures of
modern times.

Michaux was born in 1899 in Namur, Belgium.
After a period in Brussels he arrived in Paris in

EMILIO VEDOVA. *Plurimo N. 8. Feet on top.* 1962/63. Marlborough Gallery.

Emilio Vedova. *For Spain N. 6.* 1962. Marlborough Gallery.

1923, and soon thereafter undertook long voyages through America and throughout the Orient (this experience produced the book *A Barbarian in Asia*). His first exhibition was held soon after the end of the war, in the Drouin Gallery. He showed colored drawings and ink drawings of seemingly evanescent heads, figures out of a nightmare. After 1956 he began painting under the influence of mescaline, the hallucination-inducing drug. Through the stimulus of this drug his plastic technique changed to a form of rhythmic calligraphy of undulant ideograms that intermix and seemingly pullulate over the whole pictorial surface in the all-over style.

When he was asked why a poet of his stature painted with such assiduousness, Michaux answered: « Do you not see that my painting replaces words? Gestures, mimicry, sounds, lines and colors: these are the primitive, pure, and direct means of expression. » And he added: « There exists a certain inner spirit which one should be able to reproduce, not the nose, eyes, and hair, which are, really, outside. »

For Michaux nothing in creation is finished and nothing is capable of being finished. His signs and ideograms attempt to convey the idea of the interminable and ephemeral at the same time. He expects too much from painting when he states:

ASGER JORN. *Dead drunk danes.* 1960. Coll. Jon Nicholas Streep.

MATTIA MORENI. *Sun over the heath*.
Galleria Nazionale d'Arte Moderna, Roma.

« I would like to draw the consciousness of existence as well as the passage of time. »

Informalism in Germany

Emil Schumacher was born in Hagen, Westphalia, in 1912. He traveled throughout Europe, and
is one of the group centered upon Michel Tapié.
Schumacher obtains a sort of matter informalism
by means of a heavy monochrome color with a
background attenuated by faint black velaturas
run through by black branchings with light white
touches. In this way he obtains with the matter
an almost organic result, living and dramatic at
the same time, which puts him in the front rank
of the representatives of matter informalism.

EMILIO SCANAVINO. *The window*. 1964.
Del Naviglio Gallery.

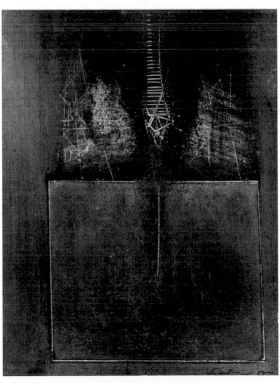

EMILIO SCANAVINO. *The gray little square*. 1965.
Del Naviglio Gallery.

K. R. H. Sønderborg (a pseudonym Kurt Hoffmann took from the name of his birthplace in Denmark) was born of German extraction in 1923. After working in Hamburg and Berlin, he went to Paris.

Sønderborg's paintings always show a dynamic direction, a rhythm achieved by short brushstrokes of a calligraphic type or by points that unite into series; they are executed with extreme rapidity and complete spontaneity. They expand, like a fugue, over the surface of the picture, like an effusion created by the rhythmic sequence. His drawings are of exceptionally high quality. Sonderborg is one of the best artists of the informal current in Germany.

Peter Brüning was born in Düsseldorf in 1929. From 1950 to 1952 he studied with Baumeister in the Academy of Art in Stuttgart, later traveled about Europe, visiting Paris, Spain, Italy and the Netherlands, and now lives in his native city. In 1961 he received the Lissone first prize in Milan.

Brüning works with the canvas spread on the floor. His painting is one of isolated action impulses, ideographs, blots, and even vague sketches of figures. He uses pure colors, each picture having one dominant color – red, blue, ocher, yellow, or soft gray – which gives great depth to the space. The space acquires an ambiguous mobility with an impression of changing depths. His latest works tend to a baroque formalism of great originality.

Hans Platschek was born in Berlin in 1923. From 1939 to 1953 he lived in Montevideo, Uruguay, where he began painting with works in the surrealist vein, in which he created images full of humor, either of animals or, more often, an unreal magical world. During this time he exhibited in Buenos Aires and Montevideo. After 1953 he moved to Germany, first to Frankfurt, then to Munich, where his painting tended toward informalism with dynamic black ideograms over a

Roberto Crippa. *Personage*. 1960. Schwarz Gallery.

monochrome background, usually in blues and reds, but vitalized by shadings and textural qualities.

He is the author of several theoretical works on modern painting, and he pursues a polemic activity through the mediums of articles and lectures. He also forms part of the *art autre* movement of Michel Tapié.

Karl Fred Dahmen was born in Stolberg, Rhineland, in 1917. Between 1951 and 1952 he traveled to Paris, Italy, and Belgium. His style is matter painting, in which he uses a heavy coat that produces an impression of plaster, of an opaque, amorphous, and cracked surface, with a rich texture and with isolated signs. He utilizes colors of somber tonalities, dark reds, browns, and blacks. He also works with collages of fabrics, paper, and the like, with which he obtains curious relief effects.

Bernard Schultze was born in Schneidemuhl, Pomerania, in 1915. From 1934 to 1939 he studied

AFRO. *Malalbergo.* 1962.

in the Academy of Art in Berlin and in Dusseldorf, then settled in Frankfort on the Main in 1947; in 1952 he visited Paris. In his work he has always searched for the multicolor activity of the picture, and sought to project himself outside the plane. The latter he attempted first by collages of small pieces of paper with the ends floating, then, later, by creating paintings in space, which consist of complicated and ramifying forms painted with the multiple colors he prefers, free in space in the manner of sculptures.

The new school in Italy

Alberto Burri was born in Città di Castello, Italy, in 1915. A physician by profession, he began painting in a prisoner-of-war camp in Texas. It is related that, not having access to conventional media, he began by using sacking, and thereby discovered the expressive quality of this material. At the end of the war, in 1945, he returned to Italy and settled in Rome. In 1947 he held his first one-man exhibition in La Margherita Gal-

lery in Rome. Together with the painters Capogrossi, Ballocco, and Colla (who later became a
sculptor of note) he formed part of the «Origine»
group.

Burri produces what could be called a renovation
of dadaist collage, and among the dadaists it is
Schwitters who seems to be Burri's direct antecedent. He resembles Schwitters in his organization of the materials and the plastic use of
them, but differs from him in that in Schwitters
they still preserve their significance as representation. Burri, on the other hand, presents them
exclusively raw and undifferentiated, precisely
because of their material quality, although they
do not lose a meaning of their own. This meaning depends not on the elementary function of
the object but on the unassuming quality of the
material and its actual state (broken, mended,
torn, and burned). It is so intimately identified
with the material itself and so subordinated to
the plastic structure of the picture, that all directly significant elements are practically canceled.
Thus it creates an expressive atmosphere, conferring a veiled dramatic quality on the picture.

It could be said that the essential element in
Burri's work is a kind of opposition between the
coarseness of the basic material, tortured and lacerated, and the severe structural scheme and almost geometric character of the composition.
This schematization first reduces the material to
its elemental and pure forms and permits the use
of the accidents of tears and holes, incorporating
them in a coherent wholeness. To permit the material to function in its visual purity, Burri uses
very little color, limiting himself generally to red,
white, and black. Color is used either to enhance
the material or to contrast with it, and only rarely to modify or dissimulate it. The coherent organization and the feeling for construction prevalent in his pictures remove them from the cate-

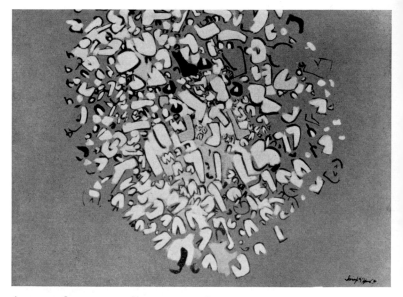

ANTONIO SANFILIPPO. *Fragment.* 1965.
Arco d'Alibert Gallery.

GIUSEPPE SANTOMASO. *Fire of Santa Maria de Mar.*
1959. Pogliani Gallery.

gory of pure informalism and place them somewhere between the formal and the informal.

Burri began by using pieces of sacking roughly stitched together; later he employed roughly cut wood (often partially burned) or fragments of sheet metal, tin, and iron, and sometimes objects made of plastic, also twisted and perforated.

In spite of the roughness and unartistic quality of the material, Burri's work is without aggressiveness; it has, instead, a lyrical impetus, although this is controlled, ascetic, severe. It opened one of the most fertile and traveled roads of the postwar period, and there is no doubt that he has contributed on a large scale to the development of the technique of assemblages that employ discarded and unartistic material.

Lucio Fontana was born in Rosario de Santa Fé, Argentina, in 1899. He was educated at the Brera Academy in Milan. In 1934 he participated in the exhibition of the «Abstraction-Création» association. From 1939 to 1946 he lived in Argentina, where he produced figural sculptures of expressionistic tendency of a high quality. He was cofounder of the Altamira art school, and in 1946 he and some of his pupils launched the White Manifesto in Buenos Aires. In 1947 he moved to Milan, and there founded the spatialist movement. Participants in this movement in the years 1951 and 1952 included Roberto Crippa, De Luigi, Dova, Donati, Cesare Peverelli, Scanavino, Ettore Sottsass, Jr., and others.

In the White Manifesto, Fontana stated his antiesthetic attitude, his break with classical easel painting, and his intention to transcend the limits imposed on the work of art, in these words: « We proclaim an art free from every esthetic artifice. » Further on he stated: « We abandon the acceptance of known forms in art, and begin the development of an art based on the unity of time and space.» Following his spatialist doctrine he undertook to introduce a real presence of space in the canvas. This he attempted by means

CARLA ACCARDI. *Labyrinth N. 19. 1957.* Stadler Gallery.

of a system of small reliefs attached to the canvas, forming a stippled salient, or else by means of incisions and perforations in the canvas, a manner he frequently employed and which came to characterize his work. These incisions are sparing and neat, with the precision of line that is characteristic of the concrete art style. The surface

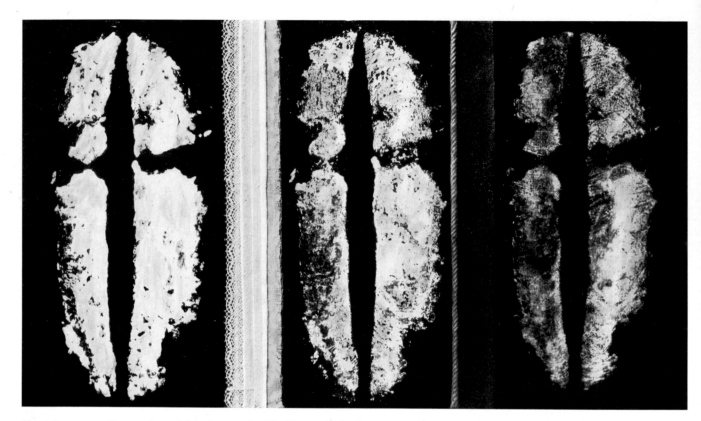

Toti Scialoja. *Repeated marble-print*. 1962. Marlborough Gallery.

of the canvas is generally monochrome and almost always smooth, with the incision or incisions (usually few) or the perforations functioning as a sign or symbol. Fontana has recently abandoned rigor and austerity to introduce ornamental motifs with heavy impasto in his canvases or by means of reliefs (always retaining, however, the monochrome tendency and generally the muted colors), but the incisions and perforations are adapted to the new style and are incorporated as decorative motifs in the general baroque construction.

But what Fontana in fact does present is an anti-art attitude, demonstrated by the mechanism of aggression against the canvas. This attitude, in a real artist like Fontana, with the added weight of the esthetic work he has already produced, has a profound significance. But any destruction of the image, when an artist performs the destruction, creates a new image.

The influence of Fontana's ideas and attitude has played an important role in Italy and in the rest of Europe. It is not improbable that this influence lies behind the origin of some of the spatial ideas of Yves Klein. The influence is also evident in the « O » group of Dusseldorf, particularly on Piene. With other modern revolutionary artists he has contributed to the turn away from the rigidity of the old esthetic prejudices, although this might necessitate having to start from scratch. In 1966 Fontana won the first prize for Italian painting at the Venice Biennale.

Luigi Spazzapan. *Abstract composition N. 1.* 1955. Marlborough Gallery.

Giuseppe Capogrossi was born in Rome in 1900 and lives there at present. He studied law and acquired a doctorate. From 1927 to 1933 he was in Paris, where he practiced figural painting of a tonal character and in the expressionist manner. The first time he employed the distinctive symbol that characterises his work was in 1949, and he held his first one-man show in 1950 at the Del Secolo Gallery in Rome. Together with Burri, Colla, and Ballocco, he belonged to the «Origine» group. Capogrossi's pictures are built around a single fundamental element, a symbol or emblem created by him, with a vaguely calligraphic quality but without any reference or significance. The outline of this symbol is semicircular (seldom rectangular) at one end and dentate (with rectangular teeth) at the other. The teeth, of which there are usually four, are set in a vertical and slightly oblique manner. This symbol, although it always retains the same general outline, appears in different ways within the same picture or from one picture to another. The number of teeth may be fewer, and at times the sign appears fragmented; at other times it is longer or shorter, blending with the long bars of the thickness of the teeth; it may take the most diverse directions, and sometimes it is multiplied, pullulating over the whole surface of the picture and so falling into the all-over category of painting; at other times it is used sparingly or alone, and gives to the free area a feeling of active space. The signs are black or gray; other variations are less frequent, although at times they may appear with slightly streaked structure. The color of the background is plain, uniform, smooth and clear and generally of one color, chosen from the pure colors but without stridency. The total impression of the picture is one of perfect control, with the rigor and precision of a concrete work.

The sign of Capogrossi is a veritable treasure chest; he has managed to confer on it an archetypal aspect, and it is undoubtedly this that gives it a curiously affective quality. A sense of something enigmatic, of mystery, surges from the picture.

But the merit of Capogrossi is that with a single element, which would appear destined to be monotonous, he has achieved an imaginative variety of plastic themes in which the sign simply acts as a dynamic signal for acquiring rhythm, to attain the mobility of a plastic ballet. Thus he distributes the sign over the surface of the picture in series or in conglomerations that are neither regular nor even but that within their looseness and apparent arbitrariness prove to be coherent and orderly. As an exponent of « sign » painting, Capogrossi is not only one of the first and most eminent, but perhaps one who has been able to delve deepest into the obscure mechanism of the sign to reveal its intensely expressive quality.

Emilio Vedova was born in Venice in 1919. In 1936 he began to exhibit landscapes and figural works of a geometric and dynamic tendency with an attenuated futuristic orientation. In 1946 he formed part of the *Fronte Nuovo delle Arti*, sponsored by the critic Marchiori. Always influenced by the dynamic-rhythmic construction of futurism, he developed along a line of violent and expressive abstraction, formed by interwoven strokes that follow lines of defined orientation

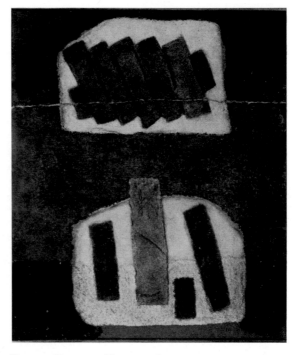

ENRICO DONATI. *Maya sandstone.* 1965.
Staempfly Gallery.

and determine a rhythmic, coherent, and organized structure. The strokes are generally black, combined with touches of intense color but applied with great restraint.

Around 1964 Vedova showed a series of experiments in spatial painting with the name of *plurimi*, consisting of panels or fragments of panels joined at various angles to form a construction in space; they constitute something of a complex of associated pictures, painted on both sides.

Mattia Moreni was born in Pavia, Italy, in 1920. He studied in Turin, and he and Spazzapan were instrumental in stimulating art in the city. In 1947 he had his first exhibition in the Galleria del Milione with works in a free figural trend; later he turned toward a semigeometrically constructed abstraction of a postcubist type. In 1953

Ennio Morlotti. *Landscape*. 1960. Odyssia Gallery.

he changed to the style of gesture painting, using wide brushstrokes, accompanied by backgrounds of color. These paintings are notable for their richness and resplendence. His pictures are sumptuous, dynamic, sensual, and always start from a theme in which the figuration at times is clearly visible, treated with a violence that is less sharp and strident than de Kooning's, whose style he approaches, in a search for a more lyrical and less aggressive feeling. He is without doubt one of the most qualified exponents of gesture painting in the world.

Emilio Scanavino was born in Genoa in 1922. He studied at the Artistic Lyceum of his native city, and belonged to the spatialist movement of Fontana. Around 1953 he arrived at his present style, which is in the informal painting idiom, and en-

Antonio Corpora. *Labyrinth.* 1960. Pogliani Gallery.

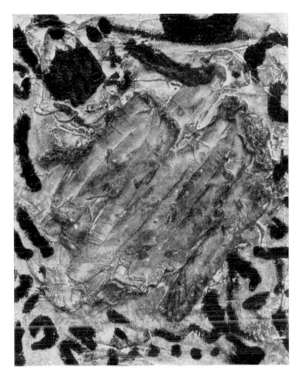

JIRO YOSHIHARA. *Untitled.* 1959. Tapié Collection.

tered some of the exhibitions of Edouard Jaguer's « Phases » group.

Scanavino's pictures cover the range from white to black, because he avoids all symbolic or emotional association that may be produced by color; but more than anything it is this kind of discipline, this restriction, which in some artists induces a deeper penetration into the mysterious dominion of plastic expression. Thus he reaches the most refined modulations of tonality in gray and black. His material is dense and luminous, and the surface is subtly toned; over it are automatically drawn calligraphic signs, extremely varied, isolated or in blocks, interlocked or forming orderly lines. The calligraphic signs are asymmetrical, disquieting, and, as he says, « not rational, but suprarational, » of an intense mobil-

ity – which creates a dynamic spatial feeling that is almost atmospheric. He is one of the foremost artists of the Italian school.

Roberto Crippa was born in 1921 in Milan, and studied there at the Brera Academy. In his latest works he uses collages of cork or wood shingles, sometimes half burned, and he often includes fragments of newspapers. These fragments are attached to one another, not as constructions, but as simple presences that create areas activated by utilizing the texture of the materials, generally with somber colors by which he obtains a sense of emptiness and solitude. At times he includes dramatic mottoes in the collages, for example, « Sono morto innocente. »

Antonio Corpora was born in 1909 in Tunis, where he studied in the School of Fine Arts. In 1929 he moved to Florence, had an exhibition there in 1930, then went to Paris that year where he remained until 1937. From 1947 to 1951 he produced abstract paintings obtained by a transposition of landscapes, with large calligraphic signs and vertical and diagonal rhythms.
He belonged to the *Fronte Nuovo delle Arti* and the Group of Eight Italian Painters. His present painting is informal, with a warm material, rich in texture, with vibrant and exquisitely shaded colors, on which are inscribed various calligraphic signs.

Afro Basaldella, known as Afro, was born in Udine in 1912. He has lived in Rome for many years. Until 1939 he was a figural painter, then he practiced a neocubistic abstraction, and in 1952 he turned to a freer style, more akin to informalism. In the same year he founded the Group of Eight Italian Painters: Birolli, Corpora, Moreni, Morlotti, Turcato, Santomaso, Vedova, and himself. He had his first one-man show in the United States in New York City in 1950, and his work

Kasuo Shiraga. *Painting.* 1961. Stadler Gallery.

appears in many museums in the States. He was commissioned to execute murals for UNESCO headquarters in Paris.

Afro's pictures show a harmonious feast of colors that are distributed without violence and are subtly shaded. He employs reds, whites, blues, blacks, and grays of refined tonalities on backgrounds of variable sizes and of imprecise forms in an ambiguous and glittering space, the whole constituting a work of intense lyricism.

Antonio Sanfilippo was born in Partanna in 1923. During the immediate postwar period he, Perilli, Dorazio, and Giulio Turcato were part of the postcubist and geometrizing group in Rome called « Forma I. » After the 1950's he turned to informalism in a style characterized by luminosity of color and activity of space heightened by dispersed signs and ideograms.

Giuseppe Santomaso was born in Venice in 1907. In 1947 he belonged to the *Fronte Nuovo delle Arti.* In 1952 he was a member of the Group of Eight Italian Painters, which was composed of the most outstanding *avant-garde* painters in Italy at that time. His paintings, of the informal category into which vague geometrizing forms are insinuated, are outstanding for their refined im-

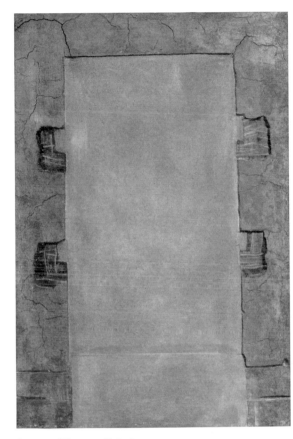

ANTONI TÀPIES. *Tabula erasa.*
Galleria Nazionale d'Arte Moderna, Roma.

pasto, their color adjustment which is always well-tempered and their luminous characteristics.

Carla Accardi, born in Trapani, Sicily, in 1925, belongs to the *art autre* group sponsored by Michel Tapié. Her pictures are characterized by the use of signs resembling ornamental ideograms, regularly repeated with slight variations, but in a free manner, over the whole surface (all-over) on a background of vibrant color. Accardi now lives in Rome.

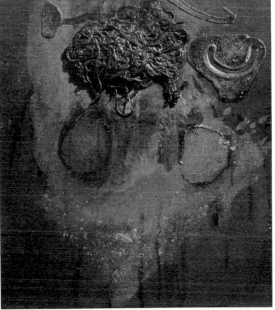

MODESTO CUIXART. Top: *Canvas-object.* 1960.
Bottom: *Ratacat.* 1961. René Metras Gallery.

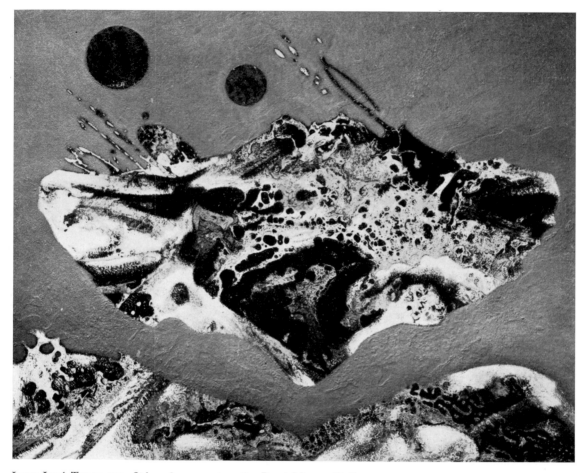

Juan José Tharrats. *Sidereal moment.* 1964. René Metras Gallery.

Toti Scialoja was born in Rome in 1914. After practicing figural painting and a neocubist abstraction, in 1958 he initiated the technique that has come to characterize his work. From one matrix he produces a series of successive impressions of abstract but not geometric motifs, usually monochrome, but of a varying intensity so that the image appears to vanish in the successive impressions. He thus obtains a kind of time arrested in two ways: by the serial rhythm produced by the repetition of images and by the sensation of fugacity or time passage provoked by the progressive intensity diminution of the image. This produces the impression of a painting in the act of becoming.

Luigi Spazzapan was born in Gradisca, Italy, in 1889; he died in 1958. In 1928 he moved permanently to Turin. Spazzapan passed through various phases of European painting, figural and abstract, including geometric art. Until about 1953 he practiced expressionism, when his work took on the characteristics of informalism, where

ROMÁN VALLÉS. *Signe 1965* series.

he found an adequate language in which to extend his profound feeling for color.

Enrico Donati was born in Milan in 1907. From 1934 to 1940 he lived in Paris, after which he went to the United States, where he formed part of the surrealist group. At present he is a follower of the *art autre* of Michel Tapié. After a period of poetic abstraction with imaginary forms and great richness of color, Donati evolved toward his present style, characterized by a matter

informalism, close to that of Dahmen or Tàpies, such as structures of eroded rocks or shingles of cement, with which he creates actual bas-reliefs of a very rich texture, with the addition of a coloration of muted range.

Ennio Morlotti was born in Lecco in 1910. He was a member of the Group of Eight Italian Painters founded by Afro. After a neocubist period he turned to matter informalism with an abstract landscape quality.

Informalism in Japan, and the « Gutai » group

The informalist movement in Japan acquires great importance for reasons that are easily explained. The gesture calligraphy that the exponents of action painting and the European informalists began to produce possessed obvious similarities with the ancient Japanese art of calligraphy. For the Japanese artists to be in the new current meant no more than to reinvigorate a traditional art.

Many of these artists emigrated to Paris or New York and joined the schools affiliated with those cities. In the New York school, Kenzo Okada and Masaki Yamaguchi distinguished themselves, while Toshimitusu Imai and Hisso Domoto were active in the School of Paris and were part of Michel Tapié's *art autre* group.

Yoshiga Saito was born in Tokyo in 1904. He now lives in Yokohama. He is one of the outstanding painters of the informalist tendency. In his work he utilizes, ably combined, effects of matter with gesture calligraphy and large areas of color.

But the most interesting and audacious gathering was the one that constituted the « Gutai » group (a word approximately corresponding to the German word *Gestalt*). It is a group of experimental nature, founded in Osaka in 1954 by young artists who gathered around a venerable master of that city, Jiro Yoshihara. Yoshihara had begun painting along surrealist lines, but in 1935 he had turned to abstraction, influenced by Kandinsky. Yoshihara became the animator of the group, and encouraged all kinds of artistic experiments. In this way the « Gutai » members were the very spearhead and vanguard for experimental art in Japan.

MANOLO MILLARES. *Untitled.*

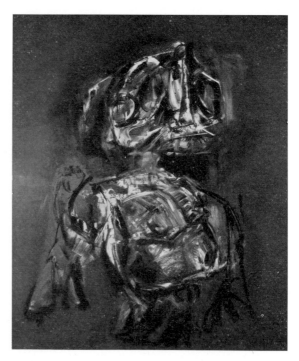

ANTONIO SAURA. *Ada.* 1962. Stadler Gallery.

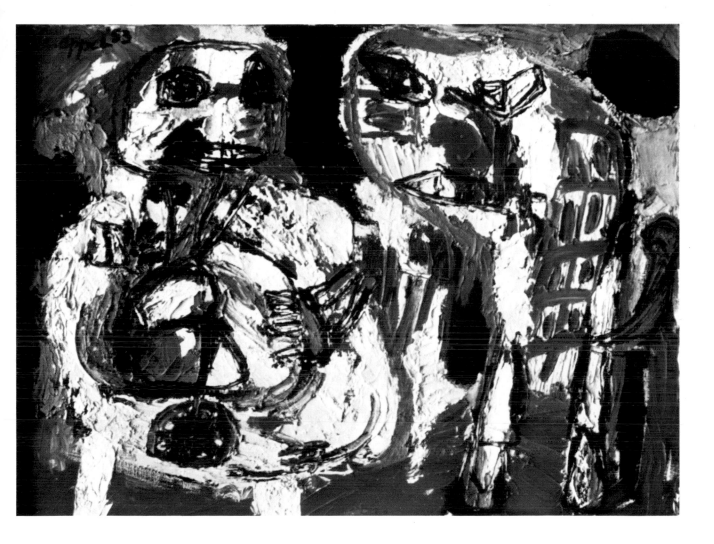

EMIL SCHUMACHER. *Red wind*. 1961. Anne Abels Gallery.

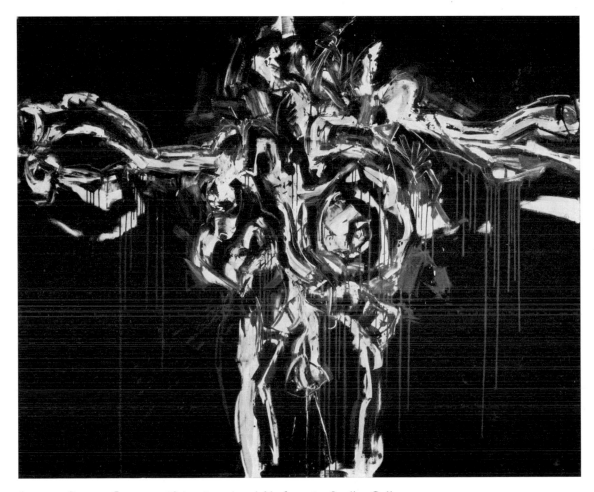

Antonio Saura. *Great crucifixion in red and black.* 1963. Stadler Gallery.

They undertook to overturn all the conventions of painting and sculpture. Experiments with new materials and new procedures of work were begun, and the group turned a remodeled old store into an exhibition hall of their own, the Gutai Picture Gallery. They are not united by a common doctrine except for a simple inclination toward abstraction and instinctive spontaneous creation. Many of their experiments have a neo-dada tinge, and the group reveal a preference for visual spectacle. Since 1957, various types of spectacles have been produced, some of which could be considered as anticipating the American « happenings. » The most important among these was the so-called « International Festival of Heaven, » produced in 1960 in Osaka, and attended by the critic Michel Tapié, who published a description of the event. It consisted of sending up in space enormous kites and globes that carried pictures painted by members of the group and by invited European and American artists.
The «Gutai» group is formed by more than twen-

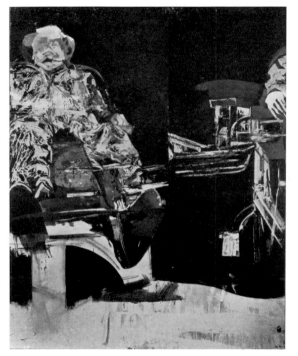

Luis Feito. *1962*. René Metras Gallery.

Rafael Canogar. *Testing of the future astronaut.* 1964.

ty artists, among whom, in addition to Yoshihara, are Kasuo Shiraga, Saburo Murakami, Atsuko Tanaka, Sadamasa Motonaga, and Ohara.

The new Spanish painting

After the Spanish Civil War and the upheaval of the Second World War there was a period of inactivity in the plastic arts in Spain. The Spanish artists appear to have ignored the trends that accumulated during the postwar period in European painting, particularly the School of Paris, and in American painting. The first signs of an awakening took place in Barcelona in 1948, when some young painters and writers founded a group called «Dau al Set» (Seven on the Die). This name must certainly have been inspired by a phrase of André Breton, the leader of surrealism: «the seventh face of the die.» The painters forming the group were Modesto Cuixart, Juan Ponç, Antoni Tàpies, and Juan José Tharrats; later they were joined by the poet-critic Juan Edmundo Cirlot. Thanks to Tharrats, who owned a printshop, they published a monthly or bimonthly artistic-literary review, which had a very limited circulation. The review continued to appear long after the group had dissolved. The breakup of the group came in 1951, and each of the painters took an independent route.

The group was of the surrealist persuasion and was influenced by Miró, the Catalan painter whom they knew and understood profoundly, and by Klee.

Tàpies was the first to abandon surrealist imagery, in 1952. He was followed by Cuixart in 1954 and by Tharrats in 1955.

Ponç, whose anguished and original imagination made him appear the most intense of the group, was born in Barcelona in 1928. In 1953, at the age of twenty-five, he went to Brazil, but his artistic activity there appears to have been scant. He returned to Barcelona in 1963, bringing drawings of superb quality done in Brazil, in which his anguished world of nightmare continued. At home he resumed his painting, with immediate success.

The awakening in Madrid came a good deal later. Several young painters there were working in the surrealist mode. In 1957 they decided to unite into a group to signify the union of the Madrid vanguard. They called their group «El Paso» (The Step), the implication being a step toward new things. It consisted of Rafael Canogar, Manolo Millares, Luis Feito, Antonio Saura, and the sculptor Pablo Serrano, who after a short time withdrew. The following year the painters Manuel Rivera and Viola joined. These artists of the group held various exhibitions and jointly published several tracts. The group was dissolved in 1960.

In spite of their brief existence, these groups were the two sources for the diffusion of the Spanish vanguard, and the members were the foundation of what became known, outside the country, as the Spanish School. Undoubtedly there are other individuals who are making themselves known, but the former members of both the original groups still remain firmly in the vanguard of painting in Spain.

The Barcelona group

Antoni Tàpies, one of the founders of the « Dau al Set,» was born in Barcelona in 1923. He began painting in 1945, frequently using heavy impastos, but his surrealist period began in 1947, coinciding with the « Dau al Set » epoch, and he changed from matter painting to depicting the image. He lived in Paris in 1950 and 1951; then, from 1952 to 1955, he went through a transition-

LUCIO MUÑOZ. *Project for an electric chair.* 1966.

al period in which he slowly returned to matter painting. His present style of painting began in 1955, and has earned him a ranking place in the international art world. In 1958 he received the Carnegie International first prize in Pittsburgh.

Tàpies is one of the painters whose work is most characteristic of matter informalism. After several attempts he achieves the preparation of his material base, which consists of varying proportions of powdered marble with latex and synthetic varnishes, resulting in a material of great solidity, which can be easily worked. The surface is then treated by rubbing, scratching, cracking, or modeling to obtain the matter-accidents that constitute the basis of his painting. The colors he uses are restrained, with a preference for the somber: grays, blacks, blues, browns, ochers, and sepias, with slate-colored or cement-toned nuances. At times he traces a solitary calligraphic line with oil and brush onto this material. The surface thus obtained may be mat or glossy, but in it there is always an extraordinary richness of texture, even though the first impression is one of ascetic sobriety. The texture derives from the grain and quality of the medium itself, from the reliefs, erosions, and flaking, from the fissures and the furrows. Sometimes he makes a deep line, or sign, in the thick impasto, and at other times he finishes it with reliefs.

From this corroded material, kneaded, chapped, and revealing its excrescences, Tàpies obtains an unexpected expressivity. Important to him is the profound sense of space he achieves in his canvases, more emphasized in productions of larger dimensions, which gives his work a sense of almost mystical concentration. An essential quality of each of Tàpies' pictures is that it has its own personality, with its own history, and with its own life. This distinct life of each picture is something few artists are able to achieve, but which is the hallmark of the elect.

Modesto Cuixart, another founder of the « Dau al Set,» was born in Barcelona in 1925. Around 1948 his pictures were surrealist and were inspired by Miró and Klee, but in 1954 his work became informal. He began incorporating collages of rags, string, or pieces of paper in his pictures; later he slowly purified his treatment until he arrived at a smooth, unobstructed background in which he searched for the action of a large space on which he inscribed magical signs, symbols, and unknown emblems in matter relief. He turned to metallic qualities from which he obtained silvered surfaces, or in dark gold, strengthening the impression of magic, secret objects. In his latest works Cuixart has abandoned informalism for the new figural painting.

Juan José Tharrats was born in Gerona in 1918. He was also one of the founders of the « Dau al Set » group, and the editor of its review, for which

MANUEL VIOLA. *Epitaph.* 1965.

he wrote a considerable number of articles on painting and painters, giving Spain at that time full information about international painting. His surrealist period ended in 1955 when he turned to informalism.

Tharrats' painting comes within the category of tachism. It consists of blots or large outlines crossed by black or dark fissures, as if there existed a struggle between color and noncolor, all forming a seductively decorative quality, neutralized by the floating mobility of the colored elements.

Román Vallés was born in Barcelona in 1923. He studied in the High School of Fine Arts of San

Jorge in Barcelona, and in 1949 he went on study tours through France, Italy, and the Low Countries. After 1956 he turned to informalism. Vallés' work is oriented toward a search for the poetry of space. Restrained brushwork in latex colors in the gesture manner calls forth a subtle play of textures over the surface of the canvas; instead of expressing violence they appear to absorb the latent energies that fill the space that surrounds us. About 1960 he produced a series of monochrome works of exceptional purity, among which the white series, where the poetry of space reaches its highest realization, is outstanding. In his most recent work, Vallés incorporates into his world – which remains intact – collages of dramatic or nostalgic prints or photographs. This irruption of the world of reality into Vallés' interior world is incorporated in a perfect synthesis. The violent or trivial world is absorbed by means of subtle transitions, unified or, more correctly, poetized by the painter. And this is where he differs in treatment from the disembodied reality that the pop artists offer.

Augusto Puig was born in Barcelona in 1929. In 1945 he began painting along abstract lines influenced by Miró and Klee. Between 1947 and 1952 he lived in Paris, and also traveled in Germany and Switzerland. At present he lives in Barcelona.
Puig's painting is in the tachist style, and employs running colors of a rich and expressive texture, which acquire an aspect of floating forms in a uniform and empty space. The refreshing imagination at the service of the invention of forms neutralizes a tendency toward sumptuousness of color that borders on the decorative.

The Madrid group

Manolo Millares, born in Las Palmas in 1926, had an initial surrealist period that lasted until 1948, when he turned to abstraction. In 1957 he became a founder of El Paso. Millares constructs his pictures with collages of torn and twisted sackcloth that protrude and hang over the surface of the picture. Almost exclusively, he uses a white oxide or a full black, by which he obtains a drama and violence that completely separates his work from the more constructed and serene work of Burri, although the material employed is similar.

Antonio Saura was born in Huesca in 1930. He is self-taught. Saura began, as did most of the painters of his generation, as a surrealist with an exhibition in Madrid in 1951. Between 1953 and 1955 he lived in Paris, and in 1954 he exhibited with the surrealist group. In 1956 he took part in an exhibition of the « Phases » group headed by Jaguer, and the next year helped found the « El Paso » group. At present he lives in Madrid. He belongs to the *art autre* group of Michel Tapié.
Saura is the most representative exponent of gesture painting in Spain. He began with abstract gesture painting, but fell gradually into figural painting. This is how he himself explained it in 1959: « By any means to fill a white surface, with an action sustained by an elemental, obsessive structualization, ruled by a mathematical-biological logic, fluid as a continuous, organic river. Not to fall into absolute chaos, not to drift toward suicide, not to lose my footing, and not to divorce myself from a tremendous reality, I have chosen, almost without reflection, the only structure that could serve me. A body, an object, a landscape could turn into a constant source as long as it did not become more than this: an endothermic support by which one could bring the need for action to a happy conclusion. »
With Saura the gesture becomes a slashing stroke. His figures call to mind de Kooning by their schematization and violence, but the aggressiveness and grotesqueness of de Kooning is trans-

formed into drama by Saura. His figures surge forth from the world of desperation to shriek at us. The colors are practically reduced to white and black, but his most subtle nuances are obtained with gray tones. The gesture lines of Saura leave the space free to act through the contrast that an inert surface offers before the vehemence of the brushstroke, heightening the lacerated characteristics of the figures. The picture acquires the hard severity, the sacred cruelty that is characteristic of the best line of traditional Spanish painting, among which figures the black painting of Goya or that of Gutierrez Solana.

Rafael Canogar, who was born in Toledo in 1935, created his first abstract pictures in 1954, and in 1957 helped found « El Paso. » He began with a surrealist period, with a magical world somewhere between Miró and Klee, but later made collages with rough materials, burlap of varying coarseness – torn, mended, eaten, and with some places burned – that transmit certain drama. Then he changed to the use of a magma base with blots or color, and of late he has assimilated certain innovations from pop art.

Luis Feito, born in Madrid in 1929, studied at the Academy of Fine Arts of San Fernando, and became another founder of « El Paso. » In his pictures Feito creates a contrast between a smooth space and the excrescences of the matter toward the center of the picture (or slightly off center), with a tendency toward circular conformations that give the impression of flattened craters. He uses thin colors without violence, especially whites, with which he achieves an intense expressiveness in opposition to the matter; his attenuated hues, rose, vague lilacs, leaden and purple colors give the impression of traces of burns. By shading the colors, nearly always with the same technique, he achieves a variability and animation of the pictorial surface.

Lucio Muñoz was born in Madrid in 1929, and, like Feito, studied at the School of Fine Arts of San Fernando. He spent the years 1955 and 1956 in Paris. On panels of heavy wood Muñoz carves the surface with deep hollows, striations, and erosions, using knife, chisel, or pyrography to produce topographical accidents in the media on which he applies restrained blots of color or liquid pitch, creating a dramatic surface, robust and full of vitality.

Manuel Viola was born in Saragossa in 1919. He lived in Paris from 1939 to 1949, after which he settled in Madrid. His painting is violent and with similarities to action painting. Viola obtains an ambiguous mixture of space and emerging forms by a technique of chiaroscuro.

Chapter four

Informalism in the United States

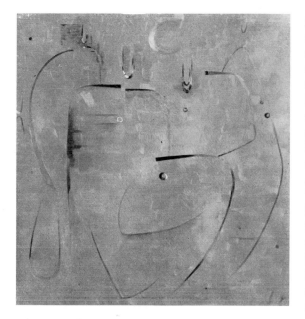

WOLFGANG PAALEN. *Painting.* 1940.

Abstract expressionism

There is no doubt that modern American painting owed its evolution to the massive influx of artists from the School of Paris, which took place with the outbreak of the Second World War, and especially after the occupation of Paris. These artists brought with them a wide experience in the *avant-garde* that became a stimulus for the young Americans in search of new directions. Among this group of artists, the surrealists were outstanding both for their number and for the artistic standing of their representatives. Around 1940, André Breton, the most original and renowned painter of the surrealist movement, came to New York, as did Max Ernst and the painters Matta (R. A. S. Matta-Echaurren), Kurt Seligman, Yves Tanguy, and Esteban Francés. Max Ernst and Matta were the most influential; they were associated with Peggy Guggenheim's

gallery, Art of This Century, which had been started in 1941, and which had launched the first wave of American artists who spearheaded abstract expressionism. Matta maintained a close friendship with Arshile Gorky and frequently saw Pollock. One must understand the missionary spirit of Matta in order to understand that this friendship provided a stimulus for reflecting on problems of creation and an impetus to experimentation. Matta's influence on Gorky is unquestionable.

These facts should refute those xenophobes who insist that the American School sprang from nothing. An original artist loses nothing by admitting that he has received his inspiration from others, in addition to the fact that it is totally impossible for an artist to evolve from nothing. As Malraux said, « An artist is born from another artist » – and this is a biological law of art, in which there exists no spontaneous generation anymore than it does in life. If the three most original artists in America Pollock, Rothko, and de Kooning had a starting point, this does not distract from their originality.

The influence of surrealism has been pointed out by several critics; even Pierre Restany, in spite of his notorious aversion to surrealism, has confirmed its decisive influence in the modern awakening of American art.* Dore Ashton also considers that the abstract expressionists are indubitably the heirs of surrealism.[+]

But even without concrete facts it is enough to examine the techniques used by the action painters to recognize that they spring from surrealism: the dripping method was used by Max Ernst (although only occasionally), and the rapid, spontaneous brushstroke is nothing else than the automatic technique propounded by Breton and used in his painting. It is also clear that the ideology

* P. RESTANY, « L'Amérique aux Américains », *Ring des Arts*, No. 2 (1961).

[+] DORE ASHTON, *Cimaise*, 4th series, No. 2 (1956).

on which action painting is founded has its roots in surrealism, which had as its principle that any freedom is permitted a creation exalting the vital and instinctive over the rational.

But in addition to the liberating influence of the surrealists, another factor of equal importance was the direct teachings of, and examples by, a European painter who had been living in the United States for many years before the war, Hans Hofmann, an expressionist painter of German origin. Hofmann belonged to an earlier invasion of European artists who had come from Germany when Hitler came to power. (The same influx brought figures who had been outstanding in the Bauhaus, from its director Walter Gropius to Moholy-Nagy and Albers). In America, Hofmann established an academy, and his teaching was very influential on many young artists. Hofmann himself became one of the foremost of the new American artists.

A possible influence, not to be overlooked, is one that has not yet been clearly defined, that of the great Austrian artist related to surrealism, Wolfgang Paalen, who was born in Vienna in 1905 and committed suicide in Mexico in 1958. Paalen went to Mexico at the outbreak of the Second World War, and there he developed a double activity, one theoretical (especially through his review *Dyn*, published in English, and a series of essays, collected into a book, *Form and Sense*, which was published in 1945 by Wittenborn and Co. in New York, and was distributed only in the United States) and the other his pictorial work. Paalen, who came to be profoundly interested in the concepts of energy and physics, wanted to transmit through his paintings the material-immaterial idea of energy. Soon after 1940 he began to produce aformal pictures, in which, by means of brushwork ordered and oriented toward undulant forms, he completely filled the canvas with all-over painting, until then unknown, and enriched with a pure, vibrant color. At the same time he produced spatial paintings with short ges-

JACKSON POLLOCK. *Cutout*. 1949.
Collection Martha Jackson Gallery.

ture signs. The high-quality work of this artist, a precursor of the new informal tendencies, has not yet been evaluated in the measure it deserves.

The influence of the European artists who emigrated to America constituted a spiritually stimulating factor in the appearance of a new school of American artists, but it is also necessary to bear in mind the material factor that served as a support to a large part of them and permitted them to work with independence and freedom during the hard times of the great economic depression. This was the Federal program of economic assistance to artists, which was created during the crisis years of the 1930's under the name of the Federal Art Project of the Works Progress Administration (WPA); it provided the painters with official commissions for murals and other works of art. The detailed biographies of the painters below will show how were helped by this program.

The historical development of abstract expressionism proceeded in an accelerated tempo along the following lines. In 1943 Peggy Guggenheim's Art of This Century gallery, founded in 1941 on a noncommercial basis, held the first one-man show of Jackson Pollock, who had been introduced by the surrealist painter Matta; the gallery then became the launching place for the first abstract expressionists and a milestone for the new American painting. Peggy Guggenheim had Pollock under contract until 1947. In 1944 Hans Hofmann had his first one-man show at the Art of This Century; in the same year Motherwell had his first one-man show there; Rothko had his first show there in 1945, and Clyfford Still in 1946. Up to this point what had passed could be called the first wave of the renewing of American painting, which ended with the closing of the Art of This Century gallery in 1947.

The second wave consisted of de Kooning, Kline, Guston, and Tomlin, and later Brooks and Tworkov, and began with de Kooning's first exhibition at the Egan Gallery in 1948. In 1950 Kline had his first one-man showing, also at the Egan Gallery, and other abstract expressionist exhibitions followed.

In the chapter on informalism we underlined the difficulties created by the use of various nomenclatures, not always the most felicitous, and often arbitrary. To designate this new American art the term « abstract expressionism » is usually employed, as it had been by the critics of the second decade of the century to designate the first works of Kandinsky. The term was used for the first time by Robert Coates, art critic of *The New Yorker* magazine, to describe the styles of Pollock, Motherwell, Clyfford Still, and Hans Hofmann. This new name stuck, and was used by the critics and the press. But when it includes painters of such

Jackson Pollock. *The deep.* 1953.
Sidney Janis Gallery.

diverse characteristics as de Kooning (actually expressionist, but not always abstract) on the one hand, and Rothko, Newman, and Tobey (who are not expressionists) on the other, the use of a name with such a precise meaning is inevitably confusing. The critic Clement Greenberg employs the more general and less compromising term « new American painting, » which precisely because of its generality is more exact.

In 1952 Harold Rosenberg introduced the term « action painting » to designate the painting of Jackson Pollock; the name was meant to indicate an art based on the instinctual muscular movement by which the brush is directed, without premeditation or control, within a climate of emotional dynamism. This term was meant to show art as a manifestation of pure life, which rejected thought and speculation, and which eliminated retouching and the controlled brushstroke in favor of improvisation. This name also caught on, but it could include only a group of these new painters, such as Pollock, de Kooning, Kline, and Motherwell, those who practiced a type of expressive automatism. In European circles the term « gesture painting » is used. For other painters whose attitude was opposed to that of other action painters (for example, Newman and Rothko) we prefer the term « quietistic » or « invisible » painting to characterize a form of painting having objectives contrary not only to action painting but also to calculated, constructed, or structural painting. Quietistic painting is based on the principle of space and the action inherent in large areas or masses. Espousing this form are, beside the artists already mentioned, Ad Reinhardt and Jules Olitski in their latest works.

There has been an attempt to make a geographical distinction between the two great styles of the new American painting. Thus it is customary to speak of a Pacific school and a New York school. The first would include artists who worked in the Far West, such as Rothko, Still, Tobey, and the second, the artists related to action painting. The Pacific school shows the influence of Oriental thought, which would explain its tendency toward quietism and contemplation, and results in a more serene art than that of the New York school. The Pacific school is divided between two centers, one in the Northwest, in Seattle, where Tobey worked, and the other in California where Rothko (very sporadically) and Still worked. The Pacific school exists only in the European version of the American panorama, which the critics in the United States have resisted, particularly those in the Pacific zone, such as Jules Langsner, who consider the trend nonexistent because there is no coordination between its supposed compo-

WILLEM DE KOONING. *Untitled.* 1963.
Collection Allen Stone Gallery.

nents. In any event, the painting as practiced in California has never at any time given evidence of having any idea of the existence of the aforementioned tendency or school.

A clearer view of the diverse tendencies that go to form the « new American painting » or « abstract expressionism » is gained by dividing them in the following manner: action painters, when the dynamic element and the expressive violence of the brushwork or the dripping method predominates; tachists, when a more static product results; calligraphic painting, when the similarity to a pictorial form of writing is dominant; and quietistic painting. A special section will be dedicated to Gorky, as a precursor, and another one to the free expressionists.

ROBERT MOTHERWELL. *Diary of a painter.* 1958. Collection Martha Jackson Gallery.

A precursor: Arshile Gorky

Arshile Gorky, the pseudonym for Nayotz Dzore, was born in Turkish Armenia in 1905, and studied in the Polytechnic Institute in Tiflis. He came to the United States in 1920, and during the depression worked on the WPA. He committed suicide in 1948.

Gorky was part of the surrealist group during Breton's stay in New York, and exhibited in the International Exhibition of Surrealism there in 1942. He was the American artist who most interested Breton. Strongly influenced by Matta and Miró, Gorky acquired a very personal style that in its turn exercised a strong influence on various of the future abstract expressionists, among whom were de Kooning, who openly avowed this in a letter published after Gorky's death. His pictures are characterized by free, abstract, organic forms, which float in an imaginary space, sometimes connected by fine lines, which confer a particularly dynamic quality on the picture.

Breton said of him that « paradoxically he placed himself before nature to paint, but used it as a stimulus or springboard to submerge himself in the most profound spiritual states, to gather from it the darkest vibration of the intimate I. »

Gorky's pictures are very complex, and the same

Franz Kline. *Accent aigu.* 1957.

forms often have spots of different color inside them. But the result as a whole is never motley, and the space acquires a luminosity that gives to the picture a sense of clearness in spite of its complexity. Black, reds, blues, and ochers were the colors Gorky preferred.

Action painters

Jackson Pollock was born in Cody, Wyoming, in 1907. He studied painting in the Manual Arts High School in Los Angeles between 1925 and 1929, and then moved to New York, where he studied with Thomas Benton at the Art Students League. From 1938 to 1942 he worked on the WPA, and his first exhibition was held at Peggy Guggenheim's Art of This Century in 1943. Pollock died in an automobile accident in 1956. Pollock's first pictures were figural and were much influenced by Orozco and his expressionistic violence; later he came under the influence of Picasso and the surrealists. His close friendship with Matta brought him into contact with Max Ernst, from whom he took the idea of dripping, which Ernst had occasionally used among his many other techniques (frottage, and so forth) for calling forth the birth of images.

The classic drip technique of Pollock has its beginnings in a picture he painted in 1943, the *She Wolf*, which is now in the Museum of Modern Art in New York. In this picture he combines brushwork with spilled paint. Part of it was done on the easel, the rest with the canvas spread on the floor. However, he continued his semifigural paintings with the *Totems* of 1945, but it could be said that this is the start of an absolutely personal style of work, which was to last until 1951. After 1951 Pollock broke away from his drip technique, which threatened to become a mannerism, and began a black-and-white period, less dense, with an eye to searching for the activity of space. This series reveals the mutual influence between the abstract expressionists, since de Kooning from 1948, Motherwell in 1949, and Kline in 1950 created their pictures in black and white. Afterward, and up to the time of his death, Pollock resumed work with the brush, returning to his first expressionist figuration, although in his last work, *Scent*, he appears to have returned to the all-over pattern of his first period of dripping – marked by *Eyes in the Heat* of 1946. Whereas other painters are interested in the theoretical conception inherent in creation, Pollock was fundamentally interested in the method of work. As he himself vividy described it: « My

Franz Kline. *Sumi ink.* 1952. Allen Stone Gallery.

painting is not done on the easel. I seldom stretch my canvas before I begin to paint. I prefer to put it up on a wall, or better still, spread it out on the floor. I need to feel the resistance of a hard surface. When the canvas is on the floor, I feel closer to it, I feel as if I am part of the painting, I can walk around it and work from all sides, literally be in the painting. This is the way the Indians in the West paint on the sand. I have eliminated the usual tools of the painter, such as easel, palette, and brushes. I prefer sticks, a trowel, ordinary spoons, or just to let the liquid color drip or spatter, or use a thick paste of sand, ground glass, or other strange materials.

« When I am painting I have no knowledge of what I am doing. Only after a moment of "returning consciousness" do I become aware of what I have been doing. Then, however, I have no hesitation about making changes, or destroying images, because the painting has a life of its own. My mission is to bring forth this life. It is only when I lose contact with the canvas that the result can be disastrous. If I maintain contact until the end, the painting surges forth like pure harmony. »

To come into Pollock's studio in that period produced a most curious impression. The floor was spattered with drops of paint, and in a corner stood a stock of cans of paint (he frequently used Duco). When beginning a picture he usually took whatever can of paint happened to be nearest. He applied paint with a thick house painter's brush or a stick or a spoon, or simply by punching a hole in the can and letting the paint run onto the canvas on the floor, he spattered, or let drip, by rapid up and down movements of the arm or the whole body. At times he would pause to let the paint run onto one spot, then resume his rhythm. On the walls and on the floor there were always several canvases in various states of progress. Pollock was wont to sit down to contemplate these canvases for long periods of time. His pictures were formed slowly, sometimes taking weeks or months.

This was Pollock's procedure in creating his paintings: after having poured out two or three colors in rhythmic waves over a canvas, he stopped the work, hung the canvas on the wall, and left it there for observation for about two weeks. In the meantime he began other pictures. After he had thoroughly studied the hung picture for two or more weeks, he once more spread it on the floor and worked feverishly over it. Afterward he again hung the canvas and subjected it to another scrutiny, until he was satisfied that no more additions or retouching were necessary. The painting had become concrete and independent of the artist: it had acquired its own life.

In his drip technique, Pollock used aluminum paint and commercial enamel paint (Duco), alone or mixed with oil, and often he poured the paint over the raw canvas so that it became impregnated. This manner of impregnating the untreated canvas was imitated not only by a large number of the abstract expressionists and many European informalists but later came to be the most fundamental technique of a tendency opposed to abstract expressionism, the « post-painterly abstraction » of such artists as Louis and Noland. Hokusai, the famous 19th-century Japanese painter, appears to have been a precursor of Pollock: it is said Hokusai wanted to use canvases of a size never before seen, and he employed brushes the size of brooms and barrelfuls of ink, with a gesture procedure that at times was very similar to Pollock's.

Pollock maintained that his procedure was not a mere automatism. It is automatic at the outset, but then a considered progress toward organization and unity develops, which is what confers on it life as a work of art. The picture acquires the consistency of a precious stone or a natural object, and its beauty must be considered as such.

« My paintings do not have a center, the same interest exists in all parts. » This is the technique called « all-over » painting. The color and the rhythm dominate everything, and the rhythm is a vital rhythm. The space becomes ambiguous and appears to be eliminated, and when the surface is filled the picture becomes a dense object, a solid body; its integration is absolute, it has become an actual organism, a unique form given it by the totality of the pictorial surface. The picture is converted finally into the result of a vital experience of the artist, because the act of creation is above all an act of vital expression.

The multiplication of the lines has come to annul the forms and the space, although, it has been held, a new pictorial space has been created. The result is a mottled surface – total, dense, and resplendent; a solid, objective thing, with the personality and shape of an object. Thus the canvas becomes a solid work, the same as a piece of sculpture, which does not contain space but is in

HANS HOFMANN. *Sun in the foliage.* 1964. Kootz Gallery.

space as a two-dimensional object, the structure of which is a surface of lines and colors organized into an indivisible whole, although open; that is, it gives the impression of being able to expand itself into infinity, and any isolated portion of it has the same importance. There are no interior forms, no centers of interest. There exists no definite and isolated color, but a streaked, motley color resulting from the intricacy of the unindividualized colored lines. Pollock represented the most advanced point in the evolution of nonfigural painting up to that time.

In spite of the fact that Pollock acted as mediator between chance and the concrete act that constitutes the work, it is evident that he possessed a will for creation, an esthetic conscience that revealed itself in those moments of contemplation dedicated to the finishing of the work.

HANS HOFMANN. *Joy sparks of the gods.* 1964.
Kootz Gallery.

Willem de Kooning was born in Rotterdam, Holland, in 1904, and studied in the Academy of Fine Arts there. In Belgium he came under the influence of the Flemish expressionists. De Kooning came to the United States in 1926, and was an intimate friend of Gorky, with whom he shared a studio from 1930 and with whom an interaction of influences developed. In 1934 de Kooning produced, practically at the same time, abstract painting and a kind of figural work that hovered between the formal realism of the new objectivity and expressionism. He worked on the WPA from 1935 to 1936.

De Kooning appears to have been influenced by Soutine's work. The first exhibition of paintings that marked the beginning of his personal style was held at the Egan Gallery in 1948 (this was the famous « black-and-white show »), and from there on he embarked on a style that was to become the most typical example of action painting, characterized by bold and violent brush-strokes outlining actual forms roughly schematized – such as his series of *Women* of 1952-1953 – or abstract forms. This oscillation between reality and abstraction put an end to the prejudice that the two tendencies were irreconcilable, as had happened in France a little earlier with Dubuffet and Fautrier and in the Low Countries with members of the « Cobra » group.

In 1951 de Kooning made the following declaration, in which he revealed the basis of his position as an artist: « Painting, to really be painting, is a way of life, a style of life, so to speak (which is the same as a negation of all style). »

De Kooning's painting generally is a product of the all-over style, and he emphatically rejects in these words the importance of space: « The space of the physicists bores me to death.»

Robert Motherwell was born in Aberdeen, Washington, in 1915. Until 1937 he lived in San Fran-

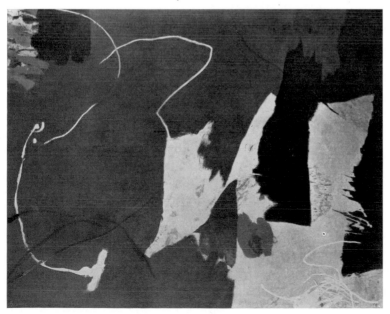

JAMES BROOKS. *Quagett.* 1964. Kootz Gallery.

cisco, and he took his Bachelor of Arts degree at Stanford University in California. He did graduate study at Harvard, 1937-1938, traveled in Europe until 1939, and studied at Columbia University, New York, in 1940-1941.

Motherwell groups himself with the surrealists; he first got to know Kurt Seligman, and, through him, Max Ernst, Tanguy, Masson, and Matta. He exhibited for the first time in Paris in 1939, and in the International Exhibition of Surrealism in New York in 1942, and also contributed to *Dyn*, the English-language review published in Mexico by Wolfgang Paalen. Motherwell is one of the most intelligent and cultured painters in the United States. He was associate editor of the review *Possibilities* from 1947 to 1948, and he was the editor of the series « The Documents of Modern Art » published by Wittenborn and Co., 1944-1957. His first one-man show was held in 1944 in New York at the Art of This Century gallery. In 1958 he married Helen Frankenthaler, also a painter. He has been Visiting Critic, Columbia University, New York.

In his pictures, which follow the style he began in 1951 with the famous « Granada » series, in black and white, Motherwell relies on an almost achromatic principle, based on the opposition of black and white. His wide black, irregular zones, of vaguely biomorphic tendency, occupy a large part of the picture, outlining over the empty whites anguished and profound canyons that produce a mysterious and dramatic quality that has become a unique characteristic. Later he introduces color marginally in low, restrained tonalities. He often uses collages, incorporated with a plastic sense into the picture.

It is interesting to know some of the thoughts of a painter of such high standing as Motherwell. Of abstract art he says: « Abstract art conveys very clearly what man, confronted with life and its conditions in modern times, feels in the way of rejection or acceptance. It expresses the desire for direct, intense, living, and immediate experience.

JACK TWORKOV. *Script.* 1962. Leo Castelli Gallery.

All that distracts from such a living experiment is eliminated in abstract art. A feeling of an abyss, of emptiness between the isolated I and modern man and the world, is produced. Abstract art is an attempt to fill this void. »

Frank Kline was born in Wilkes-Barre, Pennsylvania, in 1910, and studied in the Art Students League of Boston, and at Boston University. In 1949 he began his cycle of large calligraphies in black and white, and in 1950 he held his first one-man show at the Egan Gallery in New York. He taught at Black Mountain College, North Car-

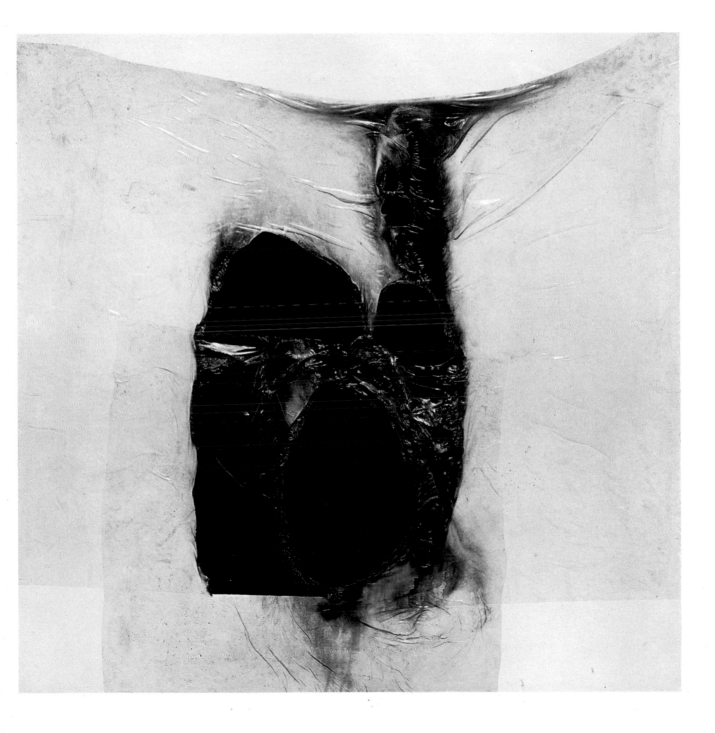

LUCIO FONTANA. *Concetto spaziale.* 1964. Marlborough Gallery.

olina, Pratt Institute, the Philadelphia Museum
Art School, and Cooper Union, New York. He
died in 1962 in New York.

Kline's painting is an expression of the pure gesture, which is the reason he eliminates the dis-
tracting action of color. His work consists of
enormous canvases in black and white in which
large, loose black brushstrokes appear as gigantic
calligraphic signs. The white does not appear as
a negative element, nor does it indicate a void,
but is presented as an active part of the picture,
acting in dialectic opposition to the black strokes.
This severe, violent and remorseless universe of
Kline was modified toward 1958, the period
when he introduced color and advanced toward
the creation of a more complex atmosphere. Actually, his pictures lost some of the impressive
vigor that had characterized them. Kline's black-
and-white painting, in its nakedness, its dramatism, expressed the utmost limit of vehemence
in painting.

Hans Hofmann was born in Weissenburg, Bavaria, in 1880. He lived in Paris between 1904 and
1914, and his first exhibition was held at the
Paul Cassirer Gallery in Berlin in 1910. Hofmann
directed a school of painting in Munich from
1915 to 1932, when he departed for the United
States. There, in a short time, he opened another
school of painting, which, because of the great
number of abstract expressionists who attended
it, came to be of fundamental importance in the
development of violence and freedom in the new
American painting. In 1944 he had his first one-
man show in New York at the Art of This Century Gallery. He died in February, 1966.

Starting from expressionism, Hofmann came under the influence of the Kandinsky of the improvisations. He began producing abstract expressionist works in 1939. Each of Hofmann's works is
a virtuosity of expressed vitality, and this man,
who was in his eighties when he died, kept producing pictures that surpass in audacity those of

PHILIP GUSTON. *Duo.* 1961.
The Solomon R. Guggenheim Museum.

the youngest artists. He uses gesture painting,
tachism, or compositions with orthogonal forms
interchangeably, but in each one the violent action spills over – vibrant, strident in color – in a
way that each picture becomes a fragment of bra-
vura; each picture is a shake-up that levels the
gentle and conventional. Everything is excellent,
powerful, vigorous, and absolutely free, without
concessions to norm or style.

James Brooks was born in Saint Louis, Missouri,
in 1906. He has lived in New York since 1926,
where he studied at the Art Students League
from 1927 to 1931. From 1938 to 1942 he worked
on the WPA. His first one-man show was at
the Peridot Gallery in New York in 1950. He received Carnegie Institute, Logan, and Art Institute of Chicago prizes. He has exhibited both nationally and internationally. He was Visiting Artist at New College, Sarasota, Florida, in 1965.
Brooks practices an action painting with ample

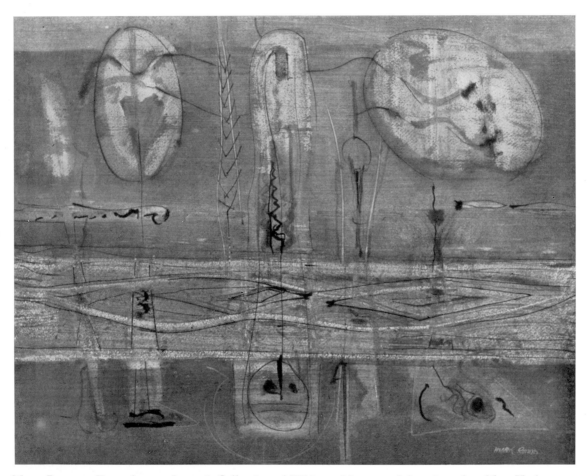

MARK ROTHKO. *Entombment, I.* 1946. Collection of Whitney Museum of American Art, New York.

brushstrokes, short and of more controlled character, less turbulent than those habitual in action painters. A sense of calm, of equilibrium, and a contained lyricism emanate from his pictures.

Jack Tworkov was born in Biala, Poland, in 1900, and came to the United States in 1913. From 1925 to 1926 he studied at the Art Students League in New York, and from 1937 to 1941 he worked on the WPA. He exhibited at the Egan Gallery in New York in 1947, 1949, 1952, and 1954, the Stable Gallery in 1957 and

1959, the Walker Art Center, and has appeared in many group shows. His painting has developed toward a gesture expression of balanced and easy rhythm. He has been Chairman of the Art Department at Yale University since 1963.

Philip Guston was born in Montreal, Canada, in 1913, and came to the United States in 1916. He is self-taught. From 1935 to 1940 he worked on the WPA, and had his first one-man show in 1945 at the Midtown Gallery in New York. Guston is an action painter who begins with a dense

BARNETT NEWMAN. *White fire N. 3.* 1964.

matter base, but his ample brushstrokes appear as if interrupted and are not directed toward the creation of a climate of violence in the picture; instead they become ordered and pacified to form a work of lyrical and contemplative quality, which includes wide gray fields and rich tonal variations of color. He has exhibited both nationally and internationally, and his work appears in many institutes and universities.

Quietistic painting

Mark Rothko was born in Dvinsk, Russia, in 1903, and was brought to the United States in 1913, in which years his family settled in Oregon. In 1925 he went to New York. Rothko began to paint in 1926 and studied for a time at the Art Students League with Max Weber; at first he was influenced by Gorky. He exhibited in New York, but without success. In 1933 he and Adolph Gottlieb founded the group called « The Ten, » and in 1936 and 1937 he worked on the WPA. During the summers of 1947 and 1949 he taught at the School of Fine Arts in San Francisco. This last occupation induced some misinformed European critics to include Rothko in the so-called Pacific school. Rothko is not only the foremost exponent of quietistic painting but also one of the most original artists of the present time; the terrain he has opened in art has been particularly fertile. Until 1939 Rothko practiced a type of expressionist painting; later he developed an abstract body of work influenced by surrealism, which he exhibited for the first time in the Art of This Century gallery, in 1945. His pictures from this period are characterized by great richness of forms, preferably curved and of biomorphic nature, that are distributed over the space; they constitute a complex of extraordinary imagination and high poetic content. After 1947 he began restricting

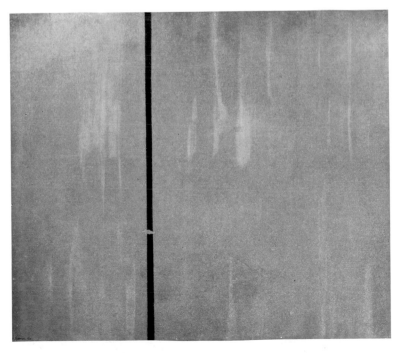

BARNETT NEWMANN. *Tundra.* 1950.

AD REINHARDT. *Number 17.* 1953. Collection of Whitney Museum of American Art, New York.

his forms, eliminating the biomorphic elements that had filled his pictures, to seek for the poetry of pure forms and color. Though his painting became simplified, approaching in sobriety some of the neoplastic works, Rothko sought something very distinct from the formal purity and coldness of the geometricists. He continued the process of purifying his work until, after 1950, he arrived at a stage consisting of large areas of pure color. His pictures dating from this time consist of

fluid rectangular zones (that is, of imprecise outlines) that become progressively larger until they
reach their final form: one large rectangle that includes almost the whole of the canvas superimposed on one or more smaller rectangles. In these
pictures composition disappears (the forms are
juxtaposed), and the forms, although apparently
regular, have indefinite outlines that gradually
dissolve in the surface of the picture through delicate, soft-edge transitions. This fluidity of the
outlines lends a quality of expansion to the masses, like some indefinite impulse toward the illimitable. The color of the surface of each large
form is solid and radiant, and although the general tone is uniform, light variations are produced
within the field of color, soft nuances, that also
give a quality of fluidity to the surface. One's attention is called to a strange lightness in the
whole form, an absence of weight, which produces an impression of floating.

The principle of the activity of masses or vast
areas of color on which Rothko's work is founded had been expressed by Gauguin, who said:
« In a meter of green more is expressed than in a
centimeter of green. » In effect, the masses of col-
or appear as if charged with energy, and even
though these pictures in no wise pretend to be
dynamic, they present a particular radiant activity of the surface, which makes the spectator,
submerged in that empty area, discover constant
elements for his attention. These resplendent areas
with borders gradually dissolving into a fleecy
amorphousness, have nothing in common with
neoplasticism and its formal precision. Nor have
they anything in common with its rational spirit;
instead they signify, as does Zen, thought in
search of the essential. It is a painting of the
essential, inducing meditation, an effect accentuated in Rothko's last pictures, which are of a
still more severe conception.

CLYFFORD STILL. *Painting, 1951.* 1951.
The Solomon R. Guggenheim Museum.

CLYFFORD STILL. *Painting N. 3.* 1951.
Betty Parsons Gallery.

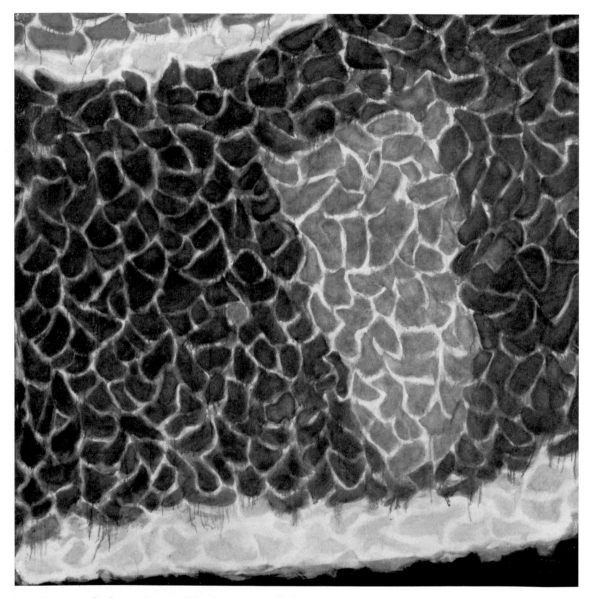

SAM FRANCIS. *Red in red.* 1965. Martha Jackson Gallery.

As with other painters, it is helpful to know Rothko's thoughts on painting. During his surrealist epoch he said: « I think of my pictures as dramas; the forms are the characters; they are the actors who move, dramatically and with absolute freedom and restraint. But these forms begin as unplanned and unknown characters in an unknown space. » And in a letter to *The New York*

PAUL JENKINS. *Phenomena nether near.* 1965.
Karl Flinker Gallery.

Times in 1947, Rothko wrote: « It is difficult
for the artist to accept the hostile incomprehen-
sion of the public. Nevertheless, this hostility can
be the instrument of his liberation. Divorced from
any false illusion of security and solidarity he can
equally well abandon the mixture of plastic conventions: the world of transcendental experience is then open to him. »

Through a painting that is all silence and solitude, Rothko manages, thanks to its radiant enchantment, to annul the silence and solitude of
the man who contemplates it.

Theodoros Stamos, born in New York in 1922,
studied at the American Artists School there in
1939. His first exhibition took place in the Wake-
field Gallery in New York in 1943. His painting, fundamentally quietistic, is along the same
lines as Rothko's. He has had numerous one-man
exhibitions, and has been an instructor.

Barnett Newman was born in New York in 1905,
and received his Bachelor of Arts degree from the
City College of New York in 1927. In 1950 he

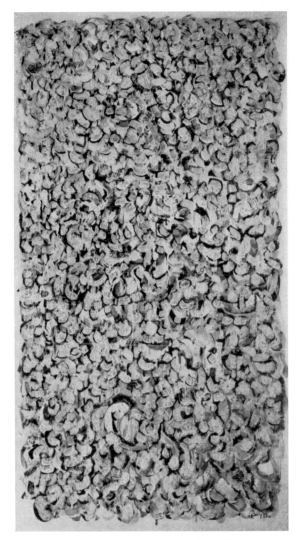

MARK TOBEY. *Pastoral.* 1964. Willard Gallery.

began his series of vast emptinesses with vertical accents in the field. He had one-man shows at
the Betty Parsons Gallery in 1947, 1950, 1951,
and 1955, at Bennington College in 1958, French
& Co. in 1959, and (with de Kooning) at the Allen Stone Gallery in 1962.

Newman is another of those artists for whom
painting takes on the role of an exercise in med-

Bradley Walker Tomlin. *N. 5-1952.*
Collection Mrs. Betty Parsons.

itation: his pictures represent an experience in space. Newman's opinion on art in general is expressed in his statement: « Only a nongeometric art can mark a new point of departure. But in no way must the art of painting be considered an instrument of energy for filling a hollow biological rhetoric. » And about his own art he says: « Painting, like a passion, is a live voice; when I hear it, I must let it speak without opposing it. » Newman produces a plastic work that is not constructivist nor arbitrary. His pictures are antisensual, ascetic. Composition and structure are eliminated. As he says, his painting is not geometric, non relational, not hierarchized. Nor is it tactile or pictorial. Finally, it is anti-emotional. All these characteristics we see repeated among the artists of the new American abstraction. The whole picture consists of a large, uniform field, with light variations of color saturation and with one or another vertical band (never pronouncedly geometric), sometimes horizontal, that crosses it or is situated on the edges and acts solely as a point of reference, or, rather, to intensify the activity of the empty space. In a sense, this is an extension of Rothko's experiments, bringing them to their final limits, but in a certain fashion opposing them. In Rothko the experience of spatiality is dominated by the expansive function of the color. In Newman we are faced with pure spatiality, and the inclusion of the smallest element (the most restrained: a simple strip, totally neutral from the point of view of form) serves to stir up the activity of the space, which otherwise would result in a passive emptiness. In this severe painting all concession is eliminated. The spectator is confronted with a space stretching into illimitability. Also in contrast to the pictures of Rothko (which close unfeelingly), Newman's pictures are open. They envelop the spectator and submerge him.

The influence of Newman on the new American abstraction, and also on the European, has been considerable. The English artist Turnbull is pursuing a very similar pictorial vision, as are others.

Ad F. Reinhardt was born in Buffalo, New York, in 1913, and at present lives in New York City. He has had many one-man shows and has exhibited and taught extensively in the United States. During 1936 and 1937 he worked under the direction of Carl Holty, by whom he was strongly

MORRIS GRAVES. *Snake, moon and rock.* 1939. The Solomon R. Guggenheim Museum.

influenced, and Francis Criss. He was part of the « American Abstract Artists » group almost from its beginning, and his painting was then a free abstraction, of intense color, although not automatic; he practiced this until 1953. From about 1954 Reinhardt began feeling distaste for the facile sensuality of color, and began to purify his painting. It tends toward a monochrome; he uses only one color, either red or blue, and if he should use more colors than one, he chooses the lowest in color value, refraining from all contrast. About 1960 he began his series of black pictures, painting them very slowly, which accounts for his production being very sparse. In these, the whole surface of the picture is a black, opaque mass, smooth and without texture, along with very subtle gradations of values, which result in a very curious spatial sensation. On observing these pictures attentively one discovers some very tenuous lines, barely perceptible, that outline strict orthogonal forms. Reinhardt's purpose is to produce an art as far removed from life as possible. These pictures, profoundly hermetic and highly refined, take a path altogether different from the monochromism of the Frenchman Yves Klein, a path of silence and concentration, in the contamination of nothingness. But the pictures of Klein are absolutely simple; those of Reinhardt, although apparently simple, become complex in the degree they are studied. His pictures are of

HELEN FRANKENTHALER. *Weather change*. 1963. Andre Emmerich Gallery.

medium size, for, as Reinhardt says, « They ought not to be taller than a man, nor wider than the extent of his outstretched arms.» The scrupulous attention that these pictures compel places them in the outermost range of quietistic painting. A mystical quality emanates from them, no doubt as a result of the spiritual position taken by the creative artist, as can be deduced from the article

Notes on Reinhardt (*International Art*, October, 1964), by Priscilla Colt.

The tachists

Clyfford Still was born in Grandin, North Dakota, in 1904. He went to San Francisco in 1941 and worked in a violent expressionism influenced by Hofmann. In California he began to interest himself in the problem of spaces and masses. From 1946 to 1950 he taught at the California School of Fine Arts, but resided in New York after 1950. Still's first exhibition in New York was held at the Art of This Century gallery, in 1946.

Still's canvases are formed by large black masses with torn contours and often with splits in the interior. These masses act on a field of flat, uniform color. A sense of serenity seems to come from the picture, an air of expectancy, and the black masses seem to be dominated by a tension downward, as if they felt the action of gravity.

With his art of large areas with or without color, Clyfford Still seems to seek, in contrast to the gesture painters of the New York school, a sensation, not of shock, but rather of serenity and meditation. He could for this reason be placed in the category of quietistic painters. He has exerted great influence over his contemporaries, particularly on Guston, Newman, and Francis.

Along the same lines as the artists of the new American painting with tachist tendencies is a group of painters who usually live in Paris, among whom Sam Francis and Paul Jenkins are outstanding. This group is generally referred to as the « Americans in Paris. »

Sam Francis was born in San Mateo, California, in 1923, studied at the University of California, where the influence of Clyfford Still was strong, and then began to paint in San Francisco. He has lived in Paris since 1950, and it was there that he had his first exhibition in 1952, in the Nina Dausset Gallery. He admits having been influenced by Monet's *Water Lilies*.

Francis works in the all-over style, which eliminates any centralized structure and in which the zones of tension and interest are equally divided over the whole picture. Thus all the perspective is destroyed, as well as any system of thematic hierarchization; all portions of the pictures have the same representative value. His whole interest in painting is based on the following phrase, which in its simplicity becomes extraordinarily profound: « I want to do something that can be used to make life bearable. »

Francis' first works are constructed by nearly juxtaposed blots, all very similar, somewhat like flakes, practically monochrome. This is not action painting, because its elements are small forms with vague contours, combining to make a serene tachism without accidents, and his work therefore falls within the group of the quietists. In his most recent creations, he appears to be turning to a search for the activity of space, which he obtains by color masses that are larger and irregular, amorphous, with broad intermediate vacuums and drips of paint over these vacuums. In contrast to his former procedure, he now uses a variety of warm, radiant colors that determine various depths in the image of the picture, with the appearance of an ambiguous, imaginary space. The result is decorative, dynamic, and highly seductive, which explains the growing success of this artist.

Paul Jenkins was born in Kansas City, Missouri, in 1923. From 1938 to 1941 he studied at the Kansas City Art Institute and from 1948 to 1952 at the Art Students League in New York. Since 1953 he has resided in Paris, with occasional seasons passed in New York. He had one-man shows at the Martha Jackson Gallery, New York, in 1958, 1960, and 1964.

Jenkins conceives of art as an incitement to life. He says, « A picture is a form of awakening. » His pictures are executed by pouring color, which he spreads with large rubber spatulas. In this fashion he obtains an aformal figuration, without violence, of a glowing coloration, with transparencies and evanescent zones of great lyrical content. He is one of the best exponents of what could be called « poetic tachism. »

Calligraphic painting

Mark Tobey was born in Centerville, Wisconsin, in 1890. In 1911 he went to New York and won fame as a portrait painter; but the profession seemed to him too commercial and worldly, and in 1922 he began teaching art in Seattle. In 1925 and 1926 he traveled in Europe and the Near East, and in 1934 he went to the Far East and visited China and Japan. In Shanghai he studied calligraphy with Teng Kwai. Later, in Japan, he became interested in Zen Buddhism, and spent a month in a Kyoto monastery. From this voyage he returned to the West with the Oriental calligraphy and the spirit of Zen, which showed him life as an open route toward the infinite. This influence was already apparent in 1936, when he produced his first white calligraphies under the title of *Broadway*, calligraphic structures outlining a modern city, with which he tried to convey the spirit of urban traffic, and more particularly the electric life of the metropolis. The word « traffic » has special significance for Tobey. To him it designates a sort of osmosis or universal interchange. In 1938 he returned to figural painting and produced a type of social painting with proletarian themes, in which, withal, there are calligraphic elements. His first free works also show influences of the art of the American Indians and other primitive art forms, which Tobey had thoroughly studied. These figural works precede his abstract period. In them, masks or totemic images appear used as pure forms and distributed along the length of the picture. In 1942 he turned to total abstraction, which slowly brought him toward calligraphy. In 1958 he received the first prize at the Venice Biennale. At present he lives in Basel.

Tobey shows a preference for water colors (tempera, gouaches, inks), and the format of his picture is usually modest, in contrast to the large format characterizing abstract expressionists in general. His calligraphy, or white script, constitutes his great contribution to contemporary plastic art. It consists of white calligraphic outlines that intercross, forming a web that occupies the whole of the space, following the all-over principle, or else that of the equality of hierarchization of all sections. The white script stands out against an iridescent background.

In spite of the multiplicity of tracings, the space does not disappear; on the contrary, the overlapping calligraphies appear to create innumerable planes of depth. But space, for Tobey, appears inhabited by mobile forces rather than by volumes subject to inertia; his white callighaphies signify the energetic displacement of the light that unifies all. Above all, this calligraphy is not symbolic, but plastic, and thus Tobey succeeds in establishing a vibratory system in the pictorial space. There is without doubt a mysticism in the origin of this sort of painting (as there also was in that of Mondrian or Herbin): the idea of cosmic communion, man listening to the constellations and the galaxies. But Tobey has known how to translate all into a plastic language that has a validity by itself. Thus he has made an original contribution to Western painting, perhaps, together with Rothko, the most original in the United States. This consists in having created a quietistic painting that does not act by the elements of a theme or through the plastic anecdote but as a totality, which does not transmit a personal feeling but an imprecise, impersonal world in which we all participate, an open world, in opposition to the closed world of the individual. Tobey's influence on the most recent tendencies is important. It is evident in the work of the Italian Dorazio and many others.

The painter Morris Graves, born in Fox Valley, Oregon, in 1910, works along the same calligra-

ADOLF GOTTLIEB. *Falling star.* 1956.
Collection Martha Jackson Gallery.

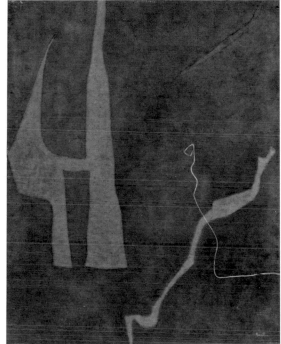

WILLIAM BAZIOTES. *Dusk.* 1958.
The Solomon R. Guggenheim Museum.

phic lines as Tobey does. He knew Tobey in
Seattle and was influenced by him; Tobey taught
him how to use the Chinese brush. Inspired by
Zen Buddhism, Graves's painting, with its fine
magical figures, has a mystical and visionary quality. He has had many one-man shows in the
United States since 1943, and in Oslo in 1955
and in Tokyo in 1957. His works are in the collections of many American museums. He is now
under contract with the National Aeronautics
and Space Agency to do paintings on space exploration.

Bradley Walker Tomlin was born in Syracuse,
New York, in 1899. He obtained his diploma
from the College of Fine Arts at Syracuse University in 1921, and in the following year established

himself in New York. In 1923 and 1924 he vis
ited England and France, and attended the Grande
Chaumière academy. He afterward worked on
murals for the WPA. In 1950 he exhibited in
the Betty Parsons Gallery in New York. He died
in 1953.
Tomlin's early works were, for a long time, cub-
istic. He turned to abstraction in 1946, and was
one of the first artists to obtain his composition
of the picture by means of signs and symbols.
Following the all-over principle, he spreads his
signs over the whole surface of the pictorial space;
the calligraphic symbols are black, white, and
red (he worked with very restrained colors) on
backgrounds that sometimes consist of actual letters or numerals. This proliferation, very know-
ingly regulated by semicalligraphic elements, elic-

its a visible vibration of the pictorial space; at the same time it provides a sensation of ambiguous depths. A serene rhythm, but of great expressive force, and a restrained and seductive lyricism emanate from his pictures. Although close to Tobey, Tomlin uses signs that have a constructive character, but at the same time he tries more for visual sensuality.

The second generation of abstract expressionists, which began to develop around 1955, has also produced notable painters. Helen Frankenthaler, born in New York in 1928, was influenced by Pollock, from whom she took the technique of direct impregnation of the canvas. Her gesture painting is more serene and of an evident lyrical quality, using the activity of the space. Her work can be placed somewhere between abstract expressionism and the chromatic abstraction of the type of Louis and Noland. The second generation includes Alfred Leslie (born in New York City in 1927) and Michael Goldberg (born in New York City in 1924), as well as two outstanding woman painters, Grace Hartigan, born in Newark, New Jersey, in 1922, and Joan Mitchell. Goldberg has had six one-man shows, in New York, California, Chicago, and Paris.

Soon after this development came the eruption of neodadaism and its consequence, pop art, which signified a limitation of its possibilities, inasmuch as some of the exponents of expressionism, Goldberg for example, tended to incorporate the pop influence.

Artists of free expressionism

Adolph Gottlieb was born in New York in 1903. In 1921 and 1922 he traveled and studied in Europe. In 1935 he and Rothko founded the « Ten » group. He won the first prize in painting in the São Paulo Biennale in 1963. He has exhibited in the United States, London, Paris, and Tokyo. After a surrealizing period, characterized by a use of ideograph or pictograph figures, he turned to a simpler form that resulted in an almost unique plastic theme. It consists of two forms placed at the extremes of an imaginary vertical axis, the upper, serene and almost geometric, contrasting with the lower one, violent and lacerated, composed of a central conglomeration from which short, heavy strokes radiate that give it the aspect of an explosion. The two forms, visually opposed, precipitate the activity of the ample space that surrounds them. This painting, of an intentionally elementary technique, which avoids composition and leans on symmetry, corresponds to what we designate as quietistic painting, based on the activity of a large empty area, heightened by the inclusion of very few formal elements. Although classified as abstract expressionism, this type of painting is opposed to it, and constitutes, together with Rothko's, the antecedent of the anti-expressionist visual tendencies that developed later in the United States.

Gottlieb has uttered some lucid thoughts about painting, for example: « The pictorial quality is without sense if it is not the expression of a sentiment. » And he adds: « Subjective images are not necessarily rational, but the performance of the painter must be rational, objective, and consciously disciplined. »

William Baziotes was born in 1912 in Pittsburgh, Pennsylvania, and went to New York in 1933. From 1936 to 1941 he worked on the WPA, and in 1944 he held his first exhibition in the Art of This Century gallery, with works strongly influenced by surrealism, and others at the Kootz Gallery from 1945 to 1954 and in 1956 and 1958. He died in 1963.

Of all the artists who turned from surrealism to abstract expressionism, Baziotes was almost the only one who continued depicting in his work a vague magical world in an imaginary space. His pictures show protoplasmic forms floating in a space of extremely sensitive pictorial quality.

Chapter five

The reaction against informalism

Informalism having fallen into a facile mannerism, empty and void of interest, the artists reacted in force. This reaction took three fundamental directions. First was the turn to the concrete world of everyday life begun by the neodadaist movement in the United States, and continued and accentuated by pop art. Second were the movements based on the purely visual, with the diverse ramifications of neoconcretism, kinetics, new tendency, programmed art, chromatic abstraction, and hard-edge, almost all of them included under the general designation « op art. » Third was the reappearance of the figural under new conditions, a movement labeled « new figuration. »

All these movements of protest, except that of new figuration, have one characteristic in common: that is, the change of attitude on the part of the artist, now searching for impersonal art, anti-individual, far from pain, passions, and torment.

Thus the currents that search for the impersonal in art, eliminating the interior world of the artist and any sort of personal art, tend to become dominant. The antiromantic spirit is emphasized by many solutions, some of them divergent, going from pop art to pure visuality.

Solutions are sought externally and not internally (even the most subjective of the new tendencies, new figuration, takes its support from the exterior world in resorting to the figure). The search extends in two directions. One is to create a strict documentation of reality as it exists in all its common trivialities, among which we live every day, that is, incorporating the very world that the artists formerly rejected, and so reconciling us to this world. The other is to search for reality in elements that are stimulating, or, one could say, vitalizing, such as light, color, movement, or purely optical play, that is, an art appealing to the physiological instead of the mind, an art that distracts instead of raising problems. Art has become playful in character. Many artists today frequently use the expression, « What I do is entertaining. » Evidently the young men of today tend to avoid problems, perhaps because the men of previous generations left too heavy a load for them.

The first impulse was to return to the tendency of the immediate past, which offered precisely these characteristics of impersonality or anti-individualism. They were found in the old constructivist formulae. Hence there was a new upsurge of constructivism, and artists who had been considered outmoded suddenly came into vogue. In the United States, older members of the « American Abstract Artists » group, such as Diller, Bolotowsky, and Glarner, regained popularity, and some found themselves allotted a new label, « hard-edge, » as happened with Feitelson and Polk Smith.

But the mere return to the same old constructivism proved to be insufficient. To many, constructivism had proved to be a failure, and the young artists aspired to something more decisive in this direction, something that dispensed not only with romantic secrecies but also with the interminable rationalizing speculations on plastic problems. The aspiration was for something more direct, something that spoke the language of the senses without need of intellectual interpretations. The new artists began to move far away from the informal as well as from the problems of Bill's « ideal form » or his mathematical speculations. In this respect they were heirs to the « intuitionism » of Newman.

A solution was sought in movement, perhaps because this appeared to be the authentic expression of the world of energy in which we are submerged. Movement in the restricted role of a displacement of the stationary was not enough; what was sought was movement in its most subtle manifestation, which is vibration, and also the optical illusion of movement. Thus the so-called « kinetic art » appeared, and immediately won adherents because the art of movement is accessible and there is no doubt that it exercises a particular fascination for the public.

In the search for a direct effect on the optical sensibility, various paths were followed, some of them diametrically opposed. Some eliminated color so as to exclude all emotional factors or the illusory associations color brings, or to get the maximum advantage of the play of total light. Others, conversely, sought in the complex activity of color the maximum possibility for optic-dynamic action and a fertile field to obtain the expressiveness of the painting.

In the United States, the latter group of artists derived from Rothko and Newman in their pure creations based on the simple action of a field of color (what we have called quietistic painting), and from the experiments with the interaction of colors by Albers. The works of Newman and Albers evoked more interest because they had fewer metaphysical or mystical components than those of Rothko. Those who followed Newman employed the empty space, seeking immersion in spatiality. Those who started out from Rothko's and from Albers's principles were interested in the activity of pure color, as were Noland and Louis.

Later, the search led to the hard-edge style, which is a naked, less speculative version of the neo-constructive. Still later, there was a turn to purely optical sensation, based on the researches in Gestalt psychology and the play of optical illusions.

In the last path all possibilities offered by the field of perception were investigated. Still other possibilities were explored by joining the resources offered by technology with what had been learned in the study of modern psychology.

Gestalt psychology has investigated the psychological necessity for the mind to organize the mosaic of « colored bubbles » the retinal image brings. It is with this compulsion to compose an image that op art and other trends relying on optical illusion play. Optical investigations have been brought to such a point that the artists have become veritable Gestalt experimenters. This penetration into the field of the psychophysiology of perception has brought the artists toward curious experiments that go beyond the simple rhythmical signal obtained by some concrete artists in the past (Strzeminsky, Berlewi, Albers, Lohse) and by Vasarely, and have a direct effect on the phenomenon of perception over which the spectator has no control; this is done by means of optical illusions that provoke the exact sensation of movement in the image.

Investigations in the moiré effects point to curious results. As the cinematographic principle is based on the retention of the image on the retina, which thus establishes a union between the successive images passing at a determined speed, so the moiré creates a sort of immobile moving picture through the inability of the eye to differentiate close-up microzones. With two series of parallel lines or concentric circles or other periodic structures superimposed by transparency, a drawing is obtained that appears to be oscillating. Thin parallels close together produce, if they undulate, a visual phenomenon very close to vertigo, or give the impression of a changing design; or if fine straight lengths of wire, or shapes of wire, are suspended and set in motion before these parallels, an apparent rupture in the continuity of the parallels is produced; or if the suspended bodies are geometrical planes, the result is a sharp sensation of vibration in the outlines of these planes. Moiré is a demonstration of lines energized. The work of the German artist Ludwig Wilding is an example of the orthodox effect of moiré. All the various techniques derived from the principle of moiré have been used by several artists of the optical tendency.

The Rubin effect * is another technique that has been utilized. Rubin observed that when a series

* E. RUBIN, *Visuell warhgenommene Figuren* (Copenhagen, 1921).

ANTONI TÀPIES. *Ocre-grey.* 1963.

ARSHILE GORKY. Allen Stone Gallery.

MORRIS LOUIS. *Tau.* 1960/61. Andre Emmerich Gallery.

of symmetrical figures partake of the same linear outline, convexity prevails over concavity.

Several of these effects had already been studied in the Bauhaus (source of many of the investigation taking place today), such as the visual illusion of Theodor Werner Schröder's reversible stairs applied by Albers in his famous ambiguous perspectives. All these effects tend to provoke a dynamic reaction of the eye.

In any event, painting has always tried to pro-voke dynamic effects: the modulation of forms, of tonalities, the action of the brush and the impasto distort the pure perceptual effect of the lines, the areas, and the colors, and these effects of ambiguity have been utilized by the informal-ists.

That artists play with optical illusion is nothing new. Perspective and, even more so, *trompe l'œil* are old methods of optical illusion. But the artists of the past used optical illusion to create

KENNETH NOLAND. *Opt.* 1966.
Andre Emmerich Gallery.

a visual sense of empirical space, the world of reality. Modern artists use it to produce an illusion of movement, and, better still, to convey an idea of the instability of reality. By this route it becomes consonant with all the other manifestations of modern art. In fact, the disintegration of the world of things that is offered us by futurism, cubism, expressionism, surrealism, each in its own way, does not signify anything but this idea of the instability of the real. Two recent, totally opposed, tendencies, new figuration and op art, do coincide in this idea. The first believes in subjectivity as the ultimate reality, the second, in pure sensation, but both reveal manifest doubts about the solidity of the real. And this is the characteristic whole of art in our days.

What remains to be clarified is what part of the *I* the artist wishes to affirm. Some lean on the world of the subconscious, the darkness where the purely vital resides (thus surrealism, informalism, and expressionism), and from which they drag up the world of the emotions; others seek support in the intellectual, the rational, such as constructivism in its many variants; others go to straight sensation, such as chromatic abstraction or op art. In these latest tendencies the artist relies on the action that stimulates the eye. What is important to him is only what the eye takes in, not what the brain tends to rectify.

But man does not want to be alone; he has a need to establish a bond that unites him to other men, and this is the fundamental mission of art. At no time as today has the artist needed to affirm himself in this other *I* who is the spectator. All the visual tendencies attempt to elicit physiological or psychological reactions of a dynamic character in the spectator. There is an actual attempt at visual provocation that is comparable to the social provocation of that other great contemporary tendency: pop art. Both want to pull the spectator out of his indifference and make him participate; they provoke him.

This idea of participation comes to be more than an expression in what some of the artists of pure visuality call « open work. » With this expression they propose that the work should be completed, or at least manipulated, by the spectator. It will now be seen how this actual participation is effected, either in transforming a picture, as in the transformable works by Agam, or by turning on a mechanism that activates the artistic machines, or regulates them, as in certain works by Le Parc, the « T » group in Milan, and generally those creations called « programed works. »

These experimentations tend toward an art that has very little to do with the traditional art contained in the concept of painting and sculpture. If Dubuffet, the informalists, and abstract expressionists broke with the traditional esthetic cate-

GENE DAVIS. *Legato in red.* 1965. Poindexter Gallery.

gorics that the cubists, the fauves, and the expressionists had in essence respected (harmony, equilibrium, compositional organization), it can be said that a large part of the new optical tendencies tend to break with materialism itself, which still sustained the exterior appearance of a picture or a sculpture. These principles justified the exhibitions with names such as « Antipainting » (held in 1962 in the G 58 Gallery, Hessenhuis, in Antwerp) and « Beyond Painting and Sculpture » (held in the Cadario Gallery in Milan in 1963). These exhibitions brought together works of different kinds, but what they had in common was that they went beyond the state of normal painting, if they used color at all, and that they employed optical and physical structures invading space without being strictly sculptures.

The diverse currents based on the principle of pure visuality have developed to an extent that makes it difficult to encompass them all under one name. As often happens lately, various designations have come up almost at the same time, but without everyone agreeing as to their mean-

ing and coverage. Some of these overlap, which means they include more than one current, as a result of which the classification of the artists becomes increasingly troublesome.

Perhaps the expression « optical » or « op art » used in America simplifies the problem. At any rate, we shall here review the diverse currents covered by this designation, and other names employed.

First, neoconcretism should be mentioned, which is found outside the op currents, and which is no more than an ulterior development of prewar geometric art, then going under such names as concretism, constructivism, and neoplasticism.

Later came the tendencies based on the activities of color, with the various names of new abstraction, post-painterly abstraction, or chromatic abstraction.

After this came the hard-edge (incorporating also new abstraction) as a formula of postconcretism. Then came kinetic art, centered on the principle of movement in art, whether supposed or real.

Recently two more designations have appeared: new tendency, embracing different currents that go beyond painting or sculpture; and programed art, which although included under the more general label of « new tendency, » tends especially to the creation of mobile works of the open kind, which invite the participation of the spectator.

The strength these tendencies were acquiring was shown at an exhibition held at the Museum of Modern Art in New York, with the title « The Responsive Eye » proposed by the organizer, William C. Seitz. The exhibition was inaugurated on February 25, 1965, with ninety-eight artists from nineteen countries participating. It had been intended in the beginning that it should be an outline of the history of the development of predominant optical tendencies, starting out from impressionism; but owing to the number of exhibitors the showing was limited to the moderns.

In the catalogue of the exhibition, Seitz undertook a classification to define the different characteristics of the pure visual currents that were presented. As an attempt at classification it was excessively forced, and did not add much clarity to the situation.

The number of denominations we have mentioned to designate the various currents of pure visuality, and others not mentioned, contribute to the confusion. They are not altogether synonymous, nor are they altogether different; the artists who intend to enter into one of these denominations go partially into others, and at times artists who have little in common come under the same classification. Let us take as an example the exhibition entitled « Post-Painterly Abstraction, » organized by Greenberg. Beside Noland, Louis, and other exponents of chromatic abstraction, Kelly and Liberman, until then addicted to hardedge, were represented, as well as artists as clearly informalist as Frankenthaler and Francis.

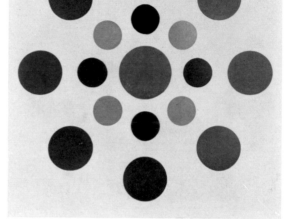

THOMAS DOWNING. *Green bias.* 1963. Stable Gallery.

JULES OLITSKI. *Demkovsky Green.* 1963.
Poindexter Gallery.

EDWARD AVEDISIAN. *Untitled.* 1965.
Robert Elkon Gallery.

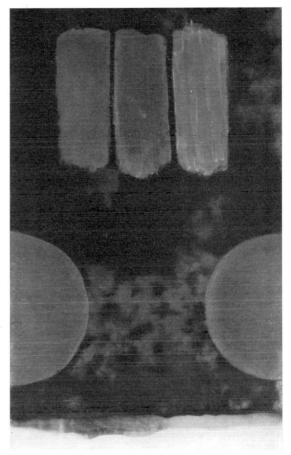

ALEXANDER LIBERMAN. *Light is as darkness.* 1966.
Betty Parsons Gallery.

On our part, we consider op art to be the general designation that includes a large part of what I would call « art of pure visuality. » Op art would include all artists of the purely visual except for the neoconstructivists, as was shown by « The Responsive Eye » exhibition.

The designation op art is a result of the influence of John Canaday, art news editor of *The New York Times*, who became enthusiastic about this art form « because it is an abstract art well done and which everyone can understand. » The denomination « op art » covers nothing new but rather a form already existing; it is a typical launching term, popularized by *Time* and *Life*, and its catchphrase quality caught on, proving the tremendous publicity power of a good label.

Op art came finally to include the following groups: first the chromatists on the order of Noland, Louis, and others similar; later, the artists considered to be strictly hard-edge, the kineticists, the members of new tendency and programed art.

We shall begin by clarifying the designations « hard-edge, » « new abstraction, » and their synonyms, and shall then take up the artists they cover.

The expression « hard-edge » has had wide acceptance. The term was employed for the first time by the California critic Jules Langsner in

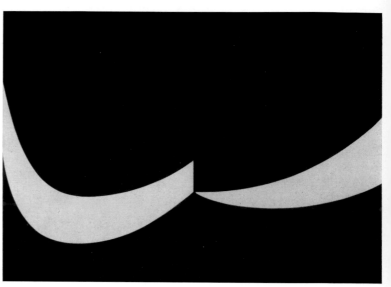

ELLSWORTH KELLY. *Atlantic.* 1956.
Collection of Whitney Museum of American Art,
New York.

AL HELD. *Blue moon greets green sailor.* 1965.
Andre Emmerich Gallery.

1959 to designate an exhibition by certain Californian nonfigural painters – Feitelson, Benjamin, Hammersley, and McLaughlin – and indicated that the fundamental characteristics here were precision, exactitude, and sharpness of outline in the forms. The designation was introduced to Paris in the Denise René Gallery, where an exhibition with this title was held that showed various old concrete pictures and various painters of that gallery, demonstrating that there was absolutely nothing new to this supposedly new current.

In any event, it is worthwhile knowing how the critic Lawrence Alloway defines hard-edge: « In hard-edge the forms are few and the surface is immaculate. The surface must be immaculate because all the parts composing it must be equivalent. There is no established relation between the figures and the field. The forms are staggered over the entire expanse of the picture; the colors are limited to two or three tones. The result of this economy is that there is no suggestion of spatial effect or of figures outlined in a field. There is no illusion of volume behind the impasto, as there is none in front, no illusion of atmosphere. What one sees is exactly what there is, although at times that which is seen contains an optical ambiguity. The positive and the negative act on one another, united on the same plane. »

In spite of its apparent precision, the definition is somewhat ambiguous. Taken literally, it would include rather few painters: Kelly in the first place, and then Ray Parker, Youngerman, Stella, Feitelson, and also Louis and Noland. But it so happens that the most characteristic hard-edge artist himself does not like to have this label put on him. Kelly says: « I am not interested in out-

JACK YOUNGERMAN. *Palma.* 1964-65.
Betty Parsons Gallery.

FRANK STELLA. *Oil.* 1963. Ileana Sonnabend Gallery.

serves me only to give quietness to the image. » *
As a consequence, in hard-edge the form can be
irregular, not geometric, but must always stand

lines, but in the masses and in color; the outline
out by the sharpness and precision of its outlines.
The denomination « new abstraction » was popularized after the big exhibition held by the Jewish
Museum in New York, in 1963, under the title
« Towards a New Abstraction. » It included, a-
mong others, Louis, Noland, Stella, Kelly, Brach,
and Youngerman. Thus it grouped artists who
before were from groups with different labels but
who evidently had much in common.

What they did have in common was that they
were situated somewhere between the rigor of
geometricity and the freedom of abstract expressionism. This was a return to the formal, but in
new fashions. These fashions referred to an elimination of all sense of composition of all tension of the field; and the forms were now abstract,
but it was not necessary that they be rigorously
geometric. The color gained an evident primacy,
with which to lighten the rigidity of the form.
The organization of the picture had to be of extreme simplicity. The treatment was something
like creating a geometry with feeling.

New abstractions of Noland's type do not pretend to show an expressive pictorial surface in
the manner of expressionism, but an object that
comes within our perceptive horizon. Nor are
they constructive works but, simply, displays.

They are not untouched by the influence of Rothko's work, centered on the function of large
areas of color, and the experiments and productions of Albers on the variability of juxtaposed
colors. These two artists furthermore demonstrated what an anticompositive, antistructural, and
symmetrical work (Rothko with his vague rectangular superimposed forms, Albers with his concentric squares) can signify for the heightening
of pure color.

This antistructural tendency, which also shows
itself in a large part of Pollock's work during his
drip-technique period and in the work of Newman, is found in a group of abstract American
painters, among whom are Noland, Louis, Olit-

* Interview with David Geldhzahler, in the catalogue from the
exhibition of Kelly (November, 1963) in the Gallery of Modern
Art in Washington.

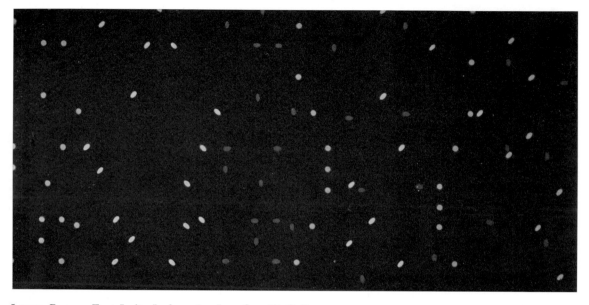

Larry Poons. *East India Jack.* 1964. Leo Castelli Gallery.

ski, and Feeley. All of them search primarily for the activity of color, while the forms they use serve only as supports for this color, which then becomes the central personality of the picture.

Clement Greenberg has been the most enthusiastic exploiter of this tendency in the United States, defending it with the same fervor that in the past he did in acclaiming and spreading the work of Pollock. He calls it « post-painterly abstraction, » considering it a reaction against the painterly abstraction of abstract expressionism. The term « painterly » is a translation of the German *malerisch,* used by Wölfflin to define the characteristics of baroque painting, as opposed to linear, which characterized classical painting. *Malerisch,* or painterly, suggests an outline of blurred forms and imprecise color. The painting defended by Greenberg must therefore be a painting in well-marked fields of color, with the color firm and precise, united, with the surface of the picture absolutely flat, that is, with the elimina-

tion of all tactile material and effects. The term « post-painterly abstraction » was used by Greenberg as the title for the exhibition of a group of new painters in the County Museum of Los Angeles in 1964. The catalog of the exhibition, with an introduction by Greenberg, contains a number of intelligently presented arguments, which are worthwhile knowing; it has been published in Number 5-6 of the *Art International* review (Summer, 1964).

To designate the painters who center their work on the activity of color we use the term « chromatic abstraction, » meaning a type of abstraction in which the color acts in its purest form, without textural or material ingredients, without the distraction of formal or compositive organizations, without optical elements that act on a different principle from that of the perception of color; and sharply outlined forms are used to avoid phenomena of imprecision and dispersion that detract from the action of the mass, that is, pure form as a support for the color. This defini-

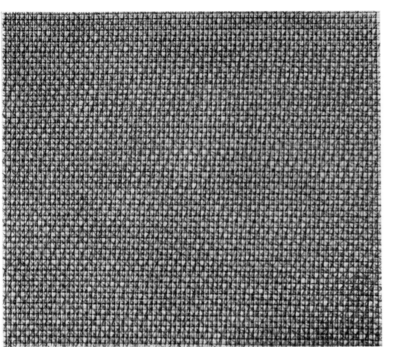

PIERO DORAZIO. *Beyond two meters.* 1964.
Marlborough Gallery.

tion does not presume to include all cases, and
undoubtedly there are to be found border situations that are more or less pure, but it is at least
in accord with the clear intention of a group of
painters to reevaluate color over any other element. These coloristic preoccupations on the part
of the painters appeared to stem from the fauve
tradition and the orphic abstractions of Delaunay.

From what has been said, it appears that the
most inclusive designation is « new abstraction, »
as it simultaneously covers painters classified as
« hard edge » and those who answer to the name
« chromatic abstractionists. » As a synonym there
is Greenberg's « post-painterly abstraction, » but
for the confusion so easily created and the arbitrariness with which painters can be so pigeon-
holed, this alternative is better dispensed with.

New American abstraction

Morris Louis was born in Baltimore in 1912 and
lived in Washington; he died in 1962. Louis
began with abstract painting along neocubist
lines, which he practiced for some years. Contact
with Pollock in his drip period transformed
Louis' concept of painting, and he became interested in questions of color. To eliminate all materiality of painting, he preferred, following Pollock's drip technique, to use water paints (acrylics) that directly impregnate the canvas in a fashion that leaves its structure visible. Almost always he left certain zones of the canvas uncol-
ored, which left a grayish white that supported
without violence the colored zone through its
neutral quality.

Between the years 1958 and 1959 Louis overlaid
the thin coats of color until he obtained a large,
grayish neutral mass, on the borders of which the
original colors appeared. Later he was seduced
by the high intensity of acrylic colors and proceeded to put them in bands, sometimes forming
small diagonals at the corners of the canvas and
finally in vertical juxtaposed bands, which often
showed the running of the poured liquid color,
forming a burst of brilliant colors at the edges
where the bare canvas showed, like a neutral and
inactive field, lacking in all spatial action. Louis's
bands are not strict forms, but sorts of « tubes
of overflow, » and reveal a continuity between
his technique and action painting, appearing as
a directed and controlled gesture in the sense
of an ordering and regularization of the dripping,
but gesture nevertheless. And although the restrained version of the gesture has as its objective,
as Greenberg says, « to eliminate whatever subjective expression so as to become purely a
vehicle for sensations, » certainly one of the
chief enchantments of the last works of Louis
is a paradoxical ascetic sensualism, an emotional
content of poetic character, with its consequent

R. J. ANUSZKIEWICZ. *Division of intensity*. 1964. Martha Jackson Gallery.

disturbing action, very distant from the cold ob- jectivity of the followers of pure visuality.

Kenneth Noland was born in Ashville, North Carolina, in 1924. He studied under Albers at

Black Mountain College, worked in Washington, and at present lives in South Shaftsbury, Vermont. For Noland, as for Louis, color took first place. His first pictures, about 1958, in this tendency, were organized about a series of perfect, circular forms drawn with a compass, showing concentric circular rings resembling targets. But although these works had the apparent characteristics of geometric painting, they obviously differed in several ways. In the first place, there was a single motive, well centered and symmetrical, that avoided all tension in the field; second, as with Louis, parts of the canvas are left unpainted which separates his work from the smooth, clean, even surface of the concretists; third, the outer circumference often shows drippings or splashed dots similar to the informalists, giving the impression by their directions that they have come from the spinning movement of the circles.

There is no question that Noland intended to evoke the idea that the circles turned and that he was searching for a sort of pulsation of color. In any event, the impregnation of the canvas in the manner of Pollock, the lack of compositive structure, and the drippings showed that Noland was heir to the abstract expressionists. In his later works this residue of informalism disappears: there is no pouring of color, and the canvas appears entirely painted, acquiring the characteristic forms of hard-edge. Further along he returns to asymmetry in a series of pictures with superimposed angular bands in the shape of a V. In this last phase of his evolution he shows himself freer in the selection of forms, which are always geometric (circular, elliptical, V-shaped, or rhomboidal), retaining the system of juxtaposed bands; but the potent and dominating color always frees the geometricity of its rigidity and coldness.

Noland's color is lively and saturated. He relies on large formats where the action of the mass makes the color more intense. If his work at this stage calls to mind anyone, it is Albers and his interaction of colors, which is not surprising because of his training at Black Mountain College. Noland's juxtaposed bands do not have the same thickness, their varying width being determined by the need to balance the nearest colors

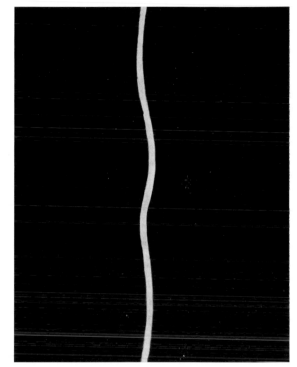

WILLIAM TURNBULL. *3-1964.*

so as to control what Noland calls the « pulsation of color. »

Of the painters who sometimes are designated as the Washington school, and who would be closest to Louis and Noland, Davis, Downing, and Reed are most prominent.

Gene Davis was born in Washington, D.C., in 1920, and works there. His work is abstract, based on equal and juxtaposed vertical bands that occupy the whole picture, painted in acrylic colors of great variety, including blacks and grays. A smooth, multicolored canvas is produced, rigorous and precise, but with great mobility of surface.

Thomas Downing was born in Suffolk, Virginia, in 1928, and now lives in Washington, D.C. He

JOHN PLUMB. *Needles*. 1963.
Collection Calouste Gulbenkian Foundation.

also works with acrylic colors in small, circular forms distributed in large circular orbits with diverse gammas of one dominant color and black.

Paul Reed specializes in semigeometrical, undulant forms of decorative character.

All these painters base themselves on the no-compositional principle of Noland and Louis and on their use of water-based colors, such as acrylic, applied directly to the untreated canvas, following the method introduced by Pollock in his drip period. For these reasons they stand apart from concrete art, although all of them use ruler and compass; the elements are not balanced, but simply related; they substitute composition for a single form indefinitely repeated, in a way that eliminates the hierarchy between the forms and suppresses the existence of any center of interest, after the fashion of all-over. The result is pictures prolonged into infinity, open pictures, in which the frame serves only as an arbitrary detention of the process. The brushstroke is suppressed so

that the picture acquires the maximum quality of impersonality.

Paul Feeley, born in Des Moines, Iowa, in 1913, belongs to the same idiom. He lives in Bennington, Vermont, and is Professor of Painting, Bennington College. His pictures are in acrylics with symmetrical, regular figures, vaguely organic.

Jules Olitski was born in Gomel, Russia, in 1922. He has a Master of Arts degree from New York University, and attended classes at the National Academy of Design and the Fine Arts Institute, also in New York. In Paris he studied at the Grand Chaumière academy and with Ossip Zadkine. He lives in Shaftsbury, Vermont, and is Chairman of the Art Department at Bennington College.
Olitski's painting is characterized by a large field of color with one or two forms, not regular but hard-edge, which activate the field. Recently he has eliminated the forms and showed a field of pure color, which would place him among the quietistic painters. He is one of the artists of highest quality in chromatic abstraction.

Guido Molinari was born in 1933 in Montreal, Canada, and now lives there. In his structures, similar to those of Gene Davis, he eliminates composition, substituting instead an apposition of a series of vertical multicolored bands, which confer a rhythmic and pulsating quality on the picture, creating an open work.

Edward Avedisian was born in Lowell, Massachusetts, in 1936, and presently lives in New York. His canvases are large, and contain, for example, one, two, or three small, perfect circles, bordered in their interior with straight bands of color, freely distributed and not balanced.

Among the painters who are classified as hard-edge, those who follow are worthy of note.

JOHN HOYLAND. *22-11-61*. 1961.

Ellsworth Kelly was born in Newburgh, New York, in 1923. In 1946 and 1948 he attended classes at the Boston Museum of Fine Arts School, and from 1946 to 1950 at the Ecole des Beaux-Arts, in Paris, where he lived until 1954.
Kelly's encounter with Arp and Vantongerloo decided him toward geometric painting. He exhibited at the Salon de Réalités Nouvelles in 1950 and 1951, and in 1951 at the Arnaud Gallery. He came to New York in 1954, where, in 1956, 1957, 1959, 1961, and 1963 he exhibited at the Betty Parsons Gallery. He has also had a one-man show at the Galerie Maeght, Paris, in 1958. He is represented in the permanent collections of the Metropolitan, Whitney, and Modern Art museums.
Kelly uses two or three forms and two or three colors, with great economy in the medium. The forms are precise, sharp, with characteristics of hard-edge, and contain one uniform color; the background, also in one flat color, is uniform and heavily saturated. There is no composition; only forms are present, and when there are two of these they are usually symmetrical.

Jack Youngerman was born in Louisville, Kentucky, in 1926, and studied at the University of North Carolina and later at the University of Missouri. He studied at the Ecole des Beaux-Arts, Paris, in 1947 and 1948, and between the years 1948 and 1956 he traveled in Europe and the Middle East, and for a time lived in Paris. He has executed some stage designs. He had one-man shows at the Betty Parsons Gallery in New York in 1958, 1960, and 1961, and in Paris in 1951 and 1962, and in Milan and Los Angeles.
Like Kelly, Youngerman appears to have been impressed by the collages of Matisse. His forms are irregular, as if cut short, with sharp borders, creating the ambiguous sensation that the background could be the form and vice versa.

Frank Stella was born in Malden, Massachusetts, in 1936, studied painting at the Phillips Academy in Princeton, and has lived in New York since 1950.
Following Noland's technique, Stella uses acrylics, but chooses the less-exploited pigments, apparently less expressive as color: black, aluminum, copper, iridescent purple. His pictures are made up of bands of equal width, sometimes mounted on irregular stretchers in the shape of an *H*, or they are polygonal with the center empty, sometimes in ordinary rectangular picture frames, but the parallel bands are disposed so as to elicit an optical effect of ambiguity. His art is in between visual illusion (op art), hard-edge, and chromatic painting, with certain influences from the pop object by its characteristic use of tinsel and the extravagance of the stretchers.

Alexander Liberman was born in Kiev, Russia, in 1912, but has been an American citizen since 1946. He studied painting with André Lhote in Paris, and in 1936 made one of the first color films of paintings for the Louvre. He is art director at Condé Nast Publications, New York. Liberman uses colored circular forms in a field of color (generally two large and two small), with pure, flat colors highly saturated. Recently he has abandoned hard-edge painting to practice abstract expressionism.

Raymond Parker, born in Beresford, South Dakota, in 1922, does work with the usual characteristics of hard-edge abstraction. He is an instructor at Hunter College, New York.

Leon Polk Smith, who has already been dealt with among the first American abstract painters, lives in New York, and can be included in the hard-edge school of Kelly's type.

Lorser Feitelson was born in Savannah, Georgia, in 1898, and now lives in Los Angeles. At the age of fifteen he felt the impact of the famous Armory Show. He was an exponent of cubism until 1917, neoclassicism until 1922 (in line with the Italian « Valori Plastici » group), and of surrealism until 1930. He then practiced a rigorous abstraction, and toward 1948 he began a period of magic forms that seem to have led him to his present production within the lines of hard-edge.
Feitelson forms part of a group in California that includes Karl Benjamin, Frederick Hammersley, and John McLaughlin, who designated their work « abstract classicism, » because it subjects itself to rules of reason and scientific thought. The painters of this group were the first to whom the appellation « hard-edge » was applied. Their forms are simple units of color; each hard-edge form can play the part of figure or background alternately in a Gestalt sense. They are not constructions, as with Mondrian and the concretists, but an apposition of elements constituting

ROBYN DENNY. *Life line II.* 1963.

form-color in such a way that no tension develops between these elements.

Al Held was born in New York in 1928, and studied at the Art Students League. From 1949 to 1951 he lived in Paris, and at present resides in New York. One of the first to straddle the line between expressionism and the new abstraction, Held uses successive coats of paint with a material base very much like that of the expressionists, although the forms are clear and hardedge; for this reason he has been classified as a concrete expressionist. He uses regular forms but without falling into the severity of pure geometry (rectangular or circular); instead he tends to break this severity with freer forms, almost decorative, at times imitating letters. He uses industrial colors of the kind frequently employed in pop painting (especially by Rosenquist). The final result approximates the hard-edge painting of Kelly.

Chromatic structures

Included among the chromatic abstractionists is a group of painters who do not use the action of mass to present the color, but who fragment it into microforms to obtain the maximum vibrating capacity that results, and the color synthesis it creates in the mechanism of perception. They may go from pointillism, in the manner of the neoimpressionists, to small homogeneous spots or a web of colored bands. It is a nonrelational painting; that is, there exists no relation between the field and a form or forms. The paintings is a continuation of similar elements. They also form open works, meaning that they tend to continue indefinitely. The originator of this type of structure was the Italian painter Dorazio.

Piero Dorazio was born in Rome in 1927. In 1945 he and Perilli founded the group and gallery L'Age d'Or, and in 1947 he was one of the founders of the « Forma I » group, oriented toward a postcubist formalist and abstractisizing concept. Beginning in 1953 he resided for some time in the United States, but now lives in Rome.
Dorazio's painting has undergone a very coherent evolution since his first essays into linear chromatism in 1947. His painting is based on chromatic structures. For this artist color has an inherent activity and capacity to stir up feelings. He creates – over a white or faintly tinted background – a web of color lines that intercross, forming a reticular chromatic structure. It forms an all-over with the characteristics of an open painting, that is, something that appears to continue into infinity. Recently he has tended to increase the thickness of the intercrossing chromatic bands at the same time that he seeks an action of space.

The following artists work within the chromatic structuralism idiom:
Lawrence (Larry) Poons, who was born in Tokyo

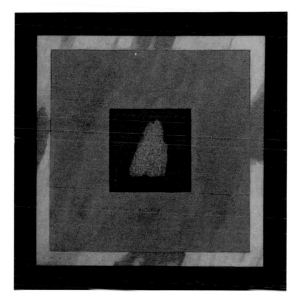

KLAUS JÜRGEN-FISCHER. *Double picture-yellow square.* 1964/65.

of American parents, in 1937, uses a chromatic structure fundamentally similar to that of Dorazio. The colors of the background are complementary to the polka dots of color disseminated over the surface in accord with a prior, basic webbing. These dots are distributed at regular intervals, resulting in a surface of complex color, very mobile, vibrant, and rhythmical. This type of structure, like the latest works of Dorazio, can be considered as proceeding from the famous *Boogie* of Mondrian.

Richard Joseph Anuszkiewicz was born in Erie, Pennsylvania, in 1930. He was a pupil of Albers. Working within chromatic structuralism with effects of optical illusion, he produces a sort of pointillism with colored vibrations and ambiguous impressions of great intensity; to create geometrical figures, he simply modifies the color of the points on the colored background. He is an instructor in design of Cooper Union Art School, New York.

Rolf-Gunter Dienst. *Diary of a moment.* 1964.

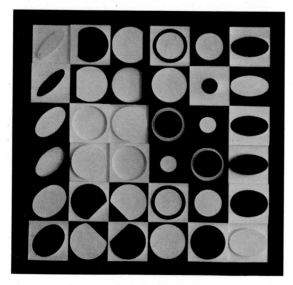

Victor Vasarely. *Black-white.* 1964.
Denise René Gallery.

There are many European artists working in the new abstraction field. Outstanding in England are Turnbull, Hoyland, and Plumb.

William Turnbull, born in Dundee, Scotland, in 1922, is equally well known as a sculptor and a painter. He had a first nonfigural period from 1949 to 1950; later he turned to figural works and to abstraction again in 1956. Since 1958 he has concerned himself especially with questions of spatial activity in large format. He began working with a heavy impasto, but was always interested in obtaining spatial sensations, and was evolving to a flat color on a smooth surface without body, suppressing all tactile qualities of the media so that the impression of space was of a purely visual quality. His pictures show an extensive emptiness given by a single uniform color, but there is always a small ribbon, in a corner or centered, or a small geometric single form, serving as a point of reference to deepen the spatial sensation.

John Hoyland was born in 1934. He seeks the activity of large areas, accentuated by an extremely fine-ruled lining or slight variations in the surface with the inclusion of small zones of color, or bands that cross the canvas, creating an animated relation between the active space and the minor areas.

John Plumb was born in Luton, Bedfordshire, in 1927. He also works with color masses segmented by fine, straight lines that determine the division of the space; in his latest pictures he combines hard-edge forms with others of intense color, which appear to be tearing themselves apart.

Robyn Denny was born in Abinger, Surrey, in 1930. On a low-key background he uses empty spaces run through by heavy lines that form a hard-edge geometric arabesque.

Various artists in Germany should also be mentioned in this context.

WILLEM DE KOONING. *July fete in Plattsburgh.* 1964. Coll. Allen Stone Gallery.

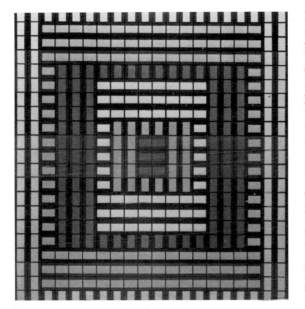

Victor Vasarely *Nanking.* 1964.
Denise René Gallery.

Rupprecht Geiger was born in Munich in 1908, the son of the painter Willy Geiger, an architect by profession. Rupprecht belonged to a Zen group. In 1951 he received the Domnick first prize in Stuttgart. He is one of the pioneers of painting of the pure field. His paintings are made up of a large mass of one highly saturated color, which frequently includes the whole picture, without any formal accident to alter the uniformity of the field. Like Newman and Rothko, he belongs to the quietistic group of painters. He exercises a strong influence over the young Germans oriented toward new abstraction.

Georg Karl Pfahler was born in Emetzheim-Weissenburg, Bavaria, in 1926. He lives in Stuttgart. After 1955, during the height of tachist painting in Germany, he produced his pictures built on geometric rigor, in an attempt to organize the informalist dispersion. In 1958 and 1959 he constructed collages with newspaper clippings. His present painting has the characteristics of hard-edge, that is, it is not a constructed geometry but one presented through a static disposition of the elements produced according to an intuitive, not a rational, order. But he knows how to break in a very subtle manner the too static and decorative effect of the geometry. He is one of the best painters in present-day Germany.

Lothar Quinte was born in Neisse in 1923. From 1957 to 1959 he worked in France, and since 1960 he has lived in Karlsruhe. Quinte exploits the action of large monochromatic areas, but animates them with subtle internal variations, and accentuates the dynamism of the field with a diagonal crossing of neutrally colored lines.

Klaus Jürgen Fischer was born in Krefeld in 1930. He is a writer, art critic, sculptor, and graphic artist. From 1949 to 1951 he studied at the Academy of Fine Arts in Dusseldorf and later

Nicolas Schöfer. *Lux-9.* 1959.
Denise René Gallery.

in Stuttgart with Baumeister; he also completed his studies in philosophy. Fischer, who publishes the review *Das Kunstwerk*, has united a group of painters who follow a theory he has formed under the name of « complex color, » by which he seeks the activity of color by various techniques, from the action of mass down to the colored microstructures that compose the picture itself. The painters who follow Jürgen Fischer in the exhibitions of « complex color » are Reimer Jochims, Bernd Berner, Eduard Micus, and R. G. Dienst.

Kinetic art

Kinetic art tends to present the most natural path for art to take if it wants to be in tune with the epoch of movement and speed. This kinetic trend appears to replace the questions of space that have occupied artists ever since the Renaissance and the advent of perspective, up to the experiments of the cubists and constructivists, not to mention such modern specialists in the spatial as Rothko, Newman, and Turnbull.

The notion of movement reveals itself to be most modern by being tied in with scientific relativity and time, on the one hand, and on the other, with vital dynamics. Plastically, more is found in some pictures by Turner than in the purely anecdotal deification of the futurists, although the experiments with serial images by Umberto Boccioni signify a step toward the present conception of this tendency in art.

It could be said that the question of animating works of art has always been a preoccupation of man. Thus the automatons and dancing and talking dolls of the 17th and 18th centuries must be considered as historical antecedents of kinetic art.

The futurists were the first to search for a solution, attempting to give an idea of movement by resorting to plastic transcription in such a traditional element as the canvas, although some of them attempted the creation of mobiles and artistic machines (Depero). Some Russian artists between the years 1914 and 1920, influenced by the message of Marinetti, concerned themselves with the problem of movement. In the Realist Manifesto, published by Gabo and Pevsner in Moscow in 1920, it was stated: « We reject the thousand-year-old illusion in art that a static rhythm is the only element of the plastic arts. We affirm in these arts a new element, kinetic rhythm, to be a basic form of perception of true time. » A piece of sculpture by Gabo, with the title *Kinetic Sculpture*, was exhibited in Berlin in 1922, in a show by Russian constructivists. In 1920 Duchamp showed a gyratory apparatus with the title *Rotative Plaque Verre* (*Optique de Précision*). In 1925 he constructed, on order, for the collector Jacques Doucet, another apparatus called *Rotative Demi-Sphere* (*Optique de Précision*), which consisted of a hemisphere of crystal decorated with concentric spirals, and was attached to a round plate covered with black velvet. It turned by means of a motor attached at the base of the apparatus. In 1935 Duchamp constructed his *Roto-reliefs* (optical disks), inspired by those utilized in his own film of 1916 with the anagrammatic title *Anemic Cinema*. The disks, six in number, could be used on phonographs and conveyed a sense of depth when turning. Moholy-Nagy constructed a *Light Machine* in 1929, which served as a theme for the film *Black, White, and Gray* (1929). This same artist, in his famous letter to Kalivoda, said: « Instead of painting with brushes and colors one could now paint with light. I dreamed of apparatuses which, thanks to a manual or automatic-mechanical device, permitted the projection of luminous visions in the air, in vast halls, on screens of undreamed-of material: mist, gases, clouds... I yearned to have at my disposition a bare hall and twelve projectors, with whose multicolored rays I'd animate the white nakedness. »

Starting in 1932, the year he exhibited mobiles simultaneously in Paris and New York, Calder became the true artist of kinetics by systematically creating those mobiles that constituted the basis of his art. In 1943 and 1945 Gabo used motors to motivate mobile parts of his kinetic works; and in 1950, Schöffer, unaware of the works of Gabo, used electric motors in his spatiodynamic clock.

In 1954 Tinguely showed his metamechanic reliefs, which consisted of formal elements in relief that turned slowly by means of an electric motor; later he produced his pseudomachines. At this point it must be kept in mind that the pseudomachines had interested various surrealists. Back in 1947 we remember having seen various pseudomachines, which were run by motor and were in no way different from those of Tinguely, in the New York studio of the Spanish surrealist De Diego.

Nor can the luminous mobiles of Ludwig Hirschfeld-Mack which he introduced in 1922 in the Bauhaus in Weimar, be overlooked as antecedents: a sort of organ to produce colored lights by means of reflectors. He created a score of « play of color » with musical notation to be played on this organ. There was also an American, Thomas Wilfred, who invented the clavilux, or color organ, an instrument with a keyboard projecting mobile forms and colors onto a screen.

The development of the art of movement during the postwar period is marked by consecutive steps that deserve enumeration, so as to give an idea of the growing interest it has awakened in the last few years.

In 1952 the Annunziata Gallery in Milan held an exhibition of works that showed movement, and also works that were transformable, organized by MAC (Movement of Concrete Art).

Then in 1955, works in motion were shown at an exhibition in the Denise René Gallery in Paris, with pieces by Calder, Marcel Duchamp, Vasarely, Bury, Tinguely, Jacobsen (sculptures on vibrating stems), Agam, and Soto.

And in 1959 Tinguely organized an international exhibition of pictures and moving objects in Antwerp.

After 1960 the kinetic exhibitions succeeded one another with increasing frequency. That year the Pater Gallery in Milan held the « Miriorama I » exhibition (with which the public activities of the « T » group were inaugurated), and the Azimuth Salon in Milan had the « Motus » exhibition (a French group that later became the « Groupe de Recherche d'Art Visuel »). The « Kinetische Kunst » exhibition was held in the Kunstgewerbe Museum in Zurich, and was repeated in Gallery One in London.

The great exhibition « Bewogen Beweging » was held during March and April of 1961 at the Stedelijk Museum in Amsterdam; it attracted fifty thousand people. This exhibition was repeated in the Louisiana Museum in Copenhagen and in the Moderna Museet in Stockholm, which attracted seventy thousand visitors.

In 1963 the art of movement appeared as the dominant tendency in the exhibition « Nove Tendencije Number 2, » in Zagreb. And in the same year the Diderot Gallery in Paris held an exhibition of the art of movement.

In the United States another important exhibition with the title « Kinetic and Optical Art Today » was held in Buffalo in 1964 in the Albright-Knox Art Gallery in cooperation with the Buffalo Fine Arts Academy. The Hanover Gallery in London held an exhibition entitled « Movement, » repeated by the Gimpel-Hanover Gallery in Zurich with the title « Bewegung. » In London, in the same year, the following exhibitions were held: « Kinetic Art » in the Center for Advanced Creative Studies; « Art in Motion » in the Royal College of Art; and « Structures Vivants » in the Redfern Gallery. In Documenta III in Kassel there is an important section with the title « Licht und Bewegung. »

International exhibitions dedicated to the theme of movement were numerous in 1965. The Denise René Gallery held its « Mouvement 2 » exhibition, and the same gallery collaborated in organizing the « Art and Movement » exhibition in Tel Aviv. The « Art and Movement » exhibition held in the Royal Scottish Academy in Edinburgh was repeated in Glasgow in the Art Gallery and Kelvingrove Museum. An exhibition with the name « Kinetik und Objetkte » was held in the Staatsgalerie in Stuttgart. The « Licht und Bewegung » (« Kinetische Kunst ») exhibition took place in the Kunsthalle in Bern. In l'Obelisco Gallery in Rome there was an exhibition titled « Perpetuum Mobile, » with an excellent catalog.

It is necessary to point out that kinetic art, as the artists accept the term today, totally rejects the figural. It is fundamentally abstract.

Very often the movement is combined with light effects, and at times these are dominant. Kinetic artists transmit movement to us by recourse to various mechanisms, which can be classified along the following lines:

1. Immobile structures. Movement is based on the energy of perception, and uses the phenomena of instability and perceptive ambiguity. As a consequence the movement is virtual or suggested and is obtained by means of optical illusion. Sometimes, to obtain this perception it is necessary that the spectator move around the object. In this group would come, first, Vasarely, then Tomasello, De Marco, Getulio, Cruz-Diez, Yvaral, and Riley and a large number who use optical illusion based especially on diagrams of Gestalt psychology.

2. Mobile pictures, or transformables: Agam and Tinguely.

3. Mobiles without a motor, which may be operated by hand or by air displacement (wind, fans): Calder, Le Parc, and George Rickey.

4. Constructions that work by magnetic forces

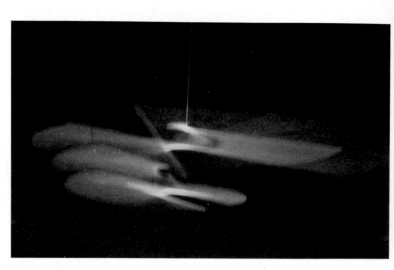

BRUNO MUNARI. *Useless machine N. 74* (*in movement*). 1946.

and are set in motion by magnets: the Greek Takis, and Boriani.

5. Lumitechnical apparatuses that create combinations of light: Schöffer, Malina, Le Parc, and Piene.

The greater number of these artists create works that correspond to kinetic sculpture, with which they redefine the limits of this work. Nevertheless, considering that a luminous projection on a screen corresponds to the planimetric and frontal view of a painting, it is to the point here to examine the work of Malina and Schöffer, and, because they combine elements of pictorial character, that of Tinguely (as will be seen in the new realist section) and Munari.

Victor Vasarely was born in Pecs, Hungary, in 1908. Though he began studying medicine, he later was a pupil at the Bauhaus in Budapest (1928 and 1929). His first one-man show was held in Budapest in 1930, and in the same year he established himself in Paris. He has been exhibiting at the Denise René Gallery since 1944. The first works of Vasarely were not essentially different from the concrete works that appeared

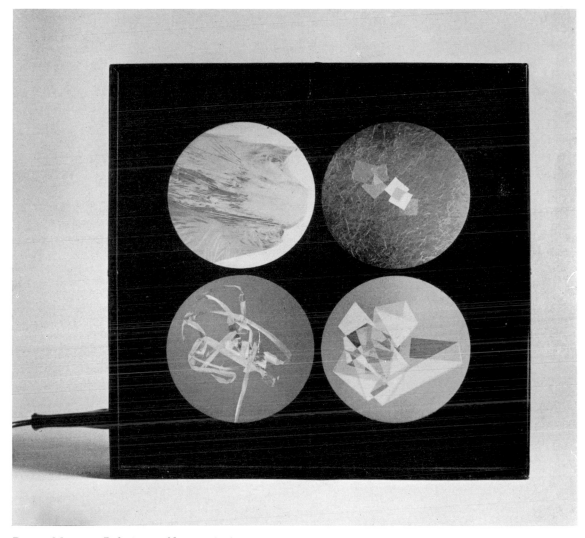

Bruno Munari. *Polariscope N. 3.* 1965. *

in the postwar period. At that time he was involved in a profound study of the theories of Kandinsky and Mondrian. In Paris he became part
of the « Espace » group. In the 1955 show,
« Mouvement, » organized by the Denise René
Gallery, he exhibited two works of kinetic tendency: compositions in transparent, staggered re-
ceding planes in depth, resulting in variations in

the picture. At the same time he published the
famous « yellow manifesto » (with the title *Mouve-*

* A programed kinetic object, which, by means of polarized light, produces chromatic mutations within otherwise
transparent and colorless materials that are contained in
luminous disks. In one minute each fragment of material
in the disks « passes from dawn to dusk. » The object is
made of iron, plexiglas, polaroid, plastic material, light
and an electric motor.

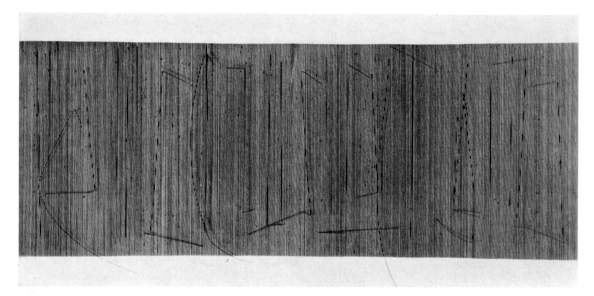

Jesús Rafael Soto. *Writing movement II*. 1964. Denise René Gallery.

ment), in which he gave a résumé of the theoretical premises that led him to research in order to solve the problem of movement in plasticity. His new concept in painting he names « kinetic plastics »; it is based on the use of a series of geometric forms with ingenious techniques of distribution and orientation that create a sense of movement. In observing his works one gets a curious sense of visual uncertainty, which justifies the title of *Ambiguïtés* he gave to his works at an exhibition in Paris in 1959.

Vasarely bases his work upon perfectly defined theories that constitute a negation of the traditional idea of easel painting. « Painting and sculpture become anachronistic terms: it is more exact to speak of a bi-, tri-, and multidimensional plastic art. We no longer have distinct manifestations of the creative sensibility, but the development of a single plastic sensibility in different spaces. » In this fashion, the initial phase of this creation, without suffering alteration, can be transported to a monumental work, a canvas, a tapestry (a craft which Vasarely developed), an album page, or a film. Thus the work « gets going. » Small format, « on the condition that it be conceived in measurable constants – constants of color: cadmium, cobalt, ultramarine; geometric constants: the rectilinear, curves, and angles; constants given by the format, relation, distance, all of which are measurable mathematical constants. » And Vasarely concludes: « Every work directed to the public irrevocably increases: (*a*) an actual increase in architecture (fresco, tapestry, glass, mosaic, etc.); (*b*) a quantitive increase in publishing (books, reviews, illustrations, albums); (*c*) an increase by still or cinematographic projection (slides, film, television). This increase or "moving on" constitutes in all cases a second creation, or re-creation. New types of artists appear, such as the "plastic scene director," etc. » And he continues, « If the art of yesterday signified "to feel and to do," today it signifies "to conceive and to order to do." If yesterday the durability of a work resided in the excellence of the materials, in their technical perfection, and in the mastery of the hand, today it rests in the

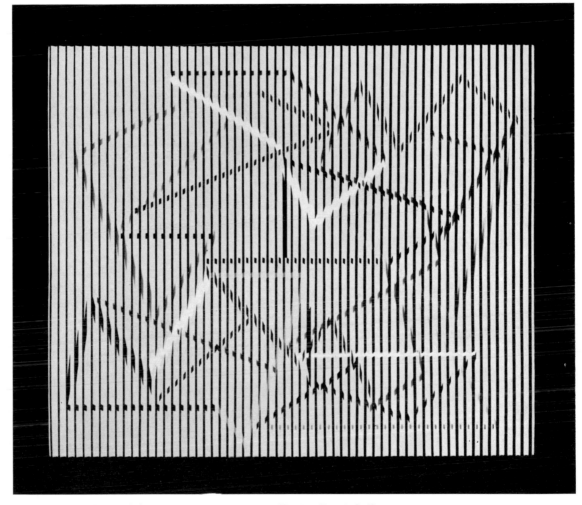

Jacob Agam. *Meta-polyformic painting.* 1960/61. Denise René Gallery.

knowledge of a possibility for *re-creation, multiplication,* and *expansion.* Thus the artifact disappears with the myth of uniqueness and the diffusible work triumphs finally, thanks to and through the machine. »

What Vasarely in fact proposes is that the artist be a creator of prototypes capable of being enlarged and multiplied, and he explains that « the value of the prototype does not consist in the rarity of the object, but in the rarity of the quality it represents. »

Vasarely accepts the fact that technical progress is the preponderant factor of present-day society; he speaks of a « technical style » that corresponds to the reality of the present. Thus modern plastic substances have the same meaning as the old pigments. And he adds: « The nature of the figural artists was that of Lamarck and Linnaeus; ours

CARLOS CRUZ-DIEZ. *Physiochrome.*

is that of Einstein, Planck, and Heisenberg. »
An ethical sense pervades the thinking of Vasarely. He says: « Abstraction is, above all, a search
for a new psychic hygiene and even a physical
one. » And further: « The title of artist is gratuitous and detestable, covering only appetites
and greed. Is it not necessary to retreat into anonymity in order to recover the honor of the profession? »
These ideas are inexorably tied to the concept
that art must function in a social context. This
Vasarely expresses clearly: « My aspiration is a
social art. Art is the plastic aspect of the community. Intelligence knows no classes. Culture is not
the prerogative of the cultured man. »

These ideas, which affirm reason and deny the
instinct, and which seek to depersonalize the
work, bring Vasarely into line with the concretist current that derives from Mondrian and Casimir Malevitch, and from them also came the
concept of the integration of the work into a social context, such as the parallelism between art
and the world of science and technology. Vasarely's ideas and work have exercised a considerable
influence on young artists in Europe, impelling
them toward experiments in plastic kineticism.
Many op artists, the « Groupe de Recherche d'Art
Visuel » in Paris, and various artists belonging to
the movement called new tendency have found in
Vasarely's ideas the initial impulse for the development of a personal search.

Vasarely's kinetic works were in the beginning
based on serial representation. At first he used
black and white exclusively to obtain nonsensory kinetic effects, but soon saw the advantage
of the spatial action of color, using purely geometric forms, to which he gave the name of
« form-color » elements, considering them basic
units in his structures. Vasarely rejected toned
colors, considering them to be a residue from
naturalism; similarly he avoided all mixing of

Jesús Rafael Soto. *Relations and harmony.* 1965.
Denise René Gallery.

colors, preferring those that were chemically pure.
He also created reliefs in which he achieved the
variation of images by the changed position of the
spectator, by superimposition of colored glass
that created moving images, and also by the use
of metallic surfaces such as the great mural he
executed for the Students' Residence Center in
the University of Caracas.

In spite of the apparent rigidity that a geometric
element as a base could create, Vasarely's works
show lightness and fluidity because of the inventiveness and skill with which he orients his elements in distributing them over the surface of
the picture and the progressive forms he creates
with them. In this way he achieves an infinite
variety of motifs that dispels the monotony otherwise inherent in serial structures.
The work of Vasarely, which today is considerable, and his continuous message have contributed to the development of kinetic art in the
world; but what puts him among the front rank

of the artists of this century is the undeniable quality of his work.

It is said that the Polish artist Henryk Berlewi, who was born in Warsaw in 1894, and is at present living in Paris, was a precursor of Vasarely. It is true that Berlewi to some extent used the serial principle, but he used it in a formal, complex structure that is closer to the dynamic paintings of El Lissitsky than to a straight kinetic purpose, as in Vasarely's work. Berlewi began his serial experiments in Berlin in 1922, and exhibited them in Warsaw in 1924 with the name of « mechano-factures. » He says that at that time he proved that the repetition of similar forms separated by regular intervals (lines or dots) created a sense of vibration, giving the impression of movement. He settled in Paris in 1928, returning to figural painting, in which he continued until 1957 when, undoubtedly inspired by Vasarely's success, he returned to his « mechano-facture » experiments.

More recognition as a precursor should, perhaps, go to the Polish artist Wladislaw Strzeminski, who was born in Minsk in 1893 and died in 1952 in Lodz. During the First World War he worked with Malevitch; with Henryk Berlewi and Henryk Stazewski he was part of the Block group. In Lodz in 1923 he launched « unism, » and in 1931 and 1932, in « Abstraction-Création, » he showed monochrome pictures with parallel lines that occupied the whole canvas, and which constituted not only the antecedents of the vibrationist compositions of the present but the monochrome concept so much in use today.

More directly related to the kinetic activity of Vasarely are the rhythmic serial pictures by Albers that he called « Exercises in Transformation on a Surface, » which were shown at the Bauhaus in 1926, and those of Carlsund exhibited in Paris in 1929.

Nicolas Schöffer was born in Kalocsa, Hungary, in 1912. He is a French citizen, and has lived in Paris since 1936. He studied at the Academy of Fine Arts in Budapest and in the School of Fine Arts in Paris. His first works were oriented toward surrealist painting and later toward expressionism. After some years of trial and error he arrived at the conclusion that the future of art lay in the production of dynamic works in actual space, and he called this doctrine « spatiodynamics. » Starting in 1950, he began constructions along geometric lines in iron or other metals. Although more closely tied to a spatial art such as sculpture, Schöffer's work should be considered in this book, became of that part which includes his luminous projections on a plane, and also because of his importance in the field of kinetics; therefore we give, as we do with other artists of equal importance whose work transcends classification (Munari, Tinguely), a brief summary of the whole of his work.

Schöffer's work in art turns into a veritable spectacle in a fashion that makes it fall outside the boundaries assigned to painting and sculpture. A new notion, that of the visual spectacle (intuitively known by a compatriot of Schöffer, Moholy-Nagy), makes its entry into the plastic arts. Thus he produced actual cybernetic ballets accompanied by luminodynamic projections and by sound. In Paris in 1956, in the Sarah Bernhardt Theater, he presented, in collaboration with the engineer François Terny of the Phillips Society, in the « Nuit de la Poésie, » his first CYSP sculpture (a name formed by the words cybernetic and spatiodynamics). The construction was equipped with an electric brain, which through photoelectric cells and microphones was sensitive to all variations of color, light intensities, and sounds produced by the surroundings.

In 1957 he enlarged his spatiodynamic conception with luminodynamism with his introduction of *Lux I*, which is now in the Museum of Modern Art in Paris. Luminodynamism consists of the projection of forms, colors, or plays of light on a surface or on a fraction of space itself (using

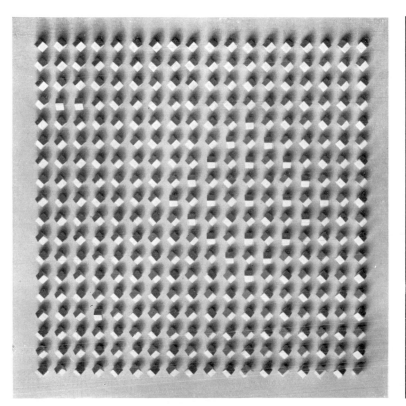

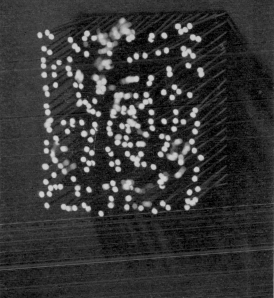

Luis Tomasello. *Chromoplastic atmosphere N. 136.*
1965.

Pol Bury. *Erectile punctuation.* 1961.
Iris Clert Gallery.

special floodlights) combined with the movement of the spatiodynamic construction itself. In 1961 he constructed next to the Palace of Congress in Liége a spatiodynamic light-and-sound tower, 52 meters high, with 60 cybernetically moved color filters, against a two-story-high screen spread over the glass façade of the Palace of Congress on which bursts of moving colored lights were projected, while music was transmitted. In 1962 he designed a luminous wall for the Museum of Decorative Arts, in Paris. In 1964 he constructed a 50-meter-high spatiodynamic sound tower for the Salon de Travaux Publics in Paris.

Schöffer has been the first to use the most modern techniques, such as electronics, in the solu-

tion of plastic problems, and the works mentioned put him at the head of the head of the artists who follow the rhythm of a technological civilization.

Frank Joseph Malina was born in Brenham, Texas, in 1912. At present he lives in Paris. An aeronautical engineer and geophysicist, he created and launched the first American high-altitude rocket (the WAC Corporal) in 1945, and is now director of the International Academy of Astronautics and permanent delegate to UNESCO of the International Federation of Astronautics.
Malina's works – « electropaintings, » as he calls them – usually contain four planes: a source of artificial light placed between gyrating, painted

EUSEBIO SEMPERE. *Untitled*. 1965. René Metras Gallery.

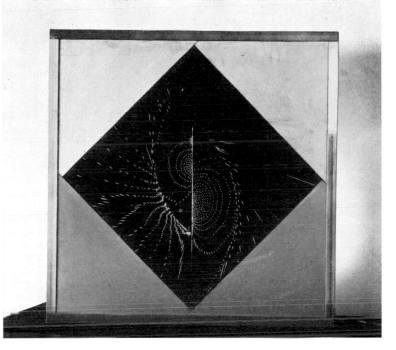

EQUIPO 57. *Untitled*. Denise René Gallery.

disks or « rotors, » set in motion by a small motor; in front of the rotor is the « stator, » a transparent plaque of plastic on which the actual composition is painted. The whole painting, combining movement, color, and drawing, appears on a
translucent plaque or screen, so that, for example, a blue on the rotor, crossing a yellow zone
in the stator, will become green on a clear screen.
Cosmic themes are frequent in Malina's works,
as their titles reveal: *Paths in Space*, *Nebula*, and
so forth; and he has a series of paintings on the
constellations. Malina is also attracted to physiol-
ogy; a work called *Heartbeats* is based on the
graphs of the palpitations of the heart of a frog.

Bruno Munari was born in Milan in 1907. He has
been active in futurism since 1926, and about
1929 he and Prampolini exhibited the first clearly abstract works in Italy. He is a pioneer in kinetics, as well as a graphic artist and designer. In
1962 he organized the first exhibition of programed art in the Olivetti plant in Milan. His
first kinetic work dates from 1933 and 1934,
when he showed his useless machine No. 2. In
1952 he showed his *Programed Fountain* at
the Biennale in Venice (now in the collection
of the Museum of Modern Art in New York),
which consists of a large exterior cylinder about
twelve feet in diameter covered with « vedril »
plates that gyrate by means of a motor, while
within it are two more cylinders, one wind-driv-
en and the other by means of a stream of water,
both covered with « Vedril » plates of various colors. In turning, the cylinders produce changing
color images. Later he turned out projections
with polarized light.

In 1958 he introduced a multipliable work entitled *Travel Sculpture*, one thousand copies of
which were made by the Danese Gallery in Milan. Munari felt that a work of art should be
within reach of every pocketbook and should be
easily transported in luggage. In 1962, in the
programed-art exhibition at the Olivetti plant,
he introduced his *Nine Spheres on a Column*,
consisting of nine spheres of transparent plastic
material forming a column held up by three vertical crystal plates. The lower sphere rests on a
rotor that puts it in motion. Each sphere has a
white band painted on it that produces changing
images as the spheres gyrate. In 1965 the Danese
Gallery in Milan showed his kinetic construction
Tetrachrome, consisting of a cubic space with
four cones within that touch each other at their
vertices. The cones are colored in two equal
zones with complementary colors (red and green)
and individual motors transmit a slow, gyratory
movement, differently timed for each: the result
is changing colored images.

These works rightly belong in the domain of
sculpture, but as an artist occupying a predomi-

A. BIASI and E. LANDI (GRUPO N). *Visual dynamics*. 1964/65. Galleria Nazionale d'Arte Moderna, Roma.

nant position Munari cannot be excluded from mention, not only because of his work as a pioneer and the quality of his production but also because of his spirit, a spirit similar to that of Marcel Duchamp, and which is characterized by not creating works in series but as unique examples that become models. That is to say, they do not become works, but laws.

Duchamp, in presenting a urinal with the title *Fountain*, created the law that the mere selection of any object by the artist converted it into a work of art. Like Duchamp, Munari combines an extraordinary inventive capacity with a sharp sense of humor – as expressed in his *Illegible Books* and in his *Twisted Forks* – which is always present, like a life-giving touch in all his works. As Seuphor accurately said of Munari: « He knew how to introduce humor into geometric art. » It is precisely this sense of humor that saves his art from coldness.

Jesús-Rafael Soto was born in Ciudad Bolívar, Venezuela, in 1923. From 1942 to 1947 he studied at the School of Plastic Arts of Caracas, and from 1947 to 1950 was the director of the School of Fine Arts in Maracaibo. In 1950 he went to Paris, where he now lives.

Soto generally prepares a background with a homogeneous and very tight series of fine white lines, vertical and parallel, over a black background. In front of this hang little rods of metal or species of curves or signs of wire, which, when set in motion by hand, create an actual vibration and rupture of the outlines of the striped background by moving against it. The same vibration occurs with stationary geometric forms before the background.

Soto's works are executed not only with perfection and finished accuracy but also with a sharp pictorial sense. The color, soberly employed and always in a low, muted key, confers on the work a climate of secret and intense poetic quality. Soto is one of the artists who has come to unite the conquest of pure visuality with the traditional expressiveness of a pictorial work.

Jacob Agam (Yaacov Gipstein), the son of a rabbi, was born in 1928 in Roshon-le-Zion in Israel. He has lived in Paris since 1951. His « transformable » pictures, shown for the first time in the Craven gallery in Paris in 1953, are each fashioned of a perforated board into which various forms equipped with pins are inserted; the spectator can change the order at will, thus creating different images. Agam also produces mobile reliefs in which the pieces are attached to the boards by flexible stems that are set in motion by a motor.

Luis Tomasello was born in La Plata, Argentina, in 1915. He lives in Paris. His works, which he calls « chromoplastic atmospheres, » are based on light; they are reliefs, fashioned by a series of cubes or cubic spaces attached to a flat white surface. The cubes on one of the faces – the one turned toward the plane – or the orthogonal spaces on the interior have one colored surface that through reflected natural or artificial light determines the coloration of the surrounding atmosphere and the projection of color on the white plane. On this plane a changing play of colors and shadows is produced, depending on the positions taken by the spectator or the changes in the luminous source.

Carlos Cruz-Diez was born in Caracas, Venezuela, in 1923, and studied in the School of Fine Arts there. He worked in advertising and as an illustrator on the newspaper *El Nacional* in Caracas. He has lived in Paris since 1960. In his pictures, which he calls « physichromes, » the color and the geometric forms change and vibrate according to the light and the position of the spectator, in the manner of a film passing before the eyes. Cruz-Diez uses a plane fashioned of close-set vertical little rods of plastic material, placed before an inactive background. The little rods produce the visible structure, and the resulting colors are determined by the optical mixture of the colors used.

Pol Bury was born in Haine-Saint-Pierre, Belgium, in 1922. He came under the influence of surrealism through the Belgian poet Chavée, belonged to the « Jeune Peinture Belge » group, and joined the « Art Abstrait » group in 1949. The first exhibition of his mobiles was held in 1953 in the Apolo Gallery in Brussels. Bury participated in the « Mouvement » exhibition at the Denise René Gallery in Paris in 1955, and since 1961 has lived in Paris.

Bury's mobiles are constructed with various mechanisms and are always set in motion by electric motors; they offer one of the most interesting phases of the art of movement. Maintaining at all times a great elegance of craftsmanship, his work differs widely from the cold and incorporeal aspect of pure geometricity (although he does use such geometric elements as the sphere) and also from the aggressively chaotic view presented by some kinetic « assemblagists, » gaining a mobile poetical image through a subtle sense of humor. Bury is undoubtedly the finest exponent of what could be designated as « poetic kinetics. »

Abraham Palatnik was born in Natal, Rio Grande do Norte, Brazil, in 1928. Educated in Israel, he returned to Brazil in 1948, and in 1951 showed his first « cinechromatics » in the First Biennale of São Paulo. Later he turned to painting on plastics and glass and to reliefs in wood, and has exhibited regularly, but his main work was studies for industrial machines. Recently he returned to his cinechromatics and exhibited them in the « Mouvement 2 » show at the Denise René Gallery in 1965 and at the « Art et Mouvement » exhibition in the museum in Tel Aviv the same year. Palatnik's cinechromatics are fashioned out of types of boxes that project moving forms and colors on a screen by means of a large number of reflectors.

Eusebio Sempere was born in Onil, Alicante, Spain, in 1924. He studied at the Academy of Fine Arts in Valencia, lived in Paris from 1949 to 1959, and showed his first « luminous reliefs » in 1955 at the Salon des Réalités Nouvelles. At present he lives in Madrid, and is an exponent of the kinetic tendency of Vasarely.

Sempere's luminous reliefs are constructed on two planes of wood (the front one cut through) in such a way that the changes of lighting produce a complete change in the work. Sempere always fashions his work by means of structures based on fine parallel lines, the monotony of which is skillfully broken by the inclusion of fragments of variable orientation. The purity and high artistry of the execution never become rigid, as the artist knows how to confer a fine poetical sense on his structures that separates them from the cold nakedness of an uncompromisingly optical activity. He has also produced a number of silk prints of exceptional quality.

Sergio Camargo, born in Rio de Janeiro in 1930, works in reliefs in wood that are highly intricate, and in which he obtains a play of light and shade.

« Equipo 57 » is the name of a group of Spanish artists who work together as a team, with the result that their works appear anonymous. They conduct Gestalt experiments applied to art, in particular along the lines of the kinetics of vision. The group was founded in Paris in 1957 (from which comes the « 57 » accompanying the word *equipo*, or team); they published a French-Spanish manifesto with the title *Interactivity of the Plastic Space*. The group is composed of Juan Cuenca, Angel Duarte, José Duarte, Agustín Ibarrola (at present a political prisoner in Burgos), and Juan Serrano. The initial meeting place of the group was Córdoba, Spain. Their manifesto says: « In the interactivity of plastic space, color, form, line, and mass do not exist as independent and autonomous elements; all is space distinguished by its dynamic function. » This search for the interactivity of the elements of plastic space is centered on the application of the serial method to art, and is based on the principle that two contiguous forms are dynamically inactive when the spacing is regular.

The work of this group is directed by the idea of art as a social function, and is revealed in declarations such as the following: « The so-called work of art, in opposition to those who insist on

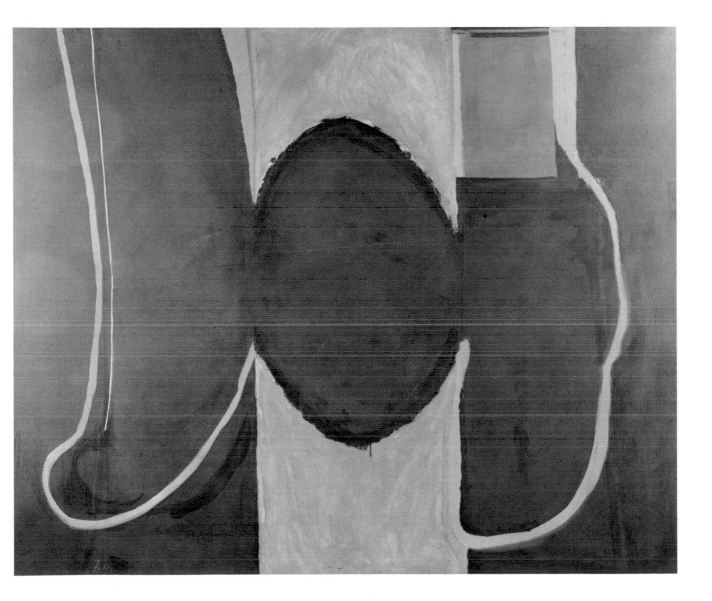

MATTA. *The space of a second N. 2.* 1957.

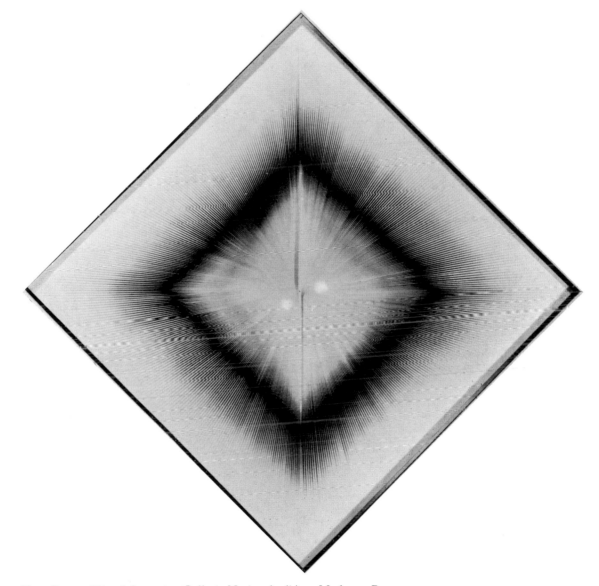

TONI COSTA. *Visual dynamics.* Galleria Nazionale d'Arte Moderna, Roma.

defending its philosophical essence or its transcendental nature, is not an important cultural
factor... Only such things as are introduced as
a daily element in daily life are authentically cultural. »

Group « T » of Milan was founded in 1959; the
members work and experiment along parallel or
divergent lines, united by a high spirit of experimentation that animates the group and by the
programmatic character of their work. Their ex-

BRIDGET RILEY. *Metamorphosis.*
Collection Calouste Gulbenkian Foundation.

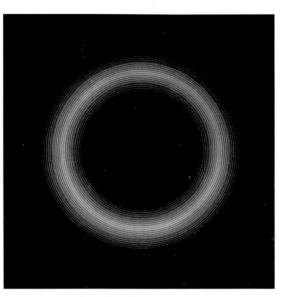

PETER SEDGELEY. *Manifestation 1964.*
Collection Calouste Gulbenkian Foundation.

periments with movement, light, and optical illusion are similar to those of the « Groupe de Recherche d'Art Visuel » in Paris.

The following fine artists are members of Group
« T » of Milan.

Giovanni Anceschi was born in Milan in 1939,
son of the well-known man of letters Luciano
Anceschi. At present he is studying at the Hochschule für Gestaltung in Ulm, Germany. A typical
work consists of an orthogonal receptacle in the
interior of which colored liquids pass through
transparent tubes. The liquid current now and
then appears to be interrupted by air bubbles,
and the circulation of the liquid creates images
that are always different. He also produces mobiles with colored lights.

Davide Boriani was born in Milan in 1936. A typical work is a large disk divided into irregular
compartments by plexiglass partitions that contain iron filings; electromagnets fitted onto the

TADASKY. *Untitled painting B. 196. 1964.*
Kootz Gallery.

Ben Cunningham. *The Tesseract*. 1966. East Hampton Gallery.

lower part of the disk attract the iron filings, resulting in the formation of changing designs.

Gianni Colombo, born in Milan in 1937, is one of the most active members of group « T. » In one of his works he shows a large, transparent plastic ribbon between glass within a metal frame; the plastic, by moving, creates images that are always different.

Gabriele Devecchi, born in Milan in 1938, and Grazia Varisco, born in Milan in 1937, complete

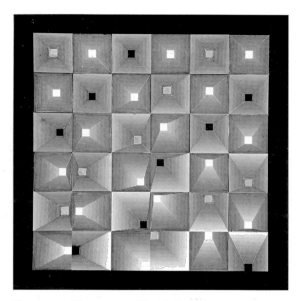

Toshihiro Katayama. *Untitled.*

to obtain works put together, not as a whole, but as simple segments of stimulating situations. The works were kinetic (usually set in motion by motors), achromatic, and programed; that is, they allow the intervention of chance within previously planned limits. In most cases the works demand the participation of the spectator.

Also in Milan, in 1964, a group of artists formed the « MID Ricerche Visive, » including Antonio Barrese, Alfonso Grassi, Gianfranco Laminarca, and Alberto Marangoni. Their experiments are centered on stroboscopic phenomena and the properties of lamps of cold light.
Within the principle of virtual kinetics, that is, using the optical illusion as the movement, the following artists are outstanding:

Bridget Riley, born in London in 1931, became a sensation at « The Responsive Eye » exhibition (the cover of the catalog was a reproduction of one of her works). Her first exhibition was held at Gallery One in 1962. She uses a technique resembling moiré and achieved by parallel lines whose curvature and thickness combine to give an effect of pulsating intensity, or else a series of small circles that diminish toward the center so as to create an illusion of depth. She is certainly the artist who has obtained the most provoking and intense optical effects.

Peter Sedgely was born in 1930 and lives in London. He began by producing works following Max Ernst's system of frottage but knowledge of Bridget Riley's work led him to work in op art. His works combine optical illusion with a rich coloring scheme.

Jeffrey Steele was born in Cardiff, Wales, in 1931, and lives in his native city. His works are decorative and have curious ambiguous perspectives.

Tadasky (Tadasuke Kuwayama) was born in Nagoya, Japan, in 1935. He lives in New York.

the Group « T » membership, both having produced works of great interest. The group has a record of very solid experiments and earnestness of spirit among the members.

Group « N » was formed in Padua in 1960, very soon after group « T » in Milan. For a time the members worked in very close cooperation on common projects that were exhibited anonymously. Belonging to the group were Alberto Biasi, Ennio Chiggio, Toni Costa, Edoardo Landi, and Manfredo Massironi. The group was dissolved in 1964, and for a year the members worked on their own. Biasi (born in Padua in 1937), Costa (born in Padua in 1935), and Landi (born in Modena in 1937) showed individual works at « The Responsive Eye » exhibition at the Museum of Modern Art in New York. In 1965 the group reformed under the name « N 1965, » with only Biasi, Landi, and Massironi. Group «N» worked on optical phenomena, movement, and instability as a visual equivalent of ambiguity. They sought indetermination, that is,

GÜNTER FRUHTRUNK. *Composition.* 1965.

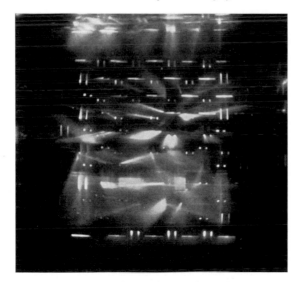

JULIO LE PARC. *Light visualized through a water volume.* 1962.

Working with concentric circles, Tadasky obtains a sensation of gyration by means of degradation of color.

Ludwig Wilding was born in Grünstadt, in the Palatinate, Germany, in 1927. He also works with moiré patterns.

John Goodyear was born in Southgate, California, in 1930. He also uses the moiré principle.

Benjamin Frazier Cunningham was born in Cripple Creek, Colorado, in 1904, and now lives in New York. He juxtaposes geometric elements that also create ambiguous perspectives.

Günter Fruhtrunk was born in Munich in 1923. He lives in Paris. Beginning with the style of Malevitch and Mondrian, he progressed toward a rhythmic style obtained by a serial juxtaposition of straight, vertical, and diagonal bands.

Bernard Sandfort was born in Cologne, Germany, in 1936, and presently lives in his native city. He uses a technique of fine parallels with variations in key and intensity, very close to the moiré effect.

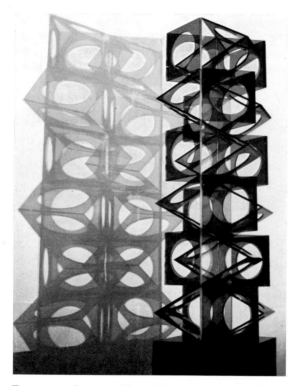

FRANCISCO SOBRINO. *Unstable transformation H2.*
1962/65.

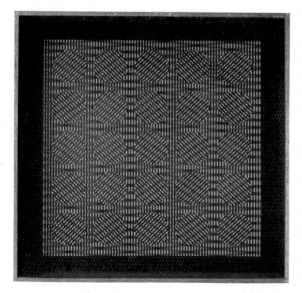

Toshihiro Katayama, a painter and industrial designer, was born in Osaka, Japan, in 1928. Through different uses of orthogonal serial elements, finely lined or varying in intensity, he obtains intense ambiguous spatial sensations.

The « *Groupe de Recherche d'Art Visuel* »

In 1960 a group was formed in Paris with the name « Groupe de Recherche d'Art Visuel. » It started out from the ideas of Vasarely, but carried them to a higher degree of development, thanks to the efficacy of teamwork.

The group, extremely active since it was first founded, has taken an experimental attitude that has opened up numerous possibilities for the new plastics. In 1961 a showing was held at the Denise René Gallery. Contact was immediately established with single solitary artists of similar tendency throughout Europe; the group participated in international exhibitions of different categories in movement, light, and visuality – three themes that constitute the fundamentals of their experiments. Some of these exhibitions the group itself organized, such as the « New Tendency » exhibition in Zagreb, and they are working for a wide diffusion of the basic ideas this name represents, in order to establish an international front.

In a pamphlet published by the Denise René Gallery in Paris in 1962, the general ideas of the « Groupe de Recherche d'Art Visuel » were summarized in the following manner: « On the question of the artist-society relation, up till now based on the idea of the artist as alone and isolated, in the myth of creation, in overrated esthetic or antiesthetic conceptions, in working for an élite, and in the production of unique works, we propose: to transform these relationships, clearing

YVARAL. *Optical acceleration.* 1964/65.
Denise René Gallery.

away the artistic conception and creation of all mystification, reducing it to a simple activity of man; to eliminate the category "work of art" and its myths; to create multipliable works; to search for new categories of achievement further than the picture and sculpture; to liberate the public from its inhibitions and from its deformations of appreciation produced by traditional estheticism. We also propose to transform the relation of object-eye, eliminating the intrinsic values of stable and recognizable form, whether in its naturalist or abstract aspect (be this last geometric or informal), to redirect the function of the eye (recognition through form and its relations) toward a new visual situation based on the peripheral vision and its instability. »

Their method of working is further explained in the following manner: « On many points, our method of working and our technique of investigation call to mind the methods and techniques of the scientists. In fact, we set out from given data and exploit them experimentally, endeavoring to control all possibilities.

« It is evident that it is necessary to make some selections of form, of color, of size, etc. – but this choice must be held down to the absolute minimum. All the rest must be a logical and biological development for the work to be done; that is, after that minimal selection, the work will begin to go by itself.

« The idea of programming... includes the manner of conceiving, executing, and showing unstable works. The question is to anticipate all the conditions of development of the work, to determine clearly its modalities so as to permit it to realize itself in space and in time, subject to the contingencies of the medium and to the nature of the participation of the spectator. »

In effect, the « Groupe de Recherche d'Art Visuel » constitutes an effort to continue the experiments on vision, movement and light begun by various pioneers from the first decade of the century, toward all fronts, renouncing the prejudice

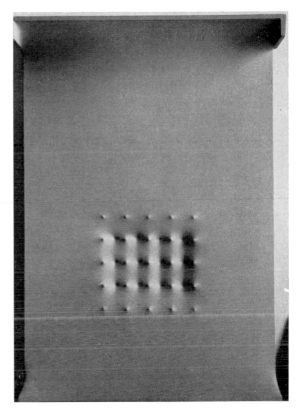

Enrico Castellani. *Pink surface.* 1963. Dell'Ariete Gallery.

for individual creation, adopting playful elements if necessary, and developing the idea of spectacle. They compose open works in the double sense that they are not concluded without the active participation of the spectator and that they also can be continued or multiplied. The idea of spectator participation is fundamental: it is intended to submerge him in the work and make him collaborate with the artist in its development and function. They definitely have broken with easel painting and with sculpture as spatial volume, that is, with the traditional categories of painting and sculpture. The notions of a unique piece of work with definite, stable character has been replaced by the idea of multiple works, transformable and unstable. From this comes the title *Instability* that has been given to many of their works. The personal achievement disappears in favor of anonymous creations, without emotional function, destined for a purely visual role.

But as artistic talent often prevails, some of these artists, gifted with sensitivity and inventiveness, offer, in spite of themselves, works that contain true poetry. Many of these works, furthermore, do not differ from the category classified as works for art galleries, and can be considered as unique examples.

Although many ideas of this group evidently originated with Vasarely, the group has handled them with great freedom and penetration, adding to them an experimental spirit, and in a short time the members have achieved some notable works. Seven artists that compose this group follow.

Julio Le Parc, born in Mendoza, Argentina, in 1928, began as a semiabstract painter whose early work won him a scholarship to study in Paris where he established himself in 1958. Two years later he abandoned traditional painting and founded the « Groupe de Recherche d'Art Visuel, » the objective of which was the study of visuality, light, and movement beyond the point to which they had previously been investigated. With these principles in mind, he has taken an active part in the « new tendency » movement and in the pursuits of the Denise René Gallery. In 1966 he won the first prize for painting at the XXXIII Biennale in Venice.

Le Parc is one the purest representatives of the « new tendency, » his work being outside the realm of art and of a fundamentally experimental nature. There is no doubt, however, that his work elicits response from a new type of modern sensitivity, the sensitivity of urban man who is beleaguered by sights, light, and movement that vie for his attention, and who is engulfed in an atmosphere of surprise and instability. Aware of

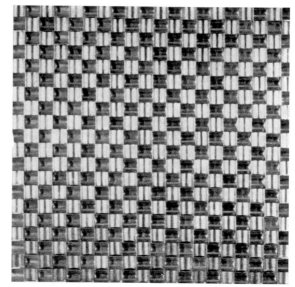

IVAN PICELJ. *Surface XLVII*. 1964. Denise René Gallery.

HUGO DEMARCO. *Spatial dynamization*. 1964. Denise René Gallery.

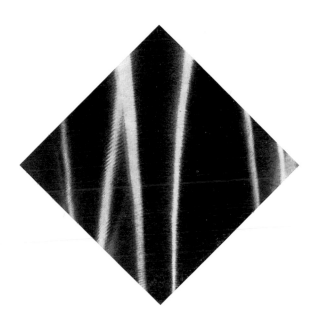

GETULIO ALVIANI. *Aluminum.* 1961.
Nuova Tendenza.

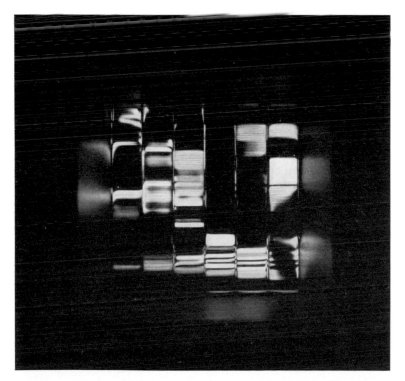

KARL GERSTNER. *Color glasses.*
Denise René Gallery.

this sensitivity, and gifted with an inexhaustible inventive capacity, Le Parc creates apparatuses, structures, and luminous mechanisms in which visual pleasure, subtle effects, and elements of surprise transport the spectator into an enchanted world. Thus, in expressing the essence of modern life, the work assumes a new dimension that opens up previously unimagined perspectives for the artist.

Francisco Sobrino, born in Guadalajara, Spain, in 1932, received his artistic education in Argentina, and also lives in Paris. Yvaral, the pseudonym for Jean Pierre Vasarely, son of Victor Vasarely, was born in Paris in 1934; he lives in Arcueil. Joël Stein was born in Boulogne-sur-Mer, France, in 1926, and resides in Paris. François Morellet was born in Cholet, Maine-et-Loire, in 1926, and still lives there. Horacio García Rossi, now living in France, was born in Buenos Aires, Argentina, in 1929. Also belonging to the group is the artist Armando Durante, who lives in Argentina.

Hugo Demarco can be considered as being linked with the « Groupe de Recherche d'Art Visuel. » He was born in Buenos Aires in 1932 and lives in Paris. He fashions serial constructions of intense chromatism by means of colored geometric elements placed within shadow boxes behind a glass pane, which produce changing images as the spectator moves.

New tendency and programed art

Tied to the kinetic arts, although not overlapping, are the movements that in Europe are called « new tendency » and « programed art. » The first sprang from a 1961 exhibition, held biennially, in Zagreb, Yugoslavia, which brought together a new group of artists who were working along the line of pure visuality, all of them with an experimental bent. It is this experimental character and the lack of constructive or compositive intentions that sets them apart, in spite of their having the same principles of clarity and rationality, from the concrete artists and the neo-concretists.

Because the members had been very active in the founding of the international movement called the « new tendency, » we shall quote the explanatory words from the pamphlet of the « Groupe de Recherche d'Art Visuel » published by the Denise René Gallery: « We employ this term [new tendency], which was used in the exhibition entitled Nove Tendencije in Zagreb in 1961, to designate a phenomenon that for the last few years has been evident among the young plastic artists simultaneously in different parts of the world. International manifestations and partial contacts are beginning to give it a more homogeneous character. The new tendency does not have a definitive character. Its evolution can bring new ways of understanding the work, of estimating it and placing it in society, which carries an implicit critical consideration before the whole panorama of present-day art. A natural reaction takes place, on the one hand against the state of sterility, to which revolutions, at one time legitimate, have fallen and which have works qualifying as lyrical abstraction, informal art, tachism, etc., by the thousands, and on the other hand against the fruitless continuation of a backward, geometric mannerism which today, in most cases, does no more than repeat the form established by a Malevitch or a Mondrian. » And it continues further along: « The new tendency is above all the search for clarity and the obligation to give precedence to the visual presence of the work, as almost all present-day currents have had to resort to extravisual, anecdotal justifications... »; and here it cites the examples of Klein and Manzoni.

Three exhibitions were held in the Suvremene

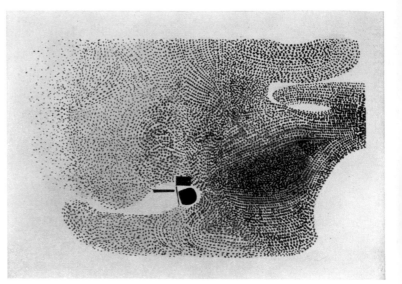

Victor Pasmore. *Blue development.* 1964. Collection British Council.

Umjetnosti Gallery in Zagreb, the first in 1961. The second was held in 1963 (and was repeated in Venice), and brought together a group of independent artists (Tomasello, von Graewenitz, Uli Pohl, Getulio, Enzo Mari, Castellani, Mavignier, Gerstner, Talman, Megert, Picelj, and others) and various experimental teams that worked in Europe: the « Groupe de Recherche d'Art Visuel » from Paris, « Equipo 57 » from Spain, group «T» from Milan, group «N» from Padua, and group «O» from Dusseldorf (Mack, Piene, Uecker). The third exhibition took place in 1965.

The experimental character of this movement is indicated by the subtitle that accompanies its name: it is called «New Tendency-Continuous Search.»

Many of these artists dispense with color, using only black and withe, or use the most neutral colors possible to avoid subjective response to the color and to eliminate all emotionalism and expressiveness. Almost all practice the strictest economy of media to obtain the maximum clarity, which is a fundamental objective of this tend-

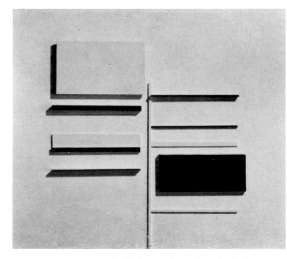

VICTOR PASMORE. *Relief in white, black, Indian red and maroon.* 1954. Collection Marlborough.

JOHN ERNEST. *Modulated plane construction II.* 1962.

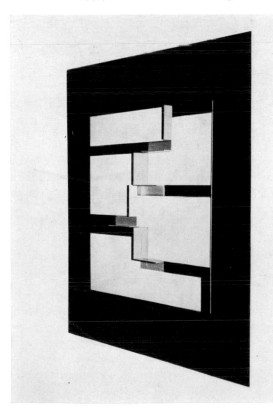

ency. Among the various artists in this movement, who up to now have not been mentioned, are the following.

Almir Mavignier was born in Rio de Janeiro in 1925. In 1951 he was in Paris, and from 1953 to 1957 he studied at the Hochschule für Gestaltung in Ulm, Germany. At present he is a professor in Hamburg. Mavignier holds that the new art ought to eliminate construction and composition and reduce itself to one element: fascination. In his works he uses continuous structures.

Enrico Castellani was born in Castelmassa (Rovigo), Italy, in 1930; he lives in Milan. Together with Piero Manzoni he published the *Azimuth* review. In his declarations Castellani uses a lan-

ANTHONY HILL. *Relief construction.* 1960. Collection Tate Gallery.

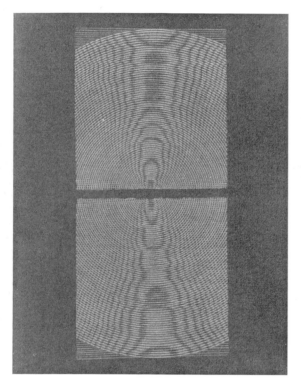

EDUARDO MAC-ENTYRE. *Painting.* 1964.

FERNÁNDEZ MURO. *Al gran pueblo argentino.*

guage evidently inspired by Klein. He speaks of the « myopia of subjectivism » and of the « necessity of the absolute that animates it. » In his works he eliminates composition and color and the heterogeneous elements that are « only good for a limited discourse and a metaphor; our discourse wants to be continuous and total. »

Castellani resolves this thirst for the absolute in canvases of even white surfaces. By inserting nails from the back he creates a series of regular protuberances in the canvas, with some zones more tightly stretched than others, thus obtaining a play of luminous reflections and a particularly seductive psychological effect through the purity and perfection with which the work is finished. Ivan Picelj is a Yugoslav; he was born in Okucani, Croatia, in 1924, and now lives in Zagreb.

He uses a serial procedure on gessoed wood panels.

Eric H. Olson, born in Malmö, Sweden, in 1909, now lives in Stockholm. His works, which he terms « optochromic compositions, » are based on the effects of forms and colors seen through polarized crystals.

Enzo Mari was born in Novara, Italy, in 1932. He lives in Milan. Since 1956 he has been creating structures that in general consist of a juxtaposed series of orthogonal boxes, frequently of polished metal, of equal size but of varying depth, in which the action of light creates a visual ambiguity, like vibration, and at the same time a curiously poetic and mystic sensation. He is one of the best artists in this tendency.

Getulio (Getulio Alviani) was born in Udine, Italy, in 1939, and still resides there. He general-

Olle Baertling. *Kortar.* 1960. Denise René Gallery

ly uses flat or slightly undulated aluminum sheets on which, by milling, he obtains luminous vibrations and startling illusions of changing volume as the spectator moves, frequently creating an actual sense of vertigo. He and the English artist Bridget Riley have achieved the most intense effects in optical illusion.

The following artists, using various new tendency techniques, are worth mentioning: the Swiss, Karl Gerstner was born in Basel in 1930 and lives in his native city; Paul Talman was born in Zurich in 1932 and lives in Basel; Christian Megert was born in Bern in 1936 and resides there; Uli Pohl was born in Munich in 1935, where he resides; Gerhard von Graewenitz, born in Schilde, Brandenburg, in 1934, lives in Munich, has exhibited

with the « O » group of Dusseldorf, and generally uses serial compositions.

The designation « programed art » became general following an exhibition arranged in the Olivetti plant in Milan by Munari; a series of works were shown that followed the plan of technological production. Different types of kinetic art were exhibited, which contained the possibility of variants (within limits previously determined in planning the movements) depending on chance, thus permitting the combination of the unforeseen with the rational-mathematical basis of construction. The work obtained in this fashion is then of a structure denominated « open » (in opposition to classical works of closed structure, or nonmodifiable) which is the same as a work of multiple structure. The exhibitors, beside Munari (who exhibited his *Nine Spheres on a Column*), were Italian artists known through their exhibitions of kinetic art and in the new tendency. The concept of programed art has spread rapidly, and permits a classification of the arts of pure visuality. Thus there are programed arts that include the kinetic arts and non-programed arts that include the neoconstructivists and the new abstraction and certain artists who rely on fixed and determined effects of optical illusion.

Neoconcrete artists

We have already said that the collapse of informalism triggered a return of the geometric tendencies. In the United States various artists forming part of the old « American Abstract Artists » association returned to favor, and the Denise René Gallery in Paris, which had remained faithful to the constructivist line during the years of the informalist storm, gained a new and accentuated impetus.

A gauge of the dimension of this reaction was given by two large exhibitions held in 1960: « Konkrete Kunst, » organized by Max Bill in Zurich, and « Construction and Geometry Painting, » held in the Chalette Gallery in New York (with a group from Denise René of Paris). This show contained a section dedicated to the pioneers (Malevitch, Kandinsky, Mondrian, Van Doesburg, Vantongerloo, El Lissitsky, Frank Kupka, Delaunay, Arp, Otto Freundlich, Sophie Teauber-Arp, Moholy-Nagy, Picabia, Herbin, and the Americans Macdonald-Wright, Russell, Bruce) and one dedicated to the contemporary artists, both those who made a name for themselves after the First World War, such as Albers, Glarner, Gorin, Cesar Domela, Diller, William Hiller, Nicholson, Stazewski, and Strzeminski, and those artists who had arrived after the second postwar period: Vasarely, Bill, Dewasne, Lohse, Picelj, Tomasello, and others.

But the most interesting phenomenon took place in England where constructivism (in spite of the presence there of Gabo) had not succeeded in taking hold before the Second World War, not even as a sort of free abstraction, with the exceptions of Nicholson and Hepworth. As if to make up for lost time, a vigorous neoconstructivist movement arose there in the postwar era, together with a resurgence of free and pictorial abstraction. Among the constructivists the dominant figure is Pasmore, and then Hill, Ernst, Mac Hale, Kenneth Martin, Mary Martin, and, later on, Peter Stroud and Robyn Denny. The strength of this reaction in England was demonstrated in the test exhibition held under the title of « Dimensions » in the O'Hana Gallery in 1957.

The majority of the English neoconstructivists were direct heirs of neoplasticism, but with the additional characteristic of rejecting traditional pictorial expression for the use of relief, and generally eliminating color, after the example of Pasmore. Because of their use of industrial material and plastics in their constructions, they are usually designated by the name « plasticists. »

Victor Pasmore was born in Chelsham, Surrey, in 1908. After some preliminary efforts he dedicated himself exclusively to painting from 1938 on: he was in the front rank of figural painters, and he sometimes alternated paintings with abstract experiments until about 1940. In 1947 he again began to experiment with abstract forms, and until 1952 he did numerous collages. In 1951 he came under the influence of the theories in Charles Biederman's book *Art as the Evolution of Visual Knowledge*. After 1953 he began producing his reliefs in black and white, which he called « projectable pictures. » At the same time he painted pictures with linear elements in which he sought to achieve a plastic rhythm; in his most recent works he has combined these very sober linear elements with large areas of color. His reliefs are actual constructions of an architectural type, in which he uses modern material, such as metals and plastics. He has abandoned the pictorial illusion of space to invade actual space. Pasmore considers creative activity in art a phenomenon that is at one and the same time social and intellectual, as is the construction of buildings. Pasmore's influence has been very important in the awakening of neoconstructivism in England.

Anthony Hill was born in London in 1930. After meeting Sam Francis, he produced his first tachist works in 1951. Until 1954 he worked with collages and abstract painting, but after that he abandoned painting and began constructing his reliefs, first along neoplastic lines, with planes vertically inserted over one sustaining plane. In his latest constructions he uses serial forms that he inserts at different angles on a base plane, creating more agile rhythms. He employs wood, metals, and plastics in his work.

John Ernest was born in Philadelphia, Pennsylvania, in 1922. He lived in New York until 1946, from 1946 to 1949 in Sweden, then in France, and in 1951 he established himself in England. His work was expressionistic until he came under the influence of the theories in Biederman's book, and since 1956 he has worked exclusively along constructivist lines. His reliefs are strictly geometrical, breaking the neoplastic rigidity by the introduction of angular forms and serial rhythms. He uses wood, metals, and plastics.

In the neoconstructivist idiom, but nearer to the American hard-edge style, is the English artist Peter Anthony Stroud, born in 1921 in Ealing. He now lives in Bennington, Vermont. His pictures search for spatial action controlled by one or two straight lines that cross the picture vertically. In Stroud's most recent works, the lines go outside the picture to shape reliefs on the canvas that accentuate the spatiality and confer on it a climate of serene meditation.

In various countries in the postwar period neoconstructivist groups or isolated artists have appeared. The « Exact 61 » group was founded in 1961 in Zagreb, with Picelj, Vjenceslav Richter, Bernardi, Bregovac, Mario Radic, Rosica, Srnee, and Zaharovic.

In Italy a neoconcrete group was formed with the name of « Gruppo Uno, » organized by Gastone Biggi, Nicola Carrino, Santoro, and Frasca.

Nicola Carrino was born in Taranto in 1932. In 1964 he received the Termoli prize. His constructions in relief, of an extreme rigor and limpidity, have an airy mobility that is not frequent in concrete works.

In Holland there is Joost Balgen, born in Middelburg in 1925. He started his neoconstructivist period in 1955. In Sweden Olle Baertling is worthy of note. Born in 1911, he now lives in Stockholm. Baertling's work is a search for large planes of color and strong, diagonal tensions. In South America the movement is especially important in Brazil and in Argentina. In Brazil there are active groups of concrete artists in Rio de Janeiro and in São Paulo. We mention Waldemar Cordeiro, who was born in Rome and works in São Paulo; Hercules Barsotti, who was born in São Paulo in 1914; Hermelindo Fiaminghi, who was born in São Paulo in 1920; Aluisio Corvao, who was born in Belém in 1918 and works in Rio de Janeiro; Decio Vieira, who was born in Petropolis in 1922; and Lygia Clark, born in Belo Horizonte in 1920. Lygia Clark is a particularly well-known sculptress, and also produces excellent reliefs in black and white along neoplastic lines.
In Argentina the artists of the concrete group have been dispersed. Tomás Maldonado fills a post as director of the Hochschule für Gestaltung in Ulm, Germany, and has practically abandoned painting. Alfredo Hlito is in Mexico, working

on free abstractions. Arden Quin is in Paris, and has not exhibited for many years. Within the last years new values have appeared, especially in a group started by Eduardo Mac Entyre, Miguel Angel Vidal, Ary Brizzi, and J. H. Silva, who produce a more sensitive geometry in search of rhythms and vibrations.

But the most important artist to come to the fore in the concrete movement in Argentina is Fernández Muro. He was born in Madrid in 1920, and arrived in Argentina in 1938. He began by developing a figuration of abstracticizing tendency, but in 1952 he began geometric abstraction, and exhibited with the concrete group. Later he evolved toward an almost monochrome concrete pointillism in which the single color reaches great intensity.

Muro now lives in the United States, where his work consists of a synthesis of certain forms out of his geometrical past, but with the mathematical qualities of informalism united to graphisms and graffiti. He uses a surface to which he gives a metallic quality, enriching it with textural suggestions. In his pictures, emblems often appear that suggest to him new exercises of material qualities. He is without doubt an exceptionally gifted artist who in his evolution with his contemporaries has known how to incorporate the new influences into a personal style that does not change but becomes enriched.

The limitation of the repertory of the neoconstructivists by their use of few elements reduces not only the possibility of creation but also of inventiveness. Very few of those who have gone far along the narrow path they have chosen have obtained any surprising variety of results, which explains why the majority of the younger artists, who are still within the confines of strictly regulated painting, now seek less circumscribed means of expression.

MARK ROTHKO. *Red and black.* 1959. Allen Stone Gallery. Coll. Noah Goldowsky.

SAM FRANCIS. *Oil*. 1953. Anne Abels Gallery.

Chapter six

Currents opposed to informalism and strict visuality

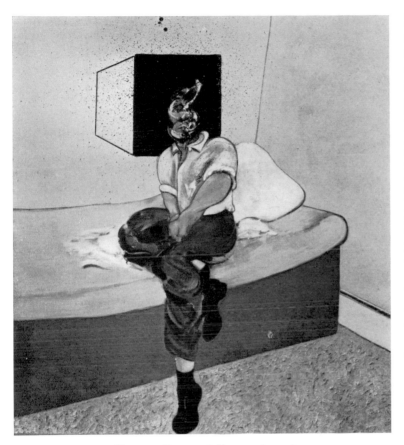

FRANCIS BACON. *Self portrait.* 1964.
Collection Peter Stuyvesant Gallery.

The problem of the « new figuration » is complex. Because of the ambiguity of the term « figuration » it can be used in misleading ways as a new name for the reactionaries in art, as a new label for old merchandise, or as a convenient term for the dealers who sense a slackening of the market for abstracts. Because those who appear first in a new movement are those who gain most by it, the new label is too hurriedly applied to everything that is not strictly abstract.

A characteristic of the second postwar period has been the attempt to fill the seemingly impassable breach between figuration and abstraction.

Some of the most important and original artists of this postwar period were either figural artists or else alternated equally between abstraction and figuration, not like someone using two different instruments, but rather as if using a single instrument to produce different notes, as did Fautrier and Dubuffet in France, the members of the « Cobra » group in Holland, Belgium, and Denmark, and de Kooning in America. Furthermore, a large number of today's abstract artists were at one time figural painters: Rothko, Tobey, Kline (whose portraits at one time enjoyed great prestige), Pollock, and many more. Some, like the English artist Pasmore, had achieved an important position in painting as figural artists, when they decided to give it up for strict geometric abstraction. Others, like Jean Hélion, start out from figuration, turn to abstraction, in which they win renown, and suddenly return to figural painting. Even De Staël returned to figuration. There has always been movement from one field to the other. Undoubtedly, until recently, the transfer most frequently made was from the figural to the abstract. Today the phenomenon is reversed, thanks to the prestige lent by the new designation, and a multitude of abstractionists become figurationists merely to be labeled with the name.

But the return to figuration is nothing new; it is merely another episode in the periodical offensive that the followers of figuration conduct against abstraction. This offensive was begun after 1920 by the so-called « new objectivity,» and it regained force at the end of the Second World War with the name of « poetic realism » (which had little realism and less poetry), and above all in the truly renewing work of Dubuffet and most recently in the pop tendencies. But because in this postwar period the offensive erased the sharp lines that existed between figuration and abstraction, the designation « figuration » does not appear to have any reason for being. However since the tendency has gained adherents, it is important to make clear what is meant today by « new figuration. »

Its name implies that it came after abstraction. Therefore it is not a return to the past, but a step forward. Supposedly, it assimilated some elements from its forerunner. But how does it differ from the figuration of the past, from cubism or expressionism that turned toward abstraction, from that which had turned from figuration toward abstraction but still had not arrived at it? The problem is not insoluble, and the key lies in the intention the work shows, without taking into account the road it previously traveled. The new figuration may be defined as a tendency that, by using modern plastic means, displays the spirit of our epoch. Thus understood, the role of precursor and most characteristic exponent of this tendency falls to Bacon because no one has managed better than he to communicate the profound drama of contemporary man.

In new figuration, subjectivity acts on the world of things, reconstructing it, deforming it. *Disfiguration*, the word used by Asger Jorn as the title for one of his works, is indicative. Jorn used it to illustrate the process in which an image taken out of reality is modified by the intervention of the artist. This « disfiguration » is a way of revealing the world of the subject in the object. It deals with a subjective reality: metamorphosis of the real by the act of spiritual projection. In this sense, new figuration occupies the spiritual terrain in the field of new tendencies formerly held by gesture painting.

What marks almost all painters in the new figuration is the strong accent on humor. The artist finds himself in conflict with the world, but now he no longer reacts dramatically, nor does he depict a climate of desperation or seek isolation or escapism in a dream world. Today he faces the world, reproducing it in its grotesque and absurd aspect, and often the image takes on an aggressive, caustic, burlesque appearance. This humor is not comical; it is wounding and brutal, often

FRANCIS BACON. *Figure in a landscape.* 1946. Collection Tate Gallery.

morose; it is what has come to be called « black humor. »

In any event, the importance of new figuration is that it reproduces the object but negates it. Such a systematic aspect of negation is built into the revolutionary character of the modern artist, revealing to us – if there were not enough proof – that we are living in a revolutionary epoch. This tendency includes representatives of various currents. In the first place, it has elements of expressionism, whose remarkable fecundity in all fields has been tested in the present epoch. In this sense, the Belgian expressionist Fritz van den Berghe (who died in 1939) must be kept in mind as a precursor; in his last period, influenced by surrealism, he achieved expressions comparable to the neofigurals of more recent date. Also Alberto Giacometti's painting achieved the distinction of being precursive, as well as that of Grosz and the expressionistic baroqueism of his American period.

Those who do not belong in the new figuration are the new artists who, quite simply, are formal imitators of cubism, expressionism, fauvism, surrealism, or informalism, without containing anything of the spirit of our epoch. They are no more than decorative painters. For this reason Roger Chastel, imitator of cubism-expressionism, is not neofigural, nor are Bernard Lorjou and Bernard Buffet, imitators of expressionism, nor André Minaux in his fauvism, nor the American painter Richard Diebenkorn. Some American critics see Diebenkorn as in the vanguard of new figuration; without entering into a discussion of his true merits, it can be taken as certain that the morphological character of his painting and the spirit from which it grows put him outside new figuration. He is simply a modernizing figural painter.

What is necessary to point out is that new figuration means, above all, a continuation of the figural experiments initiated by Dubuffet, Fautrier, Appel, Jorn, Corneille, and de Kooning.

With this as criterion, we can consider that some currents springing from different beginnings (with the logical reservation that these beginnings are often many) can be included in new figuration, and so we have:

Surrealizing neofiguration: Dado, Petlin, Gironella, Concetto Pozatti, Hultberg, Cremonini, and Vacchi.

Postexpressionistic neofiguration: Bacon, Marcel Pouget, Maryan, Antes, Seguí, Jan Lebenstein, Saura, and Bernard Dufour.

Abstracticizing neofiguration: Rebeyrolle.

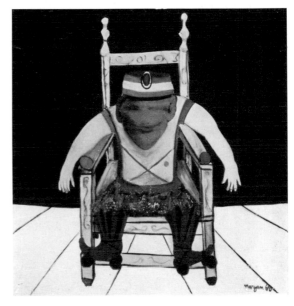

MARYAN. *Personage.* 1962.
Collection Galerie de France.

Neofiguration bordering on pop, utilizing popular images: Larry Rivers, Ronald B. Kitaj, Robert Munford, Foldes, Peter Saul, Harold Stevenson, and the Argentinian group: Macció, Noé, de la Vega, and Deira.

This classification is simply for orientation, to determine the dominant influences in each case. It is in no way final. In any event, it serves to determine how certain purely formal influences, such as cubism, have entirely disappeared.

Francis Bacon was born in Dublin in 1909. He is self-taught, and started out as a furniture designer and interior decorator. In 1927 he began to paint, just to see if he could do it. Between 1929 and 1930 he attempted semigeometric abstraction, and in 1932 and 1933 he discovered Max Ernst, and became concerned with more organic and surrealist conceptions. Because of the war and mobilization, he had to abandon painting for almost seven years, but he returned to it in 1947.

The drive for expression is fundamental with Bacon. And what he expresses is the anguish of our times. The people he paints are not grotesque; they are beings subjected to the pressure of an unbreathable atmosphere, which contorts them, which disfigures them physically. This drive for expression is supported by a pictorial quality so exceptional that it is almost miraculous. Bacon's work is a voice for order and against indifference. It is like the message of a new prophet, a message that undergoes a metamorphosis in painful and contorted images to speak to a visual epoch such as ours and to anathematize it. The mere presence of a personality such as Bacon justifies the existence of a new figuration.

In his work he relies entirely on photographs instead of on models. His studio is filled with photographs of all kinds, especially candid-camera shots from magazines, in which people are revealingly caught at unguarded moments. For movement in his subjects he carefully studies the albums of the famous Victorian photographer E. Muybridge entitled *Animals in Motion* (1899) and *Animal Locomotion* (1887), and at one time he became fascinated with Velásquez's portrait of Pope Innocent, which inspired his series of cardinals and prelates.

At first hand his pictures contrast the violence of the figures with the geometrically cold framework of the space. He uses loud, uniform, saturated colors in wide areas that make up the space. The bodies are almost without modeling; the volume and shadows are rendered with wide brushstrokes of color. There is hardly any chiaroscuro; the volumes of objects, such as large armchairs, have no more indication than the simple perspective given to geometric planes. The figures appear submerged in the most profound solitude in those geometric chambers that are their dwellings, with absolutely bare walls and one divan just as severely geometric. Does this signify, then, that Bacon's painting is literal? No,

something far more important. It signifies a reevaluation of the image, which modern, opportunistic pseudopainters and mystifiers deluxe, such as Dalí, had debased. It means to dignify the image so that the painting conveys something more than a pleasing of the eye; something more than the eternal, sensual little squirt of color or the exercises in pure visuality used as a therapy to relax tension; something more than ephemeral gratification. If every painting at any one time had a transcendental significance and was not just a divertissement, if at any time painting reflected the climate of a time, Bacon is the man of such painting today. Bacon's work is a reflection of our times, or, more precisely expressed, the reflection of a man who contemplates our times with clear eyes.

Screaming mouths, bodies turned within themselves, crushed and mangled faces, formless organic remains, all appear as if demolished by a destructive hurricane, and this hurricane is simply the magic brush of Bacon. It is there in the faces, in the bodies – the brushstroke that crushes the forms, contorting them, dragging the members along in its furious impulse. There is a great moral significance in these brushstrokes; they contain a grave accusation against man. And today, as we begin again to speak of an ethical sense of art, Bacon offers proof of profoundly ethical work. Again we say that in his unity of an expressive image of high plastic and ethical content, Bacon justifies the new figuration.

*Postexpressionist
and postsurrealist neofiguralists*

Marcel Pouget, born in Oran, Algeria, in 1923, has lived in Paris since 1949. His figures are schematic, crude, fashioned with intense colors that concede nothing to charm, leaving an impression of naked cruelty, of cold satire in which we are offered symbols of an inhuman world. He

PAUL REBEYROLLE. *Collage.* 1966.

is one of the most original painters in new figuration.

Maryan (the pseudonym of Pinchas Burstein) was
born in Nowy-Sacz, Poland, in 1927. From 1939
to 1943 he was in concentration camps in Poland,
and between 1945 and 1947 in refugee camps in
Germany. From 1947 to 1950 he lived in Israel,
and after that in Paris, where he studied at the
National Academy of Fine Arts. The image is

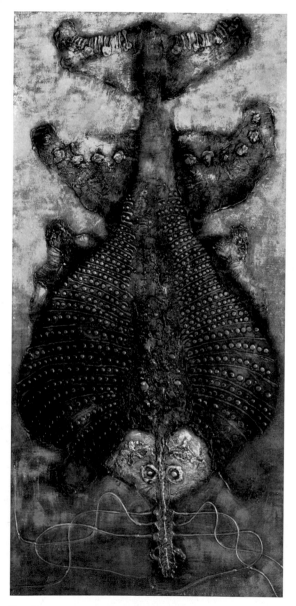

JAN LEBENSTEIN. *Aquatic.* 1965.

suddenly become vehicles for an adventure in creative and original color.

Horst Antes was born in Heppenheim, Germany, in 1936; he now lives in Rome. He produces a hard, violent figuration, with characters of fragmentary objectivity and arbitrary ordering in their distinct elements. He could be considered close to Beckmann in style, but a Beckmann gone mad.

Paul Rebeyrolle was born in Haute-Vienne, France, in 1926. Though he has exhibited as a figural painter since 1949 in the last few years he has evolved toward a synthesis that could be classified as informal figuration, in which gesture, brushstrokes, spots, and drippings cause a partial disintegration of the figure.

Jan Lebenstein was born in Brest, Poland, in 1930. He studied at the Academy of Fine Arts in Warsaw, was awarded a prize at the First Biennale in Paris, and now lives in Paris. Lebenstein's pictures are heavy, of turbulent and rough material, which have the aspect of actual bas-reliefs, of somber tones that are almost monochromes, in which what seem to be sketches of undefinable figures of vaguely human beings appear.

Antonio Seguí was born in Córdoba, Argentina, in 1934. After studying painting in Argentina, France, and Spain, he lived for a time in Mexico. Seguí began with matter abstraction, in which he achieved remarkable textures and rich colors, toned by velatura. From there he turned to figural painting; his matter became plainer, and the color gained in clarity. His figures are only shells of grotesque beings, empty wrappings with mass faces devoid of humanity. This anedoctal figuration, in very free treatment, is incorporated in a plastic organization of high pictorial quality, with measured colors of high purity.

Eduardo Arroyo, born in Madrid in 1937, has lived in Paris and in Italy since 1958. His first

important with Maryan. His figures are puppets, useless and dramatic, aggressive and lamentable at the same time; but their stiff, ridiculous bodies

Antonio Seguí. *Esperá sentado.* Collection Claude Bernard Gallery.

one-man show was at the Claude Levin Gallery in Paris in 1961. In his pictures, as in those of many of the neofiguratives, elements from previous tendencies are united. Surrealist influences are visible in the strangeness of the images, and the character of magazine illustration he sometimes gives to the landscape comes from the technique of the pop style, combined with a slant toward propaganda almost in a pamphlet style, but all embodied in a truly exceptional poetic unity.

John P. Hultberg was born in 1922 in Berkeley, California. He attended classes at the Art Students League in New York from 1949 to 1951, was in Paris in 1954, and currently lives in New York. He has been an instructor in New York and California and has exhibited nationally and internationally. Hultberg is a member of Michel Tapié's *art autre* group. His pictures show two zones, an upper one that submerges us in a profound space, and a lower one in which are accumulated ambiguous, oppressive forms of edifices or piers, and at other times walls that always debouch into the large space, and vague human silhouettes with a sense of abandon. His colors are somber in tone, and the whole always leaves

EDUARDO ARROYO. *Neuf lendemains de Waterloo*. 1965. André Schoeller Gallery.

a final impression of something like dramatic clarity.

Irving Petlin was born in Chicago, Illinois, in 1934. There he organized a number of figural artists into a group calling themselves «Momentum.» He produces anguished figures in a nightmarish atmosphere obtained through traditional pictorial means used in a personal style. They appear to be in constant flight, as if driven by a hurricane of desperation.

Bernard Dufour, born in Paris in 1922, has worked in figuration since 1955. His work follows the traditional expressionist style, with very few variations.

Leonardo Cremonini was born in Bologna in 1925, and studied at the Brera Academy in Milan. He lives in Paris. Cremonini's pictures show hallucinatory, desolate beings, seemingly corralled, who sometimes appear to be beginning to disintegrate, in interiors or in landscapes belonging to no time or place. But this climate of desolation is compensated for by an exceptionally rich and luminous color and by a very refined treatment that ends by creating an ambiguous pessimistic-optimistic atmosphere.

Concetto Pozatti was born in Padua in 1935, and now lives in Bologna. His pictures are divided into sections in which completely different

JOHN HULTBERG. *Cinema frames.* 1960. Collection Galerie du Dragon.

themes appear: in some are themes of urban or imaginary life, while in others there are bands of color in the manner of chromatic abstracts, or intercrossed organic forms, or widely varying kinds of ideograph similar to some used by Klee. The dominant colors are gray or earth-colored, and the organization is unusual and very close to surrealism.

Sergio Vacchi was born in Castenaso, close to Bologna, in 1925. He studied painting in Bologna, where he worked until 1961, when he estab-

lished himself in Rome. Vacchi's work shows the same climate of anguish and destruction that obtains in Bacon's work, but differs from it because of a dreamlike and fantastic component, a baroqueism of forms, and the frequent utilization of metallic colors (especially aluminum and old gold) which confers a frozen unreality to his compositions.

Dado, whose real name is Miodrag Djuric, is of Yugoslav origin, and was born in Cetinje, Montenegro, in 1933. He has lived in Paris since

1956. His figures are outraged images of infants strewn all over the canvas. Heads in all positions seem to blend their clamor in an anguished pictorial magma. It is the desolated chant of innocence rejecting an unacceptable world.

Neofiguratives linked with pop art

Larry Rivers, born in New York in 1923, studied with Hans Hofmann for two years. Rivers is a recorder of everyday images that obsessively invade the visual life of man today He thus expounds a popular mythology, fashioned of figures in news and happenings, sometimes blurred, like memories, reproduced with frank ordinariness, but with an evident pictorial quality. The humor does not lie in any particular deformation of the image, but rather in the subject itself and in the negligence with which it is treated, which leaves a sensation of incompleteness and ephemerality, all obtained by pictorial methods. This last factor places him within the field of new figuration, in spite of his images' similarity to pop art.

Ronald B. Kitaj was born in Ohio in 1932. He studied at the Cooper Union Institute in New York, spent some time as seaman, and since 1958 has lived in London. Kitaj depicts the everyday scene, but metamorphosized by a deep sense of the grotesque; he presents his figures as if stumped and plastered on a flat, empty space. The sensation they give is of separate episodes that have arbitrarily come together to form a picture.

Peter Foldes was born in Budapest in 1924. His pictures run in sections, like comic strips, and have the same story development, the narrations usually dealing with adventures in cosmic space. Foldes frequently includes real objects in the picture.

Peter Saul, born in San Francisco, California, in 1934, lived for a time in Paris, and at present resides in Rome. His pictures depict fragments of urban life, humorously caricaturized and arranged into insoluble puzzles in which the pieces are loose, all scrambled as if dragged along in some dizzy rhythm.

Harold Stevenson was born in Idabel, Oklahoma, in 1929. He has lived in Paris since 1959. Stevenson, who produces a sort of gigantism of academic painting, has come to be for the academic picture what Lichtenstein was for the comic strip: he creates the dynamic quality simply by an enlargement in size. He painted a fifty-five-foot-high picture of the bullfighter El Cordobés. By some he is thought to be a sensationalist, but supposedly he has nothing of the rebel in his makeup. « I am for society, » he says.

Robert W. Munford was born in Worcester, Massachusetts, in 1925. Since 1958 he has lived in Ibiza, Spain. Munford's work is on the border between figuration and pop. His motifs are the popular scene, sometimes loosely sketched and appearing like vague memories, united to an explosive color organization obtained with bold, showy poster colors, conferring on the whole a climate not of aggressiveness, but one of a particular nostalgia.

The English new figuration, falling between pop and figuration, offers not only the works of Allen Jones, David Hockney, and Howard Hodgkin, but also the pictorial part of the work of Peter Blake, who, as we shall see, is also active as a pop artist.

Allen Jones was born in Southampton in 1937, studied at the Hornsey College of Art from 1958 to 1959, at the Royal College of Art from 1959 to 1960, and was awarded a prize at the Biennale in Paris in 1963. He lives in London.

Howard Hodgkin was born in 1932 in London and now lives there. He studied at Camberwell and at the Bath Academy of Art in Corsham.

David Hockney, born in Bradford in 1937, studied at the Bradford College of Art from 1953 to 1957 and at the Royal College of Art in London from 1959 to 1962.

The works of these three artists are situated on the border between pop and figuration. They have in common the freedom with which they treat not only the figure but also the plastic conventions. The criteria of unity, coherence, and cohesion between the parts is completely cast aside, but there is in all their painting a fresh humor, an atmosphere of play, and also a true pictorial knowledge with which all these elements are handled.

The Argentine group of new figuration is represented by four painters: Macció, Noé, de la Vega, and Deira. The group, formed in Buenos Aires around 1962, became a standard-bearer for a type of new figuration that signified an actual synthesis of all contributions to painting in the past, managed with an infectious humor and creative freedom never before observed in South American painting. These artists broke with the tenets of good taste, with stiffness, and above all with the idea of art as a sacred mission.

In the work of these painters appear elements from informalism, gesture painting, pop art, and even from geometric painting, almost as ironic allusions to the fact that what they are doing has something to do with painting. At the same time they unite everyday elements with an extensive fantasy that is totally different in each one of the group, which gives the work of each an unmistakably personal character.

Rómulo Macció was born in Buenos Aires in 1931. A self-taught painter, he was awarded the International Di Tella prize in 1962; he is also an outstanding and expert advertising artist. Macció began by exhibiting paintings along surrealist lines, but later inclined toward informalism. He soon began a figural painting that was vaguely postcubistic and very pictorial, until he became acquainted with the work of de Kooning and came briefly under his influence. He then evolved a very personal combination of elements, blending gesture elements with trivial images, graffiti, and scribbles, all of intense color and powerful material quality. From there he progressed to his present painting style, purified of gesture elements, limiting his creative range to the image incorporated in planes and bands of color.

Luis Felipe Noé was born in Buenos Aires in 1933. He worked in the studio of the Argentinian painter Horacio Butler in 1952, won the National Di Tella award in 1963, and began to exhibit neofigural works in which the figures blended with a space of informal quality, with an intense coloration tending toward monochromism. Influenced by the pop venture, he turned to a freer painting, violently aggressive, inspired by the popular scene, tending to go beyond the limits of the picture by the addition of foldable parts; the partition of the work into fragments of juxtaposed pictures or several pictures held together by supports, and even avoiding the usual rectangular frame. Noé stands as the artist who is freest and least involved with the pictorial tradition of this group.

Jorge de la Vega was born in Buenos Aires in 1930. He studied architecture, only to abandon it almost at the end to dedicate himself exclusively to painting. Beginning within the concrete idiom, with a neoconstructivist painting of a very sensitive order, in which a refined texture neutralized the rigidity of the geometric forms, de la Vega later turned to informalism, but soon went on to neofiguration of a very personal kind. He uses figures often taken from children's or popular myths – elephants, faces that are imper-

LEONARDO CREMONINI. *Blindman's buff*. 1963/64. Galerie du Dragon.

sonal or out of some nightmare, or emblematic figures – and he composes them by very diversified collages, also taken from the daily world: playing cards, buttons, markers, bits of mirrors, and especially pieces of linen cloth, that he attaches with all their wrinkles and folds. On these he applies showy, loud colors, almost poster style, and he usually completes the picture with geometric motifs: circular concentric rings. He also uses serial repetition of the same image, but reproduced by different methods (printed on the canvas, varying collages). He is the artist with the richest imagination of the group.

Ernesto Deira was born in Buenos Aires in 1928. He studied with the painters Leopoldo Torres Agüero and Leopoldo Presas. He began exhibiting pictures of neoexpressionist figuration of high pictorial quality, until he turned to the synthesis of informalist and neofigural painting that now characterizes him. His pictures are products of a complete spontaneity in which are mixed graphisms, spots, fragments of figures outlined in gesture technique, and dripping, as if reflecting a condensation of different styles. The color is pure and vibrant; he has a preference for the primary colors. In his latest pictures the figure is formed by a calligraphic interplay of brushstrokes of color that trace actual labyrinths, and thus he obtains an ambiguous figure that at the same time composes and recomposes itself through the vertiginous trajectory of the line.

Another Argentinian new figuration artist is Antonio Berni, born in Rosario de Santa Fé in 1905. From 1925 to 1931 he lived in Paris, where he attended the classes of André Lhote and of Othon Friesz; his first one-man show was held in 1921. In Paris he produced surrealist pictures, but on his return to Buenos Aires he turned toward social realism, a field in which he was one of the most outstanding painters for many years. After 1960 he began to produce expressionist pictures until he reached his present idiom, which is a blend of pop and social comment. He received the International Engraving prize in the thirty-first Biennale in Venice in 1962.

Berni's pictures, of large format, are narrative: the first series concerns the life of a child, Juanito Laguna, in one of the « misery towns » of the Buenos Aires suburbs; the second series deals with the fortunes of a poor girl, Ramona Montiel, and the « loose life. » He depicts these stories in collages made up of rags, pieces of string, old cans, buttons, brooms, and junk in general. He also includes collages of photographs or illustrations from popular news magazines and even whole real objects. Aside from the collage with which he composes the figures and organizes the picture with a true sense of composition, there are parts that are summarily painted in, sketches of figures, or just brushstrokes to accentuate the effects of the collage. In this fashion Berni, without departing from the controversial intention of his former work, creates a work of stupendous imagination, of plastic richness, of indisputable originality, and, in the end, of infinitely higher efficacy than the banal pamphlets of academic socialist art.

Neodadaism and pop art

In the United States, around 1955, when informalism was in full swing, a work was introduced by an artist, Robert Rauschenberg, who using certain elements of informalism, incorporated them into a new kind of art that completely broke with the concept of frontal unity in pictures. He attached real objects to the canvas, in a dimension and in a manner inconceivable with the old collage technique, and he presented as works of art ordinary objects or collections of objects, sometimes covered with paint, and sometimes not. In 1955 he actually exhibited a real bed all made up and covered with paint, and with this it can be said that the art of using the everyday image, the common object, was born and was to become the focus of activity in pop art. A few months after this revolutionary gesture, another American artist, Jasper Johns, after a profound study of Duchamp's work, produced pictures that were remarkable in that he had reproduced infinitely the most ordinary and apparently least painterly objects: American flags, shooting-range targets, or block numbers.

Rauschenberg's exceptional inspiration opened new routes for art by an unheard-of way of introducing reality into the picture, and he started a movement that spread widely and that was modified and varied in its forms. This movement, at first called « new dada, » is what today is known as « pop art. »

This revolution, as is frequently the case with revolutions, signified a return to a past experience, that of dada; and in this sense two names are fundamental in the example they constituted for the young renewers: the names are those of the old dadaists, Marcel Duchamp and Kurt Schwitters. The ready-mades of the first and the collages of the second were the undeniable sources of inspiration in the new experience.

Robert Rauschenberg was born in Port Arthur, Texas, in 1925. Between 1946 and 1947 he studied at the Julien Academy in Paris and be-

SERGIO VACCHI. *Celebration of Michelangelo.* 1964.

CONCETTO POZZATTI. *Fall of an important monument.* 1963/64.

tween 1948 and 1949 at the Black Mountain College in North Carolina with Albers, who according to Rauschenberg was the most important teacher that he had. He married Sue Weil, whom he had known in Paris, but was soon divorced. Since 1955 he has been associated with the modern dance company of Merce Cunningham as a designer and decorator. In 1964 he was awarded the first prize in painting at the Biennale in Venice. Rauschenberg began as an abstract expressionist, and exhibited at the Betty Parsons Gallery in New York in 1951. Around 1952 he painted monochromes, white paintings, and later black paintings. In 1953 he asked de Kooning for permission

to exhibit a drawing of his carefully erased: perhaps this had the symbolic character of a rupture with abstract expressionism. The first exhibition of what he called « combined paintings, » in which he attached various objects to the canvas, was held at the Egan Gallery in January, 1955, and it can be said that with this exhibition a new panorama of American art was opened. The most violent and effectual reaction against abstract expressionism came – as customarily happens in similar cases – from an artist schooled in it.

But Rauschenberg, even if he stands for a return to the attitude of an anti-art dominated by humor, is nevertheless an indisputable descendant of the action painters. He covers his canvases, or the objects he puts in them, with paint in a manner very much like theirs. What sharply separates him from them is the fact that, instead of isolating

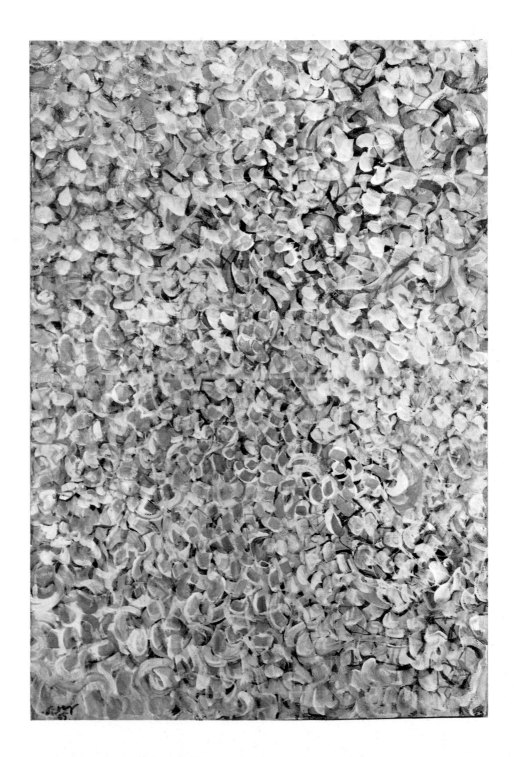

ADOLPH GOTTLIEB. *Saturnalia.* 1962. Marlborough Gallery.

R.B. KITAJ. *Notes towards a definition of nobody.* New London Gallery.

himself from the world to represent the attitude of an individual turned within himself, he faces the world about him and incorporates it in his creative act. He incorporates the world about him through direct collages of photographs of actual street scenes, ordinary merchandise, or objects of the most varied kind, such as a pillow or a chair or a garden hose.

This practice of introducing objects and actual things into a work of art has very respectable antecedents, from the cubist collage up to Schwitters, who took the technique of collages as the basis for his creation. Rauschenberg actually composes the picture in the same manner as Schwitters, following a geometric distribution proceeding from cubism. The photomontages and the photographic collages had a forerunner not only in Schwitters but in the dadaist Raoul Hausman, who used it on a large scale from 1919 to 1923. Thus the originality of Rauschenberg does not lie in the discovery of a new technique.

Rauschenberg starts from the idea that the industrial colors and the canvas are themselves articles of the same kind and significance as everything else that surrounds us, and hence may very well be combined. In a Rauschenberg picture the pigment, whether poured on or daubed, acts as a thing by itself, and not as a means of describing something (not even the actual action, as with the action painters). Thus the pigment remains a pure presence, the same as the various articles attached to the picture. The result he obtains by this technique he calls « combined painting, » and amounts to a break with the traditional idea of the canvas as a pictorial vacuum that must be filled with some illusion, of whatever sort. For Rauschenberg this last type of painting, no matter how modern it may be, is separated from life. From the beginning, he felt that his contribution fundamentally signified the closing of the breach that has always been open between art and life. In a declaration that has become famous, Rauschenberg presented his point of view on art: « Painting relates to both art and life. Neither can be made. I try to act in the gap between the two. » That is, he acts in an undetermined area in which both become fused, on the one hand the work of the artist, on the other, the penetration into the work of art by those concrete elements of life that enter into the picture, not as intruders, but as natural products of the creation.

In Rauschenberg's work there appears to be a need to grasp the passing moment, the many-faceted life that passes by us and escapes; but this moment that the artist manages to grasp, this unique instant, is the one that contains the whole. As Rauschenberg says, the idea is to inject the whole into the moment. Thus he wants to penetrate the mystery of the unity of the world and man, and reveal it to us. Reveal to us how life is made out of these particles of the world floating around us. « I try simply to obtain the maximum presence possible of the world, with the most diverse objects, and I attempt to make them function in the most alive way possible, » he says in one of his declarations. In Rauschenberg's pictures there are these fragments of the real world, but selected from those with which he is in contact and those that intrigue him, those that, without having been selected, constitute the milieu in which he is submerged. It is the universe of mass consumption and mass communication.

Rauschenberg attempts to create actual visual events, and the canvas is simply the place where the events join. Esthetic considerations do not count with this artist, and are apparently subordinated to this happening. I say « apparently » because in reality the whole picture, or the object, constitutes a conglomeration of visual metaphors in which the most varied realities are conjoined to create a climate of poetic exacerbation peculiar to this artist. And in spite of the apparent baroqueism of his construction, everything soon appears to be carefully measured and controlled, using a distribution that calls to mind the rigorousness of Mondrian.

Rauschenberg introduces us to the world of ambiguity. His pictures can be paintings and also sculptures because of the completely three-dimensional objects attached to them. As paintings they reveal pictorial impulses reminiscent of abstract expressionism, but these impulses recur only fragmentarily and as content. The attached articles present a totally dissimilar world, and can be anything from a stuffed bird to small bits of crumpled-up notepaper, or fragments of visual information, such as photographs of popular events, reproductions of classical pictures, or well-known figures like the President of the United States. These articles are gathered from the most unusual places, and in spite of the ambiguity created by the conjunction of so many apparently dissimilar objects all appear in the picture as if they were in their accustomed place, as if they had not been torn out of their routine world to inhabit the strange world of the picture. Rauschenberg also favors the ambiguity of space as it results from the juxtaposition of differing spaces, the space of the photographs or that of the objects, the pictorial space and the real space that is incorporated into the picture with the three-dimensional objects that compose it. All these divergencies soon become unified through « transitions » or mechanisms of union, often indicated by concise brushstrokes of color.

The expressionistic brushstroke, the cubist construction, and the dadaist collage give to the picture an air that is not chaotic but, so to speak,

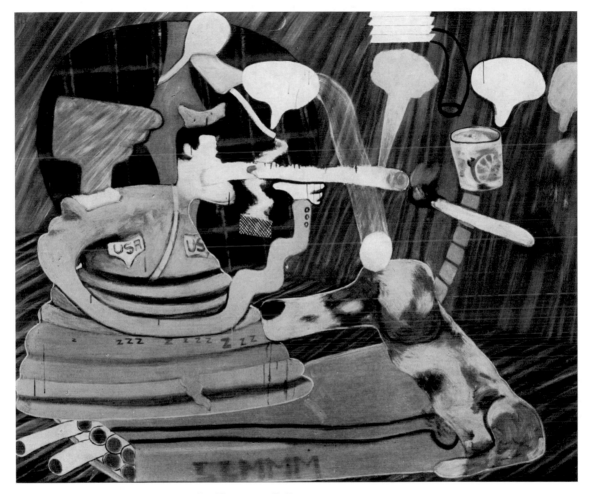

of fluid precision, because it does give us some-thing in which is mixed reality, the most ordinary and trivial, with something that has to do with dreaming or memories that pass quickly and with-out sequence through the distracted mind. The association of dissimilar images, the unusual place-ment of the image, reveal connections with sur-realism, and amply justify the surrealist invita-tion to Rauschenberg to exhibit with them in their latest exhibitions.

Jasper Johns was born in Allendale, South Caroli-na, in 1930. He has lived and painted in New York since 1952. In 1955, almost at the same time as Rauschenberg, Johns began his creative stage with his famous series of flags and shooting-range targets. Johns uses targets or flags of the ordinary type in a very special manner. Instead of in the way Cézanne, for example, used an apple as a pic-torial motif, Johns fills the whole picture with it, turning the whole picture into an object in which there is no unreal situation, no space to describe, no atmosphere. Nevertheless, the flag or the shooting-range target are fragments of reality, but a reality emptied of significance. The picture, for example, at the same time is and is not a flag, but what it really is, is a simple pictorial surface. The motifs appear selected for their quality of planes; and furthermore, as they are only valid as symbols when found in their context, they acquire when transported onto the entirety of the canvas a very individual air of neutrality. There is no doubt that what is dealt with are alienated objects, in the way Duchamp understood the ready-mades, but at the same time they become a paintable surface. Johns' painting, like that of Rauschenberg, springs from action painting. Both establish a union between the world of reality and that of the interior pictorial impulse. Both of them also regulate and domesticate this pictorial impulse, without taking away its vitality but making it serve other ends. In them – as we also shall see in Dine – exists the contained pictorial gesture, limited and always united to a sort of invasion of the world of the object. From the beginning Johns used painting in conjunction with objects and collage. His first shooting-range targets were combined with gesso masks applied in the upper part, and the flags and the targets had collages of newspapers and photographs. Later he alternated straight paintings with those in which objects, such as jars, brooms, paintbrushes, and balls, were attached. In this way he acquired that unique aspect so dear to the surrealists, which justifies, at it does with Rauschenberg, his inclusion in the surrealist exhibitions.

Johns' painting is of an uncommon quality, of an extraordinary refinement in the use of color, in the treatment of the matter, and in the sweep and orientation of the brushstroke. Thus the pictorial surface appears as if sensitized.
In the beginning he preferred grays, from which he obtained unsurpassed gammas, but at present he uses color with great freedom and true mastery, which produces an extraordinary contrast to the banality of the theme and ordinary articles used. As with Rauschenberg, his painting creates a very individual state of ambiguity, of indetermination, and more than anything a state of curious detachment that is created by the neutrality of the theme before the rich sensitiveness of the painting, and thus he obtains a strangely impersonal poetic atmosphere, impregnated with a subtle irony. This quality of detachment is very characteristic not only of Johns but of almost all pop painting that derives from these two artists. Johns does not want the work of art to be contaminated by necessities, aspirations, nostalgias, and emotions of the artist; he does not want it, as he explicitly states, to shares his « weaknesses.»

This same detachment is found in Rauschenberg and in the artists who followed him, and reflects an attitude in the contemporary artist tending toward a liberation of man from his reclusion in an interior world. But in Johns this detachment is conducive to a greater severity, to a very special asceticism, which is undoubtedly rooted in the ideas of the one who inspired him, Duchamp. Rauschenberg also stoutly affirms his detachment. « What interests me in what I do is to achieve a contact,» he says, « and not to express a message.» When Johns was asked why he produced this type of work, he answered: « It is to free me from responsibility.» These replies, and especially the last one, of Johns, ally the artist with those who voice a new type of cold, distant protest that is not polemical. In spite of the apparent detachment, there is no doubt that, as Alain Jouffroy holds, all modern art is definitely, a form of protest.

Rauschenberg and Johns initiated a new attitude among American artists. They incited the artist to integrate with his surroundings. They showed

HAROLD STEVENSON. *Oil.* 1962. Iris Clert Gallery.

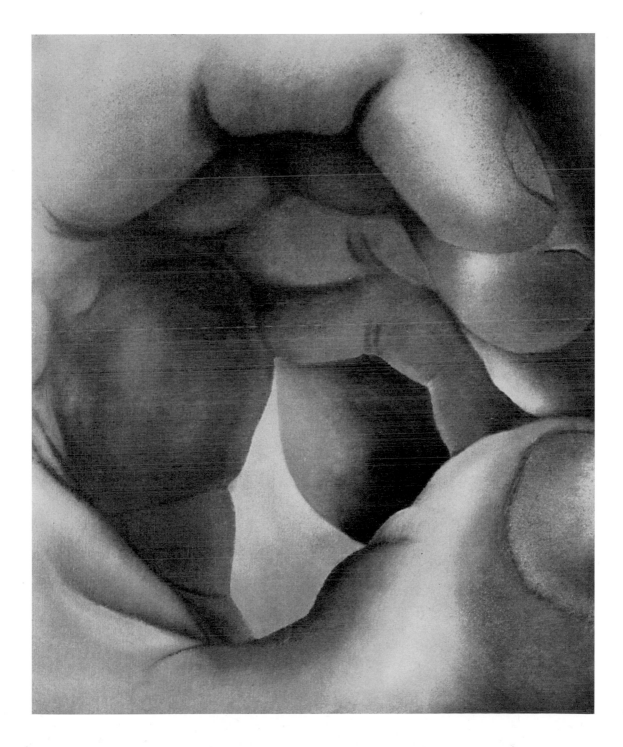

ROBERT W. MUNFORD. *And then there were none.* 1964. Dieter Brusberg Gallery.

him how to observe the real world, the importance
of the everyday, of the trivial, and they taught
him that the world forms a part of man and demands that the artist demonstrate it. This teaching caused the immediate appearance of a number of artists who threw themselves into the day-
by-day reality in search of an objective art to
oppose to nonobjective art, but with a new attitude that was not that of ordinary realism. The
explanation for this attitude is made easier by
comparing it with Duchamp's introduction of a
urinal with the title of *Fountain* into the exhibition of the Independents in New York. On this
occasion Duchamp gave the following explanation: « To take an ordinary object and present
it so that its utilitarian significance disappears
through a new designation and a new point of
view: a new significance is thus created for the
object. » This was how the ready-made emerged,
as well as the principle pronounced by Duchamp
as one of the fundamental tenets of art, which
defines the principle of selection as being the essential element in the artistic attitude: because
of the very fact that an artist does select an object, this acquires the dignity of the work of art.
And this act of selection produces the instanta-
neous alienation of the article, which then passes
from its habitual context to form part of a new
context – that of art. This explanation reveals
that the artists' new contact with reality is absolutely opposed to that of traditional realists, who
offer us an image of the object within its customary
context, a poor imitative image of reality that,
instead of bringing us nearer to it, separates us
from it.

Those artists who turned to reality with new criteria searched in it for those images which by
their frequency, by their almost obsessive repetition, were assimilated into the very life of man.
Almost all these images were products of man's
own activity, and constituted the milieu of urban
life. Their everyday use meant that they were

ALLEN JONES. *Concerning marriages 7.* 1964.
Collection British Council.

treated as trivial objects without any particular
value. For these artists, as for Dubuffet, there
were no unsuitable themes. But the *art brut* of
Dubuffet has another meaning. The new American artists resorted to standard images, the patrimony of the mass. Dubuffet searched for the
individual spontaneity of unsophisticated persons
who nevertheless were gifted with a creative impulse: they were not, in fact, part of the mass,
but exceptional beings, uncontaminated by mass
culture or a superior culture. The « Cobra » group
sought for a similar inspiration in infantile art or
in folklore, which is the creative art of the people. But the pop artists do not reproduce folklore,
the product of folk inventiveness, but the pro-

ducts manufactured in series and launched by the elite, sophisticated industrialists who prepare scientifically studied merchandise to appeal to the mass and stimulate their consumption. Highly skilled artists design these products for the mass. The Coca-Cola bottle, for example, perhaps the most obsessive object of contemporary society, was conceived by a gifted designer, Raymond Loewy.

These mass products are essentially adulterated, and furthermore contain a very insidious factor, because they tend to level the consumer to the lowest common denominator. The products selected by the pop artists are not chosen for their high quality but for their ability to please, the means of gratification: Coca-Cola, canned soups, cakes and hamburgers, movie stars, or popular singers, that is, everything that pleases the elementary collective mind, everything that levels and lulls. And if they go to less worked fields, as Warhol does with his dramatic scenes of the electric chair or his traffic accidents, they are made as trite as what appears in the more popular magazines, and they are, in the final analysis, for the delectation of aggressive, elementary minds (the electric chair and traffic accidents are also mass products of the technological supercivilization).

Pop art selects from the surrounding reality, not the exceptional, but the stereotype. It produces a replica, a faithful copy of elements or situations of daily life in their most trivial and obsessive aspects, emphasizing them by a slight trick of distortion, which can be obtained by an enlargement that distorts the size, or by serial repetition or by rough tracing, and utilizing in this replica even the same technical processes that commercial reproduction uses in mass advertising. Rosenquist, for example, resorts to billboard techniques.

The works become true mirrors of a reality that is not that of nature, not even that of man. It is fantasmal reality created by man, not for the use of man, but for the compulsive consumption by anonymous beings surrounded by forests of skyscrapers that yield only one fruit – bottles of Coca-Cola, all alike, without the possibility of the slightest variation – and to solace the spirit they are offered for consumption extremely simple comic strips that do not demand a pondering over words, because the stories are illustrated by drawings and are always absolutely simple.

Many of the critics who have to deal with these things find themselves subjected to the same mechanism of pressure, and are, consciously or not, in the service of a distorted vision of what life and reality are. Then they speak of optimism, of love of life, of contact with reality, and of holding up the mirror to the American way of life. Sometimes, no doubt, they are right. Rosenquist, in reflecting the American way of life in his montages, reveals the oppressing fatalism of technology and the desperate escape toward the erotic.

Clearly, pop artists reflect the American way of life, that is, the ideal of a society of consumption; and the themes of their works are the themes of consumption. But is this really an expression of social well being?

Is pop art then an expression of mass culture? No, it is definitely a sophisticated art for a sophisticated public, for a public with dulled sensibilities who demand new but carefully dosed sensations. Pop offers to this public the required sophistication and furthermore the delectable spice of a latent protest, but in a manner sufficiently cold and veiled so that it never reaches the point of being destructive. Pop has achieved the trick of using bad taste (the force of shock of protest), smoothing out all its aggressive and rough edges, and turning it into a bad taste in good form, into an elegant bad taste.

But pop is, in the end, an art of provocation. And the provocation can exist in the work without the artist's knowledge, when it reflects with fidelity a world to be rejected. One characteristic of the pop artists is their absolute de-

DAVID HOCKNEY. *Still life with figure and curtain.* 1963.

tachment: they do not bolster their work with any form of ideological protest. They do not explain, nor do they often talk, but when they do their statements are as ambiguous as those of the oracles. Their work also has an impersonal, objective character. This tendency toward depersonalization, to eliminate totally the world of personal impressions, is common to almost all the new tendencies in vogue, and characterizes pop as well as op art. It displays an attitude somewhat like « Nothing is gained by getting mad. » But the anger in these works exists, even if it is cold and veiled.

As is the case with other tendencies, there is no general agreement on the nomenclature. It began by being called, justifiably, « new dada, » in spite of the fervid protests of the artists involved who pointed out the differences between it and the old dada. Rauschenberg held that the fundamental difference lay in the fact that dada's stand was negative, while his, in contrast, was positive. Dada artists rejected the society in which they lived, while Rauschenberg not only accepted his but included it in his work. True enough, the real world is present in his work, but from it no acceptance of that world comes.

The English critic Lawrence Alloway, when he arrived in the United States to fill a post in the Solomon R. Guggenheim Museum, introduced the term « pop » to designate the new tendency, a term he had used in the circle of Richard Hamilton and Paolozzi in London to indicate the predilection these artists had for the images of mass media. The term gained acceptance in spite of its ambiguity, and today covers numerous artists of various intentions, and includes even the early neodadaists, like Rauschenberg and Johns, or neofigurationists, like Larry Rivers and Peter Saul. Nevertheless, they all have in common the use of what has come to be called the « popular

HOWARD HODGKIN. *Garden.* 1960/62.

RÓMULO MACCIÓ. *Emplacement*. 1965. Bonino Gallery.

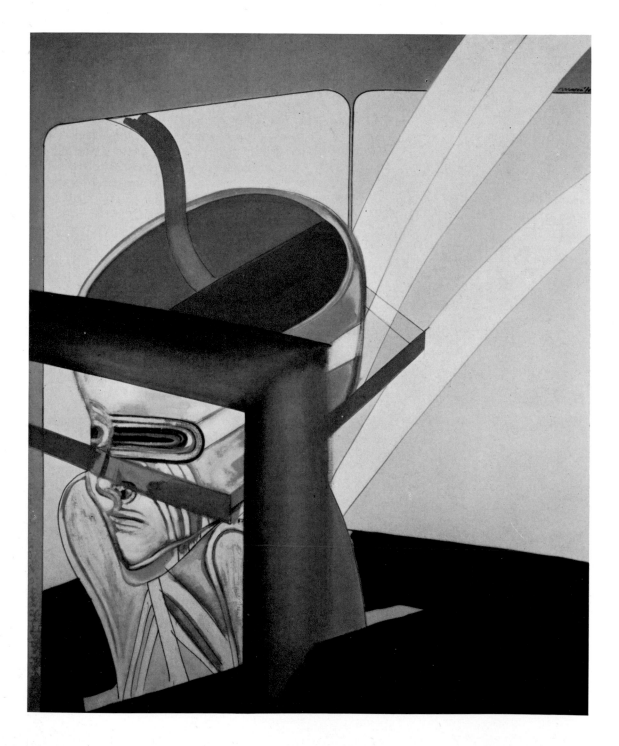

image, » or that which overwhelmingly confronts modern man, and which the sophisticated artists hitherto have scorned for its triviality. The idea is anything but original, inasmuch as the first dadaists used these popular images in a manner that was absolutely straight, especially Duchamp and Schwitters.

Still, it is to the point to establish that a fundamental difference does exist between the primitive neodadaists, Rauschenberg, Johns, and Dine, and the strict pop artists, such as Warhol, Lichtenstein, Wesselman, and Oldenburg. The first incorporate the popular image on a pictorial base coming from abstract expressionism, and reveal a real refinement, outside of composing their pictures; in their work there is a sense of warmth, a visible air of challenge, even more accentuated in Dine's work. The strict pop artist puts before us the evidence of the trivial object without any plastic elaboration, without either expressive or emotional implications, and without a trace of challenge. For this they use the most impersonal pictorial technique and even mechanical reproduction, such as silk screening. But for those who know how to look, it is just this absolute nakedness of the object placed in an artificial context to which it is alien that confers a truly dramatic quality on the pop work, and also a certain obscene quality in this « unjust nakedness. » This « obscene » quality (in the profound sense of the word, not its literal acceptance) and this manifest cruelty of pop work make it especially attractive to a public always searching for new sensations.

The inclusion of an everyday article into an artistic context always signifies – as Duchamp suggested – the alienation of that object. In a pop or neodada work an object fashioned for the use of man becomes immediately « dehumanized, » which means that the bag hanging in one of Dine's pictures has, although absolutely new, a value that has no relation to the one it had when

LUIS FELIPE NOÉ. *Three doors.* 1964. Bonino Gallery.

hanging in the store window, « ready to be used.» There the article exhibits its inanity, its existence without sense. In the neodadaists there is always a metamorphosis of the popular image, an evident change of sign, whether because of its inclusion into a strange ambience or because of the pictorial handiwork it undergoes. In the pop artists this change of sign appears not to exist, although in fact it is there in a very subtle way. In this one denies, protestations of the artists and their critics notwithstanding, the significance of the real object, and in the last instance affirms the spirit of man. Paradoxically, the pop artists arrive at the same conclusion as the informal artists they so oppose.

Without entering into a discussion about the merit of the pop artists, it is clear that in the United States they enjoy the support of nationalistic and chauvinistic critics who are desperate to declare the existence of an American painting that owes nothing to Europe; furthermore there is massive support from galleries, dealers, collectors, and others whose interests could be covered by the slogan « Buy American, » who regard with satisfaction how the United States, from having been a country that imported art, now is becoming an exporter of the commodity. This is indeed true. The interest awakened by pop art is revealed by the number of exhibitions in this tendency that have been held throughout Europe, in such major centers as London, Stockholm, Copenhagen, Amsterdam, and The Hague. The galleries Ileana Sonnabend, connected with Leo Castelli in Paris, and Alexander Iolas in Paris and Geneva are the gates through which the production of American pop flows into Europe. In addition, numerous local galleries in various parts of Europe import directly from America. But the most important phenomenon is the influence pop has had on European painters. In England, France, Germany, Italy, Spain, and even in Japan and Latin America, the number of imitators and followers of American pop is rapidly growing.

Pop artists

Roy Lichtenstein represents the purest exponent of orthodox pop. Born in New York in 1923, he studied at Ohio State University, where he re-

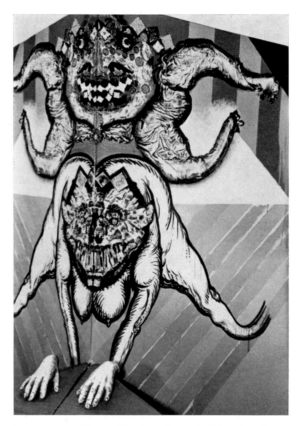

JORGE DE LA VEGA. *The four legged table* (detail). 1965. Bonino Gallery.

ceived his Master's degree in Fine Arts. In 1962 he was launched with an exhibition in the Leo Castelli Gallery, a gallery that has introduced a large number of pop artists. He is presently an instructor at Rutgers University, Rutgers, New Jersey.

Lichtenstein, who uses figures from other graphic sources, has become famous for copying scenes from the comic strips. The technique consists of an exaggerated enlargement on outsize canvases of one frame of the comic strip, faithfully reproducing it, even including the graininess of the original print, and coloring them with a flat, straight color, without modeling in the forms

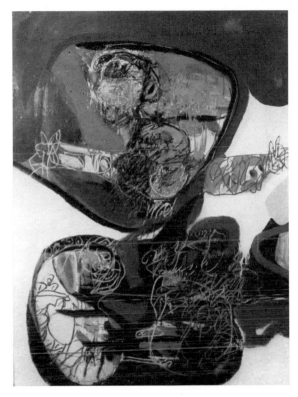

Ernesto Deira. *What's needed.* 1965.

and almost without modifying the drawing. Using the same procedure, he enlarges advertisements for automobile tires, electric mixers, and all kinds of merchandise picked from the most blatant and loud advertisements. He has also taken reproductions of paintings by Cézanne and Picasso and enlarged them with the already mentioned graininess of the print; this lends an unusual quality to his pictures and has become his permanent trademark. In this fashion, Lichtenstein obtains pictures in which the mechanical image comes forth without the personality of the commercial artist. His canvases are produced with the neatness and precision of the hard-edge painter, and this comparison is not gratuitous, because Lichtenstein's work, if one discounts the figure represented, corresponds to that type of painting in all its characteristics, in its clarity, its impersonality, and its exactitude.

In 1965 Lichtenstein exhibited a series of landscapes in New York and Paris, some almost abstract, in which he combined fragments of their planes with the grainy structure of the screen of a print and surfaces of Plexiglas, calling to mind the advertising technique because of its schematization. Referring to this change in his painting, Lichtenstein explains: « I want to do romantic things dispassionately. » In an interview given to Gene Swenson, and published in the November, 1963, issue of *Art News*, he refered to his position in this way: « The world is outside. Pop art looks at it and accepts this environment, which is neither good nor bad... and if you ask me how one can love moronization, how one can love the mechanization of work, how one can love bad art, I answer: I see it, it's here, it's the world. » In this interview Lichtenstein declared himself to be antiexperimental, anticontemplative, antigradation, anti-« let's-escape-the-tyranny-of-the-rectangle, » antimystery, antipainterly quality, anti-Zen, and anti all the brilliant ideas of preceding movements. He added: « It's customary to say that industrialization is a detestable thing. I don't know what to say, but I do know that the advertisements and the comic strips are interesting. There are useful things in commercial art, it is strong and full of vital force, and we use it. » And finally he makes a more direct observation about his technique: « The tension between the appearance of an object and the manner in which it is transformed into a flat surface is what makes the strength of pop art. » Lichtenstein, with his anti-intellectual and anti-sentimental attitude and with his idealization of the noncreative idiot image, constitutes an astonishing phenomenon in contemporary art that establishes an ambiguous mixture of the revolutionary and the conformist: he is an evident product of the enslaving force of advertising.

Andy Warhol is another exponent of the ortho-dox line of pop. He was born in Philadelphia in 1930, studied at the Carnegie Institute of Technology, and has lived in New York since 1952. He held his first exhibition at the Ferus Gallery in Los Angeles in 1962, and in 1964 exhibited at the Leo Castelli Gallery. Like Lichtenstein, he gets his subjects from news photos and other illustrated sources. He began by exactly reproducing packagings for standard merchandise: Campbell soups, Coca-Cola bottles, and Brillo – sometimes as unique units of large size, at other times repeating them in regular interminable series. From there he turned to reproducing figures of movie stars (Marilyn Monroe, Elizabeth Taylor) and popular singers (Elvis Presley full length in a cowboy outfit, taken from a publicity shot for a film). Since 1961 he has used silk screening for his reproductions (as Rauschenberg also did); he reproduces the images in a different size from the original, which serves as a base, and prints them on a white or monochrome canvas showing the image in various shades of intensity, or else he reproduces them on canvases of different colors mounted together. After this phase he became interested in scenes of violence typical of American life: scenes of executions in the electric chair, traffic accidents, repeated in juxtaposed series. These too are mass images, avidly appreciated by the masses, who feel enormously attracted by the phenomena of violence. Warhol takes these scenes from news photos, by which they acquire impersonality, a very individual sort of distance. They are mechanical images, impersonal and antisentimental. Horror thus acquires the same passive and indifferent quality as a can of Campbell soup. In 1965 he exhibited a series of flowers, also taken from advertising illustrations, as if to erase his impressions of disaster and death, but they were flat flowers, with lifeless colors, anonymous, from advertising, and they produce the same sensation of emptiness and anguished distance as his scenes of disaster. War-

hol's works convey a curious sensation of un-reality, as if we lived in an artificial world that is a reflection of another, distant and real world where the beings and the things really live. This manner of transmitting the American way of life, in spite of the total absence of opinion on Warhol's part (who limits himself to saying that everything is « pretty »), is the sharpest criticism of a mechanized and dehumanized life.

James Rosenquist, another of the artists who takes his figures from illustrations, was born in Grand Forks, North Dakota, in 1933. But his inspiration, instead of coming from the news media, is taken from the billboards. He even uses the same kind of printing method, and does not hesitate to use fluorescent paints. The fundamental difference between him and Lichtenstein and Warhol lies in the fact that his work is not just display: Rosenquist takes fragments of advertising matter and combines them, or, more precisely, composes the picture with a rigorous sense of plastic organization, and from the unnatural colors he uses he gets extremely rich effects of luminosity, tone, and transparency. From this fragmentary matter of everyday images he obtains true effects of visual metaphors, and the whole gives off a warmth and undeniably poetic atmosphere, which places Rosenquist at the extreme opposite of the unfeelingness of Lichtenstein and Warhol. That the surrealists have invited Rosenquist to participate in their exhibitions, as they did with Rauschenberg and Johns, is justifiable.

Tom Wesselmann was born in Cincinnati, Ohio, in 1931. His pictures, like those of Rosenquist, are composed. But Wesselman puts together, beside the painted parts, photographic collages and such objects as television sets and even a telephone, which, in at least one of the pictures occasionally rings. In the parts he paints he uses flat forms and well-outlined silhouettes of figures, nudes, and so forth, and includes fragments of

ANTONIO BERNI. *The great illusion.* 1962.

striped colors in the manner of the optic artists. His pictures suggest a hunger for space, and convey a certain nostalgic feeling for the life in the intimate atmosphere of American homes.

James Dine wos born in Cincinnati, Ohio, 1936, studied at the University of Ohio, and in 1958 went to live in New York. Beginning in 1959 he became known for his « happenings, » held at the

ROBERT RAUSCHENBERG. *Echo.* 1962. Ileana Sonnabend Gallery.

KENNETH NOLAND. *Up cadmium*. 1966. Andre Emmerich Gallery.

JASPER JOHNS. *Field painting.* 1964. Leo Castelli Gallery.

Reuben Gallery, where he also exhibited for the first time in 1960. Coincidental with this event he abandoned the « happenings » to dedicate himself fully to painting, and his career was meteoric. In 1963 he exhibited in the important Sidney Janis Gallery. He is one of the most outstanding artists among those included in the pop group, although the direction of his work places him at the side of Rauschenberg and Johns. Like them, he retains signs of abstract expressionism in his painting. Following the principle of the combined painting, the inclusion of actual objects acquires much more importance for Dine than for the other artists mentioned. He always uses new articles in such a way that no suggestion of decadence comes from the pictures. Furthermore, this inclusion of articles takes on very special characteristics in Dine. The article usually appears as the actual work, and the paint is merely a background or decoration, or, more precisely, it creates a fictitious space that accentuates the reality of the object. In this fashion an actual coun-

terpoint between the object and the pictorial surface is produced. The dominant presence of the object has led to a belief that Dine suffers from a sort of fetishism, but such an interpretation is wholly gratuitous. The object in Dine's work predominates by the simple fact of its presence, for its concrete reality. He has an undeniable preference for articles of dress; in his first pictures, the neckties attached and bathed in paint, or carefully reproduced, or leaving their empty mark on the canvas, and also hats, jackets, shoes, collars, and suspenders were turned into the only personalities of the picture. In the same way he used household appliances, showers, table lamps, and the like. He has also constructed pictures that directly reproduce a wall in a children's room with their clothes hanging up. In his latest pictures, which contain a collection of knives, ropes, and barbed wire accompanied with spots of intense color, the sensation of violence is accentuated. His interest also extends to work tools, carpenters' squares, saws, augurs, hammers, axes,

Roy Lichtenstein. *Stove.* 1962.
Ileana Sonnabend Gallery.

Roy Lichtenstein. *M-maybe.* 1965.
Leo Castelli Gallery.

and the tools of a painter, such as palettes and brushes. These constitute the motif of a picture, and are frequently hung, splashed over with paint, on the canvas, or all suspended from the bottom of the frame.

Many of these articles are shown in three forms: as a real object, later reproduced pictorially on the canvas, and finally with its name written on the canvas. Thus he obtains what he ironically calls three-dimensional representation of the object. In his picture *Colorful Hammering*, the hammer, suspended like a pendulum from the frame, hangs freely before the canvas on which is painted an ascending multitude of shadows of hands gripping hammers, with short lines of poured paint which confer on the picture a violence and dynamism that contrast with the serenity of the hanging object.

In Dine's pictures the object is not incorporated plastically, as is the case with the cubist collages of Schwitters and also in the works of Rauschenberg and Johns: it appears as an accompaniment, or better, a visitor before whose importance the picture yields. Nevertheless, in his later pictures, there is a closer approach to unity with the surface, and even a substantial incorporation of the objects is established, but never as plastic integrators, always as dominant presences.

In all of Dine's pictures, the canvas tends to create a sense of imaginary space, which has become a characteristic. In some of the pictures, this space acquires a density and mobility marked by brushstrokes of heavy impasto, large and violent, but rhythmically regulated. The quality of violent aggressiveness in his work, the vitality and sharp humor that emanate from it, place Dine at the opposite extreme of the complacent pictures of a Lichtenstein, a Wesselman, or even a Warhol.

Allan D'Arcangelo was born in Buffalo, New York, in 1930. He lives in New York City. His specialty is schematic perspectives of roads that

disappear in the distance, sometimes with large traffic signs in the foreground, the whole constructed with the sharpness of hard-edge, a tendency he found easier to assimilate than that of pop, in spite of his definite reference to reality. He is an instructor of arts in the New York City school system.

Robert Indiana (Robert Clark) was born in New Castle, Indiana, in 1928. He lives part of the time in New York and part of the time in Los Angeles. He has specialized in the painting of emblems in a precise and severe manner, which places him – as in the case of D'Arcangelo – in a zone between pop and optical painting.

In addition to these artists, who constitute the New York group, we should mention John Wesley, born in Los Angeles in 1928, who lives in New York, and who began painting themes with emblems, and the creators of sculpture-objects such as Oldenburg, H. C. Westermann Jr., and George Segal, although their rightful place is in a book about sculpture.

In California there is another important group of pop artists. Wayne Theibaud was born in Mesa, Arizona, in 1920, and at present lives in Sacramento, California. He is Associate Professor of Art at the University of California at Davis. He attained fame through his pictures of pastries, sandwiches, and slot machines, painted, not in the impersonal style of Lichtenstein and others like him, but with a truly pictorial impasto that is very personal and even includes the use of billboard colors.

Edward Ruscha, born in Omaha, Nebraska, in 1937, and now living in Los Angeles, constructs his pictures with mottoes painted with precision over a large, free space, obtaining an intense action in the field of uniform color, which puts him among the op artists.

Mel Ramos was born in Sacramento, California, in 1935, where he now lives. He specializes in

ANDY WARHOL. *Flowers.* 1965.
Ileana Sonnabend Gallery.

exhibitionistic female figures, imitating the cheaper tabloids, painted with shrill colors in violently bad taste.

Also working in Los Angeles is Edward Kienholz (born in Spokane, Washington, in 1927), whom it would be more accurate to place with the sculptors. Kienholz, irritated by the idiocies that he sees in daily life, the absurdities of people, produces a controversial work of a violently aggressive black humor, and has become one of the most important figures in the new American art, offering something truly authentic and charged with feeling, something really revolutionary.

Happenings

The idea of total unity between art and life and the consideration that art is an ephemeral spectacle suggested to Allen Kaprow (born in Atlantic City, New Jersey, in 1927), a professor of art

Jaмes Rosenquist. *Dishes.* 1964. Collection C. B. Wright.

history and plastic artist of the vanguard, the possibility of creating a spectacle that would unite the visual qualities of a plastic work with the intensity of action in an actual, lived event and that would later evaporate, leaving the same fleeting impact that life itself does. He hit upon the idea of a new kind of semitheatrical spectacle that would call to mind some of the dada manifestations, and frequently collaborated with Lucas Samaras (another experimental artist).

In 1959 Kaprow gave the first spectacle based on those principles, in the Reuben Gallery, with the title of « 18 Happenings in 6 Parts. » This was the first happening, and from the title came the name. Later a number of plastic artists put on a series of similar episodes, and Kaprow himself reduced his artistic activity to the staging of two types of spectacles: « environments » and « happenings. »

The art critic William Seitz, commenting on the

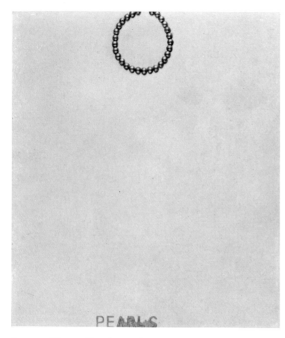

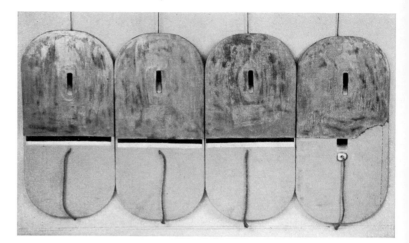

James Dine. *Four designs for a fountain in honor of the painter Balla.* 1961.
Collection Martha Jackson Gallery.

James Dine. *Pearls*, 1961.
The Solomon R. Guggenheim Museum.

first happening, considered that it had its origin in the collage. Kirby, who has written the first book on happenings,* considers them to be « a new form of theatre in the same sense that the collage was a new form of visual art. » In being considered theatre, a predominantly visual form is evident, and in this lies its tie with the plastic arts, a tie very similar to that which, for example, the noisy machines of Tinguely have. Its inclusion in the exhibition of kinetic art, organized with the title of « Bewogen-Beweging » in the Stedelijk Museum in Amsterdam, was justified. In spite of being a predominantly visual form, in which objects and people participate, it is not pure pantomime; it is accompanied by certain verbal forms consisting of monologues and dialogues, as well as by sounds and noises, and in some cases smells. The monologues consist of stacks of words and phrases picked up by chance,

* MICHAEL KIRBY, *Happenings* (E. P. Dutton & Co., New York, 1965).

ALLAN D'ARCANGELO. *Untitled 81.* 1964.
Ileana Sonnabend Gallery.

Tom Wesselmann. *Can N. 74.* 1965. Sidney Janis Gallery.

and the dialogues consist of abstract conversations. The sounds may be musical pieces (generally jazz or modern music), and the noises may be laughs, grunts, murmurs, and so forth.

The spectacles are staged indoors (most of them in the Reuben Gallery in New York) or in the open air. A very close relationship was established with the public, who were in a certain sense « submerged » in the spectacle: at any rate, there was always a very limited public, somewhere between forty and fifty people, and never more than one hundred.

The « environment » is « a work of art that surrounds and encloses the spectator on all sides. » It may or may not be associated with a « happening » (this can also be held on a stage) and undeniably establishes a new, close relation between the spectacle and the public. The space presents objects, lights, prepared walls, and at times the spectators themselves collaborate by writing inscriptions on them.

Kirby gives a definition of a « happening » that for its completeness deserves to be fully quoted: « a purposefully composed form of theatre in

ROBERT INDIANA. *USA 666.* 1964. Stable Gallery.

JOHN WESLEY. *Polly.* 1963. Robert Elkon Gallery.

which diverse alogical elements, including non-matrixed performing, are organized in a compartmented structure. »

The action is generally brief (no more than ten minutes). It does not depend on dialogue or human conflicts; the actors are limited to participating only and the objects outweigh the people in importance, and it lacks an informative structure that characterizes theatre (and even pantomime), in that it does not develop according to a logical sequence; and sometimes the scenes are produced in simultaneous compartments. There are scenes in which one or more actors appear, and at times they find themselves close to one another, though no communication exists between them; but there are also scenes in which only sounds and objects exist.

The happening, although based on the spontaneity of the situations, is not improvisation in the man-

ner of the *teatro a soggetto*; the artist who puts on the event prepares the script, in which he indicates the scenery and formulates the plan for the action, but the details of the execution are left to the actor. This freedom of execution may be what gave rise to the belief that the spectacle was an improvisation.

The best-known happenings of Kaprow bore the following titles: *18 Happenings in 6 Parts, Coca-Cola Shirley Cannonball?, A Spring Happening,* and *The Courtyard.* Happenings of equal intensity have been staged by Robert Whitman (author of constructions in cellophane), Claes Oldenburg, Red Grooms (who formely did film shorts), and Jim Dine (who has now abandoned happenings).

Among the happenings staged by Oldenburg are *Injun, World's Fair II, Gaiety,* and *Autoboyds.* What interests this artist in happenings is objects in movement, and people are included in this category of objects.

To get a clear idea of what is meant by a « happening,» it is worth while relating what takes place in the *Smiling Workman* of Jim Dine: Dine appears as painter before a white rectangular surface on which he begins to paint, taking the paint from three buckets beside him. All this is done with exaggerated, extravagant movements, splashing the paint on all sides. With great excitement he writes on the surface he has been painting, «I like what I'm doing.» After that he takes the bucket of red paint and in full view of the public pours it over himself (supposedly the paint consists of tomato juice), and finally leaps right through the extent of white paper on which he has been painting.

The hermetic, exclusive, and antibourgeois sense of the happenings throws light on the alleged conformism of the pop artists (a thesis upheld by the critic Solomon).

Taken as a whole, there is at the base of the pop movement an essential skepticism. They are young artists who realize the failure of all ideological positions that were held out in the past, and who now refuse to take a stand. Furthermore, whether conscious of it or not, they live in a world threatened by destruction. The idea of the ephemerality of everything (the extreme expression of which is the happening) appears to obsess them. Therefore they want to grasp life, and conduct their search for it in the surrounding reality; they show what the world offers them, a trivial reality that is wholly artificial, and they demonstrate their acceptance of it. It is evident that we are not dealing with an essentially optimistic art, in spite of affirmations to this effect.

This art, indeed, constitutes a denunciation of all values of the past and all cultural grounds, and a point of departure from scratch; advanced and proclaimed by various modern movements from futurism and dada, today it actually becomes reality through the systematic work by some exponents of pop.

THIEBAUD. *Oil.* 1964. Collection Allen Stone.

Pop art in England

It is curious that the name «pop» comes from England. As has been mentioned, it was proposed by Alloway, during a meeting of the Independent Group of the Institute of Contemporary Art (ICA) of London, to designate a state of mind that was inclined to consider favorably the images and appetites of the mass media. Present at the meeting were the painter Richard Hamilton and the sculptor Eduardo Paolozzi.

Richard Hamilton was born in London in 1922 and studied at the Royal Academy Schools and later at the Slade School in London. He designs and plans displays. Hamilton has exhibited engravings since 1950 and paintings since 1955; in

1960 he received the painting prize of the William and Noma Copley Foundation. He is an enthusiastic admirer of Duchamp, of whom he published a typographic version of the famous *Green Box* in book form in 1960.

Hamilton can be considered the innovator of pop in England contemporaneously with the first productions of Rauschenberg and Johns. In fact, in 1956, in the « This Is Tomorrow » exhibition held at the Whitechapel Art Gallery in London (in which architects, painters, and sculptors of all tendencies collaborated), Hamilton showed a collage composed exclusively of images from the mass media, including an enlargement of one of the famous English candies called « Pop » with the title *just what is it that makes today's homes so different, so appealing?*

Hamilton works very slowly, in the manner of his admired Duchamp, producing many projects and versions of one thing until he finally completes a picture, and even then very often in more than one version. Thus the picture acquires a notable balance, a purified precision, and a formal perfection that completely separates it from the mechanized art of the orthodox American pop artists, and from the expressionistic violence of the neodada artists. His work is just cold display; it coincides with that of the pop artists in objectivity and complete detachment, as well as in the use of mass images, but Hamilton, instead of accentuating the triviality of these images, detrivializes them, dignifying them in a certain way. For this reason he has become the only truly optimistic pop artist, a man who really does believe in life and in the future. Perhaps some of the hardness and quality of his work comes from being a designer and from his collaboration with neo-concrete artists like Pasmore (they collaborated in a show called « An Exhibit at the ICA » in London in 1957). Nevertheless, he is an admirer of American pop and in particular of Lichtenstein. Hamilton, who considers it legitimate to produce a piece of art by enlarging a section

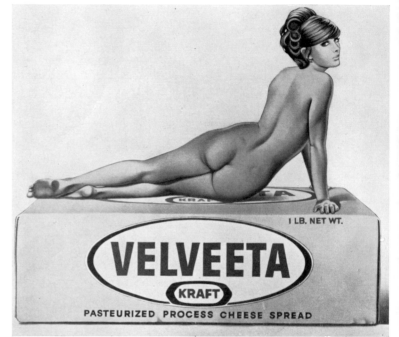

Mel Ramos. *Miss Velveeta.* 1965. Bianchini Gallery.

of another piece of art which in turn was produced by enlarging a section of a comic strip, enlarged a teardrop from one of Lichtenstein's famous pictures, the *Hopeless.*

Peter Blake is the most famous and productive of the English pop artists. Born in 1932 in Dartford, he studied at the Royal College of Art from 1953 to 1956, a time when many of the new English painters were studying there. Blake uses the mass image but with a refinement and plastic sense very much tied to the tradition of great painting. He is a revolutionary who has assimilated tradition. His collages, especially those that show the dreams of the ordinary person, appear to have been torn from some dreaming bachelor's wall in a rooming house, with its collection of pinups that represent the standard beauties of magazine covers. But all this shoddy

Allen Kaprow. *Words* (*environment*). 1962.
Smolin Gallery.

«"*Words*" *consists of two rooms within a room; one larger, brightly lit with colored, blinking bulbs, the other, smaller, dark blue, illuminated by a single weak bulb. In the first room the walls are covered with words chosen by myself and friends from a variety of sources, such as novels, comics, and newspapers, and collectively printed by hand on strips of paper and continuous cloth rollers. Sense or nonsense may be made by reading these in any*

direction. The visitor is then free to alter the arrangements by stapling over the initial composition new word-strips provided for this purpose, and also by realigning the cloth rollers. Three phonographs offer recorded advertisements, lectures, soliloquies and poems, which can be played singly or together.
In the second room, hanging from strings are many colored chalks the visitor can use to draw, write, or scribble on the blue walls whatever he wishes. Streamers torn from bed sheets dangle throughout. Visitors, helping themselves to a pad and pencil nearby, may clip onto these streamers notes written to one another. On the floor there is a recording of whispers.
Consequently, while the concept of "Words" is mine, the execution is everyone's, and it never remains the same.»

dream material is organized with strict neoplastic rigor, as can be seen in *The Girlie Door*, by means of irreproachable orthogonal divisions which seem to ennoble the poor imagery and make it immediately attractive, full of enchanting suggestions. All of Blake's work exudes a visible humor that is not found in the work of the majority of American pop artists.

Peter Phillips was born in Birmingham in 1939, and studied at the Royal College of Art from 1959 to 1962. He searches for the mass image, but to show it he tries to give to it a plastic organization. Phillips obtains this through actual baroqueism and a certain flair for advertising in his presentation of the elements.

Joe Tilson was born in London in 1928. He studied at St. Martin's School of Art and at the Royal College of Art from 1949 to 1952. Tilson produces frontally visual constructions in wood, executed with the perfectionism of a cabinetmaker, with everyday articles enlarged – large locks or keys, or displays of letters or typographical signs – with a constructive feeling for plastic organization and for the joining of the boards.

John Latham was born in Rhodesia in 1921, studied at the Chelsea School of Art from 1946 to 1951, and now lives in London. He specializes in reliefs made of books with their pages open, folded, torn, and glued, with spots of color smeared over them. Latham's work is a kind of apotheosis of the uselessness of culture, and a deserved fate for so many useless books.

Pop art in Italy and Germany

Michelangelo Pistoletto was born in Biella in 1933. He lives in Turin. His pictures consist of mirrors on which cut-out silhouettes of vague,

PETER BLAKE. *The girlie door.* 1959.

unrecognizable people are fastened. In looking at the picture the spectator sees himself reflected, and finds himself forming part of the observed work. Each spectator has his own distinct

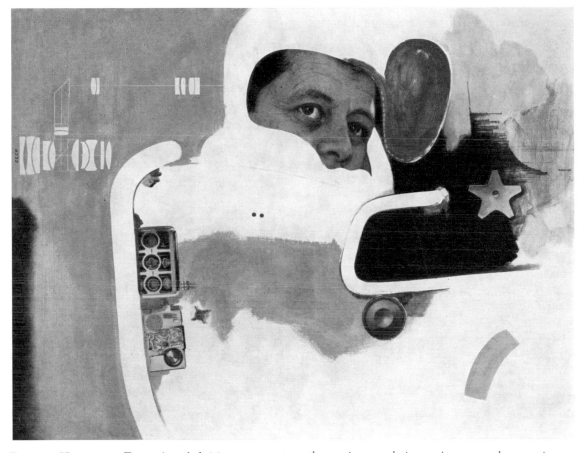

RICHARD HAMILTON. *Towards a definitive statement on the coming trends in men's wear and accesories.* Tate Gallery.

version of the work and in his own way completes the work of the artist.

Tano Festa was born in Rome in 1938, and lives in his native city. He studied at the Art Institute of Rome. In the beginning he worked in enamel on wood, and showed Venetian blinds, hermetically closed, or mirrors in which repeated and semivciled feminine faces appeared; they are like expressions of a distant and cloistered world. Later he produced repeated impressions of statues on canvas.

Mario Schifano was born in Homs, Tripoli, in 1934. He lives in Rome. After showing pictures with letters and numbers in a style recalling Jasper Johns, Schifano turned to a pop figuration in the style of Larry Rivers.

Gerhard Richter was born in Waltersdorf Kreis, Zittau, Germany, in 1932. He paints portraits imitating the quality of exaggerated photographs.

Also in Germany are the pop artists Lueg, Polke, and Herbert Kaufman.

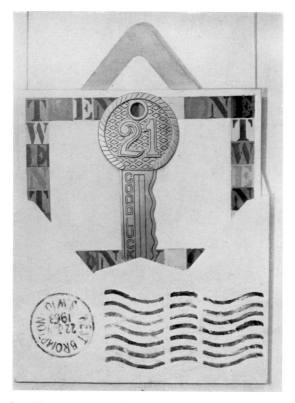

JOE TILSON. *21st.* 1963.

PETER PHILLIPS. *SUPinsetER.* 1963.

New realism

In 1960 Pierre Restany, with the group of Yves Klein, founded a movement with the name « new realism, » in an evident effort to uphold the originality of the art of the School of Paris before the overwhelming advance of the new tendencies from America. This movement would represent a European phenomenon in opposition to the American phenomenon, pop art, with baroque, romantic, and esthetically inspiring characteristics. According to Restany, this realism is new because it represents the pure and simple annexation of the elements of reality such as they actually are, in their raw state, and he says, « The new real-

ism registers the sociological reality without any controversial intention. »

The first manifesto of the new realism was published in Milan on April 16, 1960, and the group was officially organized on October 27th of that year. The first collective showing took place at the Festival of the Avant-Garde in Paris in November-December, 1960, and the second in May, 1961, in the J Gallery, with the title of « At 40° over Dada. »

The initial group was formed by nine artists: Yves Klein, Martial Raysse, Arman, César (César Baldaccini), Tinguely, Spoerri, Hains, Villeglé, and Dufresne. According to Restany, these artists appropriated directly from reality: they showed

MICHELANGELO PISTOLETTO. *Balcony with three men.* 1964. Ileana Sonnabend Gallery.

reality as it really is, reducing to a minimum the individual contribution, excluding all problems or artistic creations. What was here meant was a practical, direct art, that would give us a modern sense of reality. In sum, to use the words of the promoter of the movement: the complete possession of social reality without any transformation.

Such clarity of conception is usually not in accord with the facts, and this is precisely what happened in this case. In the first place, what sense of urban reality can the « zones of immaterial sensibility » transmit to us, which Klein proposed to show in the « Exhibition of Emptiness » held in the Iris Clert Gallery? Neither below nor above the signs indicating the « series No., » « zone No., » (with the respective numbers) was hung anything

at all. It is precisely this existentialist sense of nothingness, this preoccupation with emptiness, which has the interest of Klein and which this exhibition palpably shows; there is no doubt that Klein possesses an evident metaphysical sense that very indirectly has a relation with urban reality.

On the other hand, the purely informative character that the principles pronounced by Restany appear to convey, seems contradictory to what the majority of the artists produce. The impression that most forcefully stands out is that instead of possessing reality they have an aggressive attitude toward it. For example, the « packages » of Christo (one of the latest to come to new realism), rather than revealing reality, conceal it, and to the reply that actually to make a package

Tano Festa. *From Michelangelo.* 1965.
La Tartaruga Gallery.

of a subject means to possess it, one could answer that it was in any event a possession for no one, because the destiny of these packages is not to be opened. The same can be said of the compressed automobiles of César, and the torn posters of Hains or Villeglé in which the artists proffer us a destroyed reality.

It is more reasonable to speak of an art of behavior or of attitude when referring to these artists. For it is precisely in this that the importance of all of them lies: they are men who hierarchize the attitude in the artist, and they are not without reason. Art is, above all, and whatever the work may be, the attitude of a man *vis-à-vis* the world, other men, and, finally, himself. This attitude undoubtedly differs from that of the pop artists, although both take a position of detachment, or apparent abstention. In both there is a rejection of sentiments and individual emotion, and a search for depersonalization. The two show us a subtly distorted image of reality, in which they appear to say: I am not to blame. In both groups of artists the term « creation » could be substituted for that of intention, and this term implies a proposition that is not purely informative, deny it though the artists and the theorists who support them will. But the difference lies in that the new realists penetrate more deeply and go further. It is true that they go to a greater length than the pop artist in discounting esthetic considerations (in any event, some packages of Christo and certain machines by Tinguely are very appealing). And it is also true, furthermore, that the humor – the great unmasker – is more aggressive, purer, and less domesticated.

The new realists penetrate more deeply than the pop artists (I here refer to strict pop, not the neodadaists) because they bring us nearer to a profound sense of nothingness, because they divest the conventional reality of significance. What other sense has the work and the message of

Mario Schifano. *Space.* 1965.

GERHARD RICHTER. *Waiting (group of passengers)*. La Tartaruga Gallery.

Klein in favor of « the immaterial? » What other meaning have Christo's packages and covered showcases, Tinguely's useless machines, the torn posters, the residues of «coagulated» daily life of Spoerri? But what saves all these works from becoming dramatic is the sharp humor that animates them. And these works are not in any manner inexpressive. They express, yes: they express the attitude of a lucid man before worn-out conventions and norms that lack sense.

Yves Klein is the most important exponent of what could be called the « art of the attitude. » His influence in Europe and even in Japan and in North America and South America is recognized. The attitude mixes an anti-art conception derived from dada with certain mystic ideas derived from the Rosicrucians, dressed in a science-fiction language. Klein was born in Nice in 1928, and died of a stroke in Paris in 1962. His life was meteoric and brilliant. He practiced judo and studied Rosicrucianism and from 1948 to 1953 traveled through Europe and the Orient and to Japan, where he won an award as a judo champion. In 1954 he was in Spain as technical director of the Federation of Judo, and there published a folder with reproductions of monochrome works.

He arrived in Paris in 1955, and in 1956 he had his first exhibition of « monochrome propositions » in the Colette Allendy Gallery. One of his monochrome exhibitions, which took place in the Apollinaire Gallery, influenced the Italian painter Piero Manzoni, who thereafter achieved an outstanding place in Italy as an « artist of the attitude. » In the same year Klein had two exhibitions in Paris, one in the Iris Clert Gallery and the other in the Colette Allendy Gallery (where he showed aerostatic sculptures composed of innumerable blue globes that floated in the atmosphere). In 1957 he also exhibited in Germany in the Schmela Gallery of Dusseldorf. This exhibition influenced the painters Mack and Piene who would adopt to a great extent his ideology and found the very active group «O» in the same city. In 1958 Klein held his famous exhibition of emptiness in the Iris Clert Gallery, where more than two thousand persons attended a *vernissage* with bare walls, and where Klein put up for sale (there were several buyers) what he called « zones of immaterial pictorial sensibility, » which were to be paid for with pure gold, because, as he said, « The highest quality of the immaterial should be paid for with the highest quality of the material. » Between 1957 and 1959 he decorated the new opera house of Gelsenkirchen in the Ruhr with two large monochrome panels in blue and two large relief murals of natural sponges colored blue. In 1958, in collaboration with the architect W. Ruhnau, he planned his « aerial architecture »: constructions of air, in the air (roofs sustained by compressed air, beds where the sleepers float sustained by jets of air), accompanied by a plan of climatization of the terraqueous surface that would permit outdoor living in great permanent comfort. The plastic models for this project were shown at the exhibition entitled « Nul » in the Stedelijk Museum in Amsterdam. In 1959, in Belgium, he published a pamphlet that contained his basic theories, with the title *Le Dépassement de la Problématique de l'Art* (Ed. Montbliart, La Louvière). In 1960, together with the French critic Restany, who had turned into a permanent promoter and defender of Klein, he founded the new realism movement, which was the counterpart of American pop in the School of Paris. Also in 1960, in the Galerie Internationale d'Art Contemporaine in Paris, he showed for the first time his *Blue Anthropometrics* (marks of naked bodies on the canvas). In that same year he undertook his *Cosmogonies*, paintings produced with the help of atmospheric phenomena, such as rain, wind, and the rays of the sun (he traveled from Paris to Nice by car, on the roof of which was strapped a canvas covered with fresh blue paint), trying to obtain atmospheric markings as earlier he had produced marks of the human body in his anthropometrics. In 1961 he executed his fire paintings, produced with red and blue pigments applied to asbestos by means of flame from gas jets, and in the same year he showed his fountains of fire and water in Krefeld, the effect obtained by the shock of the flame from jet burners meeting spurts of water. Also in that year he produced his *Planetary Reliefs* (anticipatory topographical reliefs of Mars, Venus, and the earth seen from the moon).

This enumeration of Klein's works serves to give an idea of the extraordinary fantasy and audacious inventiveness of one of the most curious and passionate personalities in the variegated gallery of individuals that modern art offers us. His theoretic reflections form an integral part of the strange conglomerate of facets that constitute the personality of Klein, and it is indispensable that one have an idea of them. In the pamphlet we mentioned, he says: «For me, painting, today,

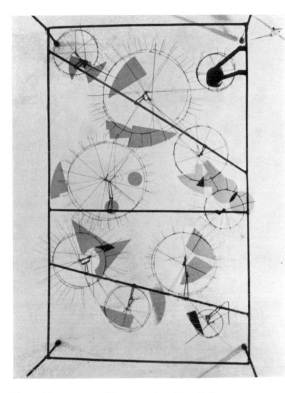

JEAN TINGUELY. *Meta-mechanic relief.* 1954.
Iolas Gallery.

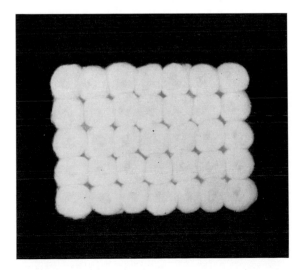

does not depend on the eye; it depends on the only thing within us that isn't ours: life. » For him, art should be reduced to an object of visual meditation, and color is the essential element of effective communication. For these reasons he showed, on his arrival in Paris in 1955, monochrome pictures in various colors, which later were reduced to blue exclusively, as being the color of the sky, and to submerge the spectator in the immensity of total space. Based on his peculiar mystical ideology, he speaks of « the universal impregnation by color. »

His monochrome pictures, in different formats and textures of canvas, show a surface covered with pure industrial pigment that is spread with a roller so that the colorwork becomes completely impersonal. After having exhibited monochromes in various tones of blue, he settled definitely on a special type of ultramarine in which he saw the « representation of the immaterial, the sovereign liberation of the spirit. » This last idea obsessed him; he spoke of the pictorial sensibility of the immaterial, which induced him to mount his exhibition of emptiness. The immaterial, the space, and « the great emptiness » constituted his themes. Later he felt attracted to fire, with its three colors – blue, red, and gold – which for him was the universal synthesis. Beside the blues, he produced monochromes in crimson and with sheets of gold. He then exhibited his « monogolds frémissants » (monochromes with small sheets of gold that trembled), in the exhibition entitled « Antagonismes » held in the Museum of Decorative Arts in Paris in 1960. Later he went on to make his impressions, first of the human body (anthropometrics) and later of the accidental atmospheric impressions (painting with rain).

The first public performance of anthropometrics

PIERO MANZONI. *Clews.*
Galleria Nazionale d'Arte Moderna, Roma.

ARMAN. *Accumulation.* Il Leone Gallery.

took place in Paris in 1960; three naked women, daubed over with blue paint, rubbed themselves against the white canvases, leaving their marks, to the sound of an orchestra of twenty who executed the *Monotonous Symphony* composed by Klein himself. This last addition consisted of a single continuous sound, which according to Klein represented « a kind of audible silence-presence. » Part of this show was recorded in the semidocumentary Italian film *Mondo Cane.*

In the pictures with rain, *Cosmogonie de la pluie,* he spread a canvas on the ground on a rainy day and threw into the air, « at the height of a man, » powdered blue pigment that was then beaten down by the rain and established a curious texture on the exposed surface.

It is necessary to point out that Klein's emphasis on space calls to mind (although it is carried to extreme limits) the ideas on spatialism propounded by Fontana since 1946; this is an antecedent that should not be underrated.

In spite of a certain mystical ingenuity in his theoretical postulates, it must be recognized that Klein had the audacity to venture into the theme of nothingness. He knew how to confront nothingness and model it and convert it into a work of art. In that lies the extraordinary magnetism of his personality and his influence on the European

ARMAN. *97/150.*

vanguard. There also lies the importance of his anti-art attitude, much more profound, more transcendental than the American pop artists. He knew how to break with all conventional structures. He said that he felt particularly enthusiastic about bad taste, adding: « I have the innermost conviction that in the very essence of bad taste exists a force capable of creating things that are situated far beyond what is traditionally called a " work of art ". » He confessed: « I want to play with human sentimentality, with its "morbidity," in a manner that is cold and ferocious. » With this ferocity he attempted to approach the impossible, materialize emptiness, and it is this anxious ferocity that places him close to two great « ferocious ones » of France: Antonin Artaud and Dubuffet.

The influence of Klein was felt first by his friends from Nice, Martial Raysse and Arman, with whom he formed what has come to be called the « Nice group, » and then by some of the members of the new realists group that was promoted by the critic Restany, particularly Tinguely and Hains. We have already mentioned his influence on Piero Manzoni in Italy and on the « O » group in Germany; the « Nul » group in the Netherlands also was stimulated by Klein's work.

Piero Manzoni, who can be considered Klein's most faithful pupil, accentuated the aggressive and anti-art tendency of his predecessor. His life was even shorter than Klein's and like him, he also had a magnetic personality that elicited deep sympathy and attachment in the circle in which he moved. He was born in Milan in 1933, and died in 1963. At the outset of his artistic career there was a short period during which he tended toward informal automatism. Following Klein's exhibition he discovered achromatics in 1957 and produced his white pictures, at times using the virgin white canvas; at other times he reduced the pictorial element to a uniform application of white pigment with a slight raise in the surface material. At that period he also showed phosphorescent pictures. In 1959 he completely eliminated any pictorial element from his work, beginning the famous series of his « lines, » which simply consisted of the tracing of a continuous line over large strips of paper of variable dimensions but which never went below several feet. These strips were then rolled up and fitted into colored and sealed cardboard tubes on which the length was marked, more with the idea of giving it a title than to establish the size. Soon, with a tension and audacity paralleling Klein's, he launched successive inventions. In 1959 he constructed his first pulsative pneumatic sculptures; later he had the idea of absolute bodies, sculptures really in space, that is, without sockles, consisting of plastic forms buoyed up in space by streams of compressed air. In an exhibition in 1960 he showed 150 eggs marked with his fingerprint, which were eaten by the public, by which the work of art was considered « incorporated » directly into the spectator. Then he planned an exhibition of living creatures that would acquire the status of works of art by being signed by him. Evidently this demonstration had its roots in Duchamp's ready-mades, which expressed the idea that mere selection by the artist was enough for any kind of object to become a work of art. Manzoni's most aggressive anti-artistic attitude was contained in his famous series «*Merde* of the Artist,» which consisted of fecal matter hermetically packed and labeled with the weight on the package. This series only carried to its extreme limits the artist's tubes with « lines. » Manzoni thus reflects the extreme stand in the negation of all utility of art and in accentuating his essen-

Daniel Spoerri. *Trick-picture.* Bischofberger Gallery.

tial and deepest «invisibility.» Together with Castellani, Manzoni published the review *Azimut*, through which he propounded his ideas, and in 1962 he organized the « Nul » exhibition, with Klein, the Dutchman Peeters, Uecker, Mack, and Piene, in the Stedelijk Museum in Amsterdam. In speaking of the monochromes of Klein and the achromatics of Manzoni, it is necessary to bear in mind that there exists, beside the white on white by Malevitch, an important antecedent in the work of the Polish painter Wladislaw Strzeminski (mentioned in connection with kinetic painting) who presented his totally monochrome « unist compositions » at the exhibition of the « Abstraction-Création » association in 1932.

Jean Tinguely

Although most of Tinguely's work goes beyond the scope of a book dedicated to painting, and

CHRISTO. *Packed Life magazine.* 1962.
La Salita Gallery.

MARTIAL RAYSSE. *Picture in the French style.* 1965.
Iolas Gallery.

belongs in the domain of sculpture, one part of it, the mobile reliefs, belongs to the pictorial section. In any event, his work is one of the most significant developments at the present moment, not only in its construction but also in its attitude, and there is no doubt that he deserves an outstanding place among those whom we have called « attitude artists. »

Jean Tinguely was born in Freiburg, Switzerland, in 1925; at the age of two he was taken to Basel, and between the years 1941 and 1945 he attended, very irregularly, the School of Fine Arts in that city. In 1952 he arrived in Paris, where he has since lived almost permanently.

From the very beginning Tinguely was obsessed with the idea of movement, as he affirms in a phrase that has made him famous: « The only

TETSUMI KUDO. *Confluent reaction in plane circulation substance.* 1960.

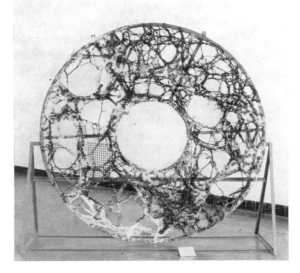

Mimmo Rotella. *Décollage.* La Salita Gallery.

stable thing is movement. » In 1954 he exhibited in the Arnaud Gallery in Paris actual mobile pictures which he called « metamechanic reliefs. » In 1955, in an exhibition at the Denise René Gallery, he showed his « sonorous metarobots » and machines for painting. The following year, at Denise René's, he exhibited new transformable pictures that consisted of large panels, either white or black, on which cut-out reliefs of simple geometric forms moved by means of a hidden motor. It is to the point to mention those works of his that contain a gesture, an attitude, or the idea of a great visual spectacle. In 1955 he had introduced a machine for painting at the Denise René Gallery, but in 1959, in the Iris Clert Gallery, he introduced his « metamatics, » machines for painting that, like slot machines, were set in motion with the insertion of a coin, and produced gesture paintings. In the Biennale of Paris in that year he exhibited his scandalous painting machine « metamatic-self-moving-olorous-and-sonorous, » which produced forty thousand gesture paintings, multicolored and free of charge. In 1960, in the Museum of Modern Art, New York, he exhibited his *Homage to New York,* an auto-destructive happening-machine that, after it starts functioning, destroys itself within twenty minutes. In 1961, in Figueras, Catalonia, together with Niki de Saint-Phalle, he constructed a bull of fire in the arena. The same year in the Louisiana Museum in Copenhagen he introduced a *Study for the End of the World,* in the shape of a « monster-sculpture-autodestructive-dynamic-and-aggressive, » as Tinguely himself classifies it. In September, 1962, in the Stedelijk Museum, Amsterdam, he organized a « dynamic labyrinth » with the title *Dylaby,* in the construction of which Martial Raysse, Per Olof Ultvedt, Rauschenberg, Niki de Saint-Phalle, and Spoerri participated.

Most of these spectacles are mixed with an exhi-

Raymond Hains. *Lacerated Biennale.* 1964. La Salita Gallery.

bitionistic drive, a love of play, but it cannot be denied that a profoundly basic sentiment impels the attitude artists: an essential skepticism, a weariness with the plethora of false values that are imposed on man and that have demonstrated their total valuelessness. To this is added an ever stronger sensation of the insubstantiality of everything and a desire to live with the utmost intensity. « Life is a game, » Tinguely says, « life is movement, life is perpetual change. From the moment in which life become fixed it stops being real; it then is dead and of no interest. » And he adds, « Everything changes, everything is modified without cessation; all attempts to catch life in its flight and to want to imprison it in a work of art, sculpture or painting, appear to me a travesty on the intensity of life. »

A great sense of humor appears dominant in Tinguely, which has earned him the sympathy of one of the champions of artistic humor, Marcel Duchamp. His machines are a sample of this humor; they are put together from all kinds of useless odds and ends: from old twisted wheels, bicycle parts, hoops of old barrels, toothless saws, old steering wheels, pulleys, crowbars, and even feathers and pieces of old fur coats. But in this there is not only humor, but also a certain tender predilection for all these useless discarded things that have lived with man, shared his dreams, and now are destined to disappear. Like Dubuffet, Tinguely appears to want to restore dignity to all this world of discards, and in some way confront man with them almost as an accusation. In any event, in his latest apparatuses Tinguely (perhaps inspired by his success) constructed machines that were truly esthetic, with new materials. A proof of his success lies in the fact that the Museum of Fine Arts in Houston, Texas, directed by the critic J. J. Sweeney, acquired early in 1965 the entire collection of a Tinguely exhibition held at the Alexander Iolas Gallery.

But there is a fundamental aspect in Tinguely's work, and he reveals it in the following concluding words: « The machine allows me, above anything, to reach poetry. »

Arman, pseudonym for Augustin Fernández, was born in Nice in 1928. A friend of Yves Klein, he shared the same leanings and ideology. In the Iris Clert Gallery he held an « Exhibition of Fullness » as a counterpart of the one of emptiness of Klein's: the gallery appeared completely blocked up by accumulated objects. From his early admiration for surrealism and Duchamp, Arman got the taste for the adventure of the object; Schwitters suggested to Arman the use of castoffs. He began showing abstract pictures in 1957, and at the same time imprinting on the canvases, with ink, marks of seals. These imprints were organized in free constructions or else filled the whole canvas according to the all-over technique; he called them his « Series of Seals. » Under the title *Allures* he showed vague impressions on the canvas of the most diverse objects – chains, bolts, wheels, and so forth; and later he included the articles themselves, but broken, destroyed. Thus in 1961 he presented a series of musical instruments, or dinner sets, broken and cracked, under the title *Colère*. After this he turned to accumulating objects that were similar, on the premise that « a thousand watch springs is more watch than a spring from one watch. » Thus he proceeded to gather together series of articles of the same kind, eyeglasses, bedside lamps, fans, cigarette cases, and so forth, behind glass in a kind of windowbox. Arman explores the domain of the castoff, pieces of useless merchandise. According to Arman, he differs from Schwitters in that Schwitters seeks these combinations for an esthetic purpose, while instead (still in Arman's words) the rejects have an expressive value in themselves, an immediate expressive value. In accumulating them, a surface is sensitized through their multiple presence. The obsessive and declamatory quality of multiplicity gains all the strength of reality. When asked the meaning of his work, Arman answers, lucidly (using terminology very much like René Guénon's), « It is an expression of quantity, the sign of our times. » In 1966, Arman was awarded the Marzotto prize.

Daniel Spoerri, of Swiss parentage, was born in Galati, Rumania, in 1930. A professional dancer, he lives in Paris.

Spoerri's are trick pictures, and consist, for example, of a board with left-over breakfast dishes – cups, small plates, glasses, an ashtray with its cigarette butt – glued to the board in the positions they occupied after the meal; this product of chance is then hung on a wall. The key to Spoerri's work lies in the word « chance » (he has written a book entitled *Anecdotal Topography of Chance*, and he, like the surrealists, feels the magic that chance contains and the power of revelation that one discovers upon fixing it fast. This whole view of daily objects and their magic qualities without doubt derives from Duchamp, a fact Spoerri himself recognized, when in an exhibition of his objects decorating a room in the Hotel Chelsea in New York there was a sign that said « I accuse Marcel Duchamp. »

Christo Javachef, known as Christo, was born in Gabrovo, Bulgaria, in 1935. From 1953 to 1957 he attended the academies of art in Sofia and in Vienna. Since 1958 he has lived in Paris. He was a member, with Bertholo, Lourdes Castro, and Voss, of the KWY group, who published the review of the same name. After various group exhibitions, he held a one-man show in 1962 at the J Gallery in Paris, a show that was accompanied by a blocking of the whole narrow Rue Visconti with oil drums.

Although his packages, as objects, generally go beyond the frontal idea of a picture, they should be studied in conjunction with the work of the new realists: these objects consist of packages made with cloth, paper, or semitransparent plastic sheets, in which the wraps are the most

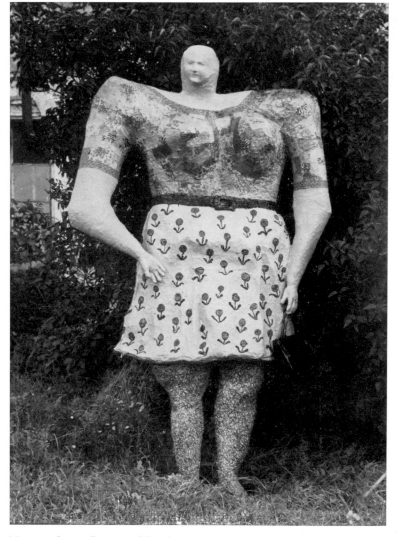

NIKI DE SAINT PHALLE. *Wanda.* 1965. Iolas Gallery.

varied things (running from the smallest packages, which look like little packaged spools, to automobile covers, perambulators, wheelbarrows, and so forth). The packages are arbitrarily tied with cord or clothesline, with numerous turns and knots. The shape of the package frequently suggests its contents.

After the packages, Christo introduced a series of store fronts with the display windows covered by a curtain. This represents the symbol of the hidden world, of which we have only inklings: we know that the article wrapped up or hidden behind a curtain is there, but we can't reach it. Within what is designated as attitude art, Christo reveals an attitude that is more severe and deeper; it no longer is a gesture of approach to social reality, but one of separation.

Martial Raysse was born in Golfe-Juan, France, in 1936. He lives in Nice, and makes frequent trips to New York and Los Angeles. He began to interest himself in merchandise made of plastic material, toilet and kitchen articles of the quality found in the five-and-ten-cent store, and with them he set up showcases of great charm. At that time he could be considered the only artist of new realism who actually resorted to reality. But later he evolved in a direction more in consonance with American pop, and this fact is perhaps significant in that his name was excluded from the last listing of new realism. In his latest works he uses photographs enlarged to life size of bathers or women's faces as they appear in advertising, and also enlargements of reproductions of female subjects from famous paintings (a *Susannah* by Tintoretto, for example, or figures by Matisse), and he covers these images with flat, toneless colors, imitating posters. Sometimes he uses cutouts of figures (as in the case of the bathers) and puts them before a screen that serves as background and frame. In the United States, where he exhibits frequently, he showed a hand in neon light holding a sort of luminous ray, a work he entitled *America.*

Tetsumi Kudo, one of the latest converts to new realism, was born in Osaka, Japan, in 1935. He has lived in Paris since 1962. Kudo has an absolute passion for the object. On arriving in Paris he turned his whole hotel room into a fantastic object, covering the walls and suspending a curious collection of phallic shapes covered by braided cord from the ceiling. From the cylinders used for compressed air, he obtained strange objects covered with braided hair (his wife's) and twine, which spread over the room. It conveyed the sensation of being inside a living being. Since then Kudo has become known for his box-objects in the style of a kind of aggressive and sarcastic Jack-in-the-box. The group under the name of *Your Portrait* has a markedly provocative function, with its enlarged anatomical sections and a selection of objects that go to make up the portrait of man today. An extraordinary imagination united to a sense of his responsibility in the world (which lends its tone to his aggressiveness) impels Kudo to construct his strange objects.

The art of décollage

This form is evidently rooted in new realism. It is the reverse of the art of collage, but more natural, as it does no more than carry out the spontaneous impulse many have on seeing a poster, namely, to tear it off. This attitude – we call it natural and spontaneous – has been translated by some artists into an art of behavior. Advertising is the obsessive monster of our days, and the poster one of its most efficient weapons. To show it dead, its hypnotic power destroyed, after it has been torn, is without doubt a gesture. And furthermore, the torn poster acquires an effective quality, a certain attractive humility the new poster in its imposing arrogance lacks.

The initiator of the genre appears to have been the Italian artist Rotella, who has practiced it in Rome since 1954. In Paris three members of new realism work in this medium: Raymond Hains, Jacques de la Villeglé, and François Dufresne (Dufresne is also a member of the letrist movement). Hains and Villeglé hold that they have used décollage since 1949, but the first exhibition of this art was held in 1957 in the Colette Allendy Gallery. Hains is a photographer who in 1948 became interested in photographing letters and posters.

The manner of procedure varies. Hains usually selects the posters already torn by the public, and sometimes he exhibits the walls or fences with their torn posters. At other times he disfigures the posters with a penknife. Dufresne habitually exhibits the lower part, the one sticking to the wall, as Rotella also does. At other times the décollage is worked, and to achieve the desired result a collage is often made of the décollage; that is, the torn pieces are remounted. The German Wolf Vostel, of Cologne, who also uses torn posters, incorporates them in his abstract pictures.

Rotella explains the function of décollage in this way: « To tear posters from the walls is the only compensation, the only way of protesting against a society that has lost the taste for transformation, for the mythical metamorphosis. »

Mimmo Rotella was born in 1918 in Catanzaro, Italy. He began by producing a type of postcubist abstraction. Rotella's décollages usually assume the character of a thematic series, such as the one he devoted to movie posters; he uses a superimposition of various posters and tears them off piece by piece until he has reached the satisfactory image.

The work of the American artist Niki de Saint-Phalle is related to new realism, particularly her pictures made with a carbine. They consist of reliefs made by an assemblage of scrap iron and various objects, among which she mixes small plastic tubes containing paint. All this is covered over with plaster. The picture is completed by firing the carbine and breaking the tubes of paint, which then floats out over the surface. The shooting is done in public, at the *vernissage*.

Finally, another aspect of the art of attitude should be mentioned, that by the well-known letrists Isidore Isou and Maurice Lemaître. They have exhibited white mice in a cage hanging before a picture with the title *Mobiles of Perpetual Movement*.

Chapter seven

The synthesis of neodadaism and strict visuality

« Group O »

« Group O » of Dusseldorf constitutes one of the most powerful and active associations in Europe. The O does not stand for zero or nothing; instead it has a connotation of optimism. It arose as the title for a publication by the group, and was inspired by the countdown of space rockets, « 6 ... 5 ... 4 ... 3 ... 2 ... 1 ... » The O in that sense represents the decisive moment, the takeoff. For the group, O means « the space not yet explored, a domain as yet not occupied by guesses, theories, and frustrated undertakings, a domain in which everything is possible and within which one can begin without suppositions, without the legacy of the burdens and chains of the past. » And finally: « A zone of silence and of pure possibilities for a fresh start. »

As one can see, the meaning of O does not constitute a negative value but a truly positive one. Like the Restany new-realism group, like American pop, and like the various optical tendencies covered by the name « op art, » it signifies a reaction against unchained instinctivity and the subjectivism of informal art. But in the case of « Group O » the reaction is especially directed against the spirit of these other tendencies, which they consider to be plagued by pessimism, offering a « psychogram of the *Homo miserabilis* » and appearing as a consequence of the anguish of the human condition threatened by war and destruction. They consider themselves as spectators of a time that looks toward the future, who dream of astronomical and cosmonautical adventures, in which man is in a condition to abandon earth and overcome the law of gravity. « We are interested in light; we are interested in the elements, fire, wind, the illimitable possibilities to plan a better and a clearer world. » These premises separate them from the French new realism, for which reason they call their new doctrine « new idealism. »

Through the review of « O » group, which Mack and Piene began to publish in 1958 and of which three numbers appeared (1 and 2 in 1958, 3 in 1961), and through numerous exhibitions organized under their name and which attracted artists from different countries, they established contact with various branches of the European vanguard. We have spoken of the strong impression left on them by Klein following his exhibition at the Schmela Gallery in Dusseldorf; to that must be added the no less important impression left by Fontana. They had a brief contact with Max Bill, which was terminated by both parties, the young men of group « O » reproaching the Swiss master for his rigid rationalism, and he being disgusted with what he considered « inconsequence » in their thought. But the attempt at this contact reveals the two currents that form the spirit with which the members of the « O » group work: a formalist current that tends toward purification and clarity in the medium, and an intuitive and vitalistic current that resorts to the imagination and exploits fantasy. As Piene says, « Painting follows the path of the spirit across the senses. » Mack, Piene, and Uecker form the fixed nucleus of the « O » group. The first two began in 1957 to form a group; Uecker joined around 1962. The three artists strive for light and movement, and this they have in common with most of the kinetic artists of the world. The movement is either implied, and the impression is realized by serial elements, or it is real, controlled by electrical apparatuses. As for the light, either it is obtained by reflection from a source of light or by direct projection of plain or colored light from an apparatus.

Of the three artists, the most orthodox in this quest is Mack. To him we are indebted for the following statements: « The beautiful is in movement and demonstrates the quietude of the disquietude as form. ... The immobile and the infinite tire the eyes and end by negating themselves... All the sense impressions generate only

HEINZ MACK. *Light relief.* 1964.
Alfred Schmela Gallery.

Heinz Mack was born in Lollar, Hesse, Germany, in 1931. He completed academic studies in painting, and finished philosophy courses at the University of Cologne. From 1956 to 1959 he worked in reliefs of polished metal cubes that produced effects of luminous reflections. He rejected color in painting in 1958, and since then has used black and white in works he calls « dynamic structures. » They are periodic, regular structures, but not similar, resembling seismographic tracings, without composition but with a very subtle variability, which in their serial rhythm create a sensation of seeing something alive.

This serial type of construction is the basis of all of Mack's work, whether for reliefs or for constructions in space. Outside of paint he uses a large variety of materials, especially aluminum, for the luminescent quality it gives the surface, but he also uses mirrors, plexiglas, glass, wood, and so on.

The concern with light is fundamental in Mack, and movement is for him movement-light. His reliefs in metal, with their radiant surfaces, manage to incorporate the vibration of light. Mack is also the author of an ambitious project: a relief in the Sahara measuring about 1600 square feet in reinforced concrete.

one sensation: movement. » And he concludes with the following impassioned phrase: « Everything is in movement, my blood, my thoughts, my desires, and everything my eye sees. » Piene wants to offer, « instead of the narrowing of the field of vision, expansion toward all parts, the view of something that gives itself, flows, and pulsates. » In this aspiration to movement and light they recognize their debt to Moholy-Nagy's ideas (*Motion in Vision*). As in all trends that follow the general direction of the new-tendency movement, the element of impersonality causes emotionalism to disappear or else reduces it to a minimum.

Otto Piene was born in Laasphe, in the former Prussian province of Westphalia, in 1928, and studied painting in Munich at the Hochschule der Bildenden Kunst and philosophy at the University of Cologne. It may be said that as light is the central element with Mack, fire is so in Piene's pictures, but a controlled fire, a diminished energy. And if in Mack it is the surfaces that tend toward continuation, to the illimitable, in Piene it is the centers of energetic expansion that dominate. He does use color, but in a very limited form, and absolutely pure. Usually it is red, the color of fire, or black, the color of smoke. At times he uses yellow; and in his im-

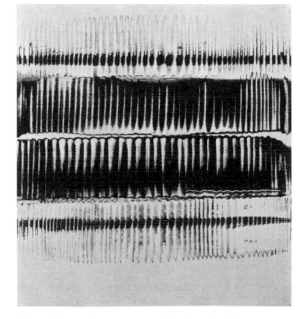

HEINZ MACK. *Structures in black and white.* 1961. Alfred Schmela Gallery.

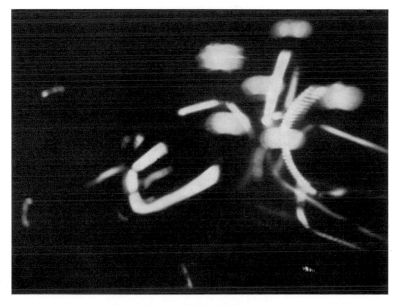

OTTO PIENE. *Light ballet.* 1965. Alfred Schmela Gallery.

ages with eyes – a frequent theme in his later pictures – he uses green, always saturated, clean in its highest quality of brilliance. He paints, as did Klein, by exposing the pigment to fire, but in a more controlled form (in accord with the synthesis of concretism and fantasy that characterizes the group), or else by applying oil paint onto drawings created with smoke, obtaining in that way circles that appear to be on the point of exploding with a curious sense of expansion. Piene does not only produce pictures. He turns out reliefs, sculptures, and especially spheres, whose surface is usually dented, intensely brilliant in their ability to reflect light. Furthermore, he has created a series of luminous spectacles (archaic luminous ballet, classical luminous ballet, mechanical luminous ballet, automatic luminous ballet) based on apparatuses that produce programed luminous projections.

Günther Uecker, born in Wendorf, Mecklenburg, in 1930, studied at the Berlin-Weissensee Academy and in the academy at Dusseldorf. In 1958 he began his works with nails on disks and boards. As the central theme in Mack is light, and in Piene the energy of fire, in Uecker it is the movement that invades his structures in an undulating impulse, until it acquires the mobility of a wave. The nail becomes at once the only sign, the element of construction, and the modifier of the surface of the objects. He uses it like a cell of a very harmonious serial structure, regular and undulant, which confers fluidity and mobility on the surface. In this way he creates frontal pictures and the most varied structural forms, or he covers furniture with nails, which confers on it a certain immateriality.

Although the works of the three artists have a perfect finish and show the greatest skill, a subtle element of humor pervades all of them, less perhaps in Mack, more accentuated in Piene, and much more in Uecker, whose invasion of nails covers tables, chairs, and pianos, with a regular

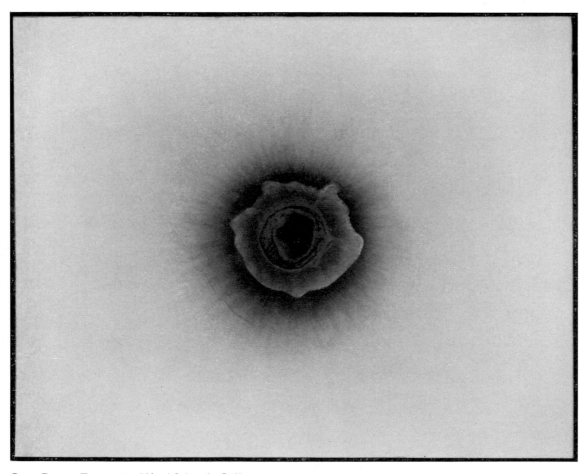

OTTO PIENE. *Eye.* 1963. Alfred Schmela Gallery.

and undulating aspect, ironic and poetic at the same time. The three have begun to produce works in collaboration, such as the ones called « luminous mills. »

Under the auspices of « Group O, » a number of international exhibitions were held, which brought together artists of similar interests. The two most important were held in the Stedelijk Museum in Amsterdam. One exhibition, in March, 1962, entitled « Nul-Zero, » brought together the following artists: Armando, Arman, Bury, J. Francis Aubertin, Castellani, Dorazio, Fontana, Hermann

Goepfert, Hans Haake, Henderikse, Oscar Holweck, Yayoi Kusama, Mack, Dadamaino, Manzoni, Mavignier, Megert, Henk Peeters, Piene, Uli Pohl, Lo Savio, J. J. Schoonhaven, Uecker, Jef Verheyen, and Her de Vries. In 1965 the second show was held, with the title of « Nul »; some new names appeared in it, among them the American kinetic artist Rickey. Also showing was the Japanese group « Gutai, » from Osaka, of evidently similar leanings, represented by their leader and teacher Jiro Yoshihara and by Akira Kanayama, Sadamasa Motonaga, Saburo Murakami, Shozo

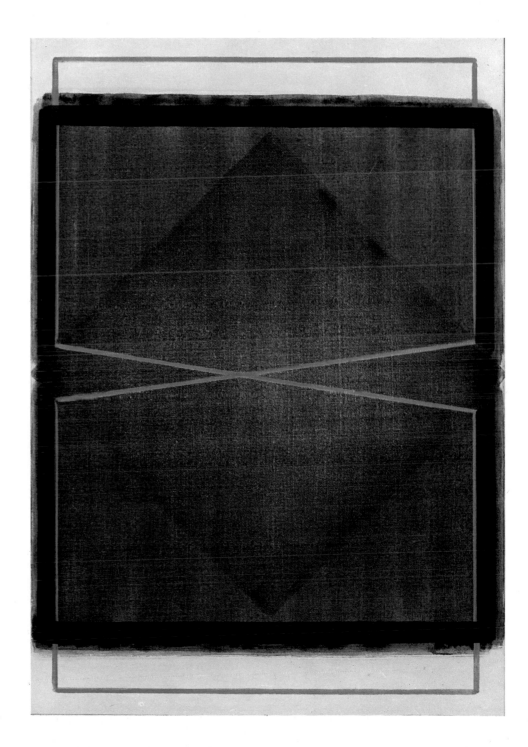

CY TWOMBLY. *Untitled.* 1962. La Tartaruga Gallery.

Shimamoto, Atsuko Tanaka, Tsuruko Yamasaki, and Michio Yoshihara.

Another group related to the Dusseldorf « O » nucleus is a Dutch group made up of Henk Peeters, Armando, and Her de Vries, who published a few numbers of the review *Nul-Zero* and recently an issue of the review *De Nieuwestijl* (The New Style), in which there is an exposition of the international vanguard with an accent on the meaning of the dada concrete-visuality synthesis. As with the « O » group, the influence of Fontana and Klein is not only visible but admitted to. They oppose at the same time informalism and cold constructivism.

The Japanese woman artist Yayoi Kusama was born in Matsumoto in 1929. She lives in New York. Her work falls between the accumulations of Arman and the surfaces covered with nails of Uecker. She covers objects and furniture with small bags of obvious phallic shape filled with plaster of Paris and covered on the outside with white plaster, until the whole room is covered.

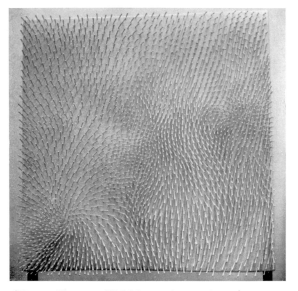

GÜNTER UECKER. *Field in motion.* 1964.
Alfred Schmela Gallery.

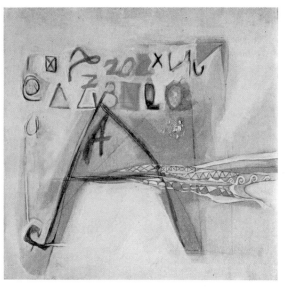

GASTONE NOVELLI. *Big A.* 1965.
Marlborough Gallery.

She does the same with cans and the like. Instead of the little bags, she sometimes uses spaghetti, and the name she gives her coverages is « alimento-sexual obsessions. »

Scribbles and graffiti

Scribbles and graffiti converted into central motives in works of art is a phenomenon that is also tied to the modern tendencies of pop and new realism, and in a certain measure represents an art of attitude, comparable to décollage in spontaneity and naturalness. In fact, to deface a bare wall when passing is an innate tendency, and to make meaningless scribbles or doodles on a paper while speaking on the telephone is an irresistible impulse. The scribble is then, in that sense, the free gesture of writing, that is, automatic writing in its pure instinctive state, with all intellectual pretension eliminated. It lacks the violence of the myokinetic gesture act (vitality in its raw state), but is connected to more subtle subconscious mechanisms.

Cy Twombly, the pioneer of the use of scribble, was born in Lexington, Virginia, in 1928. He has lived in Rome since 1957. In Twombly's work, the element is fundamentally linear. The surfaces on which his subtle lines are written or drawn are neutral, gray or white, and the scribbled lines are loose or in groups, but always allowing an intense action of space. When used, the color is reduced to light stains or sober graphic signs. At times he assembles a tenuous network of lines that appear void of automatic impulse and drawn by a ruler, but they are incorporated as another element in the writing, like a calligraphic vision of a certain aspect of man. With such simple elements, Twombly manages to produce works that have a strange enchantment of lightness, a tone of secret confidence united to an undoubted plastic quality.

Gastone Novelli was born in Vienna in 1925, of Italian parentage, and now lives in Rome. Between the years 1951 and 1953 he taught composition in the Museum of São Paulo. He collab-

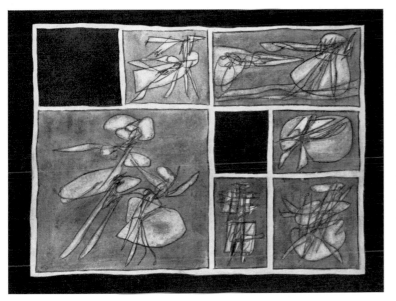

ACHILLE PERILLI. *The labyrinth of galaxies.* 1962. Marlborough Gallery.

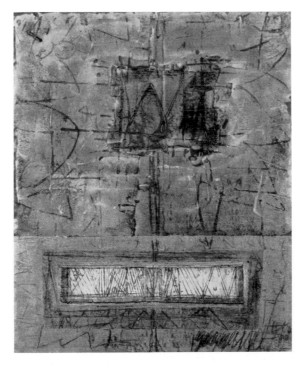

orated with Perilli on the review *Modern Experience.* In his pictures, Novelli draws in a very free manner linear signs, writings, graffiti, and communication symbols on a monochrome background of gray or white. In his latest works he tends toward the development of organic forms in a baroque organization.

Achille Perilli was born in Rome in 1927. Between 1947 and 1948 he belonged to the « Forma I » group, and founded « L'Age d'Or » group with Dorazio. He published the *avant-garde* review *Modern Experience.* Perilli began with a geometric free abstraction of neocubist orientation, then found his present manner, based on linear designs that vaguely resemble graffiti and are distributed over the picture in sequences, like the boxes of comic strips, within rectangular compartments similar to those of a neoplastic composition. The outline of the box, or sometimes all of it, presents a surface of color that is flat, uniform, and pure, in the manner of concrete painting. This contrast between the very free organic graphic lines and the coldness of the partition of the picture gives them the aspect of tracks from some mysterious but nevertheless present world. He achieves exciting animated plastic surfaces, with a rigor that is comparable to the great tradition in painting.

Georges Noël was born in Béziers, France, in 1924. He produces pictures of large format of monochromatic tendency in which calligraphic elements develop through fine lines freely distributed over the whole expanse of the canvas.

John Forrester was born in Wellington, New Zealand, in 1922; he lives in England. He began by producing constructivist work, and later changed over to a technique based on graffiti. His pictures are more organized than those of other artists of that tendency, and are built on a structure that is always linear.

GEORGES NOEL. *Great vertical palimpsest.* 1963. Paul Facchetti Gallery.

John Forrester. *Glenrowan.* 1964.

Assemblages and reliefs

A number of artists work with assemblages of objects, some along the line of spatial work, like Edoardo Paolozzi in England, Richard Stankiewicz and Elwyn Chamberlain in the United States, and César in France; others produce the assemblage on a flat surface or with a view to frontal vision, as we have seen in the work of Spoerri.

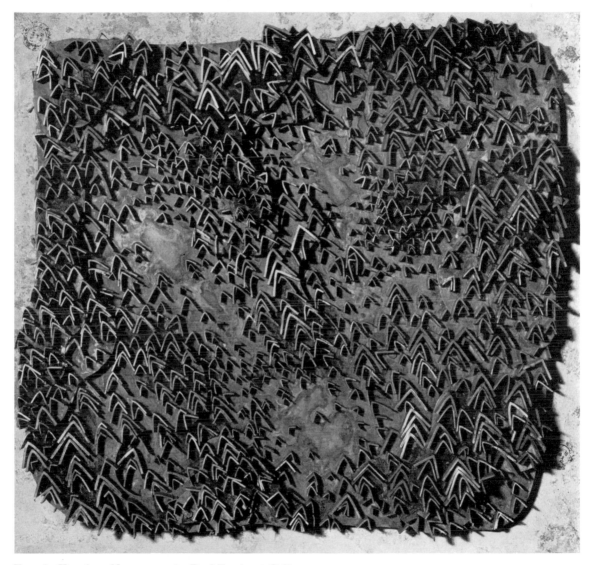

ZOLTÁN KEMÉNY. *Nature.* 1958. Paul Facchetti Gallery.

Jaap Wagmaker was born in Haarlem, The Netherlands, in 1906. He belongs to the generation before « Cobra, » although his prestige began with the exhibition of his works in the Stedelijk Museum in Amsterdam in 1957. Since 1955 Wagmaker has produced his picture-collages related to the informalist technique. To a surface of cement he attaches all sorts of elements, like pieces of wood, cloth, scrap iron, and plastic. On the other hand, the colors he uses are, in general, neutral, white, black, gray, ocher, and at times touches of live red.

ZOLTÁN KEMÉNY. *Sun suite.* 1960.
Paul Facchetti Gallery.

LOUISE NEVELSON. *Silent music I.* 1964.
The Pace Gallery.

Zoltán Kemény was born in 1907 in Banica, a village in Transylvania. He died in 1965. In his youth he learned the trade of cabinet maker. Later, he studied at the Academy of Fine Arts in Budapest; in 1940 he arrived in France, and then went to Zurich. Kemény produced reliefs on sheet metal to which are soldered various metal elements, using them in similar series – copper type, radiator grilles, nails, pipes, rings, sockets, screws, and rivets – which he arranged into tight structures until they formed something like excrescences or scales over the surface. The pictorial quality of these reliefs comes either from the natural color of the metals (the gold of the copper) or from a bath of some colored plastic liquid. For this reason Kemény sometimes called

LUCIO DEL PEZZO. *The game of solitude.* 1965.
Krugier.

K.O. Götz. *Aerochute*. 1961.

his work « my pictures » and other times « my paintings. » In the beginning he used scrap metal for his reliefs, but later he employed new metal that he had cut and shaped to order.

Louise Nevelson was born in Kiev, Russia, in 1900. She studied at the Art Students League in New York from 1929 to 1930 and in 1931 with Hans Hofmann. She has had one-man shows in Venice, London, Paris, Rome, and in Germany and South America. Her work appears in permanent exhibitions in the Whitney Museum, Brooklyn and Newark museums, Museum of Modern Art, New York, and in other American cities. She has also received United Society of Artists, Ford Foundation, and Chicago Institute awards. Her works are assemblages of various objects of wood arranged in rectangular compartments or geomet-

rical figures. The whole of the work gets its uniformity from being covered with black or silver paint, or gilt.

Lucio del Pezzo was born in Naples in 1933, and now lives in Milan. He was a member of a Neapolitan group, of which Biasi, Edoardo Persico, and del Pezzo were the most distinguished; the Naples group, of surrealist leanings, published the review *Documento-Sud*. Del Pezzo produces assemblages of various objects and geometrical bodies, placed in square compartments or very firmly attached to a supporting surface.

Present-day aspects of surrealism

The question of the existence of surrealist plastics is a very complex one. In general, the name

JACQUES LACOMBLEZ. *Easter Island marries the rain.* 1961. Collection Grubben.

GIANNI DOVA. *Personage.* 1962.

« surrealist » is given to painters of the most varied tendencies. The reason for this is that surrealism has been an artistic shrine ruled by the almost absolutist criterion of Breton, and to which artists were admitted on the condition of unconditional adherence to the surrealist dogmas and declarations (at least in a large number of cases). From the appearance of the book *Surrealism and Painting* in 1928 up to the surrealist catalogue of the 1947 exhibition, and through the different expositions and essays published by Breton, surrealist painting has embraced the most varied aggregation of styles and qualities that contemporary painting can offer. As for its quality, it varies from atrocious to excellent.

What ought really to be understood by surrealism? We shall turn to the high priest of the theories of the movement, Breton. In the book *Surrealism and Painting*, the first edition of which came out at the very outset of the movement, one reads the following: « The plastic work, in order to respond to the absolute necessity of true values, on the necessity of which all spirits are today in accord, must be referred to an interior model. » That is, the model that up to now was exterior is turning inward. We have seen that Kandinsky as early as 1912 presented his program of objectivization of the spiritual in almost the same words in his book *Of the Spiritual in Art*. But to qualify for inclusion among the surrealists, this aspect – common to a large part of modern painting – is not enough. There are other aspects that must complete the fundamental premise.

In his book, Breton gives us the guiding theme in discussing Braque's phrase « I love the rule that corrects the emotion. » Breton says, « I emphatically deny this rule. » In other words, he upholds the uncontrolled objectivization of pure emotion. But even this is not enough; in a much later essay, « Genesis and Artistic Perspectives of Surrealism, » published in the United States in 1941, Breton makes clear that the fundamental lines of surrealist plastics are automatism, in which he recognizes Klee as the initiator, and the significance of creative chance, introduced by Duchamp and Arp.

To sum it up, a surrealist plastic work implies the elimination of the voluntary, the conscious and rational, for the intervention of automatism and chance. Through these two procedures springs forth a lyrical or poetical expression that reveals the close ties between the creative sources of the plastic arts and poetry.

These theoretical premises were applied with a certain arbitrariness by Breton himself, but he sometimes seems to have subordinated them to the strategic needs of the group. The result of this was that authentically surrealist artists have never been tied to the movement, or else they have been so for a short time. On the other hand there have been in this group reactionaries and pompous artists whose fraudulence has been only too evident. It will be enough to mention Dalí among the *farceurs*. However, there are those who sincerely respond to these premises, like Klee, whom Barr, in 1936, considered the purest of the surrealists, and who exhibited in the first surrealist show, but would never become part of the group; Arp, who collaborated with them with the greatest reticence; and Hartung, who confessed to me that he did not want to hear surrealism mentioned.

In fact, surrealism constitutes the direct and pure

CARL-FREDERICK REUTERSWÄRD. *Looping the loop the masters.* 1959. Collection Alexandre Henisz.

objectivization of the vital elements that aspire to transcend the individual and to conquer a place in reality among the remaining concrete objects of the exterior world. Observed in this light, one discovers that surrealism has exercised a considerable influence on all modern plastics, and has created a direction within abstractism that has made itself evident in the predominance of instinctive-poetic or purely vital contents.

Abstract expression, or more exactly the nonfigural, has shown itself to be the most prolific in realizing the surrealist program, and even if for more than twenty years two currents – the abstract and the figural – coexisted in the very lap of the surrealist group, the division was produced

HANS MEYER-PETERSEN. *Sabbat.* 1959.

in 1944 in the United States, when Breton was in New York. Breton gives an account of this controversy between the two tendencies in his essay on Donati, not taking sides in the battle. But practically from that time on the nonfigural artists abandoned their relations with surrealism. Benjamin Peret, Breton's deputy, in the *Surrealist Almanac of the Half-Century*, published by the review *La Nef* in 1950, denied the possibility of an abstract surrealist art, or, more precisely, denied the possibility of any abstract art whatsoever.

Until the final period of the review *Minotaure* (the high point of the surrealist movement), many painters appear whose evolution toward abstraction is clearly evident: the most important

of these were the Chilean Matta Echaurren, the Englishman Onslow Ford, and the Spaniard Esteban Francés. But the great development of abstraction took place in the United States during the period of Breton's stay there from 1941 to the end of the war. In France, after the war, at the beginning of the reevaluation of the plastic arts, there was also a turn toward abstraction among the young painters of surrealist leanings. At this moment the orthodox surrealist movement directed by Breton in Paris found itself without followers in the plastic arts: the photographic current, whose greatest exponents were Dalí, Magritte, and Delvaux, and to a lesser extent Leonor Fini and Félix Labisse, found a natural refuge in the homes of the newly rich and

ALBERTO GIRONELLA. *Francisco Lezcano's atelier.* 1964.

of the aristocracy mingling with them, a logical destination for the stereotyped painting of all periods.

The development of surrealist painting of the postwar period received a fresh stimulus when the A l'Etoile Scellée Gallery opened in December, 1952, with a group show of most of the surrealist painters. In January, 1953, the second one-man show by Simon Hantai was held, with a eulogistic introduction by Breton.

In April and May, 1953, the Babylone Gallery exhibited the Swedish imaginists, which acquainted the surrealists with the work of Max Walter Svanberg, with whom the gallery had got in touch in Malmö, where he was living in retirement. Svanberg differs from the imaginists in that he places what he calls « visionary figuration » above all. The other imaginist painters incline toward abstraction.

In February, 1953, an event occurred that was

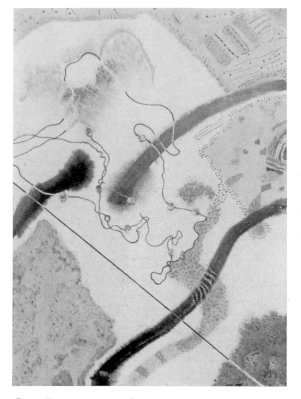

CARL BUCHHEISTER. *Composition*. 1949.

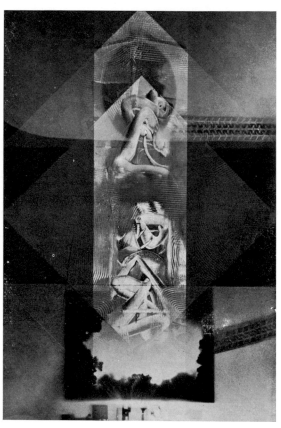

ROGELIO POLESELLO. *Kaleidoscope*. 1964.

important because it meant a shift in focus on what a surrealist painting should be: the review *Medium* reproduced an extract from an article entitled « Abstraction and Surrealism » by Charles Estienne, published in *France Observateur*. It said: « Given the death, to me very evident, of decorative abstraction and of surrealist imaginations, I think that with the most active part of abstraction and with a surrealism, not enlarged, but, on the contrary, returned to its beginnings, we have the two essential keys to modern art, the one that has already been achieved, and the one that is forming. ». The precursory signs are seen in works such as those of Paalen, Matta, and Gorky, directly tied to surrealism. A similar intention is found in the works of Hartung, Wols,

and Pollock, with their automatic signs and symbols. « It concerns a poetic order, » says Estienne, « more passionate and human than the merely plastic order. » A year later, in 1954, Edouard Jaguer, in *Phases*, argued for « an art of the imaginary » that would include all the exponents of the free exercise of the creative imagination. Estienne conferred the name « tachism » on this new tendency, using the world in a pejorative sense and with evident controversial intent.

Following this change, in 1953 Breton received four gesture painters introduced by Estienne into the A l'Etoile Scellée Gallery: René Duvillier, Jean Degottex, Marcelle Loubchansky, and Jean

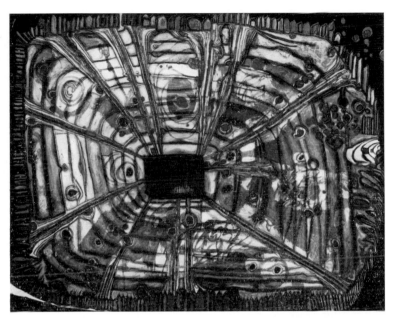

FRITZ HUNDERTWASSER. *Rain of blood falling on Japanese waters located in an Austrian garden.* 1961.

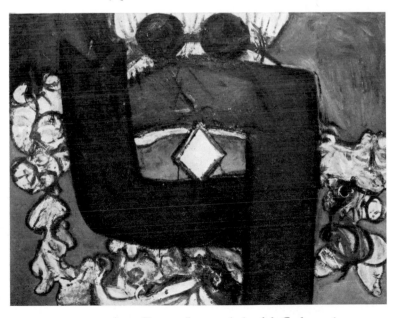

ALAN DAVIE. *Image of the fish God.* 1956. Collection British Council.

Messagier. In a later exhibition, gesture works by Judith Reigl were shown.

It is curious the first lyrical abstracts launched by the surrealist gallery with the addition of Hantai (Degottex, Loubchansky, and Reigl) were separated under Georges Mathieu's directorship. Mathieu propounded a reactionary ideology opposed to surrealism. He spoke of the « superiority of the Occidental intellect, » although everything visible in his painting is inspired by the Orient.

In 1954, the twenty-seventh Venice Biennale paid homage to surrealism, and was a tribute to its importance and its present influence artistically.

In 1960 another important event for surrealism occurred. Its ability to accept informalism had already been demonstrated during the postwar period, and that year in the International Exhibition of Surrealism, held in the d'Arcy Galleries in New York, two new-dada artists, Rauschenberg and Jasper Johns, participated. They also showed in the later International Exhibition held in Paris, as did the pop artist Rosenquist. In this fashion, surrealism accepted the most vital movement (at least some of its representatives) of this last period.

This acceptance of movements or of artists whose direction coincides with the surrealist line confirms Breton's words in the introduction to the catalog of the « Peinture Surréaliste en Europe » exhibition in Saarbrucken in 1952: « Within the fold of surrealism the artist has enjoyed total freedom of inspiration and technique, which explains the wide exterior differences in their works. What characterizes them is the intention and willingness to withdraw from the rule of the physical world to reach the field of total psychophysics (of which the conscious field is but minimal). »

On the margin of fashion, surrealism continues its work, always exploring new fields.

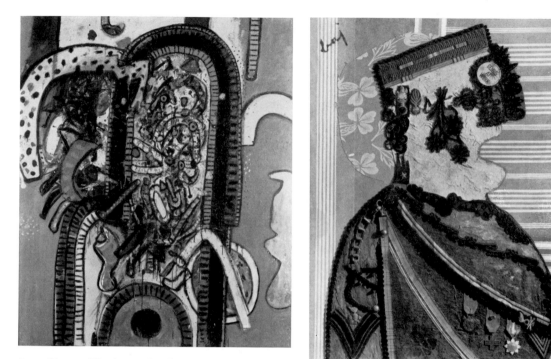

ALAN DAVIE. *The horse that has visions of immortality.* 1963.

ENRICO BAJ. *Count Joseph Tyszkiewicz, general of the lanciers.* 1965. Schwarz Gallery.

ENRICO BAJ. *Parade of six.* 1964. Schwarz Gallery.

Öyvind Fahlström. *Feast on themes of Mad.* 1958/59.

The « Phases » movement

The last issues of the reviews that had emerged from the encounter between surrealism and lyrical abstraction were printed in 1951: *Cobra* had been founded in 1948, and *Rixes* in 1949. Edouard Jaguer decided at the beginning of 1952 to regroup his forces with a program of exhibitions and publications that would centralize the efforts of various countries into a truly international movement. In January, 1954, the first issue of *Phases* appeared. In the same year the exhibitions began, first in Paris in the Paul Facchetti Gallery in 1954 with a show in which Alechinsky, Arnal, Camille Bryen, Buchheister, Capogrossi, Corneille, Claude Georges, Roger Edgard Gillet, K.-O. Götz, Otto Greis, Stanley Hayter, Roel d'Haese, Jacques Hérold, Jorn, Wifredo Lam, Matta, Francisco Nieva, Schultze, and Tajiri participated.

From this time on, exhibition followed exhibition: in 1955 in Paris, Milan, and Mexico; in 1956 in Paris and Geneva; in 1957 in the Stede-

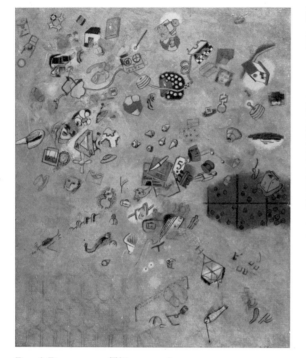

René Bertholo. *Things.* 1965.
Mathias Fels Gallery.

Bernard Rancillac. *Of what to be angry.* 1964.

lijk Museum of Amsterdam; in 1958 in Brussels, Lima, Montevideo, Buenos Aires, Wuppertal, and Tokyo; in 1959 in Santa Fé (Argentina), Crakow, Warsaw and Ljubljana; in 1960 in Brussels; in 1961 in Milan; in 1962 in Paris; in 1963 in Paris and in the National Museum of Fine Arts in Buenos Aires; in 1964 in Paris, in the Museum of Contemporary Art in São Paulo, in the Museum of Modern Art in Rio de Janeiro, and in the museum in Ixelles, Belgium.

Recognizing the fundamental surrealist principles in the « Phases » movement, an approach was made and a collaboration was effected between it and the surrealist movement, which lasted from 1959 to 1963, when the collaboration was broken, not for ideological but for personal reasons.

The following artists were connected with the « Phases » movement: Alechinsky, Camille Bryen,

Corneille, Claude Georges, K.-O. Götz, Tàpies, Asger Jorn, Karl-Heining Pedersen, Arnal, Capogrossi, Baj, Soulages, Dova, Scanavino, Oyvind Fahlström, Carl-Frederick Reuterswärd, and Requichot. The principle that brought these painters to the movement was the painting of the imaginary. As Jaguer expressed it: « Long live the painting of the imaginary! The only one worthy to express fully that knowledge of the world and that will to transform it which constitutes the primary moral qualification of the whole human search. » And he adds: « But what is the imaginary but the *future of reality*, and for what values must we battle if not for those, in a century in which we are swept by our revolutions, and why are we not at liberty to prefer this "future of reality" to the now famous "reality of the

FRANCIS BACON. *Double portrait of Lucien Freud and Frank Auerbach.* 1964.

ROBERT RAUSCHENBERG. *Quote.* 1964. Leo Castelli Gallery.

future" which at this very moment is exhibited
in full daylight and is colored with the sinister
tints of reactions, of overpopulation, and of the
bomb? »

The imaginary constitutes the world of pure invention, and has nothing to do with planned and
rationalized fantasy. A book of science-fiction is
not imaginary but imagined. The two concepts
are totally different, as Pierre Volboudt explained
in an article in the review *XXth Century* (June,
1965). There this author says, in effect, that the
imagined is what one composes with elements of
a dissociated reality, and the imaginary is, simply,
the unreal become concrete. In this way, the imaginary, thanks to an absolute freedom, can bring
us closer to the domain of the impossible.

A few of the artists who participated in the Phases exhibitions, and who have not been ecoun-
tered in preceding chapters, follow.

Karl-Otto Götz was born in Aachen, Germany,
in 1914. In 1931 and 1932 he studied at the
Academy of Decorative Arts, and from 1948 to
1953 he edited the review *Metá*. He participated
in the activities of the « Cobra » group in 1949,
and after 1953 he was part of the international
« Phases » movement directed by Edouard Jaguer
in Paris. At present he lives in Dusseldorf.

Götz is the most characteristic exponent of the
gesture tendency within the frame of « Phases. »
His pictures consist of very sober strokes of black
or gray executed with a single sweep, in wide,
generous curves that roll and unfold and appear to
spray drops of paint. The gesture is not one impelled by the brutal force of action; rather, it is
lyrical. As a whole, these gesture tracings confer
a vertiginous, explosive quality to the surface,
and transmit a sense of otherworldly nightmare.

Bernard Requichot was born in Saint-Gilles,
France, in 1928. He committed suicide in 1961. In
1954 he began to make a type of assemblage of
abstract paintings similar to those that Dubuffet
produced at the same time. He painted canvases

HERVÉ TÉLEMAQUE. *The straight path.* 1964.
Mathias Fels Gallery.

in somber colors and later cut them into pieces
and put them together again. Later he produced
collages of photographs with prints in black and
white or in color that he cut out from illustrated
magazines. Toward 1958 he began constructing
his famous reliquaries: blackened boxes, half
charred, that contained the most varied elements.
At the same time he drew and painted strangely
ramified organic forms.

Jacques Lacomblez was born in 1934 in Ixelles,
Belgium. A poet as well as a painter, Lacomblez
has participated in the « Phases » movement since

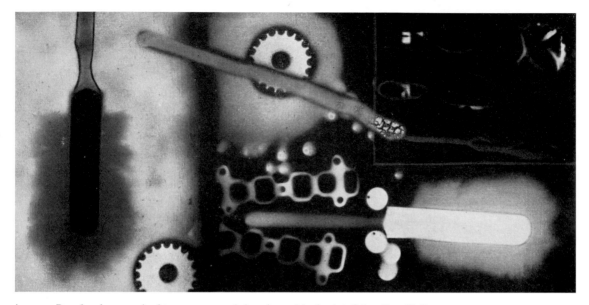

ARNAL. *Bombardment of objects attracted by the cold.* André Schoeller Gallery.

1956. He publishes the review *Edda*, associated with the movement. His pictures display a world that appears to unite, at one time, the characteristics of the vegetable, mineral, and animal worlds. Strange ramifications, at times organic, or like algae, soon take on the fascinating spectrums of gems, as if to pull us into that complex universe of the impossible that only the imagination enters.

Gianni Dova, born in Rome in 1925, now lives in Milan. He was for a short time a member of Fontana's spatial movement, and has participated in the activities of « Phases » since 1955. In his pictures he introduces strange morphologies that appear like nightmares from a mechanized and extraplanetary world. Dova justifies his activity as a painter thus: « I paint so as to formulate a judgment on my times, on society, and on today's customs. »

Carl-Frederick Reuterswärd was born in Stockholm in 1934, and lives there at present. Painter and poet, he has participated in « Phases » since

1955. In his pictures, in an imaginary space agitated by some gesture signs, variegated elements from reality are distributed in unusual juxtapositions.

Hans Meyer-Petersen, born in Copenhagen in 1937, has been active in « Phases » since 1957. His pictures offer us a magic world that appears as if immobilized by a penetrating calm, executed with pictorial refinement of particular skill.

Alberto Gironella was born in Mexico in 1929, and lives there at present. He has been active in the « Phases » movement since 1960. For a theme he may take, for example, a human figure from Velásquez, and produce a series of works in which the elements of the picture are metamorphosed into the most unusual forms. He mixes painting with collage or with the inclusion of objects.

Among other undertakings, in « Phases, » Jaguer rightly undertook to rehabilitate some of the pioneers of the modern trend who had been unjust-

GIANFRANCO BARUCHELLO. *The famous armistice-day between Variants and Constants.* 1965. Schwarz Gallery.

ly forgotten. Among them were Buchheister, Hausman, and the futurist Farfa.

Carl Buchheister was born in Hanover, Germany, in 1890, and died in his native city in 1964. He had dedicated himself to abstraction since 1923. Buchheister belonged to the « Cercle et Carré » and later to the « Abstraction-Création » association; he was a friend of Schwitters and Friedrich Vordemberge-Gildewart, with whom he founded the group of abstract artists in Ha-

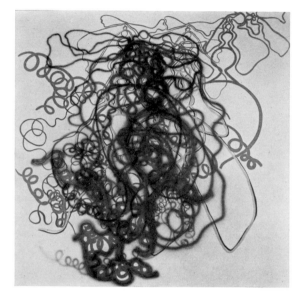

BERNARD COHEN. *Mist.* 1963.
Collection Calouste Gulbenkian Foundation.

JACK SMITH. *Various activities.* 1963.
Collection Stuyvesant Foundation.

nover in 1928. In his work Buchheister fundamentally used collage with diverse elements that he incorporated into very free plastic constructions. His painting, rich in color, created abstract forms full of poetic fantasy. He was the most faithful to the « Phases » movement, and collaborated in it uninterruptedly from its beginning.

The international « Phases » movement was associated with reviews and groups in various countries. Outside of the review *Edda*, published in Belgium by Lacomblez, three numbers of the *Boa* review were published in Buenos Aires, edited by the poet Julio Llinás (the first appeared in conjunction with a « Phases » exhibition in 1958). A group of painters formed about the review, among whom were Marta Peluffo, Victor Chab, Osvaldo Borda, and Rogelio Polesello.

Within the constants of surrealist painting, humor and poetry, activated by the motor of the imaginary, the « Phases » movement has been an indefatigable international center for planning and concentrating the efforts of the artists involved

in it, sustained by the faith and unstinting labor of its leader, the French poet Edouard Jaguer.

In the painting of the imaginary two painters must be mentioned who, although they are not directly tied to the surrealist movement, are of great importance: Hundertwasser and Davie.

Fritz Hundertwasser was born in Vienna in 1928 and for a short time attended the Academy of Fine Arts there. The pictures of Egon Schiele deeply impressed him. Hundertwasser traveled widely in Italy and Morocco, and in 1954 exhibited at the Paul Facchetti Gallery in Paris.

Hundertwasser produces paintings in the tradition of Viennese secessionism signalized by the two greatest painters of the *Jugendstil*: Gustav Klimt and Schiele. His pictures are fashioned by spiral bands with an almost organic character, which develop from a center, and enlarge irregularly as they go, strewn here and there with small colored forms that are almost geometric. The

ARNOLD LEISSLER. *Oil.* 1963.
Dieter Brusberg Gallery.

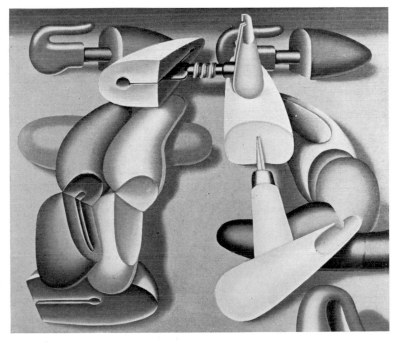

whole takes on an aspect of an imaginary labyrinth, of resplendent colors, at times silver and
gold, with greens, reds, yellows, ochers, and
sharp violets, which makes it transcend the ornamental aspect that at a certain point appears
to take over the composition. The labyrinthine
structure barely contains the eruption of this vi-
vid, saturated color, violently contrasted, and it
seems justified that Hunderwasser himself speaks
of his pictures as « a slow explosion. »
Hundertwasser, attracted by surrealism, humorously calls his creative process « transautomat-
ic, » considering it an ideal procedure against
mechanical rationalism. The baroque density of
his pictures invites them to be « read, » a perusal
along the brilliant lines of its spiral labyrinth.

Alan Davie was born in Grangemouth, Scotland,
in 1920. From 1937 to 1940 he studied at the
Edinburgh College of Art, and later became a
jazz musician and a goldsmith. His first one-man
show took place in Edinburgh in 1946, and the
first London exhibition in 1950. Davie's work
contains gesture elements and forms that are at
times visceral, at other times almost geometric,
and sometimes turn into crude scribbled lines,
which seem to call to mind figures from some
dark folklore, in a varied, almost orgiastic development of the imagination. The color is violent
– reds, greens, explosive yellows – mixed at times
with vaguely drawn lines of delicate violet color
and white backgrounds of intensively expressive
texture. The aggregate is baroque but with a vitality seldom found in modern painting. He is
undoubtedly one of the most important painters
of the present time.
On his mission as an artist, Davie voices the following opinion: « The artist must be a prophet;
that is, he must express what is full of significance in an infinite sense, and what does not proceed from reason or knowledge or the past, but

KONRAD KLAPHECK. *Life in society.* 1964.

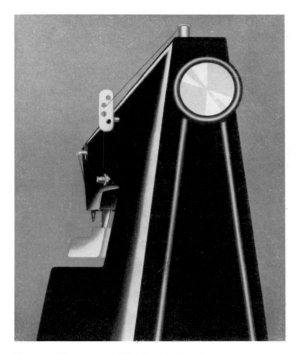

KONRAD KLAPHECK. *The logic of women.* 1965.

from the eternal present which is always new and marvellous. »

Another member of the « Phases » movement is the Italian artist Enrico Baj. He is linked on one hand with surrealism and on the other with Dubuffet, and more recently he has incorporated elements of pop art into his work. Baj was born in Milan in 1924, and still lives there. Together with Dangelo he founded the nuclear movement in 1951. Their manifesto rejected the whole previous *avant-garde*, including surrealism and the influence of the dream world, and stated that nuclear disintegration was the sign of this century. In 1953 Baj collaborated with Asger Jorn in the foundation of an international movement for an imaginist Bauhaus to oppose the *Hochschule für Gestaltung* which had been founded by Max Bill a short time before. Baj also founded the review

Il Gesto with Dangelo. From 1955 to the present he has participated in all the exhibitions of the « Phases » movement in Paris.

In his early works, Baj appears to have been under the influence of Dubuffet and *art brut.* In his nuclear period he was obsessed by science-fiction themes, and produced pictures such as the *Arrival of the Martians* and other extraplanetary fantasies. Later he turned to collage, creating a series of human figures made with old tapestries, furniture coverings and with all sorts of odds and ends. His decorated generals, done with humor, are outstanding. He works in thematic series: thus he has introduced collages of marquetry that represent the front view of furniture, imitating, with ironic fantasy, old styles that by their slight distortion accentuate the comical note. He also reproduces ordinary objects, as pop artists do, but the imaginative treatment, the poetic quality, and the humor put them closer to surrealism. He has a series of broken mirrors, and lately he has included figures of women painted in the superficial style of low-grade movie posters. Baj demonstrates ever-renewing inventiveness, and is at the head of the *avant-garde* artists in Italy.

Where is present art heading?

With the diminished activity of the informalists before the vigor of the new tendencies in the three fundamental directions that we have examined (optical tendencies, kinetics, and pop art), young artists have begun to ask themselves « Where do we go from here? » Already there are signs of tiredness.

Pop art has contributed a contact with reality that many do not wish to abandon. The latest optical currents also reveal a stimulating way to awaken visual interest, excluding all traditional concepts. Informalism itself brought a great measure of liberty and certain elements related to life, which are useful. Perhaps a syn-

PAUL VAN HOEYDONCK. *Untitled.* La Salita Gallery.

thesis is necessary. But in reality every artist, by merely living in his own time, contributes, even when not intending to, a permanent synthesis of all the new elements that appear, even as all artists contribute to enriching the plastic language and thus increase the possibilities of expression. This sort of synthesis we have seen frequently in the course of this work. What is meant here is the need to arrive at a totally different language through a synthesis of all the idioms that art of late has brought. But in what measure can the sum of so many disparate elements constitute a synthesis? Let us go over the attempts that have been made.

One of the most interesting routes toward new horizons is the one taken by those who use images, signs and symbols, and other formal elements, planted in space without gravitation and in which they appear to float. These painters take their inspiration from daily life, as do the pop artists, but they do not attempt a mere reproduction of the objects; instead, impressed by the complexity of the world of the real, they transform it into a fantastic vision. In this manner they give us a metaphoric and unusual version of the day-to-day story. In this line the Swedish painter Oyvind Fahlström must be mentioned, as well as a group in Paris that includes the Portuguese Bertholo, the Haitian Télemaque, and the Frenchman Rancillac.

Oyvind Fahlström was born in São Paulo, Brazil, in 1928, of Swedish parents; since 1939 he has lived in Stockholm. A self-taught artist, he has dedicated himself to painting since 1952. Fahlström, who participated in the « Phases » movement, first exhibited in the Numero gallery in Florence. In his work he introduces a complex world in which the most disparate elements meet and integrate into a kind of whirlwind. It appears as if he wants to capture a world to be. The turbulence of the gesture is substituted for that of the image.

René Bertholo was born in Portugal in 1935. The motley world of everyday objects floating loose, independent, in that space without gravitation of which we have spoken – this is the world of his pictures. At times he startles us, as if we were to see a mental photograph of a child's dreams.

Bernard Rancillac, born in Paris in 1931, studied with Stanley William Hayter at the famous school for engraving, Atelier 17. Characters from the comic strips mingle and fuse with a world of wheels, pipes, and indefinable forms, reproduced with evident pictorial quality.

Hervé Télemaque was born in Port-au-Prince, Haiti, in 1937. From 1957 to 1960 he lived in New York, where he studied at the Art Students League and where he could examine the new American movements, especially pop art. He be-

YAYOI KUSAMA. *Air mail stickers.* 1962. Whitney Museum of American Art, New York.

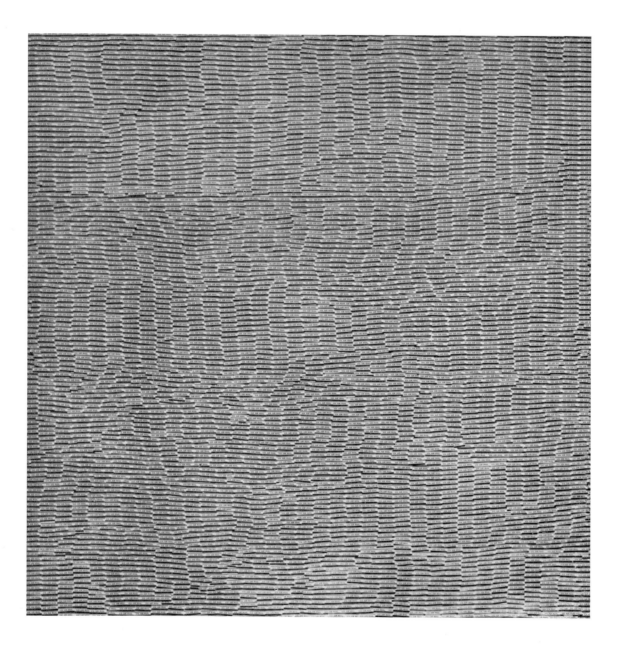

Yves Klein. *Fire painting.* 1961/62. Iolas Gallery.

longs with the surrealists. Elements of Haitian tradition, deformed mass images, characters out of comic strips, and repeated silhouettes of current events mingle in his works, as if evoked in a nightmare that condensed time in such a manner that past, present, and future were lived in a single instant.

Other artists search for a painting that has a sense of anticipation of new events in the domain of planetary exploration. The Belgian Paul van Hoeydonk, born in Antwerp in 1925, produced his first planetary reliefs, evidently influenced by a belief in the imminence of interplanetary travel. Lately he has returned to an attitude more in line with pop art in his sculpture-objects with figures of women resempling mannequins. The latest pictures by Arnal, whom we mentioned among the informalists of the School of Paris, produced by means of a printing process, show images that appear to float in stellar space; they are actually everyday objects that come to acquire an out-of-this-world character through the work of the painter.

Also with a sense of anticipation, but on the level of a new system of communication, is the painting of Gianfranco Baruchello, who was born in Leghorn in 1924 and now lives in Rome. His first one-man show was in the Tartaruga Gallery in Rome in 1963. Baruchello shows what we could designate as annotations for arranging a world in disintegration; in a space that is neither real nor mental but is rather a receptacle for exalting a new language, he distributes signs, indications, references, presentiments, and schemes that appear to form a superintelligible syntactic system of great visual potency.

Recently, some artists have been attempting a synthesis of pop art and their view of everyday reality with hard-edge techniques and formal tightness. This combination has come to be called

« poptical art. » The German painter Winfred Gaul is one of the most characteristic; other representatives of this trend are the English painter Dereck Boshier, in his latest efforts, and the young Englishman Gerald Laing.

Winfred Gaul was born in Dusseldorf in 1928. He studied with Baumeister and Henninger, and in 1956 held his first one-man show at the Facchetti Gallery in Paris. Gaul uses elements that resemble traffic signs, yet they do not correspond to the actual signs, but are inspired by them. Although the artist himself says that « they are not a negation of technique nor a romantic enlargement, they are just objects, » continuing the line of apparent detachment that characterizes the latest tendencies, it is undeniable that they are the result (although subconscious in the artist) of the coercion to which modern man finds himself subjected, a coercion symbolized by the traffic signs and the danger inherent in not obeying them. But at the same time they are concrete paintings, paintings of flat colors, pure and clear, with tight forms. They come within the hard-edge category. Formerly, Gaul had produced large uniform surfaces in monochrome that gave an overwhelming sensation of emptiness.

The work of Bernard Cohen, Jack Smith, and others in England, and Arnold Leissler in Germany, can be considered as a new perspective of formal abstraction, although steering clear of the simplicity and nakedness of hard-edge.

Bernard Cohen, the younger brother of the painter Harold Cohen, was born in London in 1933. He studied at St. Martin's School of Art and the Slade School. He embraces a free abstraction in which arabesque lines circumscribe the colored forms. His linear structure has become more complex and sharper, at the same time resulting in actual linear intricacies, but never confused, which determine levels of varying depth in the space.

Jack Smith was born in Sheffield in 1928. He was trained at the Royal College of Art. He produces branching structures of geometric character, free, in an active space.

Arnold Leissler was born in Hanover in 1939. He studied with Wendland and Geyger in the Werkkunstschule in his native city. He began with a mechanical, rigid, and sober painting very close to hard-edge, to evolve recently to a formal, very precise world, conserving the geometric line, but extraordinarily baroque and violently multicolored.

An artist who merits special mention is Konrad Klapheck, born in Dusseldorf in 1935. From 1954 to 1958 he studied at the Academy of Fine Arts in his native city with Bruno Goller. He exhibits with the surrealists and with the « Phases » group. In his pictures, Klapheck reproduces typewriters or sewing machines or semigeometric elements with precision and schematization, with a subtle humor, which unwittingly makes the reproduced objects acquire a fantastic aspect. Klapheck's work is the expression of the invisible magic that the machines have by being extensions of man. For this reason, nothing appears more reasonable than what the artist declares: « I portray myself in the machines. » His pictures are examples of what has come to be called « cold surrealism. »

These are the possible roads on which art may travel in the coming years. But no one can predict. What can be said without hesitation is that art will not be detained in its continuous search in the domain of the unknown, to which it has been drawn throughout its history.

Chapter eight

Sociological aspects of postwar art

The art of the postwar period is distinguished by various characteristics. In the first place, modern art is no longer the patrimony of an élite. Klee said, « The people are not on our side, » and this phrase contains the germ of an unpopularity that owed its origin to many factors but can be summarized in the fact that modern art demanded faculties of understanding that are not within reach of anyone not specially prepared.

Nor can it be said at present that modern art has become actually popular, in the strict sense of the word, though in a short time it has gained a vast following. In the last ten years this interest has been demonstrated in the increase in the number of collectors, the fabulous development of modern galleries, and the interest displayed by the daily press, popular magazines, and television in a measure hitherto unimagined. Museums, private showrooms, and foundations are interested in the new art and its advancement. Even governments give it official support.

We have gone a long way since the days when the first modern artists of the century had to suffer hardships. Now there is no Bateau Lavoir or any bohemia; poverty has disappeared, and with it the idea of the *artiste maudit*. The hunger and misery of Modigliani or Soutine are things that do not appear likely to be repeated.

But as late as the first year of this postwar period there were still the *maudits*. Wols died pursued by misery, and De Staël suffered until very shortly before his self-inflicted death. The American abstract artists had to battle against poverty, and many owed the solution of their struggles to the generosity of the WPA's assistance to artists.

Today the successful modern artists have magnificent studios and comfortable lives. In the United States, to be a modern painter is to belong to a social category as desirable and enviable as that of a university professor or president of a corporation.

The artist has ceased to be an outcast.

Nowadays the revolutionary manifestations in art provoke no scandals, nor do they even irritate; if anything, they provide pleasure and enjoyment for a public that is prepared for major surprises and hungry for novelty. Young artists have immediate success, particularly if they launch some newfangled invention (or what appears to be one) or merely take up the reigning fashion.

There is no greater paradox than the prestige enjoyed by art in a period that seems created for the disdain of art. But there is no question that in this prestige there often are dominant secondary factors. A great number of the collectors are collectors not only because art represents an investment but also because it automatically places them among the social élite.

The changed situation of the artist of today corresponds to a fundamental change in the attitude toward art, a change that began before the war and spread in the postwar era until it has lately become general. This change of attitude consists in that the artist, formerly a creator of a work of art, is now a manufacturer of consumer goods.

In this fashion the artist has lost his characteristic alienation of the past and has become incorporated into mass society as a normal member. This mass society is characterized by a vast, passive, and indifferent population whose fundamental function is to consume. On this population an active group of manufacturers of articles is busy. The artist has incorporated himself into this group.

The nature of these articles does not depend on the consumer's needs; it is determined by the interests of the manufacturers and is imposed on the public through the modern monster of advertising. Production and advertising together are the key to the consumer society, of which the foremost example today is the United States. Thus an egalitarian level is created, not only in the basic products – canned food with a sameness of flavor for all consumers – but also in entertainment and in cultural products. The average man is becoming more and more a passive receptacle whose life is supplied from without. In sports and entertainment he is a spectator whose reactions are perfectly calculated and measured and whose feelings are easily manipulated by the organizers of these spectacles, be they football, baseball, movies, or television. There is a simple unity within the mass that attends these entertainments, and its emotions are exactly gauged. Without doubt, television has achieved the highest degree of spectator passivity, but even sports are losing their spontaneous character, thanks to skillfully manipulated modern professionalism. In the field most readily associated with the traditional concept of culture, that of literature, the best-seller formula serves the average reader with a uniform product intended for the gratification of predictable tastes. In this way, everything is calculated to reduce the average man to a limited scheme of elementary reactions. Finally, there is the press to mold public opinion. Thus the public receives ready-made opinions conceived to be in accord with the interest of a manufacturing class, and the interest of this class is directed to offering products that can be manufactured in enormous quantities at minimum cost and that are absolutely the same. Out of this conjunction of highly standardized situations the consumer is bred, a human type without any autonomous opinions or personal tastes, and with no aspirations except to increase his capacity and ability to absorb the commodities that the consumer market offers. The phrase « consumer product » includes everything from canned soup to works of art. It is to this world that the modern artists must adapt himself.

From a cultural viewpoint it is necessary to emphasize the enormous difference existing between the « popularized » product offered modern man and authentic folklore. This reveals the true cul-

tural needs of the man of the people, of the anonymous being not yet standardized. Folk usage springs up from within man as a natural and spontaneous expression of his living world, and for this reason it varies with the surroundings. The cultural product of the mass is something imposed from outside, artificially manufactured for the use of the largest number and, as a consequence, directed to the lowest level. As these articles do not correspond to an inner necessity of man, they evidently do not need to vary with the surroundings. The cultural products of this society have the trivial features of « kitsch, » a form of communication intended only to produce effects.

These considerations are not intended to give the impression that all modern works have the features of the consumer product as we have described it. But that the artist must suffer the pressures from a society based on consumption is inevitable. In any event, the *raison d'être* of a work of art changes fundamentally when it becomes merchandise in a fluctuating market, highly sensitive to factors outside the domain of art. The notion of the artistic value of a work is confused in an alarming fashion with its economic success: the price becomes an index of real value, and this price is artificially created by publicity and artificially maintained or raised by the interest of the market. It is inevitable that in such a situation many works are produced that have no relation to any interior need for expression on the part of the artist, but are brought forth by the demands of the market. At the same time, a market so hungry for products encourages a breed of artists without any true vocation, attracted only by possible success. Artists with characteristics more of dealers than of creators come to flourish; they are manufacturers, with a sure and easy feeling for self-promotion and stupendous skill in publicity and public relations. Many of these fill private collections and museums with their abortions, for which they receive honors and official support. There is no doubt that mediocrity is not the exclusive property of the present era, but at the same time it is true that it is reaching alarming proportions.

Art dealers and the galleries

The commercial treatment accorded works of art has given them trade characteristics very similar to those that distinguish the large industrial organizations. It has become habitual in America to speak of the « New York Art Industry, Inc., » which produces assorted merchandise with the label of art. The speculative fever has taken hold of the art market, and one speculates in it as one does in the stock market.

The organization of the art market is founded on the activity of dealers who function through the art galleries. These have proliferated enormously all over the world in the last few years.

The economic fundamentals of art evolved from the patronage of the church, the leaders, the nobility, and later the first rich businessmen, up to the present system of dealers in art. The change took place during the 19th century, and with it the phenomenon of an art market began. The modern breed of dealer appeared with Paul Durand-Ruel who at the outset of the 1870's promoted the impressionists. Next in prestige was Ambroise Vollard, associated with Cézanne from 1895; in 1901 he held the first Paris exhibition of Picasso. Daniel-Henri Kahnweiler became the great art dealer associated with the cubists. All these dealers established themselves as standard-bearers for a tendency or an artist, and they where at the same time promoters, entrepreneurs, and theorists.

From these pioneers the galleries have multiplied, with only a few retaining the character of promoters and publicists of new tendencies. Most of them have assumed a fundamentally commercial character, showing themselves keenly sensitive to market values.

Outstanding among the galleries of the postwar period are René Drouin's in Paris. In his Place Vendôme gallery two exhibitions, one in 1943 and the other in 1945, introduced Fautrier. In 1945 and in 1947 there were the two important exhibitions that created the prestige of Dubuffet, and two exhibitions of Wols. Three of the most significant artists of the postwar period were launched without any immediate profit to the Drouin Gallery, as hardly any sales were made.

The Denise René Gallery from its very beginning became the promoter of the concretist line, a position it has maintained unswervingly up to the present.

The Paul Facchetti Gallery, founded in Paris in 1950, was next to Drouin's the true gallery of trial exhibitions, and introduced some of the most important informalist artists of the present.

In New York the role of pioneer in launching the first American abstract expressionists fell to Peggy Guggenheim in her Art of This Century Gallery, where the first show of Jackson Pollock was held in 1943. In 1944 the Willard Gallery held the first New York exhibitions of Tobey and of Motherwell.

Around 1948 the Betty Parsons Gallery united a large part of the American vanguard (Still, Newman, Rothko, Tobey, Tomlin, Motherwell, and others), and a similar role was played by the Charles Egan Gallery, which held the first exhibition of de Kooning in 1948. Around 1953 the Martha Jackson Gallery was founded, also dedicated to the defense of the new American painting. The promotion of the pop artists in New York is owed largely to two galleries: the Green Gallery and the Leo Castelli Gallery. Castelli and René Drouin had founded the gallery at 17 Place Vendôme in 1939, which Drouin reopened in the postwar era. Leo Castelli introduced his gallery with an exhibition entitled « New York, » in which works of the neodadaists Rauschenberg and Johns were exhibited for the first time; at present the Castelli Gallery is one of the most active in New York, and in spite of having launched some of the most important neodadaist and pop artists it is not identified only with this tendency. Connected with this gallery are Stella, who is partial to the « new geometry, » and Tworkov, an expressionist.

Galleries representing the extreme *avant-garde* usually infuse a sense of entertainment and humor into their exhibitions. An example of this is the Iris Clert Gallery. A Greek living in Paris, Iris Clert began with a small gallery in 3 Rue des Beaux Arts – « the smallest but the most advanced in the world, » she proclaimed. Later the gallery moved to its present address at 28 rue Faubourg Saint-Honoré. It was in her gallery that the famous exhibition of emptiness by Ives Klein was held, and also the one of fullness by Arman. Iris Clert periodically publishes a bulletin full of humor, and in Venice at the time of the Biennale she holds her own exhibition, which she calls the « Little Biennale. »

Some galleries that were in the vanguard in the period between the two great wars have today acquired a more tranquil tone, less sensation-seeking; for example, the Pierre Loeb Gallery in Paris, which in 1925 held the first exhibition of surrealist paintings, and the Jeanne Bucher Gallery, which in 1925 began as a gallery-bookstore, primarily interested in the surrealists Arp, Giacometti, Max Ernst. Jeanne Bucher published the famous books of collages by Max Ernst: *Histoire Naturel* and *Une Semaine de Bonté*. She died in 1946, and now her important gallery is run by Jean-François Jaeger.

The modern galleries are divided between those that search for new values and those that profit by this search by putting under contract artists who appear to be rising. These galleries are eco-nomically strong, and can defray the cost of launching the artists on a grand scale and can offer them the maximum possibility of growth.

Galleries can also be classified as those that specialize in or militate toward a tendency and those that do not specialize. Among the first is Denise René in Paris, who upholds geometric abstraction, and more recently the André Schöller Gallery, which specializes in new figuration, and the Müller Gallery in Munich, which specializes in new abstraction. Those that do not specialize are merely *avant-garde* galleries that go for the latest novelties.

The galleries have come to be almost obligatory as the middlemen between the artist and the public. It is practically impossible to get into contact with the artists except through the galleries. Outside them, the exhibition salons and collective showings are the only places where an artist's work can be evaluated. But the artists themselves look for contracts with a gallery, which means a shortcut to the customers and chances of regular sales. This fundamental importance of the galleries justifies the recent organization of a salon of galleries, and thus came into being the First Salon of Pilot Galleries in the Cantonal Museum of Fine Arts in Lausanne, in 1964, which brought together seventeen galleries from nine countries.

This is not to say that all artists operate through galleries. Many of those who are famous do not have contracts with galleries, and when their pictures are found in a gallery it has had to buy them, like any ordinary buyer, possibly in the hope of a rise in the prices or merely to gain a modest commission.

The galleries have various kinds of contracts with their artists; the less an artist is known, the less favorable is the contract for him. These contracts assure the gallery exclusive sales rights, which can be universal (including any part of the world) or limited to a country, a city, or a specific area. Sometimes, in the case of well-known artists, the contract merely gives the gallery priority in selecting a predetermined number of canvases by the artists. The forms of the contracts vary. There may be outright sales of works, or they can be on consignment for a certain monthly stipend, counted as being an advance on future sales. This last system gives the artists who are still unknown and without resources a chance to dedicate themselves wholly to their work. In this manner the gallery fills the function of financier and promoter. In the latter function the gallery guarantees to hold exhibitions and be responsible for publicity and catalogs, notices to the press, and whatever means of promotion are required to create interest in the artist, such as his participation in competitions and group exhibitions. A campaign of this kind is costly, calling for a considerable financial investment that is not always rewarded with success. This is the way the so-called pilot galleries, who are interested in discovering new talent, operate.

But there are galleries with less pretensions who simply rent space to an artist for his exhibition, and furthermore charge a commission on sales, while the artist shoulders all the expenses.

If the galleries form the base on which the art market is built, this is furthered by various influences, among which are the large national and international competitions, the annual salons dedicated to exhibiting *avant-garde* works, the activity of the modern museums that not only buy works but mount periodical exhibitions that indicate or emphasize certain tendencies, the various artistic societies, associations, and groups of artists, and even the work of critics who promote new tendencies by organizing exhibitions. To all this must be added the exploitation through such media as the daily press, popular magazines, radios, and particularly television. The publicity that accompanies the launching of a new tendency can be seen in the use of slogans and catchphrases. Designations like « hard-edge, »

« pop art, » and « op art » serve to call attention to something that pretends to be new, and they are in large part successful owing to the catchiness of the phrases.

All this complex activity of the art market mobilizes numerous resources, and around it move multiple interests that develop every imaginable strategy to attain favorable positions, attract public attention, and awaken interest among buyers. Thus there is a constant battle for awards, to be in important exhibitions, make sales to museums, and win the critics' praises.

Many large business concerns have recently demonstrated an interest in promoting art because they have discovered that it is an efficient and culture-directed means of getting valuable publicity. Also, governments give their support to modern art, finding in its diffusion a way of cultural penetration of exceptional value to the national interest.

Salons

It can be said that modern salons have their origin, as independent manifestations of official support, from the time when impressionism started the modern evolution and produced the first rupture between art and society. Thus the Salon de Refusés in 1863; in 1884 the Salon des Indépendants was founded; and from then on, various independent salons in France, Germany, Austria, and other countries indicated how the new tendencies that followed on one another were to be introduced. During the second postwar period, two unofficial salons appear as the most important in Paris: Salon de Mai and Réalités Nouvelles. The Salon de Mai, undoubtedly the most prestigious, founded immediately after the liberation, gave shelter to *avant-garde* artists who already were famous (Picasso, Matisse, Léger, and others) and to newcomers, without distinguishing between figural, abstract, and other tendencies. Thus it exhibited figural or semifigural artists such as Edouard Pignon, Charles Lapicque, and Marchand, surrealists like Matta, Hérold, Victor Brauner, and Masson, and abstract painters such as Manessier, Lanskoi, Magnelli, and Sam Francis.

The Salon des Réalités Nouvelles was founded in 1946 by Frédo Sidès, who in 1939 had organized the group called Nouvelles Réalités, the embryo of the future salon. During the first few years geometric abstracts dominated almost entirely, but during the rise of informalism it was invaded by informal expressions, in this way gathering together all the abstract expressions. From 1964 on, it was also open to new figuration, by which it lost its quality as a salon specializing in abstracts.

Later salons with official support were started, such as the Salon Comparaison, which takes place annually in the Musée d'Art Moderne de la Ville de Paris; it has been held since 1955, and is more than anything a federation of groups.

Associations for the diffusion of art are particularly widespread in Germany, where almost all important towns have a *Kunstverein* (association for plastic arts), which discharges an important function. For its work in propagating the arts the Kestner Gesellschaft of Hanover should be mentioned; under the leadership of W. Schmalenbach it has developed a sustained plan for exhibitions accompanied by important catalogs. The various German museums also mount exhibitions of instructive character; outstanding among them are the Volkwang Museum in Essen and the Haus der Kunst in Munich, the latter connected with the Neue Pinakothek.

In London the Institute of Contemporary Art (I.C.A.) fills a role similar to that of the German associations, and is active in disseminating the most diverse modern trends in the plastic arts. In the United States the function of spreading new trends is centralized in the modern museums, which periodically mount exhibitions to alert the public to new currents or to establish a general résumé of the situation. Outstanding are, first, the Museum of Modern Art, then the Solomon R. Guggenheim Museum, the Whitney Museum of American Art, and the Jewish Museum, all in New York City. All excercise a real influence on opinion, and are able to awaken immediate interest by the prestige enjoyed by their exhibitions, which usually are accompanied by important catalogs. So great is the decisive power of the exhibitions of these museums that the sculptor and theorist George Rickey, in an intelligent article with the title « The Scandal of Success, » proposed as a remedy against the artistic inflation they caused that the museums between them establish a rule not to exhibit the work of any artists who did not have a career of at least five years behind him.

International competitions

But the greatest influence in the world of art is wielded by the international competitions, of which the Biennale in Venice stands at the head both for its age and prestige. It was created in 1895, and in later years has been a sensitive indicator of dominant trends. In 1960 the tendency represented was informalism, in 1964 pop. The Venice Biennale is without doubt the great event of the art world, attracting the most important collectors and dealers who want to get an idea of the values that are forthcoming or are being established.

Similar characteristics are found in the Biennale of São Paulo in Brazil. It has the same international flavor, with pavilions for the various countries and also for those specially invited. The first exhibition there was in 1951.

In the United States there are two important international grand prizes, for which artists are invited to compete. The Pittsburgh International, usually known as the Carnegie Prize, is held every three years in the Carnegie Institute in Pittsburgh. The selection of competing artists is done by one person, the director of the Department of Fine Arts (presently Gustave von Grosschwitz, who replaced Gordon Washburn), but the prizes are awarded by an international jury. According to the rules of the competition, at least a third of the competing artists must be Americans. In 1964 four prizes for painting where awarded to the following artists: Kelly, Soulages, Pasmore, and Saura.

The other important award is the Guggenheim, instituted by the foundation of that name. Artists from various countries compete by invitation, limited as to number.

In Kassel, Germany, international exhibitions, under the name of Documenta, are held periodically, and represent an actual appraisal of the situation in modern art. Three of these exhibitions have been held: Documenta I in 1955, Documenta II in 1959, and Documenta III in 1964.

Other competitions, more restricted in scope, are the International Biennale of the Republic of San Marino, whose fourth biennale, held in 1963, had as a theme « Beyond the Informal, » and included recent tendencies; the Biennale for young artists, in Paris; the Hispano-American Biennale, which is held in Spain, and includes countries of the Spanish-speaking hemisphere; the American Biennale of Córdoba, Argentina, instituted by the Kaiser Industries of Argentina, which in its second competition in 1964 embraced the ten South American countries; the Marzotto award, instituted in Italy by the industrialist of that name, restricted to the artists of the European Community; the International Di Tella award, started in Buenos Aires by the foundation of that name; the International Lissone award in Italy; and others, less well known.

In addition to these competitions are the exhibitions of international character held by various museums, either to show a new tendency or to make an appraisal of the prevailing situation in art. Among these exhibitions the outstanding ones are those held in the Stedelijk Museum in Amsterdam, for their boldness and the international repercussions they provoke.

This intense international movement of works creates an uninterrupted traffic between the most diverse countries, and permits an immediate exchange of information as to the quality and characteristics of international art, which contributes to the internationalization of culture.

But behind the cultural motivation all kinds of economic and speculative interests are mobilized, not to mention the national struggle for artistic ascendancy. On one side there is greed, and on the other, vanity. The countries, the galleries, the collectors, and the artists resort to all sorts of subterfuges that becloud the values. Pressures of all kinds, private arrangements, and under-the-table payments are imposed on purely artistic interest and distort the results. An international award is highly coveted because it raises the prestige of an artist, and as a consequence his market quotation.

Publicity techniques

But the evaluation of an artist does not depend only on his inclusion in the international competitions. A multitude of subtle publicity techniques discharge the fundamental role. Once these moves have succeeded in stirring up interest in an artist, his work becomes part of a speculation structure comparable to stock-market quotations. An indication of the prices of works of art, particularly those by established artists, can be found by following the public auctions held by houses specializing in art works, for example, the Palais Galliera and Hôtel Drouot in Paris, Sotheby and Co. in London, and the Parke-Bernet Gallery (associated with Sotheby and Co.) in New York. In these and other auctions held in various parts of the world, merchants, collectors, and artists themselves attend to defend the prices of the works in which they have an interest.

Among the mass of publicity channels that build up the image of an artist, an outstanding role is played by publications specializing in art: books, magazines, and luxurious catalogs. Magazines devoted wholly or in part to modern art are numerous. Those enjoying high prestige include *Art International* published in Lugano, Switzerland; *Quadrum* in Belgium; *Metro* and *Rivista della Biennale di Venezia* in Italy; *Art News, Art in America, Arts*, and *Forum* (devoted primarily to defending the interest of Western artists) in the United States; *Studio International* in London, a long-established publication; and *Cimaise* in Paris, connected with the Arnaud Gallery. In Germany the two pubblications with the widest circulation are *Kunstwerk* in Baden-Baden and *Kunst* in Mainz.

An idea of the interest that this type of magazine commands can be seen by the circulation figures of a small magazine devoted to the doings of the art galleries in New York. In February, 1965, the *Art Gallery* registered a circulation of 28,258.

The sections of art news in the daily press and in some periodicals of general interest can be very influential, such as *The New York Times*, whose art critics are John Canaday and Hilton Kramer.

The function of art criticism

At this point it is valid to examine one of the fundamental aspects of the plastic arts: the function of criticism. Its task is to evalaute the artists; an artist's renown depends to a large extent on the critics. The diffusion of knowledge and of new tendencies depends also on the critics.

As a result of the growing interest in modern art, critics have proliferated, and as in all cases of proliferation the quality of the product has suffered. Being a critic today is an excellent profession; magazines, newspapers, art publications, and lectures offer innumerable possibilities; museums and art institutions scattered all over the world have many opportunities; galleries and collectors need advisers. By commanding an outlet the critics are undoubtedly an important factor in gaining or losing prestige for an artist. In that way they influence the art market. For this reason they are also subject to all sorts of pressure, flattery, and intrigue, all of which contribute to the difficulty of maintaining an impartial attitude in their judgments. At other times they themselves participate with the same fervor as the artists in the battle of tendencies. But aside from these circumstantial factors, many critics do not have the proper cultural background and knowledge for the job. And this happens to be the case with some critics of outstanding stature. For all these reasons the function of the critics becomes, in a high degree, dangerous and confusing. Add to this that those critics who are collectors will find themselves unconsciously heightening the value of the artists whose work they possess, not to mention those (fortunately few in number) who take advantage of a position with museums or institutions to promote the acquisition of the works of the artists whom it serves their interest to exploit.

The majority of the critics for the larger dailies are commentators (there are some worthy exceptions), and their copy lacks sincerity and often is not informative. These critics voice judgments that are not valid but that nevertheless exercise a strong influence on the public, thanks to the weight the man in the street attributes to the printed word.

The critic finds himself armed with the irresistible weapon of being able to sway public opinion at will, which in the end is another way of exercising power. In not a few instances this power is used to propagate extra-artistic ideologies, nationalistic or political, which can be read between the lines. This explains (when even more obscure motives do not intervene) the extolling of certain schools of artists who permit a national bias to take precedence over the pictorial or who support a political viewpoint.

And finally, are not even sincere critics influenced by the penetrating action of publicity?

The language of the critics has lately undergone a change, as have the principles that constituted the foundation of art, but the introduction of a terminology often borrowed from the new languages of science, philosophy, psychology, and sociology (frequently without any direct knowledge of these disciplines) contributes to an arcane exclusiveness of style, robbing the text of its explanatory function. Lately, some critics have come to adopt the language used in information theory, and their writing is plagued with terms such as « message, » « feedback, » and « codification. »

However, in spite of these considerations, it cannot be denied that many of the specialized publications do have the services of true experts and connoisseurs.

The critics and theorists who become promoters or defenders of a new artistic movement deserve special mention. Such guiding spirits are not exclusive to the second postwar period, but they have acquired a special importance in the last few years. In the beginning of the century, Apollinaire developed this activity by upholding the cubists, and Herwarth Walden, with his publication *Der Sturm* and his gallery, filled a similar function for the expressionists and the « Blaue Reiter. »

After the last war a critic appeared whose work was closely tied to the spread of informalism: Michel Tapié. Through his activity as an organizer of collective exhibitions and an adviser to various galleries (first with Drouin, then with Facchetti, Rive Droite Gallery, and presently with the Stadler Gallery), through his prefaces to catalogues and his own publications, through his periodic travels from the United States to Japan to search for new values and to spread those already existing, Tapié has developed a redoubtable promotional network that at the same time has permitted him to introduce and know many artists, from the American continent to the Far East. Tapié's work has introduced the American abstract expressionists and the European tachists and informalists to the Japanese, at the same time as Paris, Italy, and New York have become aware of the Japanese vanguard. He has shaped an actual cultural axis that could be called the New York-Paris-Tokyo axis. The expression he conceived, *art autre*, defines in the most precise and lucid manner the dominant phenomenon in the art of the postwar period.

Edouard Jaguer has conducted a tireless campaign in support of the art of the imaginary, and has arranged exhibitions all over Europe and North and South America. The movement he furthered is known as « Phases, » from the name of the review published by Jaguer, which serves to spread the movement and give it theoretical support.

In the United States the critic Clement Greenberg appears as the most outstanding champion of a certain tendency. Soon after the war he boldly took up the battle for abstract expressionists, and for Jackson Pollock in particular when the conformist critics still slightingly referred to him as Jack the Dripper. Recently, upholding new abstraction, his essays on Morris Louis and Noland are examples of lucid and penetrating exposition. His battle has centered on getting recognition for a « new American painting » with its own characteristics, independent of the European *avant-garde*. The success that Greenberg and other fighters have attained in their nationalistic interests must be acknowledged (no matter how tiring such nationalistic criteria become).

Recently, in France, Pierre Restany developed a kind of counteroffensive in defense of the European vanguard by creating the group of new realists, in which he ranges artists of the School of Paris against the pop artists with strictly American characteristics.

The art market

All this complex mechanism of galleries, exhibitions, battles between tendencies, critics, museums, and awards acts on the art market, which in its turn avails itself of advertising techniques and market studies that have all the characteristics of those of the industrial market with its battles for prices, inflations, and deflations.

The rapid upswing of modern works of art has made the art market a fruitful field for speculators. To give an idea of the situation it will be enough to mention that a picture by Pollock that sold for $ 8,000 in 1954 was worth $ 100,000 in 1964. A canvas by Franz Kline that sold for $ 1,200 in 1957 was worth $ 25,000 in 1964. Comparable prices of $ 20,000 to $ 25,000 were paid for works by Rothko in 1964 *. Artists of more recent popularity command the same prices: a good Morris Louis cannot be obtained for less than $ 15,000, and works by Rauschenberg, Jasper Johns, and Larry Rivers sell for $ 20,000.

The art market is primarily concentrated in two countries, the United States and France, who together govern international price quotations for the artists. In other countries there are national price quotations for artists of local interest, but the prices are sometimes totally different from the international quotations. Prices fluctuate with changing fashions, and at times there are

slumps in the market that produce actual panics, as happens on the stock exchange. An incident of this kind began in 1962 with reference to abstract art. In the October 6, 1962, issue of *Figaro Littéraire*, Maurice Tallier spoke of a 40 percent diminution in sales and of an actual panic in the abstract art market. Alain Bosquet expressed himself in similar terms in the October 2, 1962, issue of *Combat*. This evidently signified the end of interest in the informal tendency, and the galleries rushed to promote new tendencies that replaced it: new figuration, pop art and, more recently, op art and the art of movement.

But the real slump in the art market happened when Paris was replaced as the world's art capital by New York. For many years the United States was the largest importer of art from the School of Paris. American collectors went to Paris to make their purchases, and the museums in America were filled with works by the European vanguard. American artists, on the other hand, did not arouse much interest in Europe, being considered as merely imitators of the School of Paris. Suddenly, however, after the war, the situation changed: original and brilliant American artists began to appear, introducing works with a new flavor, which awakened interest in Europe. This « new American painting » began to have influence on the European painters and to acquire international value. This movement, which began with the abstract expressionists, established itself and became dominant with the appearance of pop art and new abstraction. Countering the School of Paris was the School of New York. The competition between the two schools becomes, in the final analysis, a competition between products. The American dealers no longer need to import; they prefer to export their art products, and have succeeded in doing so.

The obvious supremacy of the New York art market in the last few years has resulted in an

* Figures taken from articles by V. Marvin Elkoff in *Esquire*, January, 1965.

attempt by many European artists to conquer it. Artists of the School of Paris have emigrated to the United States. A great number of important artists from France, Italy, Spain, and Germany get their sales almost exclusively through the American galleries, or the European galleries seek agencies with those of similar bent in New York. The intense movement in the American art market is shown in its sensitivity to factors that have repercussions on the general economy. It can be observed to suffer fluctuations parallel to those of the New York Stock Exchange.

Art fashions

Another important phenomenon of the postwar period is the rapidity with which artistic fashions change. At the end of the war concrete art, an aspect of geometric abstraction, appeared to be dominant, but very soon it was literally swept away by instinctive abstraction that appeared under such different names as « lyrical abstraction, » « informalism, » and « abstract expressionism. » This movement reached its high peak between 1952 and 1956, when it in turn had to yield to pop art, which soon gave way to the public's taste for new abstraction. Recently op art and the art of movement have clearly dominated the market, even inspiring fabric designs, decoration, and advertising. New figuration, too, seems to be firmly established.

Art has become a commodity that follows the fluctuations of style with the same quick variations as the fashion in women's dress. In fact, the opening of an exhibition in one gallery was accompanied by a fashion show.

This speed in the change of orientation and objectives in art naturally is disconcerting to the artists who want to attain success (logically, those in the majority). The almost religious dedication to art has disappeared, giving way to opportunism and an unembarrassed cynicism in conduct. Those artists who have not yet achieved success (and even those who have, for the sake of staying on top) immediately attach themselves to any new fashion, even if they have no clear idea of what it is about. What is the result? A proliferation of mediocrities pretending to be innovators, who succeed only in producing a tiresome modern academism. Among these quick-acting imitators are many who became successful, thanks to poor criticism, alluring advertising, and the ignorance of a public hungry for novelties. But nothing of this invalidates the worth and the significance of the successive movements that have developed in the postwar period.

It is possible that the dulled senses of people living in this machine age need constantly stronger sensations. For this reason art becomes spectacular, and the artist includes himself in the spectacle. He becomes an entertainer of a new kind. Salvador Dalí is the grand master of this attitude. Although gifted with a great inventive faculty and indisputable technical ability, he aims fundamentally at the mystification of the spectator and his art is the art of the showman. This has undeniably brought him fame. But neither ingeniousness nor showmanship nor technical ability makes an artist, and Dalí has remained a special case as the innovator of a very peculiar phenomenon of our times. His example has been continued by various artists: Mathieu, for instance, has followed him, with less ingenuity but with more taste and restraint. Mathieu's charming improvisations are bound to delight the bourgeoisie because of their total lack of challenge. More interesting and with a deeper meaning was the activity of Yves Klein. His obsession with the cosmic, his audacious pretension to encompass emptiness in his show, had a chilling quality that transcended the farcical. He was the foremost exponent of what we designate as attitude art. Also, behind the violent humor of Tinguely's works is a meaning that leads the spectator to reflect. But the real plastic spectacle is to be found in the happenings staged by the pop artists: an ephemeral, impudent, incoherent, but human art, one that appears to be the mirror of an era.

Today the artists seek for newness at any price, because at present newness means success. But the effect of shock and surprise is quickly over when there is nothing solid behind it. This attitude of the artist is, however, not autonomous; generally it responds to a social background, or, more correctly, to the dominant tone of a certain epoch. The present tone results from disillusioned hopes for a just world and from the obvious falsification of such basic values as liberty and equal rights. All this has contributed to a state of indifference in many young people and a negative attitude toward taking a stand for any order, political, social, or moral, that have proved to be unworkable and false. Every individual appears to feel that his salvation depends on his own resources, and in a society that offers nothing any recourse is valid. On the other hand, the latent threat of the total liquidation of humanity inculcates the sensation of the ephemerality of all things, art in particular, and the need to live at an accelerated pace. It is such a state of mind that gives birth to an ephemeral art, an entertaining art.

Art and modern society

Contemporary society tends toward conformism, to convert man into a uniform article with the stamp of mass production. There is no doubt that many artists, as free men, react against this mass culture, and modern art is largely a protest art. These are the terms is which the American critic Thomas B. Hess expresses himself, and there are many who agree with him.

Dubuffet expressed the same line of thought when he said, « The true mission of art is subversive. »

The battle against mass culture in art reveals itself in different forms. In the first place it accentuates the antimechanical faculties or the instinctual and vital powers; the art of the imaginary (surrealism, « Phases » group), abstract expressionism, and informalism are expressions of this attitude. In the second place it expresses itself as aggression in the accentuation of humor and in a grotesque reproduction of the modern world; much of new figuration and pop art is of this type.

There is also no doubt that another large section of contemporary art may appear as a proof that the artist is integrating in society. The position of Vasarely (shared by the neoconstructivists in general) is defined by his own words: « Let us love our epoch which one day will be called an elevated epoch. » But in reality these artists, although they avail themselves of certain techniques of the mechanical era, seek a refuge in a pure art, highly intellectualized, that rejects every emotional implication but that for this very reason signifies a divorce from surrounding reality, an attitude that indirectly carries a protest, a protest by withdrawal.

Apparently, pop art signifies an effort to integrate with the surrounding world (this is the idea some critics and many of the artists propose that we accept), and for this reason they express themselves in a language taken directly from this same surrounding reality. But in reality they do no more than reveal the absurdity of this world, and Rauschenberg's involuntary confession is revealing: « To be a painter is to be an opposer. » As this phrase affirms, pop art, notwithstanding its appearance of integration, is, at its best, essentially nonconformist.

Nonconformism represents an important moving force in art, but because today everything is deceptive it often happens that just a plain hanker-

ing for notoriety disguises itself as nonconformism, an act that in itself is the quintessence of
conformity. Much self-styled modern art tries
for impact or shock only to attract attention,
the same as could be done with a horn or a bell.
Actually, such artists look for just one thing –
to attract attention – giving us in exchange the
most tepid and innocuous emptiness.

But even the authentic and sincere artist is today subject to all sorts of pressures that are not
helpful in the natural development of personality: pressures resulting from the exigencies of a
contract with a gallery, pressures from the critics, pressures resulting from the varying and
arbitrary demands of the market, and the necessity of remaining in the spotlight at all costs.
But from each of the schools and movements
there are always the odds that some true creators
will emerge, those whose art is a proclamation
that is implicitly an exaltation of man, and thus
a profound ethical message. And it stands as a
final affirmation that the work of every true artist,
whatever the idiom he works in, always summons
men as if to a religious ritual.

Index

Color plates

Index   314

2. 6.1% compounded annually

3. 5.58% compounded semiannually

4. 5.75% compounded quarterly

a. Which account(s) should he choose if he wants to invest the smallest amount of money now?

b. How much money must he invest to accumulate $4000 in two years' time?

39. Suppose that you have $1000 in a savings account that pays 4.8% interest per year. Suppose, also, that you owe $500 at 1.5% per month interest.

a. If you pay the interest on your loan for one month so that you can collect one month's interest on

$500 in your savings account, what is your net gain or loss?

b. If you pay the loan back with $500 from your savings account rather than pay one month's interest on the loan, what is your net gain or loss?

c. What strategy do you recommend?

40. One-fourth of the world's population is Chinese and one-fifth of the rest is Indian. What percent of the world's population is Indian?

41. A **cevian** is a line segment that joins a vertex of a triangle and a point on the opposite side. How many triangles are formed if eight cevians are drawn from one vertex of a triangle?

PROBLEMS FOR WRITING/DISCUSSION

1. A student says that if the sale price of a shirt during a 60% off sale is $27.88, then you can find the amount of money you *saved* by multiplying $27.88 times $\frac{60}{40}$ or 1.5. What would you respond?

2. Yoko says that if a car dealer pays General Motors $17,888 for a new car and he then tries to sell it for 20% over cost and it doesn't sell, he can later sell it

for 20% off and he'll still come out even. Do you agree? Explain.

3. Jerry says that if a store has a sale for 35% off and the sale price of a stairmaster is $137, then you can figure out what the original price was by taking 35% of $137 and then adding it back onto the $137. So the original price should be $184.95. But that answer doesn't check. Explain what mistake Jerry is making.

END OF CHAPTER MATERIAL

Solution of Initial Problem

A street vendor had a basket of apples. Feeling generous one day, he gave away one-half of his apples plus one to the first stranger he met, one-half of his remaining apples plus one to the next stranger he met, and one-half of his remaining apples plus one to the third stranger he met. If the vendor had one left for himself, with how many apples did he start?

Strategy: Work Backward

The vendor ended up with 1 apple. In the previous step, he gave away half of his apples plus 1 more. Thus he must have had 4 apples since the one he had plus the one he gave away was 2, and 2 is half of 4. Repeating this procedure, $4 + 1 = 5$ and $2 \cdot 5 = 10$; thus he must have had 10 apples when he met the second stranger. Repeating this procedure once more, $10 + 1 = 11$ and $2 \cdot 11 = 22$. Thus he had 22 apples when he met the first stranger.

Check:
    Start with 22.
    Give away one-half (11) plus one, or 12.

10 remain.
Give away one-half (5) plus one, or 6.
4 remain.
Give away one-half (2) plus one, or 3.
1 remains.

Additional Problems Where the Strategy "Work Backward" Is Useful

1. On a class trip to the world's tallest building, the class rode up several floors, then rode down 18 floors, rode up 59 floors, rode down 87 floors, and ended up on the first floor. How many floors did they ride up initially?

2. At a sports card trading show, one trader gave 3 cards for 5. Then she traded 7 cards for 2. Finally, she bought 4 and traded 2 for 9. If she ended up with 473 cards, how many did she bring to the show?

3. Try the following "magic" trick: Multiply a number by 6. Then add 9. Double this result. Divide by 3. Subtract 6. Then divide by 4. If the answer is 13, what was your original number?

People in Mathematics

David Blackwell (1919–   )
When David Blackwell entered college at age 16, his ambition was to earn a bachelor's degree and become an elementary teacher. Six years later, he had a doctorate in mathematics and was nominated for a fellowship at the Institute for Advanced Study at Princeton. The position included an honorary membership in the faculty at nearby Princeton University, but the university objected to the appointment of a black man as a faculty member. The director of the institute insisted on appointing Blackwell, and eventually won out. From Princeton, Blackwell went on to teach for 10 years at Howard University, then at Berkeley. He has made important contributions to statistics, probability, game theory, and set theory. "Why do you want to share something beautiful with someone else? It's because of the pleasure he will get, and in transmitting it you will appreciate its beauty all over again. My high school geometry teacher really got me interested in mathematics. I hear it suggested from time to time that geometry might be dropped from the curriculum. I would really hate to see that happen. It is a beautiful subject."

Sonya Kovalevskaya (1850–1891) As a young woman, Sonya Kovalevskaya hoped to study in Berlin under the great mathematician Karl Weierstrass. But women were barred from attending the university. She approached Weierstrass directly. Skeptical, he assigned her a set of difficult problems. When Kovalevskaya a returned the following week with solutions, he agreed to teach her privately and was influential in seeing that she was granted her degree—even though she never officially attended the university. Kovalevskaya is known for her work in differential equations and for her mathematical theory of the rotation of solid bodies. In addition, she was editor of a mathematical journal, wrote two plays (with Swedish writer Anne Charlotte Leffler), a novella, and memoirs of her childhood. Of her literary and mathematical talents, she wrote, "The poet has to perceive that which others do not perceive, to look deeper than others look. And the mathematician must do the same thing."

CHAPTER REVIEW

Review the following terms and exercises to determine which require learning or relearning—page numbers are provided for easy reference.

SECTION 7.1: Decimals

VOCABULARY/NOTATION

Decimal 265	Expanded form 265	Terminating decimal 266
Decimal point 265	Hundreds square 265	Fraction equivalents 268

EXERCISES

1. Write 37.149 in expanded form.

2. Write 2.3798 in its word name.

3. Determine which of the following fractions have a terminating decimal representation.

      a. $\dfrac{7}{2^3}$ **b.** $\dfrac{5^3}{3^2 \cdot 2^5}$ **c.** $\dfrac{17}{2^{13}}$

4. Explain how to determine the smaller of 0.24 and 0.3 using the following techniques.

   a. A hundreds square

   b. The number line

   c. Fractions

   d. Place value

5. Calculate mentally and explain what techniques you used.

   a. $(0.25 \times 12.3) \times 8$

   b. $1.3 \times 2.4 + 2.4 \times 2.7$

   c. $15.73 + 2.99$

   d. $27.51 - 19.98$

6. Estimate using the techniques given.

   a. Range: $2.51 \times 3.29 \times 8.07$

   b. Front-end with adjustment: $2.51 + 3.29 + 8.2$

   c. Rounding to the nearest tenth: $8.549 - 2.352$

   d. Rounding to compatible numbers: $421.7 \div 52.937$

SECTION 7.2: Operations with Decimals

VOCABULARY/NOTATION

Repetend ($.\overline{abcd}$)   279   Repeating decimal   279   Period   279

EXERCISES

1. Calculate the following using (i) a standard algorithm and (ii) a calculator.

   a. $16.179 + 4.83$

   b. $84.25 - 47.761$

   c. 41.5×3.7

   d. $154.611 \div 4.19$

   a. $\dfrac{5}{13}$

   b. $\dfrac{132}{333}$

   c. $\dfrac{46}{92}$

2. Determine which of the following fractions have repeating decimals. For those that do, express them as a decimal with a bar over their repetend.

3. Find the fraction representation in simplest form for each of the following decimals.

   a. $3.\overline{674}$ **b.** $24.1\overline{32}$

SECTION 7.3: Ratio and Proportion

VOCABULARY/NOTATION

Ratio 286	Whole-to-part 287	Proportion 288
Part-to-part 287	Extremes 288	Rates 288
Part-to-whole 287	Means 288	Scaling up/scaling down 290

EXERCISES

1. How do the concepts ratio and proportion differ?

2. Determine whether the following are proportions. Explain your method.

   a. $\dfrac{7}{13} = \dfrac{9}{15}$ **b.** $\dfrac{12}{15} = \dfrac{20}{25}$

3. Describe two ways to determine whether $\dfrac{a}{b} = \dfrac{c}{d}$ is a proportion.

4. Which is the better buy? Explain.

   a. 58 cents for 24 oz or 47 cents for 16 oz

   b. 7 pounds for $3.45 or 11 pounds for $5.11

5. Solve: If $3\frac{1}{4}$ cups of sugar are used to make a batch of candy for 30 people, how many cups are required for 40 people?

SECTION 7.4: Percent

VOCABULARY/NOTATION

Percent   297   Proportion approach   300   Equation approach   301

Grid approach   299

EXERCISES

1. Write each of the following in all three forms: decimal, percent, and fraction (in simplest form).

   a. 56%   **b.** 0.48   **c.** $\frac{1}{8}$

2. Calculate mentally using fraction equivalents.

   a. 48 × 25%

   b. $33\frac{1}{3}$% × 72

   c. 72 × 75%

   d. 20% × 55

3. Estimate using fraction equivalents.

   a. 23% × 81   **b.** 49% × 199

   c. 32% × 59   **d.** 67% × 310

4. Solve:

   a. A car was purchased for $17,120 including a 7% sales tax. What was the price of the car before tax?

   b. A soccer player has been successful 60% of the times she kicks toward goal. If she has taken 80 kicks, what percent will she have if she kicks 11 out of the next 20?

PROBLEMS FOR WRITING/DISCUSSION

1. Mary Lou said she knows that when fractions are written as decimals they either repeat or terminate. So 12/17 must not be a fraction because when she divided 12 by 17 on her calculator, she got a decimal that did not repeat or terminate. How would you react to this?

2. A student in your class says that if the ratio of oil to vinegar in a salad dressing is 3 : 4, that means that 75% of the salad dressing is oil. Another student says less than 50% is oil. Can you explain this?

3. A student tells you that 6.45 is greater than 6.5 because 45 is greater than 5. How would you explain?

4. Can you use lattice multiplication for decimals? For example, how would you multiply 3.24 times 1.7?

5. Caroline is rounding decimals to the nearest hundredth. She takes 19.67472 and she changes it to 19.6747, then 19.675, then 19.68. Her teacher says the answer is 19.67. Caroline says, "I thought I was supposed to round up when the next digit is 5 or more." Can you help explain this problem?

6. Looking at the same problem that Caroline had, Amir comes up with the answer 19.66. When his teacher asks him how he got that answer, he says, "because of the 4, I had to round down." What is Amir's misconception?

7. There is a new student in your class whose family has just moved to your district from Germany. When he writes out the number for π, he writes 3,14 instead of 3.14, and when you tell him he's wrong, he gets upset. The next day he brings a note from home saying that 3,14 is correct. What is going on here? How would you explain?

8. Merilee said her calculator changed $\frac{2}{3}$ to .6666667, so obviously it does not repeat. Therefore it must be a terminating decimal. How would you respond to Merilee?

9. How do you calculate a 15% tip in a restaurant? Explain your method. What do you think is the best way to do it mentally?

10. Hair stylists tell you that human hair typically grows $\frac{1}{2}$ inch per month. How would you translate that into miles per hour? How would you explain your method to students?

CHAPTER TEST

Knowledge

1. True or false?

   a. The decimal 0.034 is read "thirty-four hundredths."

   b. The expanded form of 0.0271 is $\frac{2}{100} + \frac{7}{1000} + \frac{1}{10,000}$.

   c. The fraction $\frac{27}{125}$ has a terminating decimal representation.

   d. The repetend of $0.03\overline{74}$ is "374."

   e. The fraction $\frac{27}{225}$ has a repeating, nonterminating decimal representation.

   f. Forty percent equals two-fifths.

   g. The ratios $m:n$ and $p:q$ are equal if and only if $mq = np$.

   h. If p% of n is x, then $\frac{100x}{n}$.

2. Write the following in expanded form.

   a. 32.198   **b.** .000342

3. What does the "cent" part of the word *percent* mean?

4. In a bag of 23 Christmas candies there were 14 green candies and 9 red candies. Express the following types of ratios.

   a. Part to part

   b. Part to whole

Skill

5. Compute the following problems without a calculator. Find approximate answers first.

   a. $3.71 + 13.809$

   b. $14.3 - 7.961$

   c. 7.3×11.41

   d. $6.5 \div 0.013$

6. Determine which number in the following pairs is larger using (i) the fraction representation, and (ii) the decimal representation.

   a. 0.103 and 0.4

   b. 0.0997 and 0.1

7. Express each of the following fractions in its decimal form.

   a. $\frac{2}{7}$ **b.** $\frac{5}{8}$ **c.** $\frac{7}{48}$ **d.** $\frac{4}{9}$

8. Without converting, determine whether the following fractions will have a terminating or nonterminating decimal representation.

   a. $\dfrac{9}{16}$ **b.** $\dfrac{17}{78}$ **c.** $\dfrac{2^3}{2^7 \cdot 5^3}$

9. Express each of the following decimals in its simplest fraction form.

   a. $0.\overline{36}$ **b.** $0.3\overline{6}$ **c.** 0.3636

10. Express each of the following in all three forms: decimal, fraction, and percent.

   a. 52%   **b.** 1.25   **c.** $\frac{17}{25}$

11. The ratio of boys to girls is 3:2 and there are 30 boys and girls altogether. How many boys are there?

12. Estimate the following and describe your method.

   a. 53×0.48

   b. $1469.2 \div 26.57$

   c. $33 \div 0.76$

   d. 442.78×18.7

13. Arrange the following from smallest to largest.

$$\frac{1}{3}, \quad 0.3, \quad 3\%, \quad \frac{2}{7}$$

Understanding

14. Without performing any calculations, explain why $\frac{1}{123456789}$ must have a repeating, nonterminating decimal representation.

15. Suppose that the percent key and the decimal point key on your calculator are both broken. Explain how you could still use your calculator to solve problems like "Find 37% of 58."

16. Write a word problem involving percents that would have the following proportion or equation as part of its solution.

   a. $80\% \cdot x = 48$

   b. $\dfrac{x}{100} = \dfrac{35}{140}$

17. When adding 1.3 and 0.2, the sum has 1 digit to the right of the decimal. When multiplying 1.3 and 0.2, the product has 2 digits to the right of the decimal. Explain why the product has 2 digits to the right of the decimal and not just 1.

Problem-Solving/Application

18. What is the 100th digit in $0.\overline{564793}$?

19. If the cost of a new car is $12,000 (plus 5% sales tax) and a down payment of 20% (including the tax) is required, how much money will a customer need to drive out in a new car?

20. A television set was to be sold at a 13% discount, which amounted to $78. How much would the set sell for after the discount?

21. A photograph measuring 3 inches by $2\frac{1}{2}$ inches is to be enlarged so that the smaller side, when enlarged, will be 8 inches. How long will the enlarged longer side be?

22. Find three numbers between 5.375 and 5.3751.

23. Dr. Fjeldsted has 91 students in his first-quarter calculus class. If the ratio of math majors to non-math majors is 4 to 9, how many math majors are in the class?

24. In a furniture store advertisement it was stated "our store offers six new sofa styles—that's 40% more than the competition." Explain why the person writing this advertisement does not understand the mathematics involved.

25. A refrigerator was on sale at the appliance store for 20% off. Marcus received a coupon from the store for an additional 30% off any current price in the store. If he uses the coupon to buy the refrigerator, the price would be $487.20 before taxes. What was the original price?

References for Reflections from Research

BELL, A. (1986). Diagnostic teaching 2. Developing conflict–discussion lessons. *Mathematics Teacher*, *116*, 26–29.

GREER, B. (1987). Nonconservation of multiplication and division involving decimals. *Journal for Research in Mathematics Education*, *18*, 37–45.

HIEBERT, J., & WEARNE, D. (1987). Procedure over concept: The acquisition of decimal number knowledge. In J. Hiebert (Ed.), *Conceptual and procedural knowledge: The case of mathematics* (pp. 199–233). Hillsdale, NJ: Erlbaum.

IRWIN, K. (1996). Children's understanding of the principles of covariation and compensation in part-whole relationships. *Journal for Research in Mathematics Education*, *27*, 25–40.

LO, J., & WATANABE, T. (1997). Developing ratio and proportion schemes: A story of a fifth grader. *Journal for Research in Mathematics Education*, *28*, 216–236.

LOPEZ-REAL, F. (1995). How important is the reversal error in algebra? In B. Atweh & S. Flavel (Eds.),

MERGA 18: GALTHA, *Proceedings of the 18th annual conference* (pp. 390–396). Darwin, Australia: Northern Territory University.

OWENS, D. T. (1990). Thinking on rational number concepts. A teaching experiment. Final Report to Social Sciences and Humanities Research Council of Canada Grant #410-88-0678.

RESNICK, L. B., NESHER, P., LEONARD, F., MAGONE, M., OMANSON, S., & PELED, I. (1989). Conceptual bases of arithmetic errors: The case of decimal fractions. *Journal for Research in Mathematics Education*, *20*, 8–27.

SWAFFORD, J. O., & LANGRALL, C. W. (2000). Grade 6 students' preinstructional use of equations to describe and represent problem situations. *Journal for Research in Mathematics Education*, *31*, 89–110.

TRAFTON, P. R., & ZAWOJEWSKI, J. S. (1984). Teaching rational number division: A special problem. *Arithmetic Teacher*, *31*(6), 20–22.

FOCUS ON *A Brief History of Negative Numbers*

No trace of the recognition of negative numbers can be found in any of the early writings of the Egyptians, Babylonians, Hindus, Chinese, or Greeks. Even so, computations involving subtraction, such as $(10 - 6) \cdot (5 - 2)$, were performed correctly where rules for multiplying negatives were applied. The first mention of negative numbers can be traced to the Chinese in 200 B.C.

In the fourth century in his text *Arithmetica*, Diophantus spoke of the equation $4x + 20 = 4$ as "absurd," since x would have to be -4! The Hindu Brahmagupta (circa A.D. 630) spoke of "negative" and "affirmative" quantities, although these numbers always appeared as subtrahends. Around 1300, the Chinese mathematician Chu Shi-Ku gave the "rule of signs" in his algebra text. Also, in his text *Ars Magna* (1545) the Italian mathematician Cardano recognized negative roots and clearly stated rules of negatives.

Various notations have been used to designate negative numbers. The Hindus placed a dot or small circle over or beside a number to denote that it was negative; for example, 6̇ or 6̊ represented -6. The Chinese used red to denote positive and black to denote negative integers, and indicated negative numbers by drawing a slash through a portion of the numeral; for example, $-10,200$ was written 10 ✗ ✗ 00. Cardano used the symbol m: (probably for "minus") for negative; for example, -3 was written m:3.

In this chapter we use black chips and red chips to motivate the concepts underlying positive ("in the black") and negative ("in the red") numbers much as the Chinese may have done, although with the colors reversed.

Both zeros and negative terms occur in this page from Chu Shih-Chieh's book on algebra, *Precious Mirror of the Four Elements*, published in 1303. Each box, consisting of a group of squares containing signs, represents a "matrix" form of writing an algebraic expression. The frequent occurrence of the sign "0" for zero may be clearly seen. (In these cases it means that terms corresponding to those squares do not occur in the equation.) The diagonal lines slashed through some of the numbers in the squares indicate that they are negative terms. (The number "one" is one vertical line, the number "two" is two vertical lines, etc.)

Strategy
Use Cases

Many problems can be solved more easily by breaking the problem into various cases. For example, consider the following statement: The square of any whole number n is a multiple of 4 or one more than a multiple of 4. To prove this, we need only consider two cases: n is even or n is odd. If n is even, then $n = 2x$ and $n^2 = 4x^2$, which is a multiple of 4. If n is odd, then $n = 2x + 1$ and $n^2 = 4x^2 + 4x + 1$, which is one more than a multiple of 4. The following problem can be solved easily by considering various cases for a, b, and c.

Initial Problem

Prove or disprove: 2 is a factor of $(a - b)(b - c)(c - a)$ for any integers a, b, c. (*Hint*: Try a few examples first.)

$a = 8$, $b = 5$, $c = 1$.
$(a - b)(b - c)(c - a) = -84$.
$2 \mid -84$.

Clues

The Use Cases strategy may be appropriate when

- A problem can be separated into several distinct cases.
- A problem involves distinct collections of numbers such as odds and evens, primes and composites, and positives and negatives.
- Investigations in specific cases can be generalized.

A solution of the Initial Problem appears on page 347.

INTRODUCTION

Whole numbers and fractions are useful in solving many problems and applications in society. However, there are many situations where negative numbers are useful. For example, negative numbers are very helpful in describing temperature below zero, elevation below sea level, losses in the stock market, and an overdrawn checking account. In this chapter we study the integers, the set of numbers that consists of the whole numbers, together with the negative numbers that are the opposites of the nonzero whole numbers. The four basic operations of the integers are introduced together with order relationships.

8.1   ADDITION AND SUBTRACTION

STARTING POINT

In the above introduction, temperature, elevation, stocks, and banking are presented as situations where positive and negative numbers are used. Using one of these scenarios, write a word problem for each of the following expressions.

$$-30 + 14 \qquad -30 - 14 \qquad -30 + (-14)$$

Integers and the Integer Number Line

Reflection from Research
An understanding of integers is crucial to an understanding of future work in algebra (Sheffield & Cruikshank, 1996).

Reflection from Research
It is important to introduce children to negative numbers using manipulatives (Thompson, 1988).

The introduction to this chapter lists several situations in which negative numbers are useful. There are other situations in mathematics in which negative numbers are needed. For example, the subtraction problem $4 - 7$ has no answer when using whole numbers. Also, the equation $x + 7 = 4$ has no whole-number solution. To remedy these situations, we introduce a new set of numbers, the integers. Our approach here will be to introduce the integers using a physical model. This model is related to a procedure that was used in accounting. Numerals written in black ink represent amounts above zero ("in the black" is positive) and in red ink represent accounts below zero ("in the red" is negative). We will use the integers to represent these situations.

DEFINITION

Integers

The set of **integers** is the set

$$I = \{. \ . \ . \ , -3, -2, -1, 0, 1, 2, 3, . \ . \ .\}.$$

The numbers 1, 2, 3, . . . are called **positive integers** and the numbers -1, -2, -3, . . . are called **negative integers.** Zero is neither a positive nor a negative integer.

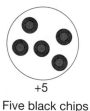

+5
Five black chips

−3
Three red chips
Figure 8.1

In a set model, chips can be used to represent integers. However, *two* colors of chips must be used, one color to represent positive integers (black) and a second to represent negative integers (red) (Figure 8.1). One black chip represents a credit of 1 and one red chip represents a debit of 1. Thus *one black chip and one red chip cancel each other*, or "make a zero" [Figure 8.2(a)]. Using this concept, each integer can be represented by chips in many different ways [Figure 8.2(b)].

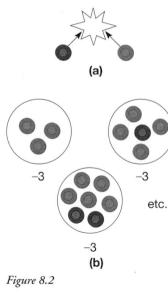

An extension from the examples in Figure 8.2 is that each integer has infinitely many representations using chips. (Recall that every fraction also has an infinite number of representations.)

Another way to represent the integers is to use a measurement model, the **integer number line** (Figure 8.3). The integers are equally spaced and arranged sym-

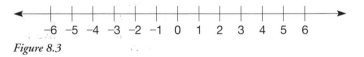

Figure 8.3

-3 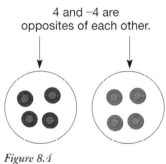 -3

etc.

-3

(b)

Figure 8.2

metrically to the right and left of zero on the number line. This symmetry leads to a useful concept associated with positive and negative numbers. This concept, the opposite of a number, can be defined using either the measurement model or the set model of integers. The **opposite** of the integer a, written $-a$ or $(-a)$, is defined as follows:

Set Model The opposite of a is the integer that is represented by the same number of chips as a, but of the opposite color (Figure 8.4).

Measurement Model The opposite of a is the integer that is its mirror image about 0 on the integer number line (Figure 8.5).

4 and −4 are
opposites of each other.

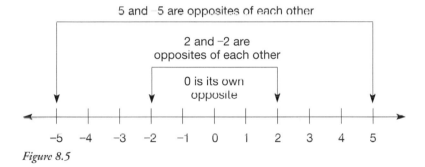

Figure 8.5

Figure 8.4

The opposite of a positive integer is negative, and the opposite of a negative integer is positive. Also, the opposite of zero is zero. The concept of opposite will be seen to be very useful later in this section when we study subtraction.

Addition and Its Properties

Consider the following situation. In a football game, a running back made 12 running attempts and was credited with the following yardage for each attempt: 12, 7, −6, 8, 13, −1, 17, −5, 32, 16, 14, −7. What was his total yardage for the game? Integer addition can be used to answer this question. The definition of addition of integers can be motivated using both the set model and the measurement model.

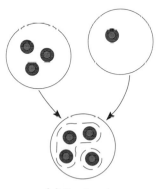

(a) 3 + 1 = 4

Figure 8.6a

Set Model Addition means to put together or form the union of two disjoint sets (Figure 8.6).

www.wiley.com/
college/musser

Spotlight on Technology The set model using black and red chips is illustrated in the Chapter 8 eManipulative activity, *Chips Plus*. After trying a few examples, answer the following question: "In general, when will the sum of two integers be negative?"

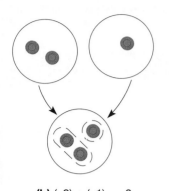

Measurement Model Addition means to put directed arrows end to end starting at zero. Note that positive integers are represented by arrows pointing to the right and negative integers by arrows pointing to the left (Figure 8.7).

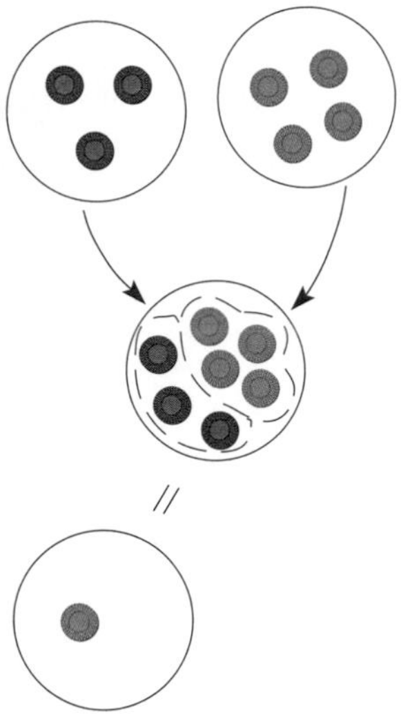

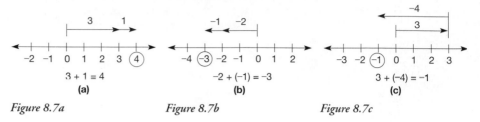

(a)	(b)	(c)
$3 + 1 = 4$	$-2 + (-1) = -3$	$3 + (-4) = -1$

Figure 8.7a   *Figure 8.7b*   *Figure 8.7c*

(b) $(-2) + (-1) = -3$

Figure 8.6b

The examples in Figures 8.6 and 8.7 lead to the following definition of integer addition.

● DEFINITION

Addition of Integers

Let a and b be any integers.

1. *Adding zero*: $a + 0 = 0 + a = a$.
2. *Adding two positives*: If a and b are positive, they are added as whole numbers.
3. *Adding two negatives*: If a and b are positive (hence $-a$ and $-b$ are negative), then $(-a) + (-b) = -(a + b)$, where $a + b$ is the whole-number sum of a and b.
4. *Adding a positive and a negative*:
   a. If a and b are positive and $a \geq b$, then $a + (-b) = a - b$, where $a - b$ is the whole-number difference of a and b.
   b. If a and b are positive and $a < b$, then $a + (-b) = -(b - a)$, where $b - a$ is the whole-number difference of a and b.

(c) $3 + (-4) = -1$

Figure 8.6c

These rules for addition are abstractions of what most people do when they add integers—namely, compute mentally using whole numbers and then determine whether the answer is positive, negative, or zero.

Example 8.1   Calculate the following using the definition of integer addition.
a. $3 + 0$ **b.** $3 + 4$ **c.** $(-3) + (-4)$
d. $7 + (-3)$ **e.** $3 + (-7)$ **f.** $5 + (-5)$

Solution

a. *Adding zero*: $3 + 0 = 3$
b. *Adding two positives*: $3 + 4 = 7$
c. *Adding two negatives*: $(-3) + (-4) = -(3 + 4) = -7$
d. *Adding a positive and a negative*: $7 + (-3) = 7 - 3 = 4$
e. *Adding a positive and a negative*: $3 + (-7) = -(7 - 3) = -4$
f. *Adding a number and its opposite*: $5 + (-5) = 0$ ■

The problems in Example 8.1 have interpretations in the physical world. For example, $(-3) + (-4)$ can be thought of as the temperature dropping 3 degrees one

PRACTICE

LESSON
22

Using Negative Numbers

In many real-life situations we need to describe things using numbers that are less than 0. In this lesson you'll review how to identify and name these negative numbers.

◆ Can you think of times when it might be useful to use numbers less than 0?

Suppose the temperature is 10°C and it goes down 15°C. What will the temperature be?

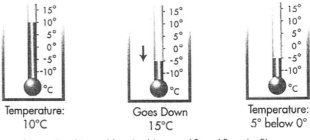

| Temperature: 10°C | Goes Down 15°C | Temperature: 5° below 0° |

We can then write this problem in this way: 10 − 15 = (−5)

−5 is read "negative 5."

We often call a temperature of 5° below 0°C a temperature of −5°C.

You can show negative numbers on a number line.

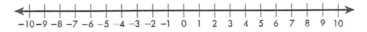

Write the missing items.

	Temperature Before Change	Temperature Change	Temperature After Change
1	15°C	up 5°	■
2	10°C	down 15°	■
3	−5°C (5° below 0°C)	down 5°	■
4	−10°C	up 2°	■
5	−5°C	up 5°	■

McGraw-Hill, MCGRAW-HILL MATHEMATICS "Using Negative Numbers," Grade 6, p. 82. Copyright © 2002 by The McGraw-Hill Companies. Reproduced with permission of the publisher.

322

hour and 4 degrees the next for a total of 7 degrees. In football, $3 + (-7)$ represents a gain of 3 and a loss of 7 for a net loss of 4 yards.

The integer models and the rules for the addition of integers can be used to justify the following properties of integers.

Reflection from Research
Students should be able to make generalizations to integers from their experience with arithmetic (Thompson & Dreyfus, 1988).

PROPERTIES

Properties of Integer Addition

Let a, b, and c be any integers.

Closure Property for Integer Addition

$$a + b \text{ is an integer.}$$

Commutative Property for Integer Addition

$$a + b = b + a$$

Associative Property for Integer Addition

$$(a + b) + c = a + (b + c)$$

Identity Property for Integer Addition

0 is the unique integer such that $a + 0 = a = 0 + a$ for all a.

Additive Inverse Property for Integer Addition

For each integer a there is a unique integer, written $-a$, such that $a + (-a) = 0$. The integer $-a$ is called the **additive inverse** of a.

In words, this property states that any number plus its additive inverse is zero. A useful result that is a consequence of the additive inverse property is **additive cancellation.**

THEOREM

Additive Cancellation for Integers

Let a, b, and c be any integers. If $a + c = b + c$, then $a = b$.

Proof Let $a + c = b + c$. Then

$$(a + c) + (-c) = (b + c) + (-c) \qquad \textit{Addition}$$
$$a + [c + (-c)] = b + [c + (-c)] \qquad \textit{Associativity}$$
$$a + 0 = b + 0 \qquad \textit{Additive inverse}$$
$$a = b \qquad \textit{Additive identity}$$

Thus, if $a + c = b + c$, then $a = b$. ■

Observe that $-a$ need not be negative. For example, the opposite of -7, written $-(-7)$, is 7, a positive number. In general, if a is positive, then $-a$ is negative; if a is negative, then $-a$ is positive; and if a is zero, then $-a$ is zero. As shown in Figure 8.8, using colored chips or a number line, it can be seen that $-(-a) = a$ for any integer a. (NOTE: The three small dots are used to allow for enough chips to represent any integer a, not necessarily just -3 and 3 as suggested by the black and red chips.)

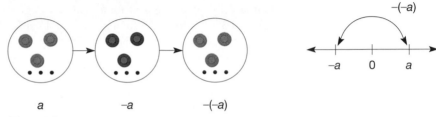

Figure 8.8

THEOREM

Let a be any integer. Then $-(-a) = a$.

Proof   Notice that $a + (-a) = 0$ and $-(-a) + (-a) = 0$.
Therefore, $a + (-a) = -(-a) + (-a)$.
Finally, $a = -(-a)$, since the $(-a)$s can be canceled by additive cancellation.   ■

Properties of integer addition, together with thinking strategies, are helpful in doing computations. For example,

$$3 + (-10) = 3 + [(-3) + (-7)]$$
$$= [3 + (-3)] + (-7) = 0 + (-7) = -7$$

and

$$(-7) + 21 = (-7) + (7 + 14)$$
$$= [(-7) + 7] + 14 = 0 + 14 = 14.$$

Problem-Solving Strategy
Look for a Pattern.

Each preceding step can be justified using a property or the definition of integer addition. When one does the preceding problem mentally, not all the steps need to be carried out. However, it is important to understand how the properties are being applied.

Subtraction

Subtraction of integers can be viewed in several ways.

Pattern

*THE FIRST COLUMN
REMAINS 4.
THE SECOND COLUMN
DECREASES BY 1 EACH
TIME.*

$4 - 2 = 2$ } *1 MORE*
$4 - 1 = 3$ } *1 MORE*
$4 - 0 = 4$ } *1 MORE*
$4 - (-1) = 5$ } *1 MORE*
$4 - (-2) = 6$

Take-Away

Example 8.2   Calculate the following differences.

a. $6 - 2$
b. $-4 - (-1)$
c. $-2 - (-3)$
d. $2 - 5$

Solution See Figure 8.9.   ■

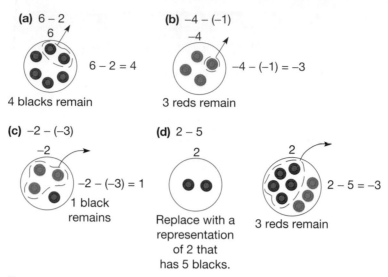

Figure 8.9

Adding the Opposite Let's reexamine the problem in Example 8.2(d). The difference $2 - 5$ can be found in yet another way using the chip model (Figure 8.10).

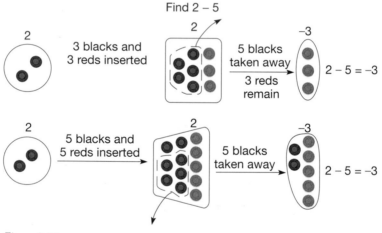

Figure 8.10

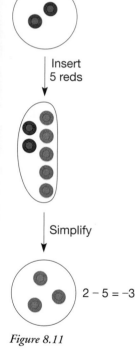

Figure 8.11

This second method can be simplified. The process of inserting 5 blacks and 5 reds and then removing 5 blacks can be accomplished more simply by inserting 5 reds, since we would just turn around and take the 5 blacks away once they were inserted.

Simplified Second Method Find $2 - 5$. The simplified method in Figure 8.11 finds $2 - 5$ by finding $2 + (-5)$. Thus the method of subtraction replaces a subtraction problem with an equivalent addition problem—namely, adding the opposite.

Spotlight on Technology The set model using black and red chips for subtraction is illustrated in the Chapter 8 eManipulative activity, *Chips Minus*. A key idea in using the chips to model integer operations is that adding 1 black chip and 1 red chip to a set does not change the value of the set because it is the same as adding 0. In fact, a pair of chips where one is black and the other is red is often referred to as a **zero pair.** After doing a few examples of integer subtraction on the eManipulative explain why the concept of a zero pair is important.

www.wiley.com/
college/musser

> ## DEFINITION
>
> **Subtraction of Integers: Adding the Opposite**
>
> Let *a* and *b* be any integers. Then
> $$a - b = a + (-b).$$

Adding the opposite is perhaps the most efficient method for subtracting integers because it replaces any subtraction problem with an equivalent addition problem.

Example 8.3 Find the following differences by adding the opposite.

a. $(-8) - 3$ **b.** $4 - (-5)$

Solution

a. $(-8) - 3 = (-8) + (-3) = -11$ **b.** $4 - (-5) = 4 + [-(-5)] = 4 + 5 = 9$ ■

Missing Addend Recall that another approach to subtraction, the missing-addend approach, was used in whole-number subtraction. For example,

$$7 - 3 = n \quad \text{if and only if} \quad 7 = 3 + n.$$

In this way, subtraction can be done by referring to addition. This method can also be extended to integer subtraction.

Example 8.4 Find $7 - (-3)$.

Solution $7 - (-3) = n$ if and only if $7 = -3 + n$. But $-3 + 10 = 7$. Therefore, $7 - (-3) = 10$. ■

Using variables, we can state the following.

> ## ALTERNATIVE DEFINITION
>
> **Subtraction of Integers: Missing-Addend Approach**
>
> Let *a*, *b*, and *c* be any integers. Then $a - b = c$ if and only if $a - b + c$.

In summary, there are three equivalent ways to view subtraction in the integers.

1. Take-away
2. Adding the opposite
3. Missing addend

Notice that both the take-away and the missing-addend approaches are extensions of whole-number subtraction. The adding-the-opposite approach is new because the additive inverse property is a property the integers have but the whole numbers do not. As one should expect, all of these methods yield the same answer. The following argument shows that adding the opposite is a consequence of the missing-addend approach.

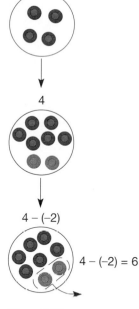

Figure 8.12

Let $a - b = c$.
Then $a = b + c$ by the missing-addend approach.
Hence $a + (-b) = b + c + (-b) = c$, or
$$a + (-b) = c.$$
Therefore, $a - b = a + (-b)$.

It can also be shown that the missing-addend approach follows from adding the opposite.

Example 8.5 Find $4 - (-2)$ using all three methods of subtraction.

Solution

a. Take-Away: See Figure 8.12
b. Adding the Opposite: $4 - (-2) = 4 + [-(-2)] = 4 + 2 = 6$.
c. Missing Addend: $4 - (-2) = c$ if and only if $4 = (-2) + c$. But $4 = -2 + 6$.
 Therefore, $c = 6$. ■

Spotlight on Technology Using a scientific calculator to do integer computation requires an understanding of the difference between subtracting a number and a negative number. On a calculator the subtraction key is $\boxed{-}$ and the negative key is $\boxed{(-)}$. The number -9 is found by pressing $\boxed{(-)}$ 9 $\boxed{-9}$. To calculate $(-18) - (-3)$, press these keys: $\boxed{(-)}$ 18 $\boxed{-}$ $\boxed{(-)}$ 3 $\boxed{=}$ $\boxed{-15}$. (NOTE: On some calculators there is a change-of-sign key $\boxed{+/-}$ instead of a negative key $\boxed{(-)}$. In those cases a -9 is entered as 9 $\boxed{+/-}$.)

As you may have noticed, the "$-$" symbol has three different meanings. Therefore, it should be read in a way that distinguishes among its uses. First, the symbol "-7" is read "negative 7" (*negative* means "less than zero"). Second, since it also represents the opposite or additive inverse of 7, "-7" can be read "the opposite of 7" or "the additive inverse of 7." Remember that "opposite" and "additive inverse" are not synonymous with "negative integers." For example, the opposite or additive inverse of -5 is 5 and 5 is a positive integer. In general, the symbol "$-a$" should be read "the opposite of a" or "the additive inverse of a." It is confusing to children to call it "negative a" since $-a$ may be positive, zero, or negative, depending on the value of a. Third, "$a - b$" is usually read "a minus b" to indicate subtraction.

MATHEMATICAL MORSEL

Often, very surprising results in mathematics spring from simple problems. One such result is the following: Take any collection of seven integers, say a, b, c, d, e, f, and g. Form all consecutive sums from the left; $a, a + b, a + b + c, \ldots, a + b + \cdots + g; b, b + c, b + c + d, \ldots, b + c + \cdots + g$; and so on. Then one of these sums must have a factor of 7. For example, in $\{2, -3, 5, -1, 3, -4, -5\}$, the consecutive sum $(-1) + 3 + (-4) + (-5)$ is $7(-1)$ and hence has a factor of 7. It is interesting that the preceding result holds for any collection of integers, not just 7. That is, if one takes any collection of n integers, there is always a consecutive sum of these integers that has a factor of n.

Section 8.1   EXERCISE / PROBLEM SET A

EXERCISES

1. Which of the following are integers? If they are, identify as positive, negative, or neither.

    a. 25   **b.** −7   **c.** 0

2. Represent the opposites of each of the numbers represented by the following models, where B = black chip and R = red chip.

    a. *BBBBR*   **b.** *RBBRRRRR*

    c.

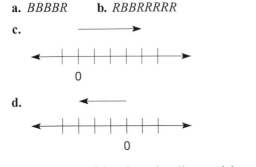

    d.

3. Use the set model and number-line model to represent each of the following integers.

    a. 3   **b.** −5   **c.** 0

4. Write the opposite of each integer.

    a. 3   **b.** −4   **c.** 0

    d. −168   **e.** 56   **f.** −1235

5. Given I = integers, $N = \{-1, -2, -3, -4, . . .\}$, $P = \{1, 2, 3, 4, . . .\}$, W = whole numbers, list the members of the following sets.

    a. $N \cup W$ **b.** $N \cup P$ **c.** $N \cap P$

6. Dixie had a balance of $115 in her checking account at the beginning of the month. She deposited $384 in the account and then wrote checks for $153, $86, $196, $34, and $79. Then she made a deposit of $123. If at any time during the month the account is overdrawn, a $10 service charge is deducted. At the end of the month, what was Dixie's balance?

7. Show how you could find the following sums (i) using a number-line model and (ii) using black and red chips. Look at the Chapter 8 eManipulative activity, *Chips Plus*, to gain a better understanding of how to use the black and red chips.

    a. $5 + (-3)$ **b.** $(-3) + (-2)$

8. Use thinking strategies to compute the following sums. Identify your strategy.

    a. $-14 + 6$ **b.** $17 + (-3)$

9. Identify the property illustrated by the following equations.

    a. $3 + [6 + (-3)] = 3 + (-3 + 6)$

    b. $[3 + (-3)] + 6 = 0 + 6$

10. Apply the properties and thinking strategies to compute the following sums mentally.

    a. $-126 + (635 + 126)$

    b. $84 + (-67) + (-34)$

11. The Chapter 8 eManipulative activity, *Chips Minus*, demonstrates how to use black and red chips to model integer subtraction. After doing a few examples on the eManipulative, sketch how the chip model could be used to do the following problems.

    a. $3 - 7$ **b.** $4 - (-5)$

12. Calculate.

    a. $3 - 7$ **b.** $8 - (-4)$

    c. $(-2) + 3$ **d.** $(-7) - (-8)$

13. Find the following using your calculator and the $\boxed{(-)}$ key. Check mentally.

    a. $-27 + 53$

    b. $(-51) - (-46)$

    c. $123 - (-247)$

    d. $-56 - 72$

14. The existence of additive inverses in the set of integers enables us to solve equations of the form $x + b = c$. For example, to solve $x + 15 = 8$, add (-15) to both sides; $x + 15 + (-15) = 8 + (-15)$ or $x = -7$. Solve the following equations using this technique.

    a. $x + 21 = 16$ **b.** $(-5) + x = 7$

    c. $65 + x = -13$ **d.** $x - 6 = -5$

    e. $x - (-8) = 17$ **f.** $x - 53 = -45$

15. True or false?

    a. Every whole number is an integer.

    b. The set of additive inverses of the whole numbers is equal to the set of integers.

    c. Every integer is a whole number.

    d. The set of additive inverses of the negative integers is a proper subset of the whole numbers.

16. Write out in words (use *minus, negative, opposite*).

a. $5 - 2$

b. -6 (two possible answers)

c. -3 d. $-(-5)$

e. $10 - [-(-2)]$

f. $-p$ (two possible answers)

17. The **absolute value** of an integer a, written $|a|$, is defined to be the distance from a to zero on the integer number line. For example, $|3| = 3$, $|0| = 0$, and $|-7| = 7$. Evaluate the following absolute values.

a. $|5|$ b. $|-17|$ c. $|5 - 7|$

d. $|5| - |7|$ e. $-|7 - 5|$ f. $|-(7 - 5)|$

18. Fill in each empty square so that the number in the square will be the sum of the pair of numbers beneath the square.

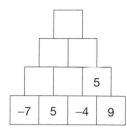

PROBLEMS

19. Which of the following properties hold for integer subtraction? If the property holds, give an example. If it does not hold, disprove it by a counterexample.

a. Closure b. Commutative

c. Associative d. Identity

20. Assume that the adding-the-opposite approach is true, and prove that the missing-addend approach is a consequence of it. (*Hint*: Assume that $a - b = c$, and show that $a = b + c$ using the adding-the-opposite approach.)

21. a. If possible, for each of the following statements find a pair of integers a and b that satisfy the equation or inequality.

i. $|a + b| = |a| + |b|$

ii. $|a + b| < |a| + |b|$

iii. $|a + b| > |a| + |b|$

iv. $|a + b| \le |a| + |b|$

b. Which of these conditions will hold for all pairs of integers?

22. Complete the magic square using the following integers.

$$10, 7, 4, 1, -5, -8, -11, -14$$

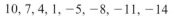

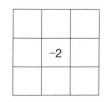

23. a. Let A be a set that is closed under subtraction. If 4 and 9 are elements of A, show that each of the following are also elements of A.

i. 5 ii. -5 iii. 0

iv. 13 v. 1 vi. -3

b. List all members of A.

c. Repeat part (b) if 4 and 8 are given as elements of A.

d. Make a generalization about your findings.

24. Fill in each empty square so that the number in a square will be the sum of the pair of numbers beneath the square.

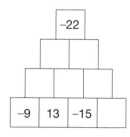

25. A student suggests the following algorithm for calculating $72 - 38$.

$$
\begin{array}{r}
72 \\
-38 \\
\hline
-6 \\
40 \\
\hline
34
\end{array}
$$

Two minus eight equals negative six.

Seventy minus thirty equals forty.

Forty plus negative six equals thirty-four, which therefore is the result.

As a teacher, what is your response? Does this procedure always work? Explain.

26. A **squared rectangle** is a rectangle whose interior can be divided into two or more squares. One example of a squared rectangle follows. The number written inside a square gives the length of a side of that square. Determine the dimensions of the unlabeled squares.

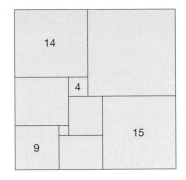

Section 8.1 EXERCISE / PROBLEM SET B

EXERCISES

1. Which of the following are integers? Identify those that are as positive, negative, or neither.

   a. $\frac{3}{4}$ **b.** 556 **c.** $-252/5$

2. Identify each of the integers represented by the following models, where B = black chip and R = red chip.

   a. *BBBRR* **b.** *BRRRRBRR*

   c.

   d.
   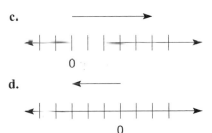

3. Use the set model and number-line model to represent each of the following integers.

   a. -3 **b.** 6

4. What is the opposite or additive inverse of each of the following (a and b represent integers)?

   a. a **b.** $-b$ **c.** $a + b$ **d.** $a - b$

5. Given I = integers, $N = \{-1, -2, -3, -4, \ldots\}$, $P = \{1, 2, 3, 4, \ldots\}$, W = whole numbers, list the members of the following sets.

   a. $N \cap I$ **b.** $P \cap I$ **c.** $I \cap W$

6. Write an addition statement for each of the following sentences and then find the answer.

   a. In a series of downs, a football team gained 7 yards, lost 4 yards, lost 2 yards, and gained 8 yards. What was the total gain or loss?

   b. In a week, a given stock gained 5 points, dropped 12 points, dropped 3 points, gained 18 points, and dropped 10 points. What was the net change in the stock's worth?

   c. A visitor in an Atlantic City casino won $300, lost $250, and then won $150. Find the gambler's overall gain or loss.

7. Show how you could find the following sums (i) using a number-line model and (ii) using black and red chips. Look at the Chapter 8 eManipulative activity, *Chips Plus*, to gain a better understanding of how to use the black and red chips.

   a. $4 + (-7)$ **b.** $(-3) + (-5)$

8. Use thinking strategies to compute the following sums. Identify your strategy.

   a. $14 + (-6)$ **b.** $21 + (-41)$

9. Identify the property illustrated by the following equations.

   a. $3 + [(-3) + 6] = [3 + (-3)] + 6$

   b. $0 + 6 = 6$

10. Apply the properties and thinking strategies to compute the following sums mentally.

    a. $-165 + 3217 + 65$

    b. $173 + (-43) + (-97)$

11. The Chapter 8 eManipulative activity, *Chips Minus*, demonstrates how to use black and red chips to model integer subtraction. After doing a few examples on the eManipulative, sketch how the chip model could be used to do the following problems.

    a. $(-3) - (-6)$ **b.** $0 - (-4)$

12. Calculate the following sums and differences.

    a. $13 - 27$ **b.** $38 - (-14)$

    c. $(-21) + 35$ **d.** $-26 - (-32)$

13. Find the following using your calculator and the $\boxed{(-)}$ key. Check mentally.

    a. $-119 + 351 + (-463)$

    b. $-98 - (-42)$

    c. $632 - (-354)$

    d. $-752 - (-549) + (-352)$

14. For each of the following equations, find the integer that satisfies the equation.

    a. $-x = 5$ **b.** $x + (-3) = -10$

    c. $x - (-5) = -8$ **d.** $6 - x = -3$

    e. $-5 - x = -2$ **f.** $x = -x$

15. If p and q are arbitrary negative integers, which of the following is true?

    a. $-p$ is negative.

    b. $p - q = q - p$

    c. $-(p + q) = q - p$

    d. $-p$ is positive.

16. Is $-x$ positive or negative if x is

    a. positive?   **b.** negative?   **c.** zero?

17. An alternate definition of absolute value is

$$|a| = \begin{cases} a \text{ if } a \text{ is positive or zero} \\ -a \text{ if } a \text{ is negative.} \end{cases}$$

(NOTE: $-a$ is the opposite of a.) Using this definition, calculate the following values.

    a. $|-3|$ **b.** $|7|$

    c. $|x|$ if $x < 0$ **d.** $|-x|$ if $-x > 0$

    e. $-|x|$ if $x < 0$ **f.** $-|-x|$ if $-x > 0$

18. Fill in each empty square so that the number in the square will be the sum of the pair of numbers beneath the square.

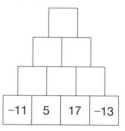

19. Under what conditions is the following equation true?

$$(a - b) - c = (a - c) - b$$

    a. Never

    b. Always

    c. Only when $b = c$

    d. Only when $b = c = 0$

20. On a given day, the following Fahrenheit temperature extremes were recorded. Find the range between the high and low temperature in each location.

CITY	HIGH	LOW
Philadelphia	65	37
Cheyenne	35	-9
Bismarck	-2	-13

21. A student claims that if $a \neq 0$, then $|a| = -a$ is never true, since absolute value is always positive. Explain

PROBLEMS

why the student is wrong. What two concepts is the student confusing?

22. Switch two numbers to produce an additive magic square.

140	-56	-42	-28
-14	70	56	28
42	14	0	84
98	112	126	-70

23. If a is an element of $\{-3, -2, -1, 0, 1, 2\}$ and b is an element of $\{-5, -4, -3, -2, -1, 0, 1\}$, find the smallest and largest values for the following expressions.

    a. $a + b$

    b. $b - a$

    c. $|a + b|$

24. Fill in each empty square so that a number in a square will be the sum of the pair of numbers beneath the square.

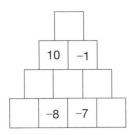

25. a. Demonstrate a 1-1 correspondence between the sets given.

    i. Positive integers and negative integers

    ii. Positive integers and whole numbers

    iii. Whole numbers and integers

b. What does part (iii) tell you about the number of whole numbers compared to the number of integers?

26. A **squared square** is a square whose interior can be subdivided into two or more squares. One example of a squared square follows. The number written inside a square gives the length of a side of that square. Determine the dimensions of the unlabeled squares.

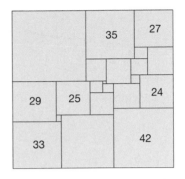

PROBLEMS FOR WRITING/DISCUSSION

1. Using the black and red chip model, how would you explain to students why you were inserting 5 black and 5 red chips to the circle in order to subtract 8 from 3?

2. Some people learn this rule for adding two numbers whose signs are different: "Subtract the numbers and take the sign of the larger." Explain why this rule might lead to some confusion for students when doing the problem "4 + (−6)."

3. In the additive inverse property there is the phrase "there is a unique integer." How would you explain the meaning of that phrase to students?

8.2 MULTIPLICATION, DIVISION, AND ORDER

STARTING POINT

Recall that for positive exponents, the following properties hold:

$$7^4 = 7 \cdot 7 \cdot 7 \cdot 7 \qquad 7^0 = 1 \qquad 7^5 \div 7^3 = 7^{5-3} = 7^2 \qquad 7^5 \cdot 7^3 = 7^{5+3} = 7^8$$

It is important that the properties of negative exponents are consistent with the properties of exponents above. If the properties were consistent, what would 7^{-2} be equal to? Justify your conclusion. (*Hint*: Consider $7^3 \div 7^5$ or $7^2 \cdot 7^{-2}$.)

Reflection from Research

If students understand multiplication as repeated addition, then a positive times a negative, such as 7×-6, can be taught as "seven negative 6s" (Bley & Thornton, 1989).

Multiplication and Its Properties

Integer multiplication can be viewed as extending whole-number multiplication. Recall that the first model for whole-number multiplication was repeated addition, as illustrated here:

$$3 \times 4 = 4 + 4 + 4 = 12.$$

Now suppose that you were selling tickets and you accepted three bad checks worth $4 each. A natural way to think of your situation would be $3 \times (−4) = (−4) + (−4) + (−4) = −12$ (Figure 8.13).

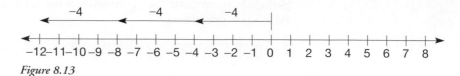

Figure 8.13

Rules for integer multiplication can be motivated using the following pattern.

THE FIRST COLUMN REMAINS 3 THROUGHOUT.	$3 \times 4 = 12$ *3 LESS*
	$3 \times 3 = 9$ *3 LESS*
THE SECOND COLUMN IS DECREASING BY 1 EACH TIME.	$3 \times 2 = 6$ *3 LESS*
	$3 \times 1 = 3$ *ETC.*
	$3 \times 0 = 0$
	$3 \times (-1) = ?$
	$3 \times (-2) = ?$
	$3 \times (-3) = ?$
	$3 \times (-4) = ?$

This pattern extended suggests that $3 \times (-1) = -3$, $3 \times (-2) = -6$, $3 \times (-3) = -9$, and so on. A similar pattern can be used to suggest what the product of two negative integers should be, as follows.

THE FIRST COLUMN REMAINS (-3).	$(-3) \times 3 = -9$
	$(-3) \times 2 = -6$ *3 MORE*
	$(-3) \times 1 = -3$ *3 MORE*
	$(-3) \times 0 = 0$ *3 MORE*
THE SECOND COLUMN DECREASES BY 1 EACH TIME.	$(-3) \times (-1) = ?$ *ETC.*
	$(-3) \times (-2) = ?$
	$(-3) \times (-3) = ?$

Problem-Solving Strategy
Look for a Pattern.

This pattern suggests that $(-3)(-1) = 3$, $(-3)(-2) = 6$, $(-3)(-3) = 9$, and so on.

Integer multiplication can also be modeled using black and red chips. Since 4×3 can be thought of as "combine 4 groups of 3 black chips," the operation 4×-3 can be thought of as "combine 4 groups of 3 red chips" (see Figure 8.14).

Notice that the sign on the second number in the operation determines the color of chips being used. Since the first number in 4×-3 is positive, we *combined* 4 groups of -3. How would the situation of -4×3 be handled? In this case the first number (4) is negative, which indicates that we should "*take away* 4 groups of 3 black chips" rather than combine. When the first number is positive, the groups are *combined* into a new set that has a value of 0. When the first number is negative, the groups are *taken away* from a set that has a value of 0. In order to take something away from a set with a value of 0, we must add some chips with a value of 0 to the set. This is done by adding an equal number of red and black chips to the set. After taking away 4 groups of 3 black chips, the resulting set has 12 red chips or a value of -12 (Figure 8.15).

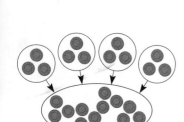

$4 \times -3 = -12$

Figure 8.14

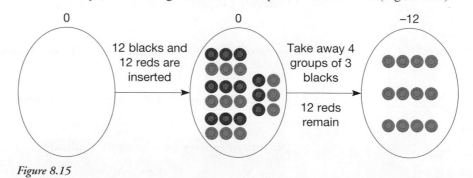

Figure 8.15

The number-line model, the patterns, and the black and red chips model all lead to the following definition.

DEFINITION

Multiplication of Integers

Let a and b be any integers.

1. *Multiplying by 0*: $a \cdot 0 = 0 = 0 \cdot a$.
2. *Multiplying two positives*: If a and b are positive, they are multiplied as whole numbers.
3. *Multiplying a positive and a negative*: If a is positive and b is positive (thus $-b$ is negative), then

$$a(-b) = -(ab),$$

   where ab is the whole-number product of a and b. That is, the product of a positive and a negative is negative.

4. *Multiplying two negatives*: If a and b are positive, then

$$(-a)(-b) = ab,$$

   where ab is the whole-number product of a and b. That is, the product of two negatives is positive.

Example 8.6 Calculate the following using the definition of integer multiplication.

a. $5 \cdot 0$ **b.** $5 \cdot 8$ **c.** $5(-8)$ **d.** $(-5)(-8)$

Solution

a. *Multiplying by zero*: $5 \cdot 0 = 0$
b. *Multiplying two positives*: $5 \cdot 8 = 40$
c. *Multiplying a positive and a negative*: $5(-8) = -(5 \cdot 8) = -40$
d. *Multiplying two negatives*: $(-5)(-8) = 5 \cdot 8 = 40$ ■

The definition of multiplication of integers can be used to justify the following properties.

PROPERTIES

Properties of Integer Multiplication

Let a, b, and c be any integers.
Closure Property for Integer Multiplication

$$ab \text{ is an integer.}$$

Commutative Property for Integer Multiplication

$$ab = ba$$

Associative Property for Integer Multiplication

$$(ab)c = a(bc)$$

Identity Property for Integer Multiplication
1 is the unique integer such that $a \cdot 1 = a = 1 \cdot a$ for all a.

As in the system of whole numbers, our final property, the distributive property, connects addition and multiplication.

PROPERTY

Distributivity of Multiplication over Addition of Integers

Let a, b, and c be any integers. Then

$$a(b + c) = ab + ac.$$

Using the preceding properties of addition and multiplication of integers, some important results that are useful in computations can be justified.

THEOREM

Let a be any integer. Then

$$a(-1) = -a.$$

Proof   First, $a \cdot 0 = 0$ by definition.

$$
\begin{aligned}
\text{But } a \cdot 0 &= a[1 + (-1)] & & \textit{Additive inverse} \\
&= a(1) + a(-1) & & \textit{Distributivity} \\
&= a + a(-1). & & \textit{Multiplicative identity}
\end{aligned}
$$

Therefore, $a + a(-1) = 0$.

$$
\begin{aligned}
\text{Then } \quad a + a(-1) &= a + (-a). & & \textit{Additive inverse} \\
\text{Finally, } a(-1) &= -a & & \textit{Additive cancellation} \quad ■
\end{aligned}
$$

Stating the preceding result in words, we have "the product of negative one and any integer is the opposite (or additive inverse) of that integer." Notice that, on the integer number line, multiplication by -1 is equivalent geometrically to reflecting an integer about the origin (Figure 8.16).

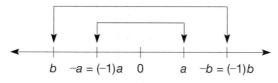

$$b \quad -a = (-1)a \quad 0 \quad a \quad -b = (-1)b$$

Figure 8.16

THEOREM

Let a and b be any integers. Then

$$(-a)b = -(ab).$$

Proof

$$
\begin{aligned}
(-a)b &= [(-1)a]b & & \textit{(−1)a = −a} \\
&= (-1)(ab) & & \textit{Associativity for multiplication} \\
&= -(ab) & & \textit{(−1)a = −a}
\end{aligned}
$$

Using commutativity with this result gives $a(-b) = -(ab)$.   ■

THEOREM

Let a and b be any integers. Then

$$(-a)(-b) = ab \text{ for all integers } a, b.$$

Proof

$$
\begin{aligned}
(-a)(-b) &= [(-1)a][(-1)b] & (-1)a = -a \\
&= [(-1)(-1)](ab) & \text{Associativity and commutativity} \\
&= 1ab & \text{Definition of integer multiplication} \\
&= ab & \text{Multiplicative identity} \quad \blacksquare
\end{aligned}
$$

NOTE: The three preceding results encompass more than just statements about multiplying by negative numbers. For example, $(-a)(-b) = ab$ is read "the opposite of a times the opposite of b is ab." The numbers a and b may be positive, negative, or zero; hence $(-a)$ and $(-b)$ also may be negative, positive, or zero. Thus there is a subtle but important difference between these results and parts 3 and 4 of the definition of multiplication of integers.

Example 8.7 Calculate the following products.
a. $3(-1)$ **b.** $(-3)5$ **c.** $(-3)(-4)$ **d.** $(-1)(-7)$ **e.** $(-x)(-y)(-z)$

Solution

a. $3(-1) = -3$, since $a(-1) = -a$.
b. $(-3)5 = -(3 \cdot 5) = -15$, since $(-a)b = -(ab)$.
c. $(-3)(-4) = (3 \cdot 4) = 12$, since $(-a)(-b) = ab$.
d. $(-1)(-7)$ can be found in two ways: $(-1)(-7) = -(-7) = 7$, since $(-1)a = a$, and $(-1)(-7) = 1 \cdot 7 = 7$, since $(-a)(-b) = ab$.
e. $(-x)(-y)(-z) = xy(-z)$, since $(-a)(-b) = ab$; and $xy(-z) = -(xyz)$, since $a(-b) = -(ab)$. $\blacksquare$

Finally, the next property will be useful in integer division.

PROPERTY

Multiplicative Cancellation Property

Let a, b, c be any integers with $c \neq 0$. If $ac = bc$, then $a = b$.

Notice that the condition $c \neq 0$ is necessary, since $3 \cdot 0 = 2 \cdot 0$, but $3 \neq 2$.
    The multiplicative cancellation property is truly a *property* of the integers (and whole numbers and counting numbers) because it cannot be proven from any of our previous properties. However, in a system where nonzero numbers have multiplicative inverses (such as the fractions), it is a theorem. The following property is equivalent to the multiplicative cancellation property.

PROPERTY

Zero Divisors Property

Let a and b be integers. Then $ab = 0$ if and only if $a = 0$ or $b = 0$ or a and b both equal zero.

Division

Recall that to find $6 \div 3$ in the whole numbers, we sought the whole number c, where $6 = 3 \cdot c$. Division of integers can be viewed as an extension of whole-number division using the missing-factor approach.

DEFINITION

Division of Integers

Let a and b be any integers, where $b \neq 0$. Then $a \div b = c$ if and only if $a = b \cdot c$ for a unique integer c.

Example 8.8 Find the following quotients (if possible).

a. $12 \div (-3)$
b. $(-15) \div (-5)$
c. $(-8) \div 2$
d. $7 \div (-2)$

Solution

a. $12 \div (-3) = c$ if and only if $12 = (-3) \cdot c$. From multiplication, $12 = (-3)(-4)$. Since $(-3) \cdot c = (-3)(-4)$, by multiplicative cancellation, $c = -4$.
b. $(-15) \div (-5) = c$ if and only if $-15 = (-5) \cdot c$. From multiplication, $-15 = (-5) \cdot 3$. Since $(-5) \cdot c = (-5) \cdot 3$, by multiplicative cancellation, $c = 3$.
c. $(-8) \div 2 = c$ if and only if $(-8) = 2 \cdot c$. Thus $c = -4$, since $2(-4) = -8$.
d. $7 \div (-2) = c$ if and only if $7 = (-2) \cdot c$. There is no such integer c. Therefore, $7 \div (-2)$ is undefined in the integers. ■

Considering the results of this example, the following generalizations can be made about the division of integers: Assume that b divides a; that is, that b is a factor of a.

1. *Dividing by 1: $a \div 1 = a$.*
2. *Dividing two positives (negatives):* If a and b are both positive (or both negative), then $a \div b$ is positive.
3. *Dividing a positive and a negative:* If one of a or b is positive and the other is negative, then $a \div b$ is *negative.*
4. *Dividing zero by a nonzero integer:* $0 \div b = 0$, where $b \neq 0$, since $0 = b \cdot 0$. As with whole numbers, division by zero is undefined for integers.

Example 8.9 Calculate.

a. $0 \div 5$
b. $40 \div 5$
c. $40 \div (-5)$
d. $(-40) \div (-5)$

Solution

a. *Dividing into zero:* $0 \div 5 = 0$
b. *Dividing two positives:* $40 \div 5 = 8$
c. *Dividing a positive and negative:* $40 \div (-5) = -8$ and $(-40) \div 5 = -8$
d. *Dividing two negatives:* $(-40) \div (-5) = 8$ ■

Spotlight on Technology The negative-sign key can be used to find $-306 \times (-76) \div 12$ as follows:

$$\boxed{(-)}\; 306\; \boxed{\times}\; \boxed{(-)}\; 76\; \boxed{\div}\; 12\; \boxed{=}\; \boxed{1938}$$

However, this calculation can be performed without the negative-sign key by observing that there are an even number (two) of negative integers multiplied together. Thus the product is positive. In the case of an odd number of negative factors, the product is negative.

Negative Exponents and Scientific Notation

When studying whole numbers, exponents were introduced as a shortcut for multiplication. As the following pattern suggests, there is a way to extend our current definition of exponents to include integer exponents.

Problem-Solving Strategy
Look for a Pattern.

$$a^3 = a \cdot a \cdot a$$
$$a^2 = a \cdot a \qquad \Big\rangle \div a$$
$$a^1 = a \qquad \Big\rangle \div a$$
$$a^0 = 1 \qquad \Big\rangle \div a$$
$$a^{-1} = \frac{1}{a} \qquad \Big\rangle \div a$$
$$a^{-2} = \frac{1}{a^2} \qquad \Big\rangle \div a$$
$$a^{-3} = \frac{1}{a^3} \qquad \Big\rangle \div a$$
$$\vdots$$

etc.

This pattern leads to the next definition.

⬡ DEFINITION

Negative Integer Exponent

Let a be any nonzero number and n be a positive integer. Then

$$a^{-n} = \frac{1}{a^n}.$$

For example, $7^{-3} = \frac{1}{7^3}$, $2^{-5} = \frac{1}{2^5}$, $3^{-10} = \frac{1}{3^{10}}$, and so on. Also, $\frac{1}{4^{-3}} = \frac{1}{1/4^3} = 4^3$.

The last sentence indicates how the definition leads to the statement $a^{-n} = \frac{1}{a^n}$ *for all integers n.*

It can be shown that the theorems on whole-number exponents given in Section 3.3 can be extended to integer exponents. That is, for any nonzero numbers a and b, and integers m and n, we have

$$a^m \cdot a^n = a^{m+n}$$

$$a^m \cdot b^m = (ab)^m$$

$$(a^m)^n = a^{nm}$$

$$\frac{a^m}{a^n} = a^{m-n}.$$

NCTM Standards 2000
Number and Operations
Grades 6–8
All students should develop an understanding of large numbers and recognize and appropriately use exponential, scientific, and calculator notations.

In Section 4.1 scientific notation was discussed in the context of using a scientific calculator. Numbers are said to be in **scientific notation** when expressed in the form $a \times 10^n$, where $1 \le a < 10$ and n is any integer. The number a is called the **mantissa** and n the **characteristic** of $a \times 10^n$. The following table provides some examples of numbers written in scientific notation.

	SCIENTIFIC NOTATION	STANDARD NOTATION
Diameter of Jupiter	1.438×10^8 meters	143,800,000 meters
Total amount of gold in Earth's crust	1.2×10^{16} kilograms	12,000,000,000,000,000 kilograms
Mass of a human egg	1.5×10^{-9} kilogram	0.0000000015 kilogram
Diameter of a proton	1×10^{-11} meter	0.00000000001 meter

Example 8.10   Convert as indicated.
a. 38,500,000 to scientific notation
b. 7.2×10^{-14} to standard notation
c. 4.135×10^{11} to standard notation
d. 0.0000961 to scientific notation

Solution

a. $38,500,000 = 3.85 \times 10^7$
b. $7.2 \times 10^{-14} = 0.000000000000072$
c. $4.135 \times 10^{11} = 413,500,000,000$
d. $0.0000961 = 9.61 \times 10^{-5}$ ■

Spotlight on Technology Conversions from standard notation to scientific notation can be performed on most scientific calculators. For example, the following keystrokes convert 38,500,000 to scientific notation.

$$38500000 \;\boxed{\text{2nd}}\; \boxed{\text{Sci}}\; \boxed{\qquad 3.85^{07}}$$

The raised "07" represents 10^7. Since the number of digits displayed by calculators differs, one needs to keep these limitations in mind when converting between scientific and standard notations.

Scientific notation is used to solve problems involving very large and very small numbers, especially in science and engineering.

Example 8.11   The diameter of Jupiter is about 1.438×10^8 meters, and the diameter of Earth is about 1.27×10^7 meters. What is the ratio of the diameter of Jupiter to the diameter of Earth?

Solution

$$\frac{1.438 \times 10^8}{1.27 \times 10^7} = \frac{1.438}{1.27} \times \frac{10^8}{10^7} \approx 1.13 \times 10 = 11.3 \qquad ■$$

When performing calculations involving numbers written in scientific notation, it is customary to express the answer in scientific notation. For example, the product $(5.4 \times 10^7)(3.5 \times 10^6)$ is written as follows:

$$(5.4 \times 10^7)(3.5 \times 10^6) = 18.9 \times 10^{13} = 1.89 \times 10^{14}.$$

NCTM Standards 2000
Number and Operations
Grades 6–8
All students should develop meaning for integers and represent and compare quantities with them.

Ordering Integers

The concepts of **less than** and **greater than** in the integers are defined to be extensions of ordering in the whole numbers. In the following, ordering is viewed in two equivalent ways, the number-line approach and the addition approach. Let a and b be any integers.

Number-Line Approach The integer a *is less than* the integer b, written $a < b$, if a is to the left of b on the integer number line. Thus, by viewing the number line, one can see that $-3 < 2$ (Figure 8.17). Also, $-4 < -1$, $-2 < 3$, and so on.

$-3 < 2$

Figure 8.17

Addition Approach The integer a *is less than* the integer b, written $a < b$, if and only if there is a *positive* integer p such that $a + p = b$. Thus $-5 < -3$, since $-5 + 2 = -3$, and $-7 < 2$, since $-7 + 9 = 2$. Equivalently, $a < b$ if and only if $b - a$ is positive (since $b - a = p$). For example, $-27 < -13$, since $-13 - (-27) = 14$, which is positive.

The integer a **is greater than** the integer b, written $a > b$, if and only if $b < a$. Thus, the discussion of greater than is analogous to that of less than. Similar definitions can be made for $\leq$ and $\geq$.

Example 8.12 Order the following integers from the smallest to largest using the number-line approach.

$$2, 11, -7, 0, 5, -8, -13.$$

Solution

See Figure 8.18.

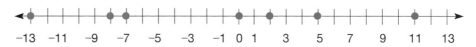

$-13 < -8 < -7 < 0 < 2 < 5 < 11$

Figure 8.18

■

Example 8.13 Determine the smallest integer in the set $\{3, 0, -5, 9, -8\}$ using the addition approach.

Solution

$-8 < -5$, since $(-8) + 3 = -5$. Also, since any negative integer is less than 0 or any positive integer, -8 must be the smallest.

■

The following results involving ordering, addition, and multiplication extend similar ones for whole numbers.

PROPERTY

Properties of Ordering Integers

Let a, b, and c be any integers, p a positive integer, and n a negative integer.

Transitive Property for Less Than

$$\text{If } a < b \text{ and } b < c, \text{ then } a < c.$$

Property of Less Than and Addition

$$\text{If } a < b, \text{ then } a + c < b + c.$$

Property of Less Than and Multiplication by a Positive

$$\text{If } a < b, \text{ then } ap < bp.$$

Property of Less Than and Multiplication by a Negative

$$\text{If } a < b, \text{ then } an > bn.$$

The first three properties for ordering integers are extensions of similar statements in the whole numbers. However, the fourth property deserves special attention because it involves multiplying both sides of an inequality by a *negative* integer. For example, $2 < 5$ but $2(-3) > 5(-3)$. [Note that 2 *is less than* 5 but that $2(-3)$ *is greater than* $5(-3)$.] Similar properties hold where $<$ is replaced by $\leq$, $>$, and $\geq$. The last two properties, which involve multiplication and ordering, are illustrated in Example 8.14 using the number-line approach.

Example 8.14

a. $-2 < 3$ and $4 > 0$; thus $(-2) \cdot 4 < 3 \cdot 4$ by the property of less than and multiplication by a positive (Figure 8.19).

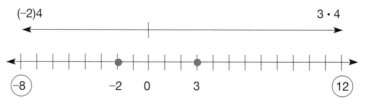

Figure 8.19

b. $-2 < 3$ and $-4 < 0$; thus $(-2)(-4) > 3(-4)$ by the property of less than and multiplication by a negative (Figure 8.20).

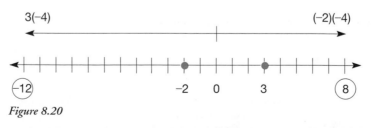

Figure 8.20

Notice how -2 was to the left of 3, *but* $(-2)(-4)$ is to the *right* of $(3)(-4)$. ■

To see why the property of less than and multiplication by a negative is true, recall that multiplying an integer a by -1 is geometrically the same as reflecting a across

the origin on the integer number line. Using this idea in all cases leads to the following general result.

If $a < b$, then $(-1)a > (-1)b$ (Figure 8.21).

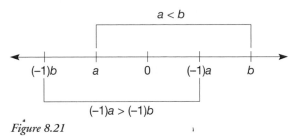

$$a < b$$

$$(-1)a > (-1)b$$

Figure 8.21

To justify the statement "if $a < b$ and $n < 0$, then $an > bn$," suppose that $a < b$ and $n < 0$. Since n is negative, we can express n as $(-1)p$, where p is positive. Then $ap < bp$ by the property of less than and multiplication by a positive. But if $ap < bp$, then $(-1)ap > (-1)bp$, or $a[(-1)p] > b[(-1)p]$, which, in turn, yields $an > bn$. Informally, this result says that "multiplying an inequality by a negative number 'reverses' the inequality."

MATHEMATICAL MORSEL

In January 1999, a 16-year-old high school student from Cork County, Ireland, named Sarah Flannery, caused quite a stir in the technology world. She devised an advanced mathematical code used to encrypt information sent electronically. Her algorithm uses the properties of 2×2 matrices and is said to be up to 30 times faster than the previous algorithm, Rivest, Shamir, and Adlemann (RSA), which was created by three students at Massachusetts Institute of Technology in 1977. She named her algorithm the Cayley-Purser algorithm, after nineteenth-century mathematician Arthur Cayley and Michael Purser, a Trinity College professor who gave her the initial ideas and inspired her. Because such an advancement can have a significant impact in the computer and banking industries, Sarah had computer firms offering her consulting jobs and prestigious universities inviting her to sign up when she graduated.

Section 8.2 EXERCISE / PROBLEM SET A

EXERCISES

1. Write one addition and one multiplication equation represented by each number-line model.

a.

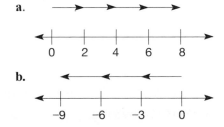

b.

c.

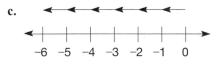

2. a. Extend the following patterns by writing the next three equations.

i. $6 \times 3 = 18$ **ii.** $9 \times 3 = 27$
    $6 \times 2 = 12$ $9 \times 2 = 18$
    $6 \times 1 = 6$ $9 \times 1 = 9$
    $6 \times 0 = 0$ $9 \times 0 = 0$

b. What rule of multiplication of negative numbers is suggested by the equations you have written?

3. Find the following products.

a. $6(-5)$ **b.** $(-2)(-16)$

c. $-(-3)(-5)$ **d.** $-3(-7-6)$

4. Represent the following products using black and red chips and give the results.

a. $3 \times (-2)$

b. $(-3) \times (-4)$

5. The uniqueness of additive inverses and other properties of integers enable us to give another justification that $(-3)4 = -12$. By definition, the additive inverse of $3(4)$ is $-(3 \cdot 4)$. Provide reasons for each of the following equations.

$$(-3)(4) + 3 \cdot 4 = (-3 + 3) \cdot 4$$
$$= 0 \cdot 4$$
$$= 0$$

Thus we have shown that $(-3)4$ is also the additive inverse of $3 \cdot 4$ and hence is equal to $-(3 \cdot 4)$.

6. Extend the meaning of a whole-number exponent.

$$a^n = \underbrace{a \cdot a \cdot a \cdots a,}_{n \text{ factors}}$$

where a is any integer. Use this definition to find the following values.

a. 2^4 **b.** $(-3)^3$ **c.** $(-2)^4$

d. $(-5)^2$ **e.** $(-3)^5$ **f.** $(-2)^6$

7. If a is an integer and $a \neq 0$, which of the following expressions are always positive and which are always negative?

a. a **b.** $-a$ **c.** a^2

d. $(-a)^2$ **e.** $(-a)^2$ **f.** a^3

8. Provide reasons for each of the following steps.

$$a(b - c) = a[b + (-c)]$$
$$= ab + a(-c)$$
$$= ab + [-(ac)]$$
$$= ab - ac$$

Which property have you justified?

9. Find each quotient.

a. $-18 \div 3$ **b.** $-45 \div (-9)$

c. $75 \div (-5)$ **d.** $(-5 + 5) \div (-2)$

e. $[144 \div (-12)] \div (-3)$

f. $144 \div [-12 \div (-3)]$

10. Make use of the $\boxed{(-)}$ key on a calculator to calculate each of the following problems.

a. -36×72 **b.** $-51 \times (-38)$

c. $-128 \times (-765)$ **d.** $-658 \div 14$

e. $3588 \div (-23)$ **f.** $-108,697 \div (-73)$

11. Consider the statement $(x + y) \div z = (x \div z) + (y \div z)$. Is this a true statement in the integers for the following values of x, y, and z?

a. $x = 16, y = -12, z = 4$

b. $x = -20, y = 36, z = -4$

c. $x = -42, y = -18, z = -6$

d. $x = -12, y = -8, z = 3$

12. Write each of the following as a fraction without exponents.

a. 10^{-2} **b.** 4^{-3} **c.** 2^{-6} **d.** 5^{-3}

13. a. Simplify $4^{-2} \cdot 4^6$ by expressing it in terms of whole-number exponents and simplifying.

b. Simplify $4^{-2} \cdot 4^6$ by applying $a^m \cdot a^n = a^{m+n}$.

c. Repeat parts (a) and (b) to simplify $5^{-4} \cdot 5^{-2}$.

d. Does it appear that the property $a^m \cdot a^n = a^{m+n}$ still applies for integer exponents?

14. a. Simplify $\dfrac{3^{-2}}{3^5}$ by expressing it in terms of whole-number exponents and simplifying.

b. Simplify the expression in part (a) by applying

$$\frac{a^m}{a^n} = a^{m-n}.$$

c. Repeat parts (a) and (b) to simplify $\dfrac{6^3}{6^{-7}}$.

d. Does it appear that the property $\dfrac{a^m}{a^n} = a^{m-n}$ still applies for integer exponents?

15. Use the definition of integer exponents and properties of exponents to find a numerical value for the following expressions.

a. $3^{-2} \cdot 3^5$ **b.** $\dfrac{6^{-3}}{6^{-4}}$ **c.** $(3^{-4})^{-2}$

16. Each of the following numbers is written in scientific notation. Rewrite each in standard decimal form.

a. 3.7×10^{-5} **b.** 2.45×10^{-8}

17. Express each of the following numbers in scientific notation.

a. 0.0004 **b.** 0.0000016 **c.** 0.000000000495

d. $0.00000000000000000008071$

18. You can use a scientific calculator to perform arithmetic operations with numbers written in scientific notation. If the exponent is negative, use your $\boxed{+/-}$ or $\boxed{\text{CHS}}$ or $\boxed{(-)}$ key to change the sign.

    For example, see the following multiplication problem.

$$(1.6 \times 10^{-4})(2.7 \times 10^{-8})$$

    1.6 $\boxed{\text{SCI}}$ 4 $\boxed{+/-}$ $\boxed{\times}$ 2.7 $\boxed{\text{SCI}}$ 8 $\boxed{+/-}$ $\boxed{=}$

    $\boxed{\;4.32\;-\;12}$

    (NOTE: The sequence of steps or appearance of the answer in the display window may be slightly different on your calculator.)
    Use your calculator to evaluate each of the following. Express your results in scientific notation.

    a. $(7.6 \times 10^{10})(9.5 \times 10^{-36})$

    b. $(2.4 \times 10^{-6})(3.45 \times 10^{-20})$

    c. $\dfrac{1.2 \times 10^{-15}}{4.8 \times 10^{-6}}$

    d. $\dfrac{(7.5 \times 10^{-12})(8 \times 10^{-17})}{(1.5 \times 10^{9})}$

    e. $\dfrac{480{,}000{,}000}{0.0000006}$

    f. $\dfrac{0.000000000000123}{0.0000006}$

19. Show that each of the following is true by using the number-line approach.

    a. $-3 < 2$ b. $-6 < -2$ c. $-3 > -12$

20. Write each of the following lists of integers in increasing order from left to right.

    a. $-5, 5, 2, -2, 0$ b. $12, -6, -8, 3, -5$

    c. $-2, -3, -5, -8, -11$

    d. $23, -36, 45, -72, -108$

21. Complete the following statements by inserting $<$, $=$, or $>$ in the blanks to produce true statements.

    a. If $x < 4$, then $x + 2$ ___ 6.

    b. If $x > -2$, then $x - 6$ ___ -8.

PROBLEMS

22. Fill in each empty square so that a number in a square is the product of the two numbers beneath it.

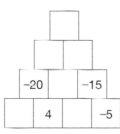

23. a. Which of the following integers when substituted for x make the given inequality true: -6, -10, -8, -7?

$$3x + 5 < -16$$

    b. Is there a largest integer value for x that makes the inequality true?

    c. Is there a smallest integer value for x that makes the inequality true?

24. a. The rules of integer addition can be summarized in a table as follows:

+	+	−
+	+	?
−		

Positive + positive = positive ($+$ sign)
Positive + negative = positive or negative or zero ($?$ sign)
Complete the table.

    b. Make a similar table for

        i. subtraction.

        ii. multiplication.

        iii. division (when possible).

25. a. If possible, find an integer x to satisfy the following conditions.

        i. $|x| > x$ ii. $|x| = x$

        iii. $|x| < x$ iv. $|x| \geq x$

    b. Which, if any, of the conditions in part (a) will hold for all integers?

26. A student suggests that she can show $(-1)(-1) = 1$ using the fact that $-(-1) = 1$. Is her reasoning correct? If yes, what result will she apply? If not, why not?

27. A student does not believe that $-10 < -5$. He argues that a debt of $10 is greater than a debt of $5. How would you convince him that the inequality is true?

28. In a multiplicative magic square, the product of the integers in each row, each column, and each diagonal is the same number. Complete the multiplication magic square given.

29. If $0 < x < y$ where x and y are integers, prove that $x^2 < y^2$.

30. There are 6.022×10^{23} atoms in 12.01 grams of carbon. Find the mass of one atom of carbon. Express your answer in scientific notation.

31. Hair on the human body can grow as fast as 0.0000000043 meter per second.

   a. At this rate, how much would a strand of hair grow in one month of 30 days? Express your answer in scientific notation.

   b. About how long would it take for a strand of hair to grow to be 1 meter in length?

32. A farmer goes to market and buys 100 animals at a total cost of $1000. If cows cost $50 each, sheep cost $10 each, and rabbits cost 50 cents each, how many of each kind does he buy?

33. Prove or disprove: The square of any whole number is a multiple of 3 or one more than a multiple of 3.

34. A shopper asked for 50 cents worth of apples. The shopper was surprised when she received five more than the previous week. Then she noticed that the price had dropped 10 cents per dozen. What was the new price per dozen?

35. Assume that if $ac = bc$ and $c \neq 0$, then $a = b$. Prove that if $ab = 0$, then $a = 0$ or $b = 0$. (*Hint*: Assume that $b \neq 0$. Then $ab = 0 = 0 \cdot b$. . . .)

Section 8.2   **EXERCISE / PROBLEM SET B**

EXERCISES

1. Illustrate the following products on an integer number line.

   a. $2 \times (-5)$ **b.** $3 \times (-4)$

   c. $5 \times (-2)$

2. Extend the following patterns by writing the next three equations. What rule of multiplication of negative numbers is suggested by the equations you have written?

   a. $-5 \times 3 = -15$ **b.** $-8 \times 3 = -24$
      $-5 \times 2 = -10$ $-8 \times 2 = -16$
      $-5 \times 1 = -5$ $-8 \times 1 = -8$
      $-5 \times 0 = 0$ $-8 \times 0 = 0$

3. Find the following products.

   a. $(-2)(-5)(-3)$

   b. $(-10)(7)(-6)$

   c. $5[(-2)(13) + 5(-4)]$

   d. $-23[(-2)(6) + (-3)(-4)]$

4. Represent the following products using black and red chips and give the results.

   a. $(-3) \times 4$ **b.** $(2) \times (-4)$

   c. $(-2) \times (-1)$

5. The following argument shows another justification for $(-3)(-4) = 12$. Provide reasons for each of the following equations.

$$(-3)(-4) + (-3) \cdot 4 = (-3)(-4 + 4)$$
$$= (-3) \cdot 0$$
$$= 0$$

Therefore, $(-3)(-4)$ is the additive inverse of $(-3)4 = -12$. But the additive inverse of -12 is 12, so $(-3)(-4) = 12$.

6. Are the following numbers positive or negative?

   a. $(-2)^5$ **b.** $(-2)^8$ **c.** $(-5)^3$

   d. $(-5)^{16}$ **e.** $(-1)^{20}$ **f.** $(-1)^{33}$

   g. a^n if $a < 0$ and n is even

   h. a^n if $a < 0$ and n is odd

7. If a is an integer and $a \neq 0$, which expressions are always positive and which are always negative?

   a. a^3 **b.** $(-a)^3$ **c.** $-(a^3)$

   d. a^4 **e.** $(-a)^4$ **f.** $-(a^4)$

8. Expand each of the following products.

   a. $-6(x + 2)$ **b.** $-5(x - 11)$

   c. $-3(x - y)$ **d.** $x(a - b)$

   e. $-x(a - b)$ **f.** $(x - 3)(x + 2)$

9. Solve the following equations using the missing-factor approach.

   a. $-3x = -9$ **b.** $-15x = 1290$

   c. $11x = -374$ **d.** $-9x = -8163$

10. Compute using a calculator.

a. $(-36)(52)$ b. $(-83)(-98)$

c. $(127)(-31)(-57)$ d. $(-39)(-92)(-68)$

e. $-899 \div 29$ f. $-5904 \div (-48)$

g. $7308 \div (-126)$

h. $[-1848 \div (-56)] \div (-33)$

11. Consider the statement $x \div (y + z) = (x \div y) + (x \div z)$. Is this statement true for the following values of $x, y,$ and z?

a. $x = 12, y = -2, z = -4$

b. $x = 18, y = 2, z = -3$

12. Write each of the following as a fraction without exponents.

a. 4^{-2} b. 2^{-5} c. 7^{-3}

13. a. Simplify $(3^2)^{-3}$ by expressing it in terms of whole-number exponents and simplifying.

b. Simplify $(3^2)^{-3}$ by applying $(a^m)^n = a^{mn}$.

c. Repeat parts (a) and (b) to simplify $(5^{-3})^{-2}$.

d. Does it appear that the property $(a^m)^n = a^{mn}$ still applies for integer exponents?

14. a. Simplify $(2^{-3})(4^{-3})$ by expressing it in terms of whole-number exponents and simplifying.

b. Simplify $(2^{-3})(4^{-3})$ by applying $(a^m)(b^m) = (ab)^m$.

c. Repeat parts (a) and (b) to simplify $(3^{-4})(5^{-4})$.

d. Does it appear that the property $(a^m)(b^m) = (ab)^m$ still applies for integer exponents?

15. Apply the properties of exponents to express the following values in a simpler form.

a. $\dfrac{5^{-2} \cdot 5^3}{5^{-4}}$ b. $\dfrac{(3^{-2})^{-5}}{3^{-6}}$

c. $\dfrac{8^3}{2^3 \cdot 4^{-2}}$ d. $\dfrac{2^6 \cdot 3^2}{(3^{-3})^{-2} \cdot 4^5}$

16. Each of the following numbers is written in scientific notation. Rewrite each in standard decimal form.

a. 9.0×10^{-6} b. 1.26×10^{-13}

17. Express each of the following numbers in scientific notation.

a. 0.000000691 b. 0.0000000000003048

18. Use your calculator to evaluate each of the following. Express your answers in scientific notation.

a. $(9.62 \times 10^{-12})(2.8 \times 10^{-9})$ b. $\dfrac{3.74 \times 10^{-6}}{8.5 \times 10^{-30}}$

c. $(4.35 \times 10^{-40})(7.8 \times 10^{19})$

d. $\dfrac{(1.38 \times 10^{12})(4.5 \times 10^{-16})}{1.15 \times 10^{10}}$

e. $(62,000)(0.00000000000033)$

f. $\dfrac{0.000000000000000232}{0.000000145}$

19. Show that each of the following inequalities is true by using the addition approach.

a. $-7 < -3$ b. $-6 < 5$ c. $-17 > -23$

20. Fill in the blanks with the appropriate symbol — $<$, $>$, or $=$ — to produce true statements.

a. -4 ___ 9 b. 3 ___ -2 c. -4 ___ -5

d. 0 ___ -2 e. $3 + (-5)$ ___ $2 \times (-3)$

f. $(-12) \div (-2)$ ___ 2 (___ 3)

g. $15 - (-6)$ ___ $(-3) \times (-7)$

h. $5 + (-5)$ ___ $(-3) \times (-6)$

21. Complete the following statements by inserting $<$, $=$, or $>$ in the blanks to produce true statements.

a. If $x < -3$, then $4x$ ___ -12.

b. If $x > -6$, then $-2x$ ___ 12.

PROBLEMS

22. Fill in each empty square so that a number in a square is the product of the two numbers beneath it.

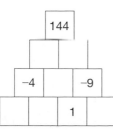

23. a. Which of the following integers when substituted for x make the given inequality true: $-4, -3, -2, -1$?

$$5x - 3 \geq -18$$

b. Is there a largest integer value for x that makes the inequality true?

c. Is there a smallest integer value for x that makes the inequality true?

24. a. Is there a largest whole number? integer? negative integer? positive integer? If yes, what is it?

b. Is there a smallest whole number? integer? negative integer? positive integer? If yes, what is it?

25. Use absolute-value notation to write the following two parts of the definition of integer multiplication.
    a. If p is positive and q is negative, then $pq =$ ___.
    b. If p is negative and q is negative, then $pq =$ ___.

26. Use the absolute-value notation to express the answers for these division problems.
    a. If p is positive and q is negative, then $p \div q =$ ___.
    b. If both of p and q are negative, then $p \div q =$ ___.

27. If $x < y$, where x and y are integers, is it always true that $x^2 < y^2$? Prove or give a counterexample.

28. If $x < y$, where x and y are integers, is it always true that $z - y < z - x$, if z is an integer? Prove or give a counterexample.

29. The mass of one electron is 9.11×10^{-28} grams. A uranium atom contains 92 electrons. Find the total mass of the electrons in a uranium atom. Express your answer in scientific notation.

30. A rare gas named "krypton" glows orange when heated by an electric current. The wavelength of the light it emits is about 605.8 nanometers, and this wavelength is used to define the exact length of a meter. If one nanometer is 0.000000001 meter, what is the wavelength of krypton in meters? Express your answer in scientific notation.

31. The mass of one molecule of hemoglobin can be described as 0.11 attogram.
    a. If 1 attogram $= 10^{-21}$ kilogram, what is the mass in kilograms of one molecule of hemoglobin?

    b. The mass of a molecule of hemoglobin can be specified in terms of other units, too. For example, the mass of a molecule of hemoglobin might be given as 68,000 daltons. Determine the number of kilograms in 1 dalton.

32. Red blood corpuscles in the human body are constantly disintegrating and being replaced. About 73,000 of them disintegrate and are replaced every 3.16×10^{-2} second.
    a. How many red blood corpuscles break down in 1 second? Express your answer in scientific notation.
    b. There are approximately 25,000,000,000,000 red blood corpuscles in the blood of an adult male at any given time. About how long does it take for all of these red blood corpuscles to break down and be replaced?

33. Prove or disprove: If $x^2 + y^2 = z^2$ for whole numbers x, y, and z, either x or y is a multiple of 3.

34. A woman born in the first half of the nineteenth century (1800 to 1849) was X years old in the year X^2. In what year was she born?

35. Assume that the statement "If $ab = 0$, then $a = 0$ or $b = 0$" is true. Prove the multiplication cancellation property. [*Hint:* If $ac = bc$, where $c \neq 0$, then $ac - bc = 0$, or $(a - b)c = 0$. Since $(a - b)c = 0$, what can you conclude based on the statement assumed here?]

PROBLEMS FOR WRITING/DISCUSSION

1. In an example, the answer to $(-x)(-y)(-z)$ is given as $-xyz$. You have a student who asks, "How do you know the answer is negative if you don't know what x, y, and z are?" How do you respond?

2. A student asks if 3 can equal 0. He is looking at the equation $3x = 0$, and he explains that since that means $3 = 0$ or $x = 0$, then 3 and x must both equal zero. How would you explain?

3. Maurice says that $a^2 + b^2 = (a + b)(a + b)$. Is this always true, never true, or sometimes true? Explain.

END OF CHAPTER MATERIAL

Solution of Initial Problem

Prove or disprove: 2 is a factor of $(a - b)(b - c)(c - a)$ for any integers a, b, c.

Strategy: Use Cases

Note that if x and y are integers with $x \neq 0$, then $x \mid y$ means $x = y$ for some integer n.

CASE 1: Assume that at least two of a, b, or c are even (say, a and b are even). Then $a = 2m$, $b = 2n$, and $a - b = 2m - 2n = 2(m - n)$. Thus $2 \mid (a - b)$, so $2 \mid (a - b)(b - c)(c - a)$.

CASE 2: Assume that at least two of a, b, or c are odd (say, a and b are odd). Then $a = 2m + 1$, $b = 2n + 1$, and $a - b = (2m + 1) - (2n + 1) = 2(m - n)$. Thus $2 \mid (a - b)$, so $2 \mid (a - b)(b - c)(c - a)$.

Since either at least two of a, b, or c are even or at least two are odd, we have covered all cases.

Additional Problems Where the Strategy "Use Cases" Is Useful

1. If the sum of three consecutive numbers is even, prove that two of the numbers must be odd.

2. If m and n are integers, under what circumstances will $m^2 - n^2$ be positive?

3. Show that the square of any whole number is either a multiple of 5, one more than a multiple of 5, or one less than a multiple of 5.

People in Mathematics

Grace Chisholm Young (1868–1944) Grace Chisholm Young, who was born in England, became the first woman to receive a doctoral degree in Germany. She married William Young, a mathematician who had been her tutor in England. A curious collaboration developed between the two. Both had done important mathematical research independently, but together they produced 220 mathematical papers, several books, and six children. Their joint papers were usually published under Will's name alone because of prejudice against women mathematicians. In a letter to Grace, Will wrote, "Our papers ought to be published under our joint names, but if this were done neither of us get the benefit of it." Their daughter Cecily describes their collaboration: "My mother had decision and initiative and the stamina to carry an undertaking to its conclusion. If not for [her skill] my father's genius would probably have been abortive, and would not have eclipsed hers and the name she had already made for herself."

Martin Gardner (1914–) Martin Gardner wrote the lively and thoughtful "Mathematical Games" column in *Scientific American* magazine for more than 20 years. Readers were served an eclectic blend of diversions — logical puzzles, number problems, card tricks, game theory, and much more. Perhaps more than anyone else in our time, Gardner has succeeded in popularizing mathematics, which he calls "a kind of game that we play with the universe." There are now 14 book collections of his *Scientific American* features, and he has written more than 50 books in all. He wrote, "A good mathematical puzzle, paradox, or magic trick can stimulate a child's imagination much faster than a practical application (especially if the application is remote from the child's experience), and if the game is chosen carefully, it can lead almost effortlessly into significant mathematical ideas."

CHAPTER REVIEW

Review the following terms and exercises to determine which require learning or relearning—page numbers are provided for easy reference.

SECTION 8.1: Addition and Subtraction

VOCABULARY/NOTATION

Integers 319	Opposite 320	Adding the opposite 325
Positive integers 319	Additive inverse 320	Zero pair 325
Negative integers 319	Additive cancellation 323	Missing-addend approach 326
Integer number line 320	Take-away 324	

EXERCISES

1. Explain how to represent integers in two ways using the following:

   a. A set model

   b. A measurement model

2. Show how to find $7 + (-4)$ using (a) colored chips and (b) the integer number line.

3. Name the property of addition of integers that is used to justify each of the following equations.

   a. $(-7) + 0 = -7$ b. $(-3) + 3 = 0$

   c. $4 + (-5) = (-5) + 4$

   d. $(7 + 4) + (-4) = 7 + [4 + (-4)]$

   e. $(-9) + 7$ is an integer

4. Show how to find $3 - (-2)$ using each of the following approaches.

   a. Take-away   b. Adding the opposite

   c. Missing addend

5. Which of the following properties hold for integer subtraction?

   a. Closure   b. Commutative

   c. Associative   d. Identity

SECTION 8.2: Multiplication, Division, and Order

VOCABULARY/NOTATION

Scientific notation   339   Characteristic   339   Less than, greater than   340

Mantissa   339

EXERCISES

1. Explain how you can provide motivation for the following.

   a. $5(-2) = -10$ b. $(-5)(-2) = 10$

2. Name the property of multiplication of integers that is used to justify each of the following equations.

   a. $(-3)(-4) = (-4)(-3)$

   b. $(-5)[2(-7)] = [(-5)(2)](-7)$

   c. $(-5)(-7)$ is an integer

   d. $(-8) \times 1 = -8$

   e. If $(-3)n = (-3)7$, then $n = 7$.

3. Explain how $(-a)(-b) = ab$ is a generalization of $(-3)(-4) = 3 \times 4$.

4. If $3n = 0$, what can you conclude? What property can you cite for justification?

5. Explain how integer division is related to integer multiplication.

6. Which of the following properties hold for integer division?

   a. Closure

   b. Commutative

   c. Associative

   d. Identity

7. Without doing the indicated calculations, determine whether the answers are positive, negative, or zero. Explain your reasoning.

   a. $(-3)(-7)(-5) \div (-15)$

   b. $(-27) \div 3 \times (-4) \div (-3)$

   c. $35(-4) \div 5 \times 0 \times (-2)$

8. Explain how you can motivate the fact that $7^{-4} = \dfrac{1}{7^4}$.

9. Convert as indicated.

   a. 0.000079 to scientific notation

   b. 3×10^{-4} to standard notation

   c. 458.127 to scientific notation

   d. 2.39×10^7 to standard notation

10. Explain how to determine the smaller of -17 and -21 using the following techniques.

    a. The number-line approach

    b. The addition approach

11. Complete the following, and name the property you used as a justification.

    a. If $(-3) < 4$, then $(-3)(-2)$ ___ $4(-2)$.

    b. If $-5 < 7$ and $7 < 9$, then -5 ___ 9.

    c. If $-3 < 7$, then $(-3)2$ ___ $7 \cdot 2$.

    d. If $-4 < 5$, then $(-4) + 3$ ___ $5 + 3$.

PROBLEMS FOR WRITING/DISCUSSION

1. Suppose you were working out the following problem with a student. What would be your explanation for each step? For each step write out how you would read it (when would you say "minus" and when "negative," for example) and what reason you would give for each change.

$$-3 - (-2) = -3 + 2$$
$$= -1$$

2. Students often get confused when working a problem like $-5 - 7$. A common mistake is to rewrite the problem as $(-5) + (+7) = 2$. Why might the student be making this mistake? How would you explain the right way to do it?

3. Students know that when there is a negative sign in front of a number, it means that the number is negative. "-3" means "negative 3." Therefore, many students assume that "$-n$" is also a negative number. How would you explain to students that "$-n$" is sometimes positive and sometimes negative (and sometimes neither)?

4. Joe and Misha are using their calculators to do the problem -7^2. Joe types the negative sign, the seven, the exponent character ^, and then 2. He gets the answer -49. Misha's calculator won't allow him to type the negative sign first, so he types 7, then the negative sign, then the exponent character ^, then 2. His calculator says the answer is 49. What's going on here?

5. Mary Lou is trying to find 2^{42} using her calculator. She tells you that her calculator says the answer is 4.398 to the 12th power, which equals 52,367,603.57. Where did she go wrong?

6. Roger tells you that 3^7 means 3 multiplied times itself 7 times, so 3^{-7} must mean 3 multiplied times itself -7 times. He wants to know how to do that. How would you explain?

7. List all the real-life applications of negative numbers you can think of.

8. Students can model $4(-3)$ with successive additions by writing $(-3) + (-3) + (-3) + (-3)$. How would you explain how to multiply $(-4)(-3)$?

9. A student performing the subtraction problem $4 - (-3)$ says, "A negative times a negative is a positive, so this problem means $4 + 3$." How would you respond?

10. One student says that since $7x > -28$, then $x < -4$, because when you have a negative, you reverse the inequality. What do you say?

CHAPTER TEST

Knowledge

1. True or false?
   a. The sum of any two negative integers is negative.
   b. The product of any two negative integers is negative.
   c. The difference of any two negative integers is negative.
   d. The result of any positive integer subtracted from any negative integer is negative.
   e. If $a < b$, then $ac < bc$ for integers a, b, and nonzero integer c.
   f. The opposite of an integer is negative.
   g. If $c = 0$ and $ac = bc$, then $a = b$.
   h. The sum of an integer and its additive inverse is zero.

2. What does the notation a^{-n} mean, where a is not zero and n is a positive integer?

3. Which of the following is a property of the integers but not of the whole numbers? (circle all that apply)
   a. Additive identity
   b. Additive inverse
   c. Closure for subtraction

4. Identify three different approaches to the subtraction of integers.

Skill

5. Compute each of the following problems without using a calculator.
   a. $37 + (-43)$ b. $(-7)(-6)$
   c. $45 - (-3)$ d. $16 \div (-2)$
   e. $(-13) - 17$ f. $(-24) \div (-8)$
   g. $(-13)(4)$ h. $[-24 - (-27)] \times (-4)$

6. Evaluate each of the following expressions in two ways to check the fact that $a(b + c)$ and $ab + ac$ are equal.

a. $a = 3, b = -4, c = 2$
b. $a = -3, b = -5, c = -2$

7. Express the following in scientific notation.
   a. $(9.7 \times 10^8)(8.5 \times 10^3)$
   b. $(5.5 \times 10^{-7}) \div (9.1 \times 10^{-2})$

8. Solve for n in the following expression.

$$\frac{(2^5)^{-2} \cdot 2^3}{2^{-3}} = 2^n$$

Understanding

9. Name the property or properties that can be used to simplify these computations.
   a. $(-37 + 91) + (-91)$ **b.** $[(-2)17] \cdot 5$
   c. $(-31)17 + (-31)83$ **d.** $(-7)13 + 13(17)$

10. Compute using each of the three approaches: (i) take-away, (ii) adding the opposite, and (iii) missing addend.
    a. $8 - (-5)$ **b.** $(-2) - (-7)$

11. If a and b are negative and c is positive, determine whether the following are positive or negative.
    a. $(-a)(-c)$ **b.** $(-a)(b)$
    c. $(c - b)(c - a)$ **d.** $a(b - c)$

12. Illustrate the following operations using a (i) number line, and (ii) black and red chips.
    a. $8 + -3$ **b.** $-2 + 4$ **c.** $3 + -5$

13. Illustrate with black and red chips the operation $-2 - 3$ using the (i) take-away and the (ii) missing-addend approaches.

14. **a.** Building from the fact that $3 \times 4 = 12$, use patterns to illustrate why $-2 \times 4 = -8$.
    b. Building from the fact established in part (a), use patterns to illustrate why $-2 \times -4 = 8$.

15. Explain whether or not $a(b \cdot c)$ is equal to $(a \cdot b) \times (a \cdot c)$.

Problem Solving/Application

16. If $30 \le a \le 60$ and $-60 \le b \le -30$, where a and b are integers, find the largest and smallest possible *integer* values for the following expressions.
    a. $a + b$
    b. $a - b$
    c. ab
    d. $a \div b$

17. Complete this *additive* magic square of integers using $9, -12, 3, -6, 6, -3, 12, -9$.

	0	

18. Complete this *multiplicative* magic square of integers.

		-64
	32	128
		-4

19. Find all values of a and b such that $a - b = b - a$.

20. On Hideki's history exams he gets 4 points for each problem answered correctly, he loses 2 points for each incorrect answer, and he gets 0 points for each question left blank. On a 25-question test, Hideki received a score of 70.
    a. What is the largest number of questions that he could have answered correctly?
    b. What is the fewest number of questions that he could have answered correctly?
    c. What is the largest number of questions that he could have left blank?

References for Reflections from Research

BLEY, N. S., & THORNTON, C. A. (1989). *Teaching mathematics to the learning disabled* (2nd ed.). Austin, TX: PRO-ED.

SHEFFIELD, L. J., & CRUIKSHANK, D. E. (1996). *Teaching and learning elementary and middle school mathematics* (3rd ed.). Upper Saddle River, NJ: Prentice Hall.

THOMPSON, F. M. (1998). Algebraic instruction for the younger child. In A. Coxford (Ed.), *The ideas of algebra,* K-12 (pp. 8–19). Reston, VA: National Council of Teachers of Mathematics.

THOMPSON, P. W., & DREYFUS, T. (1988). Integers as transformations. *Journal of Research in Mathematics Education, 19,* 115–133.

Rational Numbers and Real Numbers, with an Introduction to Algebra

FOCUS ON *The Pythagoreans and Irrational Numbers*

Pythagoras

Pythagoras (circa 570 B.C.) was one of the most famous of all Greek mathematicians. After his studies and travels, he founded a school in southern Italy. This school, an academy of philosophy, mathematics, and natural science, developed into a closely knit brotherhood with secret rites and observances. The society was dispersed, but the brotherhood continued to exist for at least two centuries after the death of Pythagoras.

Much of the work of the Pythagoreans was done in whole numbers, but they also believed that *all* measurements could be done with fractions. However, the hypotenuse of the unit right triangle caused them some alarm, since they could not find a fraction to measure it and still fit the Pythagorean theorem. One feeble attempt was to say that $c = \frac{7}{5}$. Then $c^2 = \frac{49}{25}$ (or *almost* 2).

Hippasus is attributed with the discovery of incommensurable ratios, that is, numbers not expressible as the ratio of two whole numbers. This discovery caused a scandal among the Pythagoreans, since their theory did not allow for such a number. Legend has it that Hippasus, a Pythagorean, was drowned because he shared the secret of incommensurables with others outside the society. Actually, according to Aristotle, the Pythagoreans gave the first proof (using an indirect proof) that there is no fraction whose square is 2. However, they still would not accept the existence of a number whose square is 2.

By 300 B.C. many other irrational numbers were known, such as $\sqrt{3}, \sqrt{5}, \sqrt{6}$, and $\sqrt{8}$. Eudoxus, a Greek mathematician, developed a geometric method for handling irrationals. This treatment was presented in Euclid's *Elements*. (See the Focus On section for Chapter 14.)

In the first century A.D. the Hindus began to treat irrationals like other numbers, replacing expressions such as $5\sqrt{2} + 4\sqrt{2}$ with $9\sqrt{2}$, and so on. Finally, in the late nineteenth century, irrationals were fully accepted as numbers.

Irrationals cannot be expressed exactly as decimals. For example, $\pi = 3.141592654$ . . . has been calculated to over one billion places, but it has no exact decimal representation. This may seem strange to you at first, but if you have difficulty grasping the concept of an irrational number, keep in mind that many famous mathematicians throughout history had similar difficulties.

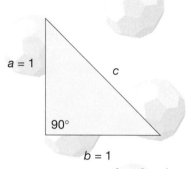

Pythagorean theorem: $a^2 + b^2 = c^2$

3000 B.C.	Babylonians and Egyptians
500 B.C.	Pythagoreans
300 B.C.	Greeks
A.D. 100	Hindus
A.D. 1880	Acceptance of irrationals

Strategy
Solve an Equation

Often, when applying the Use a Variable strategy to solve a problem, the representation of the problem will be an equation. The following problem yields such an equation. Techniques for solving simple equations are given in Section 9.2.

Initial Problem

A man's boyhood lasted for $\frac{1}{6}$ of his life, he played soccer for the next $\frac{1}{12}$ of his life, and he married after $\frac{1}{7}$ more of his life. A daughter was born 5 years after his marriage, and the daughter lived $\frac{1}{2}$ as many years as her father did. If the man died 4 years after his daughter did, how old was the man when he died?

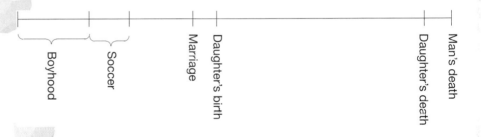

Clues

The Solve an Equation strategy may be appropriate when

- A variable has been introduced.
- The words *is*, *is equal to*, or *equals* appear in a problem.
- The stated conditions can easily be represented with an equation.

A solution of the Initial Problem appears on page 406.

INTRODUCTION

In this book we have introduced number systems much the same as they are developed in the school curriculum. The counting numbers came first. Then zero was included to form the whole numbers. Because of the need to deal with parts of a whole, fractions were introduced. Since there was a need to have numbers to represent amounts less than zero, the set of integers was introduced. The relationships among these sets are illustrated in Figure 9.1, where each arrow represents "is a subset of." For example, the set of counting numbers is a subset of the set of whole numbers, and so on. Recall that as number systems, both the fractions and integers extend the system of whole numbers.

NCTM Standards 2000
Number and Operations
Grades 6–8
All students should understand the meaning and effects of arithmetic operations with fractions, decimals, and integers.

Figure 9.1

It is the objective of this chapter to introduce our final number systems, first the rational numbers and then the real numbers. Both of these are extensions of our existing number systems. The set of rational numbers is composed of the fractions and their opposites, and the real numbers include all of the rational numbers together with additional numbers such as π and $\sqrt{2}$. Finally, we use the real numbers to solve equations and inequalities, and we graph functions.

9.1 THE RATIONAL NUMBERS

STARTING POINT

The fraction $\frac{2}{3}$ can be thought of as the number $0.\overline{6}$, which lies on the number line between 0 and 1. It can also be thought of as one whole broken into 3 parts where 2 of those parts are of interest.

How are the symbols $-\frac{2}{3}$ and $\frac{-2}{3}$ related to each other or to either of the meanings described to the right.

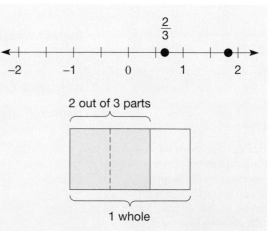

Rational Numbers: An Extension of Fractions and Integers

There are many reasons for needing numbers that have both reciprocals, as fractions do, and opposites, as integers do. For example, the fraction $\frac{2}{3}$ satisfies the equation $3x = 2$, since $3(\frac{2}{3}) = 2$, and -3 satisfies the equation $x + 3 = 0$, since $-3 + 3 = 0$. However, there is neither a fraction nor an integer that satisfies the equation $3x = -2$. To find such a number, we need the set of rational numbers.

There are various ways to introduce a set of numbers that extends both the fractions and the integers. Using models, one could merge the shaded-region model for fractions with the black and red chip model for integers. The resulting model would

represent rational numbers by shading parts of wholes—models with black shaded parts to represent positive rational numbers and with red shaded parts to represent negative rational numbers.

For the sake of efficiency and mathematical clarity, we will introduce the rational numbers abstractly by focusing on the two properties we wish to extend; namely, that every nonzero number has a reciprocal and that every number has an opposite. There are two directions we can take. First, we could take all the fractions together with their opposites. This would give us a new collection of numbers, namely the fractions and numbers such as $-\frac{2}{3}, -\frac{5}{7}, -\frac{11}{2}$. A second approach would be to take the integers and form all possible "fractions" where the numerators are *integers* and the denominators are *nonzero integers*. We adopt this second approach, in which a rational number will be defined to be a *ratio* of integers. The set of rational numbers defined in this way will include the opposites of the fractions.

DEFINITION

Rational Numbers

The set of **rational numbers** is the set

$$Q = \left\{ \frac{a}{b} \mid a \text{ and } b \text{ are integers, } b \neq 0 \right\}.$$

Examples of rational numbers are $\frac{2}{3}, \frac{-5}{7}, \frac{4}{-9}, \frac{0}{1}$, and $\frac{-7}{-9}$. Mixed numbers such as $-3\frac{1}{4} = \frac{-13}{4}$, $-5\frac{2}{7} = \frac{-37}{7}$ and $2\frac{1}{3} = \frac{7}{3}$ are also rational numbers, since they can be expressed in the form $\frac{a}{b}$, where a and b are integers, $b \neq 0$. Notice that every fraction is a rational number; for example, in the case when $a \geq 0$ and $b > 0$ in $\frac{a}{b}$. Also, every integer is a rational number; for example, in the case when $b = 1$ in $\frac{a}{b}$. Thus we can extend our diagram in Figure 9.1 to include the set of rational numbers (Figure 9.2).

Reflection from Research
Rational number programs which report success in deeper understanding have a common feature of "highlighting rather than glossing over the difference between rational and whole numbers" (Moss & Case, 1999).

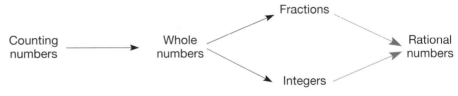

Figure 9.2

Equality of rational numbers and the four basic operations are defined as natural extensions of their counterparts for fractions and integers.

DEFINITION

Equality of Rational Numbers

Let $\frac{a}{b}$ and $\frac{c}{d}$ be any rational numbers. Then $\frac{a}{b} = \frac{c}{d}$ if and only if $ad = bc$.

The equality-of-rational-numbers definition is used to find equivalent representations of rational numbers (1) to simplify rational numbers and (2) to obtain common denominators to facilitate addition, subtraction, and comparing rational numbers.

As with fractions, each rational number has an infinite number of representations. That is, by the definition of equality of rational numbers, $\frac{1}{2} = \frac{2}{4} = \frac{3}{6} = \cdots = \frac{-1}{-2} = \frac{-2}{-4} = \frac{-3}{-6} = \cdots$. The rational number $\frac{1}{2}$ can then be viewed as the idea represented by all of its various representations. Similarly, the number $\frac{-2}{3}$ should come to mind when any of the representations $\frac{-2}{3}, \frac{2}{-3}, \frac{-4}{6}, \frac{4}{-6}, \frac{-6}{9}, \frac{6}{-9}, \cdots$ are considered.

By using the definition of equality of rational numbers, it can be shown that the following theorem holds for rational numbers.

THEOREM

Let $\frac{a}{b}$ be any rational number and n any nonzero integer. Then

$$\frac{a}{b} = \frac{an}{bn} = \frac{na}{nb}.$$

A rational number $\frac{a}{b}$ is said to be in **simplest form** or in **lowest terms** if a and b have no common prime factors and b is *positive*. For example, $\frac{2}{3}, \frac{-5}{7},$ and $\frac{-3}{10}$ are in simplest form, whereas $\frac{5}{-7}, \frac{4}{6},$ and $\frac{-3}{81}$ are not because of the -7 in $\frac{5}{-7}$, and because $\frac{4}{6} = \frac{2}{3}$ and $\frac{-3}{81} = \frac{-1}{27}$.

Example 9.1 Determine whether the following pairs are equal. Then express them in simplest form.

a. $\frac{5}{-7}, \frac{-5}{7}$　　**b.** $\frac{-20}{-12}, \frac{5}{3}$　　**c.** $\frac{16}{-30}, \frac{-8}{15}$　　**d.** $\frac{-15}{36}, \frac{20}{-48}$

Solution

a. $\frac{5}{-7} = \frac{-5}{7}$, since $5 \cdot 7 = (-7)(-5)$. The simplest form is $\frac{-5}{7}$.

b. $\frac{-20}{-12} = \frac{(-4)5}{(-4)3} = \frac{5}{3}$ due to simplification. The simplest form is $\frac{5}{3}$.

c. $\frac{16}{-30} = \frac{-8}{15}$, since $16 \cdot 15 = 240$ and $(-30)(-8) = 240$. The simplest form is $\frac{-8}{15}$.

d. $\frac{-15}{36} = \frac{20}{-48}$, since $(-15)(-48) = 720 = 36 \times 20$. The simplest form is $\frac{-5}{12}$. ■

Addition and Its Properties

Addition of rational numbers is defined as an extension of fraction addition.

> ### DEFINITION
>
> **Addition of Rational Numbers**
>
> Let $\dfrac{a}{b}$ and $\dfrac{c}{d}$ be any rational numbers. Then
>
> $$\frac{a}{b} + \frac{c}{d} = \frac{ad + bc}{bd}.$$

It follows from this definition that $\dfrac{a}{b} + \dfrac{c}{b} = \dfrac{a + c}{b}$ also.

Example 9.2 Find these sums.

a. $\dfrac{3}{7} + \dfrac{-5}{7}$ **b.** $\dfrac{-2}{5} + \dfrac{4}{-7}$ **c.** $\dfrac{-2}{5} + \dfrac{0}{5}$ **d.** $\dfrac{5}{6} + \dfrac{-5}{6}$

Solution

a. $\dfrac{3}{7} + \dfrac{-5}{7} = \dfrac{3 + (-5)}{7} = \dfrac{-2}{7}$

b. $\dfrac{-2}{5} + \dfrac{4}{-7} = \dfrac{(-2)(-7) + 5 \cdot 4}{5(-7)} = \dfrac{14 + 20}{-35} = \dfrac{34}{-35} = \dfrac{-34}{35}$

c. $\dfrac{-2}{5} + \dfrac{0}{5} = \dfrac{-2 + 0}{5} = \dfrac{-2}{5}$

d. $\dfrac{5}{6} + \dfrac{-5}{6} = \dfrac{5 + (-5)}{6} = \dfrac{0}{6}$ ■

Example 9.2(c) suggests that just as with the integers, the rationals have an additive identity. Also, Example 9.2(d) suggests that there is an additive inverse for each rational number. These two observations will be substantiated in the rest of this paragraph.

$$\frac{a}{b} + \frac{0}{b} = \frac{a + 0}{b} \qquad \text{\textit{Addition of rational numbers}}$$

$$= \frac{a}{b} \qquad \text{\textit{Identity property for integer addition}}$$

Thus $\dfrac{0}{b}$ is an identity for addition of rational numbers; moreover, it can be shown to be unique. For this reason, we write $\dfrac{0}{b}$ as 0, where b can represent any nonzero integer.

Next, let's consider additive inverses.

$$\frac{a}{b} + \frac{-a}{b} = \frac{a + (-a)}{b} \qquad \text{\textit{Addition of rational numbers}}$$

$$= \frac{0}{b} \qquad \text{\textit{Additive inverse property for integer addition}}$$

Thus the rational number $\dfrac{-a}{b}$ is an additive inverse of $\dfrac{a}{b}$. Moreover, it can be shown that each rational number has a unique additive inverse.

Notice that $\dfrac{-a}{b} = \dfrac{a}{-b}$, since $(-a)(-b) = ab = ba$. Therefore, $\dfrac{a}{-b}$ is the additive inverse of $\dfrac{a}{b}$ also. The symbol $-\dfrac{a}{b}$ is used to represent this additive inverse. We summarize this in the following result.

THEOREM

Let $\dfrac{a}{b}$ be any rational number. Then

$$-\dfrac{a}{b} = \dfrac{-a}{b} = \dfrac{a}{-b}.$$

We can represent the rational numbers on a line that extends both the fraction number line and the integer number line. Since every fraction and every integer is a rational number, we can begin to form the rational number line from the combination of the fraction number line and the integer number line (Figure 9.3).

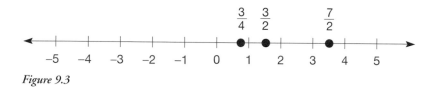

Figure 9.3

Just as in the case of fractions, we cannot label the entire fraction portion of the line, since there are infinitely many fractions between each pair of fractions. Furthermore, this line does not represent the rational numbers, since the additive inverses of the fractions are not yet represented. The additive inverses of the nonzero fractions, called the negative rational numbers, can be located by reflecting each nonzero fraction across zero (Figure 9.4). In particular, $-\frac{2}{3}$, $-\frac{5}{7}$, $-\frac{13}{4}$, and so on, are examples of negative rational numbers. In general, $\dfrac{a}{b}$ is a **positive rational number** if a and b are both positive or both negative integers, and $\dfrac{a}{b}$ is a **negative rational number** if one of a or b is positive and the other is negative.

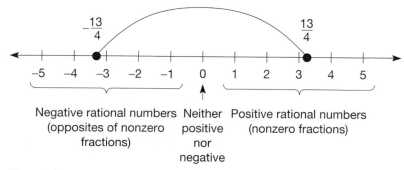

Figure 9.4

Next we list all the properties of rational-number addition. These properties can be verified using similar properties of integers.

PROPERTIES

Rational-Number Addition

Let $\dfrac{a}{b}, \dfrac{c}{d}$, and $\dfrac{e}{f}$ be any rational numbers.

Closure Property for Rational-Number Addition

$$\frac{a}{b} + \frac{c}{d} \text{ is a rational number.}$$

Commutative Property for Rational-Number Addition

$$\frac{a}{b} + \frac{c}{d} = \frac{c}{d} + \frac{a}{b}$$

Associative Property for Rational-Number Addition

$$\left(\frac{a}{b} + \frac{c}{d}\right) + \frac{e}{f} = \frac{a}{b} + \left(\frac{c}{d} + \frac{e}{f}\right)$$

Identity Property for Rational-Number Addition

$$\frac{a}{b} + 0 = \frac{a}{b} = 0 + \frac{a}{b} \qquad \left(0 = \frac{0}{m}, m \neq 0\right)$$

Additive Inverse Property for Rational-Number Addition

For every rational number $\dfrac{a}{b}$ there exists a unique rational number $-\dfrac{a}{b}$ such that

$$\frac{a}{b} + \left(-\frac{a}{b}\right) = 0 = \left(-\frac{a}{b}\right) + \frac{a}{b}.$$

NCTM Standards 2000
Number and Operations
Grades 6–8
All students should use the associative and commutative properties of addition and multiplication and the distributive property of multiplication over addition to simplify computations with integers, fractions, and decimals.

Example 9.3 Apply properties of rational-number addition to calculate the following sums. Try to do them mentally before looking at the solutions

a. $\left(\dfrac{3}{4} + \dfrac{5}{6}\right) + \dfrac{1}{4}$ **b.** $\left(\dfrac{5}{7} + \dfrac{3}{8}\right) + \dfrac{-6}{16}$

Solution

a. $\left(\dfrac{3}{4} + \dfrac{5}{6}\right) + \dfrac{1}{4} = \dfrac{1}{4} + \left(\dfrac{3}{4} + \dfrac{5}{6}\right)$ *Commutativity*

$\qquad\qquad = \left(\dfrac{1}{4} + \dfrac{3}{4}\right) + \dfrac{5}{6}$ *Associativity*

$\qquad\qquad = 1 + \dfrac{5}{6}$ *Addition*

$\qquad\qquad = 1\dfrac{5}{6}$ or $\dfrac{11}{6}$ *Addition*

b. $\left(\dfrac{5}{7} + \dfrac{3}{8}\right) + \dfrac{-6}{16} = \dfrac{5}{7} + \left(\dfrac{3}{8} + \dfrac{-6}{16}\right)$ *Associativity*

$\qquad\qquad = \dfrac{5}{7} + 0$ *Additive inverse*

$\qquad\qquad = \dfrac{5}{7}$ *Additive identity* ■

The following two consequences of the rational-number properties are extensions of corresponding integer results. Their verifications are left for the Problem Set (Problems 29 in Part A and 26 in Part B).

THEOREM

Additive Cancellation for Rational Numbers

Let $\dfrac{a}{b}, \dfrac{c}{d}$, and $\dfrac{e}{f}$ be any rational numbers.

$$\text{If } \frac{a}{b} + \frac{e}{f} = \frac{c}{d} + \frac{e}{f}, \text{ then } \frac{a}{b} = \frac{c}{d}.$$

THEOREM

Opposite of the Opposite for Rational Numbers

Let $\dfrac{a}{b}$ be any rational number. Then

$$-\left(-\frac{a}{b}\right) = \frac{a}{b}.$$

Subtraction

Since there is an additive inverse for each rational number, subtraction can be defined as an extension of integer subtraction.

DEFINITION

Subtraction of Rational Numbers: Adding the Opposite

Let $\dfrac{a}{b}$ and $\dfrac{c}{d}$ be any rational numbers. Then

$$\frac{a}{b} - \frac{c}{d} = \frac{a}{b} + \left(-\frac{c}{d}\right).$$

The following discussion shows that this definition is also an extension of fraction subtraction.

Common Denominators

$$\frac{a}{b} - \frac{c}{b} = \frac{a}{b} + \left(-\frac{c}{b}\right) = \frac{a}{b} + \left(\frac{-c}{b}\right) = \frac{a + (-c)}{b} = \frac{a - c}{b}$$

That is,

$$\frac{a}{b} - \frac{c}{b} = \frac{a - c}{b}.$$

Thus rational numbers with common denominators can be subtracted as is done with fractions that have common denominators, namely by subtracting numerators.

Unlike Denominators

$$\frac{a}{b} - \frac{c}{d} = \frac{ad}{bd} - \frac{bc}{bd} = \frac{ad - bc}{bd} \qquad \textit{Using common denominators}$$

Example 9.4   Calculate the following differences and express the answers in simplest form.

a. $\dfrac{3}{10} - \dfrac{4}{5}$ **b.** $\dfrac{8}{27} - \dfrac{-1}{12}$

Solution

a. $\dfrac{3}{10} - \dfrac{4}{5} = \dfrac{3}{10} - \dfrac{8}{10} = \dfrac{3-8}{10} = \dfrac{-5}{10} = \dfrac{-1}{2}$

b. $\dfrac{8}{27} - \left(\dfrac{-1}{12}\right) = \dfrac{32}{108} - \left(\dfrac{-9}{108}\right) = \dfrac{32}{108} + \left[-\left(\dfrac{-9}{108}\right)\right] = \dfrac{41}{108}$ ■

The fact that the missing-addend approach to subtraction is equivalent to the adding-the-opposite approach is discussed in the Problem Set. (Problem 26 in Part A).

Spotlight on Technology A fraction calculator can be used to find sums and differences of rational numbers just as we did with fractions, except that the $\boxed{(-)}$ key may have to be used. For example $\dfrac{5}{27} - \left(\dfrac{-7}{15}\right)$ can be found as follows: 5 $\boxed{/}$ 27 $\boxed{-}$ $\boxed{(-)}$ 7 $\boxed{/}$ 15 $\boxed{=}$ $\boxed{88/135}$. On some calculators, there is a change-of-sign key $\boxed{+/-}$ instead of a negative key $\boxed{(-)}$. In those cases, a -7 is entered as 7 $\boxed{+/-}$. Notice that the keystrokes 7 $\boxed{/}$ $\boxed{(-)}$ 15 would also be correct because $\dfrac{-7}{15} - \dfrac{7}{-15}$. Using a decimal calculator, the numerator, $5 \cdot 15 + 27 \cdot 7$, and the denominator, $27 \cdot 15$, can be calculated. The result, $\dfrac{264}{405}$, can be simplified to $\dfrac{88}{135}$.

Multiplication and Its Properties

Multiplication of rational numbers is defined as an extension of fraction multiplication as follows.

DEFINITION

Multiplication of Rational Numbers

Let $\dfrac{a}{b}$ and $\dfrac{c}{d}$ be any rational numbers. Then

$$\frac{a}{b} \cdot \frac{c}{d} = \frac{ac}{bd}.$$

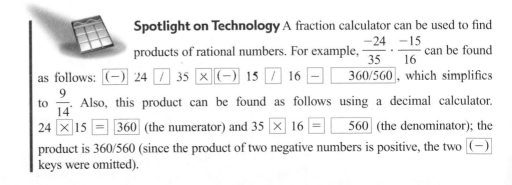

Spotlight on Technology A fraction calculator can be used to find products of rational numbers. For example, $\dfrac{-24}{35} \cdot \dfrac{-15}{16}$ can be found as follows: $\boxed{(-)}$ 24 $\boxed{/}$ 35 $\boxed{\times}$ $\boxed{(-)}$ 15 $\boxed{/}$ 16 $\boxed{-}$ $\boxed{360/560}$, which simplifies to $\dfrac{9}{14}$. Also, this product can be found as follows using a decimal calculator. 24 $\boxed{\times}$ 15 $\boxed{=}$ $\boxed{360}$ (the numerator) and 35 $\boxed{\times}$ 16 $\boxed{=}$ $\boxed{560}$ (the denominator); the product is 360/560 (since the product of two negative numbers is positive, the two $\boxed{(-)}$ keys were omitted).

Reasoning by analogy to fraction multiplication, the following properties can be verified using the definition of rational-number multiplication and the corresponding properties of integer multiplication.

PROPERTIES

Rational-Number Multiplication

Let $\dfrac{a}{b}, \dfrac{c}{d}$, and $\dfrac{e}{f}$ be any rational numbers.

Closure Property for Rational-Number Multiplication

$$\frac{a}{b} \cdot \frac{c}{d} = \frac{ac}{bd} \text{ is a rational number.}$$

Commutative Property for Rational-Number Multiplication

$$\frac{a}{b} \cdot \frac{c}{d} = \frac{c}{d} \cdot \frac{a}{b}$$

Associative Property for Rational-Number Multiplication

$$\left(\frac{a}{b} \cdot \frac{c}{d}\right)\frac{e}{f} = \frac{a}{b}\left(\frac{c}{d} \cdot \frac{e}{f}\right)$$

Identity Property for Rational-Number Multiplication

$$\frac{a}{b} \cdot 1 = \frac{a}{b} = 1 \cdot \frac{a}{b} \qquad \left(1 = \frac{m}{m}, m \neq 0\right)$$

Multiplicative Inverse Property for Rational-Number Multiplication

For every nonzero rational number $\dfrac{a}{b}$ there exists a unique rational number $\dfrac{b}{a}$

such that $\dfrac{a}{b} \cdot \dfrac{b}{a} = 1.$

Recall that the multiplicative inverse of a number is also called the **reciprocal** of the number. Notice that the reciprocal of the reciprocal of any nonzero rational number is the original number.

It can be shown that distributivity also holds in the set of rational numbers. The verification of this fact takes precisely the same form as it did in the set of fractions and will be left for the Problem Set (Problem 27 in Part A).

PROPERTY

Distributive Property of Multiplication over Addition of Rational Numbers

Let $\dfrac{a}{b}, \dfrac{c}{d}$, and $\dfrac{e}{f}$ be any rational numbers. Then

$$\frac{a}{b}\left(\frac{c}{d} + \frac{e}{f}\right) = \frac{a}{b} \cdot \frac{c}{d} + \frac{a}{b} \cdot \frac{e}{f}.$$

The distributive property of multiplication over subtraction also holds.

Example 9.5 Use properties of rational numbers to compute the following problems (mentally if possible).

a. $\dfrac{2}{3} \cdot \dfrac{5}{7} + \dfrac{2}{3} \cdot \dfrac{2}{7}$ **b.** $\dfrac{-3}{5}\left(\dfrac{13}{37} \cdot \dfrac{10}{3}\right)$ **c.** $\dfrac{4}{5} \cdot \dfrac{7}{8} - \dfrac{1}{4} \cdot \dfrac{4}{5}$

Solution

a. $\dfrac{2}{3} \cdot \dfrac{5}{7} + \dfrac{2}{3} \cdot \dfrac{2}{7} = \dfrac{2}{3}\left(\dfrac{5}{7} + \dfrac{2}{7}\right) = \dfrac{2}{3}\left(\dfrac{7}{7}\right) = \dfrac{2}{3}$

b. $\dfrac{-3}{5}\left(\dfrac{13}{37} \cdot \dfrac{10}{3}\right) = \left(\dfrac{13}{37} \cdot \dfrac{10}{3}\right)\left(\dfrac{-3}{5}\right) = \dfrac{13}{37}\left(\dfrac{10}{3} \cdot \dfrac{-3}{5}\right) = \dfrac{-26}{37}$

NOTE: Just as with fractions, we could simplify before multiplying as follows.

$$\frac{-3}{5}\left(\frac{13}{37} \cdot \frac{10}{3}\right) = \frac{-\overset{-1}{\cancel{3}}}{\cancel{5}}\left(\frac{13}{37} \cdot \frac{\overset{2}{\cancel{10}}}{\cancel{3}}\right) = \frac{-26}{37}$$

c. $\dfrac{4}{5} \cdot \dfrac{7}{8} - \dfrac{1}{4} \cdot \dfrac{4}{5} = \dfrac{4}{5} \cdot \dfrac{7}{8} - \dfrac{4}{5} \cdot \dfrac{1}{4} = \dfrac{4}{5}\left(\dfrac{7}{8} - \dfrac{1}{4}\right) = \dfrac{4}{5} \cdot \dfrac{5}{8} = \dfrac{1}{2}$ ■

Division

Division of rational numbers is the natural extension of fraction division, namely, "invert the divisor and multiply" or "multiply by the reciprocal of the divisor."

DEFINITION

Division of Rational Numbers

Let $\dfrac{a}{b}$ and $\dfrac{c}{d}$ be any rational numbers where $\dfrac{c}{d}$ is nonzero. Then

$$\frac{a}{b} \div \frac{c}{d} = \frac{a}{b} \times \frac{d}{c}.$$

The common-denominator approach to fraction division also holds for rational-number division, as illustrated next.

$$\frac{a}{b} \div \frac{c}{b} = \frac{a}{b} \times \frac{b}{c} = \frac{a}{c}, \text{ that is, } \frac{a}{b} \div \frac{c}{b} = \frac{a}{c}$$

Also, since $a \div b$ can be represented as $\dfrac{a}{b}$, the numerator and denominator of the quotient of two rationals can also be found by dividing numerators and denominators in order from left to right. That is,

$$\frac{a}{b} \div \frac{c}{d} = \frac{a}{b} \times \frac{d}{c} = \frac{a}{c} \times \frac{d}{b} = \frac{a}{c} \div \frac{b}{d} = \frac{a \div c}{b \div d};$$

in summary, $\dfrac{a}{b} \div \dfrac{c}{d} = \dfrac{a \div c}{b \div d}$. When c is a divisor of a, the rational number $\dfrac{a}{c}$ equals the integer $a \div c$ and, if d is a divisor of b, $\dfrac{b}{d}$ equals $b \div d$.

Thus, just as with fractions, there are three equivalent ways to divide rational numbers.

THEOREM

Three Methods of Rational-Number Division

Let $\dfrac{a}{b}$ and $\dfrac{c}{d}$ be any rational numbers where $\dfrac{c}{d}$ is nonzero. Then the following are equivalent.

1. $\dfrac{a}{b} \div \dfrac{c}{d} = \dfrac{a}{b} \times \dfrac{d}{c}$

2. $\dfrac{a}{b} \div \dfrac{c}{b} = \dfrac{a}{c}$

3. $\dfrac{a}{b} \div \dfrac{c}{d} = \dfrac{a \div c}{b \div d}$

Example 9.6 Express the following quotients in simplest form using the most appropriate of the three methods of rational-number division.

a. $\dfrac{12}{-25} \div \dfrac{4}{5}$ **b.** $\dfrac{13}{17} \div \dfrac{-4}{9}$ **c.** $\dfrac{-18}{23} \div \dfrac{-6}{23}$

Solution

a. $\dfrac{12}{-25} \div \dfrac{4}{5} = \dfrac{12 \div 4}{-25 \div 5} = \dfrac{3}{-5} = \dfrac{-3}{5}$ by dividing the numerators and denominators using method (3) of the previous theorem, since $4 \mid 12$ and $5 \mid 25$.

b. $\dfrac{13}{17} \div \dfrac{-4}{9} = \dfrac{13}{17} \times \dfrac{-9}{4} = \dfrac{-117}{68}$ by multiplying by the reciprocal using method (1).

c. $\dfrac{-18}{23} \div \dfrac{-6}{23} = \dfrac{-18}{-6} = 3$ by the common-denominator approach using method (2), since the denominators are equal. ■

Figure 9.5 shows how rational numbers are extensions of the fractions and the integers.

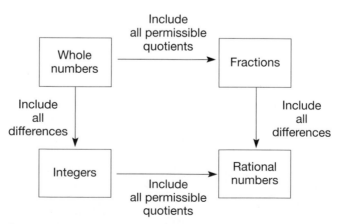

Figure 9.5

Ordering Rational Numbers

There are three equivalent ways to order rationals in much the same way as the fractions were ordered.

Number-Line Approach $\frac{a}{b} < \frac{c}{d}\left(\text{or } \frac{c}{d} > \frac{a}{b}\right)$ if and only if $\frac{a}{b}$ is to the left of $\frac{c}{d}$ on the rational-number line.

Common-Positive-Denominator Approach $\frac{a}{b} < \frac{c}{b}$ if and only if $a < c$ and $b > 0$. Look at some examples where $a < c$ and $b < 0$. What can be said about $\frac{a}{b}$ and $\frac{c}{b}$ in these cases? In particular, consider the pair $\frac{3}{-5}$ and $\frac{4}{-5}$ to see why a positive denominator is required in this approach.

Addition Approach $\frac{a}{b} < \frac{c}{d}$ if and only if there is a *positive* rational number $\frac{p}{q}$ such that $\frac{a}{b} + \frac{p}{q} = \frac{c}{d}$. An equivalent form of the addition approach is $\frac{a}{b} < \frac{c}{d}$ if and only if $\frac{c}{d} - \frac{a}{b}$ is positive.

Example 9.7 Order the following pairs of numbers using one of the three approaches to ordering.

a. $\frac{-3}{7}, \frac{5}{2}$ **b.** $\frac{-7}{13}, \frac{-2}{13}$ **c.** $\frac{-5}{7}, \frac{-3}{4}$

Solution

a. Using the number line, all negatives are to the left of all positives, hence $\frac{-3}{7} < \frac{5}{2}$.

b. Since $-7 < -2$, we have $\frac{-7}{13} < \frac{-2}{13}$ by the common-positive-denominator approach.

c. $\frac{-5}{7} - \left(\frac{-3}{4}\right) = \frac{-5}{7} + \frac{3}{4} = \frac{-20}{28} + \frac{21}{28} = \frac{1}{28}$, which is positive.

Therefore, $\frac{-3}{4} < \frac{-5}{7}$ by the addition approach. Alternately, using the common-positive-denominator approach, $\frac{-3}{4} = \frac{-21}{28} < \frac{-20}{28} = \frac{-5}{7}$. ■

As was done with fractions, the common-positive-denominator approach to ordering can be used to develop a shortcut for determining which of two rationals is smaller.

Suppose that $\frac{a}{b} < \frac{c}{d}$, where $b > 0$ and $d > 0$.

Then $\frac{ad}{bd} < \frac{bc}{bd}$. Since $bd > 0$, we conclude that $ad < bc$.

Similarly, if $ad < bc$, where $b > 0$ and $d > 0$, then $\frac{ad}{bd} < \frac{bc}{bd}$, so $\frac{a}{b} < \frac{c}{d}$.

We can summarize this as follows.

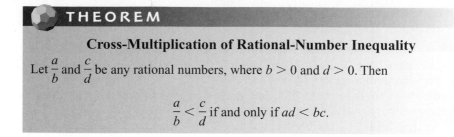

THEOREM

Cross-Multiplication of Rational-Number Inequality

Let $\dfrac{a}{b}$ and $\dfrac{c}{d}$ be any rational numbers, where $b > 0$ and $d > 0$. Then

$$\frac{a}{b} < \frac{c}{d} \text{ if and only if } ad < bc.$$

Cross-multiplication of inequality can be applied immediately when the two rational numbers involved are in simplest form, since their denominators will be positive.

Spotlight on Technology To compare $\dfrac{-37}{56}$ and $\dfrac{63}{-95}$, first rewrite both numbers with a positive denominator: $\dfrac{-37}{56}$ and $\dfrac{-63}{95}$. Now $(-37)95 = -3515$, and $(-63)(56) = -3528$, and $-3528 < -3515$. Therefore, $\dfrac{-63}{95} < \dfrac{-37}{56}$. Of course, one could also compare the two numbers using their decimal representations: $\dfrac{-37}{56} \approx -0.6607$, $\dfrac{63}{-95} \approx -0.6632$, and $-0.6632 < -0.6607$. Therefore, $\dfrac{63}{-95} < \dfrac{-37}{56}$. One could also use the fact that $\dfrac{a}{b} < \dfrac{c}{d}$ if and only if $\dfrac{ad}{b} < c \left(\dfrac{a}{b} > \dfrac{c}{d} \text{ if and only if } \dfrac{ad}{b} > c \right)$, where $b, d > 0$, as we did with fractions.

The following relationships involving order, addition, and multiplication are extensions of similar ones involving fractions and integers. The verification of these is left for the Problem Set (Problems 28 Part A and 29–31 Part B).

PROPERTIES

Ordering Rational Numbers

Transitive Property for Less Than
Property of Less Than and Addition
Property of Less Than and Multiplication by a Positive
Property of Less Than and Multiplication by a Negative
Density Property

Similar properties hold for $>$, $\leq$, and $\geq$. Applications of these properties are given in Section 9.2.

MATHEMATICAL MORSEL

To approximate $\sqrt{2}$, the Greeks built the "ladder" of numbers. The fourth rung "12, 17" is obtained from the third rung as follows: $12 = 5 + 7$, and $17 = 12 + 5$. In general, the nth rung, obtained by the $(n-1)$st rung "a,b," is "$a + b$, $2a + b$." The ratio of the number in the second column to the number in the first column (like 7/5 in rung 3) approaches $\sqrt{2}$.

Column 1	Column 2	Ratio	Rung
1	1	$1 : 1 = 1$	1
2	3	$3 : 2 = 1.5$	2
5	7	$7 : 5 = 1.4$	3
12	17	$17 : 12 = 1.41\overline{6}$	4
29	41	$41 : 29 = 1.413\cdots$	5
$\cdot$	$\cdot$	$\cdot$	$\cdot$
$\cdot$	$\cdot$	$\cdot$	$\cdot$
$\cdot$	$\cdot$	$\cdot$	$\cdot$
a	b	$b : a$	$n - 1$
$a + b$	$2a + b$	$(2a + b) : (a + b)$	n
$\cdot$	$\cdot$	$\cdot$	$\cdot$
$\cdot$	$\cdot$	$\cdot$	$\cdot$
$\cdot$	$\cdot$	$\cdot$	$\cdot$

Section 9.1 EXERCISE / PROBLEM SET A

EXERCISES

1. Explain how the following numbers satisfy the definition of a rational number.
   a. $-\frac{2}{3}$ b. $-5\frac{1}{6}$ c. 10

2. Which of the following are equal to -3?

$$\frac{-3}{1}, \frac{3}{1}, \frac{3}{-1}, -\frac{3}{1}, \frac{-3}{-1}, -\frac{-3}{1}, -\frac{-3}{-1}$$

3. Determine which of the following pairs of rational numbers are equal (try to do mentally first).

   a. $\frac{-3}{5}$ and $\frac{63}{-105}$ b. $\frac{-18}{-24}$ and $\frac{45}{60}$

4. Rewrite each of the following rational numbers in simplest form.

   a. $\frac{5}{-7}$ b. $\frac{21}{-35}$ c. $\frac{-8}{-20}$ d. $\frac{-144}{180}$

5. Add the following rational numbers. Express your answers in simplest form.

   a. $\frac{4}{9} + \frac{-5}{9}$ b. $\frac{-5}{12} + \frac{11}{-12}$

   c. $\frac{-2}{5} + \frac{13}{20}$ d. $\frac{-7}{8} + \frac{1}{12} + \frac{2}{3}$

6. Apply the properties of rational-number addition to calculate the following sums. Do mentally, if possible.

   a. $\frac{5}{7} + \left(\frac{9}{7} + \frac{5}{8}\right)$ b. $\left(\frac{5}{9} + \frac{3}{5}\right) + \frac{4}{9}$

7. Find the additive inverses of each of the following numbers.

   a. -2 b. $\frac{5}{3}$

8. Perform the following subtractions. Express your answers in simplest form.

   a. $\frac{5}{6} - \frac{1}{6}$ b. $\frac{3}{4} - \frac{-5}{4}$

   c. $\frac{-4}{7} - \frac{-9}{7}$ d. $\frac{-7}{12} - \frac{5}{18}$

9. Perform each of the following multiplications. Express your answers in simplest form.

   a. $\frac{2}{3} \cdot \frac{7}{9}$ b. $\frac{-5}{6} \cdot \frac{7}{3}$

   c. $\frac{-3}{10} \cdot \frac{-25}{27}$ d. $\frac{-2}{5} \cdot \frac{-15}{24}$

10. Use the properties of rational numbers to compute the following (mentally, if possible).

a. $-\dfrac{3}{5} \cdot \left(\dfrac{11}{17} \cdot \dfrac{5}{3}\right)$ b. $\left(-\dfrac{3}{7} \cdot \dfrac{10}{12}\right) \cdot \dfrac{6}{10}$

c. $\dfrac{2}{3} \cdot \left(\dfrac{3}{2} + \dfrac{5}{7}\right)$ d. $\dfrac{5}{9} \cdot \dfrac{2}{7} + \dfrac{2}{7} \cdot \dfrac{4}{9}$

11. Find the following quotients using the most appropriate of the three methods of rational-number division.

a. $\dfrac{-40}{27} \div \dfrac{-10}{9}$ b. $\dfrac{-1}{4} \div \dfrac{3}{2}$

c. $\dfrac{-3}{8} \div \dfrac{5}{6}$ d. $\dfrac{21}{25} \div \dfrac{-3}{5}$

12. Calculate and express in simplest form.

a. $\dfrac{25}{33} + \dfrac{-23}{39}$ b. $\dfrac{47}{49} - \dfrac{19}{-35}$

13. Order the following pairs of rational numbers using any of the approaches.

a. $\dfrac{-9}{11}, \dfrac{-3}{11}$ b. $\dfrac{-1}{3}, \dfrac{2}{5}$

c. $\dfrac{-5}{6}, \dfrac{-9}{10}$ d. $\dfrac{-10}{9}, \dfrac{-9}{8}$

14. Using a calculator and cross-multiplication of inequality, order the following pairs of rational numbers.

a. $\dfrac{-232}{356}, \dfrac{-152}{201}$ b. $\dfrac{-761}{532}, \dfrac{-500}{345}$

15. Let W = the set of whole numbers

F = the set of (nonnegative) fractions

I = the set of integers

N = the set of negative integers

Q = the set of rational numbers.

List all the sets that have the following properties.

a. -5 is an element of the set.

b. $-\dfrac{3}{4}$ is an element of the set.

c. The set is closed under addition.

d. The set is closed under subtraction.

e. The set is closed under multiplication.

16. State the property that justifies each statement.

a. $\dfrac{-2}{3} + \left(\dfrac{1}{6} + \dfrac{3}{4}\right) = \left(\dfrac{-2}{3} + \dfrac{1}{6}\right) + \dfrac{3}{4}$

b. $\left(\dfrac{5}{6} \cdot \dfrac{7}{8}\right) \cdot \dfrac{-8}{3} = \left(\dfrac{7}{8} \cdot \dfrac{5}{6}\right) \cdot \dfrac{-8}{3}$

c. $\dfrac{1}{4}\left(\dfrac{8}{3} + \dfrac{-5}{4}\right) = \dfrac{1}{4}\left(\dfrac{8}{3}\right) + \dfrac{1}{4}\left(\dfrac{-5}{4}\right)$

d. $\dfrac{4}{9} + \dfrac{3}{5} < \dfrac{5}{9} + \dfrac{3}{5}$, since $\dfrac{4}{9} < \dfrac{5}{9}$

17. The property of less than and addition for ordering rational numbers can be used to solve simple inequalities. For example,

$$x + \dfrac{3}{5} < \dfrac{-7}{10}$$

$$x + \dfrac{3}{5} + \left(-\dfrac{3}{5}\right) < \dfrac{-7}{10} + \left(-\dfrac{3}{5}\right)$$

$$x < -\dfrac{13}{10}.$$

Solve the following inequalities.

a. $x + \dfrac{1}{2} < -\dfrac{5}{6}$ b. $x - \dfrac{2}{3} < \dfrac{-3}{4}$

18. Some inequalities with rational numbers can be solved by applying the property of less than and multiplication by a positive for ordering rational numbers. For example,

$$\dfrac{2}{3}x < -\dfrac{5}{6}$$

$$\left(\dfrac{3}{2}\right)\left(\dfrac{2}{3}x\right) < \left(\dfrac{3}{2}\right)\left(-\dfrac{5}{6}\right)$$

$$x < -\dfrac{5}{4}.$$

Solve the following inequalities.

a. $\dfrac{5}{4}x < \dfrac{15}{8}$ b. $\dfrac{3}{2}x < -\dfrac{9}{8}$

19. When the property of less than and multiplication by a negative for ordering rational numbers is applied to solve inequalities, we need to be careful to change the inequality sign. For example,

$$-\dfrac{2}{3}x < \dfrac{5}{-6}$$

$$\left(-\dfrac{3}{2}\right)\left(-\dfrac{2}{3}x\right) > \left(-\dfrac{3}{2}\right)\left(-\dfrac{5}{6}\right)$$

$$x > \dfrac{5}{4}.$$

Solve each of the following inequalities.

a. $-\dfrac{3}{4}x < -\dfrac{15}{16}$ b. $-\dfrac{3}{5}x < \dfrac{9}{10}$

20. Calculate the following in two ways: (i) exactly as written and (ii) calculating an answer using all positive numbers and then determining whether the answer is positive or negative.

  a. $(-37)(-43)(-57)$ **b.** $\dfrac{(-55)(-49)}{-35}$

21. Calculate and express in simplest form.

  a. $\dfrac{13}{27} + \dfrac{-21}{31}$ **b.** $\dfrac{-15}{22} - \dfrac{-31}{48}$

22. Order the following pairs of numbers, and find a number between each pair.

  a. $\dfrac{-37}{76}, \dfrac{-43}{88}$ **b.** $\dfrac{59}{-97}, \dfrac{-68}{113}$

23. The set of rational numbers also has the density property. Recall some of the methods we used for fractions, and find three rational numbers between each pair of given numbers.

  a. $\dfrac{-3}{4}$ and $\dfrac{-1}{2}$ **b.** $\dfrac{-5}{6}$ and $\dfrac{-7}{8}$

PROBLEMS

24. Using the definition of equality of rational numbers, prove that $\dfrac{a}{b} = \dfrac{an}{bn}$, where n is any nonzero integer.

25. Using the corresponding properties of integers and reasoning by analogy from fraction properties, prove the following properties of rational-number multiplication.

  a. Closure   **b.** Commutativity

  c. Associativity   **d.** Identity

  e. Inverse

26. a. Complete the following statement for the missing-addend approach to subtraction.

  $$\frac{a}{b} - \frac{c}{d} = \frac{e}{f} \text{ if and only if } \underline{\hspace{1cm}}.$$

  b. Assuming the adding-the-opposite approach, prove that the missing-addend approach is true.

  c. Assume that the missing-addend approach is true, and prove that the adding-the-opposite approach is true.

27. Verify the distributive property of multiplication over addition for rational numbers: If $\dfrac{a}{b}, \dfrac{c}{d}$, and $\dfrac{e}{f}$ are rational numbers, then

$$\frac{a}{b}\left(\frac{c}{d} + \frac{e}{f}\right) = \frac{a}{b} \cdot \frac{c}{d} + \frac{a}{b} \cdot \frac{e}{f}.$$

28. Verify the following statement.

$$\text{If } \frac{a}{b} < \frac{c}{d}, \text{ then } \frac{a}{b} + \frac{e}{f} < \frac{c}{d} + \frac{e}{f}.$$

29. Prove that additive cancellation holds for the rational numbers.

$$\text{If } \frac{a}{b} + \frac{e}{f} = \frac{c}{d} + \frac{e}{f}, \text{ then } \frac{a}{b} = \frac{c}{d}.$$

30. Using a 5-minute and an 8-minute hourglass timer, how can you measure 6 minutes?

Section 9.1   EXERCISE / PROBLEM SET B

EXERCISES

1. Explain how the following numbers satisfy the definition of a rational number.

  a. $\frac{7}{3}$ **b.** $7\frac{1}{8}$ **c.** -3

2. Which of the following are equal to $\dfrac{5}{6}$?

  $$-\frac{5}{6}, \frac{-5}{6}, \frac{5}{-6}, \frac{-5}{-6}, -\frac{-5}{6}, \frac{5}{-6}$$

3. Determine whether the following statements are true or false.

  a. $\dfrac{-32}{22} = \dfrac{48}{-33}$ **b.** $\dfrac{-75}{-65} = \dfrac{21}{18}$

4. Rewrite each of the following rational numbers in simplest form.

  a. $\dfrac{4}{-6}$ **b.** $\dfrac{-60}{-84}$ **c.** $\dfrac{64}{-144}$ **d.** $\dfrac{96}{-108}$

5. Add the following rational numbers. Express your answers in simplest form.

  a. $\dfrac{3}{10} + \dfrac{-8}{10}$ **b.** $\dfrac{-5}{4} + \dfrac{1}{9}$

  c. $\dfrac{-5}{6} + \dfrac{5}{12} + \dfrac{-1}{4}$ **d.** $\dfrac{-3}{8} + \dfrac{5}{12}$

6. Apply the properties of rational-number addition to calculate the following sums. Do mentally, if possible.

a. $\left(\dfrac{3}{11} + \dfrac{-18}{66}\right) + \dfrac{17}{23}$ **b.** $\left(\dfrac{3}{17} + \dfrac{6}{29}\right) + \dfrac{3}{-17}$

7. Find the additive inverses of each of the following numbers.

a. $\dfrac{2}{-7}$ **b.** $-\dfrac{5}{16}$

8. Perform the following subtractions. Express your answers in simplest form.

a. $\dfrac{8}{9} - \dfrac{2}{9}$ **b.** $\dfrac{-3}{7} - \dfrac{3}{4}$

c. $\dfrac{2}{9} - \dfrac{-7}{12}$ **d.** $\dfrac{-13}{24} + \dfrac{-11}{24}$

9. Multiply the following rational numbers. Express your answers in simplest form.

a. $\dfrac{3}{5} \cdot \dfrac{-10}{21}$ **b.** $\dfrac{-6}{11} \cdot -\dfrac{-33}{18}$

c. $\dfrac{5}{12} \cdot \dfrac{48}{-15} \cdot \dfrac{-9}{8}$ **d.** $\dfrac{-6}{11} \cdot \dfrac{-22}{21} \cdot \dfrac{7}{-12}$

10. Apply the properties of rational numbers to compute the following (mentally, if possible).

a. $\dfrac{2}{9} + \left(\dfrac{3}{5} + \dfrac{7}{9}\right)$ **b.** $\dfrac{3}{7}\left(\dfrac{-11}{21}\right) + \left(\dfrac{-3}{7}\right)\left(\dfrac{-11}{21}\right)$

c. $\dfrac{3}{7} + \left(\dfrac{5}{6} + \dfrac{-3}{7}\right)$ **d.** $\left(\dfrac{-9}{7} \cdot \dfrac{23}{-27}\right) \cdot \left(\dfrac{-7}{9}\right)$

11. Find the following quotients. Express your answer in simplest form.

a. $\dfrac{-8}{9} \div \dfrac{2}{9}$ **b.** $\dfrac{12}{15} \div \dfrac{-4}{3}$

c. $\dfrac{-10}{9} \div \dfrac{-5}{4}$ **d.** $\dfrac{-13}{24} \div \dfrac{-39}{-48}$

12. Calculate and express in simplest form.

a. $\dfrac{67}{42} \times \dfrac{51}{59}$ **b.** $\dfrac{213}{76} \div \dfrac{-99}{68}$

13. Put the appropriate symbol, $<$, $=$, or $>$, between each pair of rational numbers to make a true statement.

a. $-\dfrac{5}{6}$ —— $-\dfrac{11}{12}$ **b.** $-\dfrac{1}{3}$ —— $\dfrac{5}{4}$

c. $\dfrac{-12}{15}$ —— $\dfrac{36}{-45}$ **d.** $-\dfrac{3}{12}$ —— $\dfrac{-4}{20}$

14. Using a calculator and cross-multiplication of inequality, order the following pairs of rational numbers.

a. $\dfrac{475}{652}, \dfrac{-308}{-421}$ **b.** $\dfrac{372}{487}, \dfrac{-261}{-319}$

15. Let W = the set of whole numbers
F = the set of (nonnegative) fractions
I = the set of integers
N = the set of negative integers
Q = the set of rational numbers.

List all the sets that have the following properties.

a. The set is closed under division.

b. The set has an additive identity.

c. The set has a multiplicative identity.

d. The set has additive inverses for each element.

e. The set has multiplicative inverses for each nonzero element.

16. State the property that justifies each statement.

a. $-\dfrac{2}{3}\left(\dfrac{3}{2} \cdot \dfrac{3}{5}\right) = \left(-\dfrac{2}{3} \cdot \dfrac{3}{2}\right) \cdot \dfrac{3}{5}$

b. $\dfrac{-7}{9}\left(\dfrac{3}{2} + \dfrac{-4}{5}\right) = \dfrac{-7}{9}\left(\dfrac{-4}{5} + \dfrac{3}{2}\right)$

c. $\left(\dfrac{-3}{5}\right) + \left(\dfrac{-5}{6}\right) < \left(\dfrac{-1}{5}\right) + \left(\dfrac{-5}{6}\right)$, since $\dfrac{-3}{5} < \dfrac{-1}{5}$

d. $\dfrac{5}{11} \cdot \left(\dfrac{-1}{3}\right) > \dfrac{6}{11} \cdot \left(\dfrac{-1}{3}\right)$, since $\dfrac{5}{11} < \dfrac{6}{11}$

17. Solve the following inequalities.

a. $x - \dfrac{6}{5} < \dfrac{-12}{7}$ **b.** $x + \left(\dfrac{-3}{7}\right) > \dfrac{-4}{5}$

18. Solve the following inequalities.

a. $\dfrac{1}{6}x < \dfrac{-5}{12}$ **b.** $\dfrac{2}{5}x < -\dfrac{7}{8}$

19. Solve the following inequalities.

a. $-\dfrac{1}{3}x < -\dfrac{5}{6}$ **b.** $\dfrac{-3}{7}x > \dfrac{8}{5}$

20. Calculate the following in two ways: (i) exactly as written and (ii) calculating an answer using all positive numbers and then determining whether the answer is positive or negative.

a. $\dfrac{(-1111)(-23)(49)}{-77}$ **b.** $(-43)^2(-36)^3$

21. Calculate and express in simplest form.

a. $\dfrac{-65}{72} \times \dfrac{7}{48}$ **b.** $\dfrac{43}{57} \div \dfrac{37}{72}$

22. Order the following pairs of numbers and find a number between each pair.

a. $\dfrac{-113}{217}, \dfrac{-163}{314}$ **b.** $\dfrac{-812}{779}, \dfrac{545}{-522}$

23. Find three rational numbers between each pair of given numbers.

a. $\dfrac{-5}{4}$ and $\dfrac{-6}{5}$ **b.** $\dfrac{-1}{10}$ and $\dfrac{-1}{11}$

PROBLEMS

24. The closure property for rational-number addition can be verified as follows:

$$\frac{a}{b} + \frac{c}{d} = \frac{ad + bc}{bd} \text{ by definition of addition.}$$

$ab + bc$ and bd are both integers by closure properties of integer addition and multiplication and $bd \neq 0$. Therefore, by the definition of rational number,

$$\frac{ad + bc}{bd} \text{ is a rational number.}$$

In a similar way, verify the following properties of rational-number addition.

a. Commutative   **b.** Associative

25. Which of the following properties hold for subtraction of rational numbers? Verify the property or give a counterexample.

a. Closure   **b.** Commutative   **c.** Associative

d. Identity   **e.** Inverse

26. Using additive cancellation, prove $-\left(-\dfrac{a}{b}\right) = \dfrac{a}{b}$.

27. The positive rational numbers can be defined as those a/b where $ab > 0$. Determine whether the following are true or false. If true, prove; if false, give a counterexample.

a. The sum of two positive rationals is a positive rational.

b. The difference of two positive rationals is a positive rational.

c. The product of two positive rationals is a positive rational.

d. The quotient of two positive rationals is a positive rational.

28. Given: $\dfrac{a}{b} \cdot \left(\dfrac{c}{d} + \dfrac{e}{f}\right) = \dfrac{a}{b} \cdot \dfrac{c}{d} + \dfrac{a}{b} \cdot \dfrac{e}{f}$

Prove: $\dfrac{a}{b} \cdot \left(\dfrac{c}{d} - \dfrac{e}{f}\right) = \dfrac{a}{b} \cdot \dfrac{c}{d} - \dfrac{a}{b} \cdot \dfrac{e}{f}$

29. Prove: If $\dfrac{a}{b} < \dfrac{c}{d}$ and $\dfrac{c}{d} < \dfrac{e}{f}$, then $\dfrac{a}{b} < \dfrac{e}{f}$.

30. Prove each of the following statements.

a. If $\dfrac{a}{b} < \dfrac{c}{d}$ and $\dfrac{e}{f} > 0$, then $\dfrac{a}{b} \cdot \dfrac{e}{f} < \dfrac{c}{d} \cdot \dfrac{e}{f}$.

b. If $\dfrac{a}{b} < \dfrac{c}{d}$ and $\dfrac{e}{f} < 0$, then $\dfrac{a}{b} \cdot \dfrac{e}{f} > \dfrac{c}{d} \cdot \dfrac{e}{f}$.

31. Prove: If $\dfrac{a}{b} < \dfrac{c}{d}$, then there is an $\dfrac{e}{f}$ such that $\dfrac{a}{b} < \dfrac{e}{f} < \dfrac{c}{d}$.

32. José discovered what he thought was a method for generating a **Pythagorean triple,** that is, three whole numbers a,b,c such that $a^2 + b^2 = c^2$. Here are his rules: Take any odd number (say, 11). Square it (121). Subtract 1 and divide by 2 (60). Add 1 (61). (NOTE: $11^2 + 60^2 = 121 + 3600 = 3721 = 61^2$.) Try another example. Prove that José's method always works by using a variable.

PROBLEMS FOR WRITING/DISCUSSION

1. Maria multiplied $\dfrac{15}{7}$ and $\dfrac{14}{9}$ to obtain $\dfrac{210}{63}$. She says the answer in simplest form is $\dfrac{10}{3}$. Karl says the answer in simplest form is $3\dfrac{1}{3}$. Who is correct (or are they both correct)? Explain.

2. On another problem. Maria got an answer of $\dfrac{-3}{4}$, Billy got an answer of $\dfrac{3}{-4}$, and Karl got an answer of $\dfrac{-3}{-4}$.

Karl said, "We all have the same answer." How would you respond?

3. Explain how you know why the sum of two rational numbers, say $\dfrac{3}{7}$ and $\dfrac{2}{5}$, will be a rational number. In other words, explain why the closure property holds for rational number addition.

9.2   THE REAL NUMBERS

STARTING POINT

In Chapter 6, it was stated that fractions could be written as terminating or repeating decimals. The same is true for rational numbers. (Remember that terminating decimals are those decimals that repeat zero.) What are some examples of nonterminating, nonrepeating decimal numbers?

$$-\frac{3}{8} = -0.375$$

$$\frac{13}{5} = 4.333333\ldots$$

$$-\frac{5}{7} = -0.\overline{714285714285}$$

Real Numbers: An Extension of Rational Numbers

Every repeating decimal (this includes terminating decimals because of the repeating zero) can be written as a rational number $\frac{a}{b}$ where a and b are integers. Therefore, numbers with decimal representations that do not repeat are not rational numbers. What type of numbers are such decimals? Let's approach this question from another point of view.

The equation $x - 3 = 0$ has a whole-number solution, namely 3. However, the equation $x + 3 = 0$ does not have a *whole*-number solution. But the equation $x + 3 = 0$ does have an *integer* solution, namely -3. Now consider the equation $3x = 2$. This equation has neither a whole-number nor an integer solution. But the *fraction* $\frac{2}{3}$ is a solution of $3x = 2$. What about the equation $-3x = 2$? We must move to the set of *rationals* to find its solution, namely $-\frac{2}{3}$. Since solving equations plays an important role in mathematics, we want to have a number system that will allow us to solve many types of equations. Mathematicians encountered great difficulty when attempting to solve the equation $x^2 = 2$ using rational numbers. Because of its historical significance, we give a proof to show that it is actually *impossible* to find a rational number whose square is 2.

◆ THEOREM

There is no rational number whose square is 2.

Problem-Solving Strategy
Use Indirect Reasoning

Proof Use indirect reasoning. Suppose that there is a rational number $\frac{a}{b}$ such that $\left(\frac{a}{b}\right)^2 = 2$. Then we have the following.

$$\left(\frac{a}{b}\right)^2 = 2$$

$$\frac{a^2}{b^2} = 2$$

$$a^2 = 2b^2$$

Now the argument will become a little subtle. By the Fundamental Theorem of Arithmetic, the numbers a^2 and $2b^2$ have the same prime factorization. Because squares have prime factors that occur in pairs, a^2 must have an *even* number of prime factors in its prime factorization. Similarly, b^2 has an even number of prime factors in its prime factorization. But 2 is a prime also, so $2 \cdot b^2$ has an *odd* number of prime factors in its prime factorization. (Note that b^2 contributes an even number of prime factors, and the factor 2 produces one more, hence an odd number of prime factors.) Recapping, we

have (i) $a^2 = 2b^2$, (ii) a^2 has an even number of prime factors in its prime factorization, and (iii) $2b^2$ has an odd number of prime factors in its prime factorization. According to the Fundamental Theorem of Arithmetic, it is impossible for a number to have an even number of prime factors *and* an odd number of prime factors in its prime factorization. Thus there is *no* rational number whose square is 2. ■

Using similar reasoning, it can be shown that for every prime p there is no rational number, $\dfrac{a}{b}$, whose square is p. We leave that verification for the problem set.

Using a calculator, one can show that the square of the rational number 1.414213562 is very close to 2. However, we have proved that *no* rational number squared is exactly 2. Consequently, we have a need for a new system of numbers that will include infinite nonrepeating decimals, such as 0.020020002 . . . , as well as numbers that are solutions to equations such as $x^2 = p$, where p is a prime.

DEFINITION

Real Numbers

The set of **real numbers**, R, is the set of all numbers that have an infinite decimal representation.

Thus the real numbers contain all the rationals (which are the infinite *repeating* decimals, positive, negative, or zero) together with a new set of numbers called, appropriately, the irrational numbers. The set of **irrational numbers** is the set of numbers that have infinite *nonrepeating* decimal representations. Figure 9.6 shows the different types of decimals. Since irrational numbers have infinite nonrepeating decimal representations, rational-number approximations (using finite decimals) have to be used to perform approximate computations in some cases.

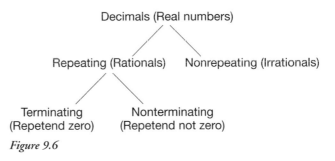

Figure 9.6

Example 9.8 Determine whether the following decimals represent rational or irrational numbers.
a. 0.273   **b.** 3.14159 . . .   **c.** $-15.\overline{76}$

Solution

a. 0.273 is a rational number, since it is a terminating decimal.
b. 3.14159 . . . should be considered to be irrational, since the three dots indicate an infinite decimal and there is no repetend indicated.
c. $-15.\overline{76}$ is rational, since it is a repeating decimal. ■

Now we can extend our diagram in Figure 9.2 to include the real numbers (Figure 9.7).

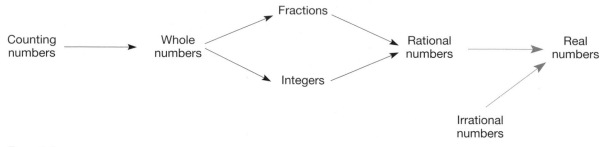

Figure 9.7

In terms of a number line, the points representing real numbers completely fill in the gaps in the rational number line. In fact, the points in the gaps represent irrational numbers (Figure 9.8).

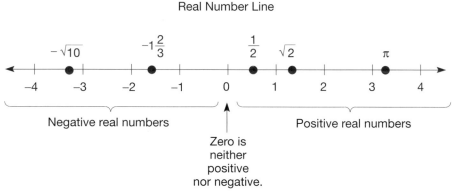

Figure 9.8

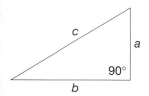

Figure 9.9

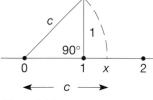

Figure 9.10

NCTM Standards 2000
Number and Operations
Grades 6–8
All students should understand and use the inverse relationships of addition and subtraction, multiplication and division, and squaring and finding square roots to simplify computations and solve problems.

Let's take this geometric representation of the real numbers one step further. The Pythagorean theorem from geometry states that in a right triangle whose sides have lengths a and b and whose hypotenuse has length c, the equation $a^2 + b^2 = c^2$ holds (Figure 9.9).

Now consider the construction in Figure 9.10. The length c is found by using the Pythagorean theorem:

$$1^2 + 1^2 = c^2 \quad \text{or} \quad c^2 = 2.$$

Moreover, the length of the segment from 0 to x is c also, since the dashed arc in Figure 9.10 is a portion of a circle. Thus $x = c$ where $c^2 = 2$. Since we know the number whose square is 2 is not rational, c must have an infinite *nonrepeating* decimal representation. To represent c with numerals other than an infinite nonrepeating decimal, we need the concept of square root.

Since both $(-3)^2$ and 3^2 equal 9, -3 and 3 are called *square roots* of 9. The symbol $\sqrt{a}$ represents the *nonnegative* square root of a, called the **principal square root.** For example, $\sqrt{4} = 2$, $\sqrt{25} = 5$, $\sqrt{144} = 12$, and so on. We can also write symbols such as $\sqrt{2}$, $\sqrt{3}$, and $\sqrt{17}$. These numbers are not rational, so they have infinite nonrepeating decimal representations. Thus it is necessary to leave them written as $\sqrt{2}, \sqrt{3}, \sqrt{17}$, and so on. According to the definition, though, we know that $(\sqrt{2})^2 = 2$, $(\sqrt{3})^2 = 3$, and $(\sqrt{17})^2 = 17$.

DEFINITION

Square Root

Let a be a nonnegative real number. Then the **square root** of a (i.e., the principal square root of a), written $\sqrt{a}$, is defined as

$$\sqrt{a} = b \qquad \text{where } b^2 = a \quad \text{and} \quad b \geq 0.$$

Spotlight on Technology Calculators can be used to find square roots. First, a $\boxed{\sqrt{}}$ key can be used. For example, to find $\sqrt{3}$ press $\boxed{\sqrt{}}$ 3 $\boxed{=}$ $\boxed{1.732050808}$ or simply $3\,\boxed{\sqrt{}}$. (Some calculators have "$\sqrt{}$" as a second function.) The $\boxed{\sqrt[x]{y}}$ key may also be used where x is 2 for square root. To find $\sqrt{3}$ using $\boxed{\sqrt[x]{y}}$, press $2\,\boxed{\sqrt[x]{y}}$ 3 $\boxed{=}$ $\boxed{1.732050808}$. Notice that this entered in the same way that it would be read, namely "the second root of three." Some calculators, however, use the following syntax: $3\,\boxed{\sqrt[x]{y}}\,2$, where the y is entered first. NOTE: The calculator displayed number is an *approximation* to $\sqrt{3}$.

One can observe that there are infinitely many irrational numbers, namely $\sqrt{p}$, where p is a prime. However, the fact that there are many more irrationals will be developed in the problem set. The number pi (π), of circle fame, was proved to be irrational around 1870; π is the ratio of the circumference to the diameter in any circle.

Using the decimal representation of real numbers, addition, multiplication, subtraction, and division of real numbers can be defined as extensions of similar operations in the rationals. The following properties hold (although it is beyond the scope of this book to prove them).

PROPERTIES

Real-Number Operations

ADDITION	MULTIPLICATION
Closure	Closure
Commutativity	Commutativity
Associativity	Associativity
Identity (0)	Identity (1)
Inverse ($-a$)	Inverse $\left(\dfrac{1}{a} \text{ for } a \neq 0\right)$

Distributivity of Multiplication over Addition

Also, subtraction is defined by $a - b = a + (-b)$, and division is defined by $a \div b = a \cdot \dfrac{1}{b}$, where $b \neq 0$. "Less than" and "greater than" can be defined as extensions of ordering in the rationals, namely $a < b$ if and only if $a + p = b$ for some positive real number p. The following order properties also hold. Similar properties hold for $>$, $\leq$, and $\geq$.

PROPERTIES

Ordering Real Numbers

Transitive Property of Less Than
Property of Less Than and Addition
Property of Less Than and Multiplication by a Positive
Property of Less Than and Multiplication by a Negative
Density Property

You may have observed that the system of real numbers satisfies all of the properties that we have identified for the system of rational numbers. The main property that distinguishes the two systems is that the real numbers are "complete" in the sense that this is the set of numbers that finally fills up the entire number line. Even though the rational numbers are dense, there are still infinitely many gaps in the rational-number line, namely, the points that represent the irrationals. Together, the rationals and irrationals comprise the entire real number line.

Rational Exponents

Now that we have the set of real numbers, we can extend our study of exponents to rational exponents. We begin by generalizing the definition of square root to more general types of roots. For example, since $(-2)^3 = -8$, -2 is called the cube root of -8. Because of negative numbers, the definition must be stated in two parts.

DEFINITION

n*th Root*

Let a be a real number and n be a positive integer.

1. If $a \geq 0$, then $\sqrt[n]{a} = b$ if and only if $b^n = a$ and $b \geq 0$.
2. If $a < 0$ and n is odd, then $\sqrt[n]{a} = b$ if and only if $b^n = a$.

Example 9.9   Where possible, write the following values in simplest form by applying the previous two definitions.

a. $\sqrt[4]{81}$
b. $\sqrt[5]{-32}$
c. $\sqrt[6]{-64}$

Solution

a. $\sqrt[4]{81} = b$ if and only if $b^4 = 81$. Since $3^4 = 81$, we have $\sqrt[4]{81} = 3$.
b. $\sqrt[5]{-32} = b$ if and only if $b^5 = -32$. Since $(-2)^5 = -32$, we have $\sqrt[5]{-32} = -2$.
c. It is tempting to begin to apply the definition and write $\sqrt[6]{-64} = b$ if and only if $b^6 = -64$. However, since b^6 must always be positive or zero, there is no real number b such that $\sqrt[6]{-64} = b$.   ■

The number a in $\sqrt[n]{a}$ is called the **radicand** and n is called the **index.** The symbol $\sqrt[n]{a}$ is read **the *n*th root of *a*** and is called a **radical.** Notice that $\sqrt[n]{a}$ has not been defined for the case when n is even and a is negative. The reason is that $b^n \geq 0$ for any real number b and n an even positive integer. For example, there is no real number b such that $b = \sqrt{-1}$, for if there were, then b^2 would equal -1. This is impossible since, by the property of less than and multiplication by a positive (or negative), it can be shown that the square of any nonzero real number is positive.

Spotlight on Technology Roots of real numbers can be calculated by using the $\boxed{\sqrt[x]{y}}$ key. For example, to find $\sqrt[5]{30}$, enter it into the calculator just as it is read: the fifth root of thirty, or 5 $\boxed{\sqrt[x]{y}}$ 30. $\boxed{=}$ $\boxed{1.9743505}$. (NOTE: Some calculators require that you press the second function key, $\boxed{2nd}$, to get to the $\boxed{\sqrt[x]{y}}$ function.) Also, as a good mental check, since $2^5 = 32$, a good estimate of $\sqrt[5]{30}$ is a number somewhat less than 2. Hence, the calculator display of 1.9743505 is a reasonable approximation for $\sqrt[5]{30}$.

Using the concept of radicals, we can now proceed to define rational exponents. What would be a good definition of $3^{1/2}$? If the usual additive property of exponents is to hold, then $3^{1/2} \cdot 3^{1/2} = 3^{1/2 + 1/2} = 3^1 = 3$. But $\sqrt{3} \cdot \sqrt{3} = 3$. Thus $3^{1/2}$ should represent $\sqrt{3}$. Similarly, $5^{1/3} = \sqrt[3]{5}, 2^{1/7} = \sqrt[7]{2}$, and so on. We summarize this idea in the next definition.

> ### DEFINITION
>
> *Unit Fraction Exponent*
>
> Let a be any real number and n any positive integer. Then
> $$a^{1/n} = \sqrt[n]{a}$$
> where
>
> 1. n is arbitrary when $a \geq 0$, and
> 2. n must be odd when $a < 0$.

For example, $(-8)^{1/3} = \sqrt[3]{-8} = -2$, and $81^{1/4} = \sqrt[4]{81} = 3$.

The combination of this last definition with the definitions for integer exponents leads us to this final definition of **rational exponent.** For example, taking into account the previous definition and our earlier work with exponents, a natural way to think of $27^{2/3}$ would be $(27^{1/3})^2$. For the sake of simplicity, we restrict our definition to rational exponents of nonnegative real numbers.

> ### DEFINITION
>
> *Rational Exponents*
>
> Let a be a nonnegative number and $\dfrac{m}{n}$ be a rational number in simplest form. Then
> $a^{m/n} = (a^{1/n})^m = (a^m)^{1/n}$.

Example 9.10 Express the following values without exponents.
a. $9^{3/2}$ **b.** $16^{5/4}$ **c.** $125^{-4/3}$

Solution

a. $9^{3/2} = (9^{1/2})^3 = 3^3 = 27$
b. $16^{5/4} = (16^{1/4})^5 = 2^5 = 32$

c. $125^{-4/3} = (125^{1/3})^{-4} = 5^{-4} = \dfrac{1}{5^4} = \dfrac{1}{625}$ ■

The following properties hold for rational exponents.

PROPERTIES

Rational Exponents

Let a, b represent positive real numbers and m, n positive rational exponents. Then

$$a^m a^n = a^{m+n}$$
$$a^m b^m = (ab)^m$$
$$(a^m)^n = a^{mn}$$
$$a^m \div a^n = a^{m-n}.$$

Real-number exponents are defined using more advanced mathematics, and they have the same properties as rational exponents.

Spotlight on Technology An exponent key such as $\boxed{\wedge}$ or $\boxed{y^x}$ can be used to calculate real exponents. For example, to calculate $3^{\sqrt{2}}$, press 3 $\boxed{\wedge}$ $\boxed{\sqrt{}}$ 2 $\boxed{=}$ $\boxed{4.7288044}$.

Introduction to Algebra

Reflection from Research
Sixth-grade students with no formal instruction in algebra are "generally able to solve problems involving specific cases and showed remarkable ability to generalize the problem situations and to write equations using variables. However, they rarely used their equations to solve related problems" (Swafford & Langrall, 2000).

Solving equations and inequalities is one of the most important processes in mathematics. Traditionally, this topic has represented a substantial portion of an entire course in introductory algebra. An **equation** is a sentence involving numbers, or symbols representing numbers, where the verb is *equals* (=). There are various types of equations:

$$3 + 4 = 7 \qquad \textit{True equation}$$
$$3 + 4 = 9 \qquad \textit{False equation}$$
$$x + 4 = 9 \qquad \textit{Conditional equation}$$
$$2x + 5x = 7x \qquad \textit{Identity}$$

An **inequality** is a sentence whose verb is one of the following: $<$, $\leq$, $>$, $\geq$, or $\neq$. Examples of conditional equations and inequalities follow.

EQUATIONS
$$x + 3 = 7$$
$$\frac{1}{3}x + \frac{2}{5} = \frac{2}{7}x - \frac{4}{13}$$

INEQUALITIES
$$2x + 4 < -17$$
$$(\sqrt{2})x - \frac{2}{5} \leq 8x - \frac{1}{\sqrt{3}}$$

NCTM Standards 2000
Algebra
Grades 6–8
All students should develop an initial conceptual understanding of different uses of variables.

The following treatment will be limited to solving equations of the form $ax + b = cx + d$, where a, b, c, d, and x are real numbers, as well as inequalities of the form $ax + b \leq cx + d$. The symbol x is a **variable.** We will permit variables to represent real numbers. When a particular number replaces a variable to produce a true equation (or inequality), that number is called a **solution.** The set of all solutions for a given equation (inequality) is called the **solution set** of the equation (inequality). For example, the solution set of the equation $x + 3 = 7$ is $\{4\}$, of $x + 4 < 7$ is $\{x \mid x < 3\}$, and so on. To **solve** an equation or inequality means to find its solution set.

Solving Equations Before we solve equations of the form $ax + b = cx + d$, the next example shows three different ways to solve equations of the form $ax + b = c$.

Example 9.11 Solve the equation $3x + 4 = 19$.

Solution

Guess and Test As the name of this method suggests, one guesses values for the variable and substitutes to see if a true equation results.

Try $x = 1 : 3(1) + 4 = 7 \neq 19$.
Try $x = 4 : 3(4) + 4 = 16 \neq 19$.
Try $x = 5 : 3(5) + 4 = 19$. Therefore, 5 is a solution of the equation.

Problem-Solving Strategy
Draw a Diagram

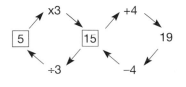

Cover Up In this method we cover up the term with the variable: $\square + 4 = 19$. To make a true equation, the $\square$ must be 15. Thus $3x = 15$. Since $3 \cdot 5 = 15$, x must be 5.

Work Backward The left side of the equation shows that x was *multiplied* by 3 and then 4 was *added* to obtain 19. Thus if we *subtract* 4 from 19 and *divide* by 3, we can work backward to the value of x. Here $19 - 4 = 15$ and $15 \div 3 = 5$, so $x = 5$. The diagram to the left summarizes this.   ■

Next we develop a systematic approach for solving more complex equations and inequalities, which we call the **balancing method**. Consider equations of the form $ax + b = cx + d$, where x is a variable and a, b, c, and d are fixed real numbers. Here, a and c are called **coefficients** of the variable x; they are numbers multiplied by a variable. We begin with an elementary form and proceed to more complex forms.

Problem-Solving Strategy
Draw a Picture

Form 1

$$x + a = b$$
Solve: $x + 4 = 7$.

Concrete/Pictorial Representation	**Abstract Representation**

$$x + 4 = 7$$

Reflection from Research
The use of objects and containers as analogues for variables helped students solve linear equations. The analogue positively influenced not only students' achievement, but also their attitude toward the topic (Quinlan, 1995).

There are four coins and some more hidden from view behind the square. Altogether they balance seven coins. How many coins are hidden?

(NOTE: Throughout this section we are assuming that the coins are identical.)

Add (-4) to both sides

$$x + 4 + (-4) = 7(-4)$$
$$x + 0 = 3$$
$$x = 3$$

Remove four coins from each side. There are three coins hidden.

Form 2

$$ax + b = c$$
Solve: $3x + 6 = 12$.

Concrete/Pictorial Representation	**Abstract Representation**

$$3x + 6 = 12$$

Objective: Solve addition equations.

 10·8 Explore Addition Equations

Algebra & functions

Learn

You can use counters and cups to solve equations.

Work Together

You Will Need
• counters
• cups

▶ You can use counters and cups to solve the equation $d + 9 = 24$.
  - Use a sheet of paper to represent each side of the equation.
  - Use counters to represent the numbers and a cup to stand for the variable, d.

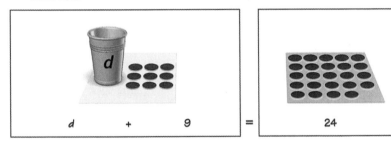

$$d \qquad + \qquad 9 \qquad = \qquad 24$$

  - Take 9 counters away from each side of the equation.
    Note: If you add or subtract the same number from both sides of an equation, the equation will still be true.
  - The variable d is equal to the number of counters left on the right side of the equal sign.
  - Record your work.
▶ Use counters and cups to solve each equation. Record your work.

$$9 + x = 23 \qquad 3 + t = 12 \qquad y + 9 = 14 \qquad t + 7 = 19$$

454 Cluster B

McGraw-Hill, MCGRAW-HILL MATHEMATICS "Explore Addition Equations," Grade 5, p. 454. Copyright © 2002 by The McGraw-Hill Companies. Reproduced with permission of the publisher.

Remove six coins from each side.

Add (-6) to both sides (equivalently, subtract 6 from both sides).

$$3x + 6 + (-6) = 12 + (-6)$$
$$3x = 6$$

Divide the coins into three equal piles (one pile for each square). Each square hides two coins.

Multiply both sides by $\frac{1}{3}$ (equivalently, divide both sides by 3).

$$\left(\frac{1}{3}\right)3x = \left(\frac{1}{3}\right)6$$
$$\left(\frac{1}{3} \cdot 3\right)x = 2$$
$$1 \cdot x = 2$$
$$x = 2$$

Form 3

$$ax + b = cx + d$$
$$Solve: 4x + 5 = 2x + 13.$$

Concrete/Pictorial Representation

Abstract Representation

$$4x + 5 = 2x + 13$$

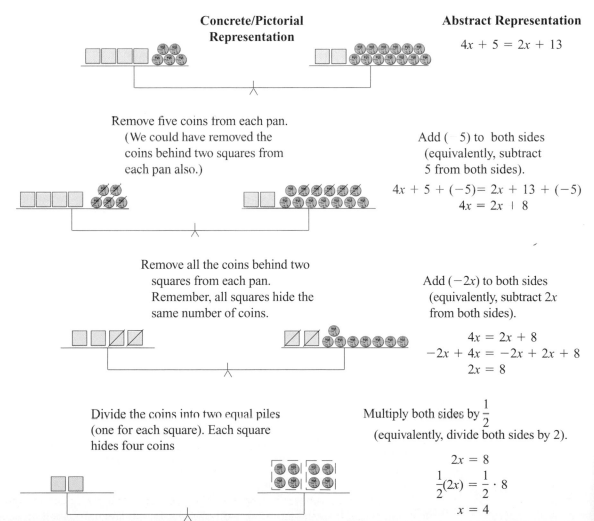

Remove five coins from each pan. (We could have removed the coins behind two squares from each pan also.)

Add (5) to both sides (equivalently, subtract 5 from both sides).

$$4x + 5 + (-5) = 2x + 13 + (-5)$$
$$4x = 2x + 8$$

Remove all the coins behind two squares from each pan. Remember, all squares hide the same number of coins.

Add $(-2x)$ to both sides (equivalently, subtract $2x$ from both sides).

$$4x = 2x + 8$$
$$-2x + 4x = -2x + 2x + 8$$
$$2x = 8$$

Divide the coins into two equal piles (one for each square). Each square hides four coins

Multiply both sides by $\frac{1}{2}$ (equivalently, divide both sides by 2).

$$2x = 8$$
$$\frac{1}{2}(2x) = \frac{1}{2} \cdot 8$$
$$x = 4$$

(NOTE: In the preceding three examples, all the coefficients of *x* were chosen to be positive. However, the same techniques we have applied hold for negative coefficients also.)

Spotlight on Technology The Chapter 9 eManipulative activity, *Balance Beam Algebra*, models the solution of algebraic equations using a balance beam. Use the eManipulative to solve the equation www.wiley.com/ college/musser $2(x + 3) = 10$. When students solve such a problem, they often write $2(x + 3) = 2x + 3$ because they forget to use the distributive property properly. How does the balance beam model help students avoid making this mistake?

The previous examples show that to solve equations of the form $ax + b = cx + d$, you should add the appropriate values to each side to obtain another equation of the form $mx = n$. Then multiply both sides by $\dfrac{1}{m}$ (or, equivalently, divide by *m*) to yield the solution $x = \dfrac{n}{m}$.

Example 9.12 Solve these equations.

a. $5x + 11 = 7x + 5$ **b.** $\dfrac{2}{3}x + \dfrac{5}{7} = \dfrac{9}{4}x - \dfrac{2}{11}$

Solution

a.
$$5x + 11 = 7x + 5$$
$$(-5x) + 5x + 11 = (-5x) + 7x + 5$$
$$11 = 2x + 5$$
$$11 + (-5) = 2x + 5 + (-5)$$
$$6 = 2x$$
$$\frac{1}{2} \cdot 6 = \frac{1}{2} \cdot 2x$$
$$3 = x$$

To check, substitute 3 for *x* into the initial equation:
Check: $5 \cdot 3 + 11 = \mathbf{26}$,   and $7 \cdot 3 + 5 = \mathbf{26}$

b. This solution incorporates some shortcuts.

$$\frac{2}{3}x + \frac{5}{7} = \frac{9}{4}x - \frac{2}{11}$$
$$\frac{2}{3}x = \frac{9}{4}x - \frac{2}{11} - \frac{5}{7}$$
$$\frac{2}{3}x - \frac{9}{4}x = -\frac{69}{77}$$
$$\frac{-19}{12}x = \frac{-69}{77}$$
$$x = \left(-\frac{12}{19}\right)\left(-\frac{69}{77}\right) = \frac{828}{1463}$$

Check: $\dfrac{2}{3} \cdot \dfrac{828}{1463} + \dfrac{5}{7} = \dfrac{552}{1463} + \dfrac{5}{7} = \dfrac{\mathbf{1597}}{\mathbf{1463}}$ and

$\dfrac{9}{4} \cdot \dfrac{828}{1463} - \dfrac{2}{11} = \dfrac{1863}{1463} - \dfrac{2}{11} = \dfrac{\mathbf{1579}}{\mathbf{1463}}$ ■

In the solution of Example 9.12(a), the same term was added to both sides of the equation or both sides were multiplied by the same number until an equation of the

form $x = a$ (or $a = x$) resulted. In the solution of Example 9.12(b), terms were moved from one side to the other, changing signs when addition was involved and inverting when multiplication was involved. This method is called **transposing.**

Solving Inequalities Inequalities can be solved in much the same manner using the following properties of order.

> *Property of less than and addition*: If $a < b$, then $a + c < b + c$.
> *Property of less than and multiplication by a positive*: If $a < b$ and $c > 0$, then $ac < bc$.
> *Property of less than and multiplication by a negative*: If $a < b$ and $c < 0$, then $ac > bc$.

Notice that in the third property, the property of less than and multiplication by a negative, the inequality $a < b$ "reverses" to the inequality $ac > bc$, since c is *negative*. Also, similar corresponding properties hold for "greater than," "less than or equal to," and "greater than or equal to."

Example 9.13 Solve these inequalities.

a. $3x - 4 < x + 12$ **b.** $\frac{1}{3}x - 7 > \frac{3}{5}x + 3$

Solution

a.

$$3x - 4 < x + 12 \qquad \text{\textit{Property of less than and addition}}$$
$$3x + (-4) + 4 < x + 12 + 4$$
$$3x < x + 16 \qquad \text{\textit{Property of less than and addition}}$$
$$(-x) + 3x < (-x) + x + 16$$
$$2x < 16$$
$$\frac{1}{2}(2x) < \frac{1}{2}(16) \qquad \text{\textit{Property of less than and multiplication by a positive}}$$
$$x < 8$$

b.

$$\frac{1}{3}x - 7 > \frac{3}{5}x + 3$$
$$\frac{1}{3}x - 7 + 7 > \frac{3}{5}x + 3 + 7 \qquad \text{\textit{Property of greater than and addition}}$$
$$\frac{1}{3}x > \frac{3}{5}x + 10$$
$$-\frac{3}{5}x + \frac{1}{3}x > -\frac{3}{5}x + \frac{3}{5}x + 10 \qquad \text{\textit{Property of greater than and addition}}$$
$$-\frac{4}{15}x > 10$$
$$\left(-\frac{15}{4}\right)\left(-\frac{4}{15}x\right) < \left(\frac{15}{4}\right)10 \qquad \text{\textit{Property of greater than and multiplication by a negative}}$$
$$x < \frac{-75}{2} = -37.5 \qquad ■$$

Solutions of equations can be checked by substituting the solutions back into the initial equation. In Example 9.12(a), the substitution of 3 into the equation $5x + 11 = 7x + 5$ yields $5 \cdot 3 + 11 = 7 \cdot 3 + 5$, or $26 = 26$. Thus 3 is a solution of this equation. The process of checking inequalities is more involved. Usually, there are infinitely many numbers in the solution set of an inequality. Since there are infinitely many numbers to check, it is reasonable to check only a few (perhaps two or three) well-chosen numbers. For example, let's consider Example 9.13(b). The solution set for the inequality $\frac{1}{3}x - 7 > \frac{3}{5}x + 3$ is $\{x \mid x < -37.5\}$ (Figure 9.11).

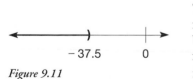

$-37.5 \qquad 0$

Figure 9.11

To check the solution, substitute into the inequality one "convenient" number from the solution set and one outside the solution set. Here -45 (in the solution set) and 0 (not in the solution set) are two convenient values.

1. In $\frac{1}{3}x - 7 > \frac{3}{5}x + 3$, substitute 0 for x: $\frac{1}{3} \cdot 0 - 7 > \frac{3}{5} \cdot 0 + 3$, or $-7 > 3$, which is false. Therefore, 0 does *not* belong to the solution set.

2. To test -45: $\frac{1}{3}(-45) - 7 > \frac{3}{5}(-45) + 3$, or $-22 > -24$ which is true. Therefore, -45 does belong to the solution set.

You may want to check several other numbers. Although this method is not a complete check, it should add to your confidence that your solution set is correct.

Algebra has important uses in addition to solving equations and inequalities. For example, the problem-solving strategy Use a Variable is another application of algebra that is very useful.

Example 9.14 Prove that the sum of any five consecutive whole numbers has a factor of 5.

Solution Let x, $x + 1$, $x + 2$, $x + 3$, $x + 4$ represent any five consecutive whole numbers.

Then

$$x + (x + 1) + (x + 2) + (x + 3) + (x + 4) = 5x + 10 = 5(x + 2),$$

which has a factor of 5. ■

MATHEMATICAL MORSEL

Throughout history there have been many interesting approximations of π as well as many ways of computing them. The value of pi to seven decimal places can easily be remembered using the mnemonic "May I have a large container of coffee?", where the number of letters in each word yields 3.1415926.

1. Found in an Egyptian papyrus:

$$\pi \approx \left(2 \times \frac{8}{9}\right)^2.$$

2. Due to Archimedes: $\pi \approx \frac{22}{7}$, $\pi \approx \frac{355}{113}$.

3. Due to Wallis:

$$\pi = 2 \cdot \frac{2}{1} \cdot \frac{2}{3} \cdot \frac{4}{3} \cdot \frac{4}{5} \cdot \frac{6}{5} \cdot \frac{6}{7} \cdot \frac{8}{7} \cdot \cdot \cdot$$

4. Due to Gregory:

$$\pi = 4\left(1 - \frac{1}{3} + \frac{1}{5} - \frac{1}{7} + \cdot \cdot \cdot\right).$$

5. Due to Euler and Bernoulli:

$$\pi^2 = 6\left(\frac{1}{1^2} + \frac{1}{2^2} - \frac{1}{3^2} + \cdot \cdot \cdot\right).$$

6. In 1989, Gregory V. and David V. Chudnovsky calculated π to 1,011,196,691 places.

Section 9.2 EXERCISE / PROBLEM SET A

EXERCISES

1. Which of the following numbers are rational, and which are irrational? Assume that the decimal patterns continue.

    a. 6.233233323333 . . .   **b.** $\sqrt{49}$ **c.** $\sqrt{61}$

    d. −5.235723572357 . . .

    e. 7.121231234 . . .

    f. $\sqrt{37}$ **g.** $\sqrt{64}$ **h.** 4.233233233 . . .

2. The number π is given as an example of an irrational number. Often the value $\frac{22}{7}$ is used for π. Does $\pi = \frac{22}{7}$? Why or why not?

3. Arrange the following real numbers in increasing order.

    0.56 $0.5\overline{6}$ $0.5\overline{66}$ 0.56565556 . . .

    $0.\overline{566}$ 0.56656665 . . .

    0.565566555666 . . .

4. Find an irrational number between $0.\overline{37}$ and $0.\overline{38}$.

5. Find four irrational numbers between 3 and 4.

6. a. Which property of real numbers justifies the following statement?

$$2\sqrt{3} + 5\sqrt{3} = (2 + 5)\sqrt{3} = 7\sqrt{3}$$

    b. Can this property be used to simplify $5\pi + 3\pi$? Explain.

    c. Can this property be used to simplify $2\sqrt{3} + 7\sqrt{5}$? Explain.

7. Compute the following pairs of expressions.

    a. $\sqrt{4} \times \sqrt{9}, \sqrt{4 \times 9}$

    b. $\sqrt{4} \times \sqrt{25}, \sqrt{4 \times 25}$

    c. $\sqrt{9} \times \sqrt{16}, \sqrt{9 \times 16}$

    d. $\sqrt{9} \times \sqrt{25}, \sqrt{9 \times 25}$

    e. What conclusion do you draw about $\sqrt{a}$ and $\sqrt{b}$ and $\sqrt{a \times b}$? (NOTE: a and b must be nonnegative.)

8. Estimate the following values; then check with a calculator.

    a. $\sqrt{361}$ **b.** $\sqrt{729}$

9. The result $\sqrt{a} \times \sqrt{b} = \sqrt{a \times b}$ may be used to simplify square roots. For example, $\sqrt{20} = \sqrt{4 \times 5} = \sqrt{4} \times \sqrt{5} = 2\sqrt{5}$. Simplify the following so that the radical is as small a whole number as possible.

    a. $\sqrt{20} \times \sqrt{5}$

    b. $\sqrt{11} \times \sqrt{44}$

10. Construct the lengths $\sqrt{2}, \sqrt{3}, \sqrt{4}, \sqrt{5}, \ldots$ as follows.

    a. First construct a right triangle with both legs of length 1. What is the length of the hypotenuse?

    b. This hypotenuse is a leg of the next right triangle. The other leg has length 1. What is the length of the hypotenuse of this triangle?

    c. Continue drawing right triangles, using the hypotenuse of the preceding triangle as a leg of the next triangle until you have constructed one with length $\sqrt{7}$.

11. Use the Pythagorean theorem to find the length of the indicated side of the following right triangles. (NOTE: The square-like symbol indicates the 90° angle.)

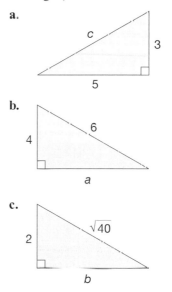

a.

b.

c.

12. Since the square roots of some numbers are irrational, their decimal representations do not repeat. Approximations of these decimal representations can be made by a process of squeezing. For example, from Figure 9.9, we see that $1 < \sqrt{2} < 2$. To improve this approximation, find two numbers between 1 and 2 that "squeeze" $\sqrt{2}$. Since $(1.4)^2 = 1.96$ and $(1.5)^2 = 2.25$, $1.4 < \sqrt{2} < 1.5$. To obtain a closer approximation, we could continue the squeezing process by choosing numbers close to 1.4 (since 1.96 is closer to 2 than 2.25). Since $(1.41)^2 = 1.9981$ and $(1.42)^2 = 2.0164$, $1.41 < \sqrt{2} < 1.42$, or $\sqrt{2} \approx 1.41$. Use the squeezing process to approximate square roots of the following to the nearest hundredth.

    a. 7   **b.** 15.6   **c.** 0.036

13. Using a calculator with a square-root key, enter the number 2. Press the square-root key several times consecutively. What do you observe about the numbers displayed? Continue to press the square-root key until no new numbers appear in the display. What is this number?

14. Using the square-root key on your calculator, find the square roots of the following numbers. Then order the given number and its square root in increasing order. What do you observe?

    a. 0.3   **b.** 0.5

15. Express the following values without exponents.

    a. $25^{1/2}$ **b.** $32^{1/5}$ **c.** $9^{5/2}$

    d. $(-27)^{4/3}$ **e.** $16^{3/4}$ **f.** $25^{-3/2}$

16. Write the following radicals in simplest form if they are real numbers.

    a. $\sqrt[3]{-27}$ **b.** $\sqrt[4]{-16}$ **c.** $\sqrt[5]{32}$

17. Calculate the following to three decimal places.

    a. $625^{0.5}$ **b.** $37^{0.37}$ **c.** $11111^{1.7}$ **d.** $7^{8.23}$

18. Determine the larger of each pair.

    a. $\pi, \frac{22}{7}$ **b.** $\sqrt[3]{37}, 1.35^4$

19. Solve the following equations using any method.

    a. $x + 15 = 7$ **b.** $x + (-21) = -16$

    c. $x + \frac{11}{9} = \frac{2}{3}$ **d.** $x + 2\sqrt{2} = 5\sqrt{2}$

20. Solve the following equations using each of the three methods of Example 9.11.

    a. $2x - 5 = 13$ **b.** $3x + 7 = 22$

    c. $-5x + 13 = -12$ **d.** $\frac{2}{3}x + \frac{1}{6} = \frac{11}{22}$

    e. $-\frac{3}{5}x - \frac{1}{4} = \frac{9}{20}$ **f.** $3x + \pi = 7\pi$

21. Solve these inequalities.

    a. $3x - 6 < 6x + 5$ **b.** $2x + 3 \geq 5x - 9$

    c. $\frac{2}{3}x - \frac{1}{4} > \frac{1}{9}x + \frac{3}{4}$ **d.** $\frac{6}{5}x - \frac{1}{3} \leq \frac{3}{10}x + \frac{2}{5}$

PROBLEMS

22. Prove that $\sqrt{3}$ is not rational. (*Hint*: Reason by analogy from the proof that there is no rational number whose square is 2.)

23. Show why, when reasoning by analogy from the proof that $\sqrt{2}$ is irrational, an indirect proof does not lead to a contradiction when you try to show that $\sqrt{9}$ is irrational.

24. Prove that $\sqrt[3]{2}$ is irrational.

25. a. Show that $5\sqrt{3}$ is an irrational number. (*Hint*: Assume that it is rational, say a/b, isolate $\sqrt{3}$, and show that a contradiction occurs.)

    b. Using a similar argument, show that the product of any nonzero rational number with an irrational number is an irrational number.

26. a. Prove that $1 + \sqrt{3}$ is an irrational number.

    b. Show, similarly, that $m + n\sqrt{3}$ is an irrational number for all rational numbers m and n ($n \neq 0$).

27. Show that the following are irrational numbers.

    a. $6\sqrt{2}$ **b.** $2 + \sqrt{3}$ **c.** $5 + 2\sqrt{3}$

28. A student says to his teacher, "You proved to us that $\sqrt{a} \cdot \sqrt{b} = \sqrt{ab}$. Reasoning by analogy, we get $\sqrt{a} + \sqrt{b} = \sqrt{a + b}$. Therefore, $\sqrt{9} + \sqrt{16} = \sqrt{25}$ or $3 + 4 = 5$. Right?" Comment!

29. A student says to her teacher, "You proved that $\sqrt{a} \cdot \sqrt{b} = \sqrt{ab}$. Therefore,

$$-1 = (\sqrt{-1})^2 = \sqrt{-1}\sqrt{-1} = \sqrt{(-1)(-1)} = \sqrt{1} = 1,$$

so that $-1 = 1$." What do you say?

30. Recall that a Pythagorean triple is a set of three nonzero whole numbers (a, b, c) where $a^2 + b^2 = c^2$. For example, $(3, 4, 5)$ is a Pythagorean triple. Show that there are infinitely many Pythagorean triples.

31. A **primitive Pythagorean triple** is a Pythagorean triple whose members have only 1 as a common prime factor. For example, $(3, 4, 5)$ is primitive, whereas $(6, 8, 10)$ is not. It has been shown that all primitive Pythagorean triples are given by the three equations:

$$a = 2uv \qquad b = u^2 - v^2 \qquad c = u^2 + v^2,$$

where u and v are relatively prime, one of u or v is even and the other is odd, and $u > v$. Generate five primitive triples using these equations.

32. You have three consecutive integers less than 20. Add two of them together, divide by the third, and the answer is the smallest of the three integers. What are the numbers?

33. Can a rational number plus its reciprocal ever be an integer? If yes, say precisely when.

34. If you are given two straight pieces of wire, is it possible to cut one of them into two pieces so that the length of one of the three pieces is the average of the lengths of the other two? Explain.

35. Messrs. Carter, Farrell, Milne, and Smith serve the little town of Milford as architect, banker, druggist, and grocer, though not necessarily respectively. The druggist earns exactly twice as much as the grocer,

the architect earns exactly twice as much as the druggist, and the banker earns exactly twice as much as the architect. Although Carter is older than anyone who makes more money than Farrell, Farrell does not make twice as much as Carter. Smith earns exactly $3776 more than Milne. Who is the druggist?

36. At a contest, two persons were asked their ages. Then, to test their arithmetical powers, they were asked to add the two ages together. One gave 44 as the answer and the other gave 1280. The first had subtracted one age from the other, while the second person had multiplied them together. What were their ages?

Section 9.2   EXERCISE / PROBLEM SET B

EXERCISES

1. Which of the following numbers are rational, and which are irrational?
   a. 2.375375 . . .   **b.** 3.0120123 . . .   **c.** $\sqrt{169}$
   d. 2π **e.** $3.\overline{12}$ **f.** $\sqrt{7}$
   g. $\dfrac{35}{0.72}$ **h.** 5.626626662 . . .

2. The number $\sqrt{2}$ is often given as 1.414. Doesn't this show that $\sqrt{2}$ is rational, since it has a terminating decimal representation? Discuss.

3. Arrange the following real numbers in increasing order.
   0.876   0.8$\overline{76}$ 0.$\overline{876}$ 0.876787677876 . . .
   0.$\overline{8766}$ 0.8766876667 . . .
   0.8767876677887666 . . .

4. Find an irrational number between $0.5\overline{777}$ and $0.5\overline{778}$.

5. Find three irrational numbers between 2 and 3.

6. Simplify the following square roots.
   a. $\sqrt{40}$ **b.** $\sqrt{80}$ **c.** $\sqrt{180}$

7. Compute and simplify the following expressions.
   a. $\sqrt{18} \times \sqrt{2}$ **b.** $\sqrt{27} \times \sqrt{3}$
   c. $\sqrt{60} \times \sqrt{12}$ **d.** $5\sqrt{2} - 9\sqrt{2}$
   e. $\sqrt{18} \times \sqrt{32}$ **f.** $\sqrt{20} - \sqrt{5} + \sqrt{45}$

8. Estimate the following values; then check with a calculator.
   a. $\sqrt{3136}$ **b.** $\sqrt{5041}$

9. Simplify the following so that the radical is as small a whole number as possible.
   a. $\sqrt{16} \times \sqrt{48}$ **b.** $\sqrt{12} \times \sqrt{216}$

10. Use the Pythagorean theorem to find the lengths of the given segments drawn on the following square lattices.

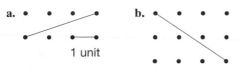

c.

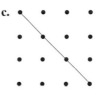

11. Use the Pythagorean theorem to find the missing lengths in the following diagrams.

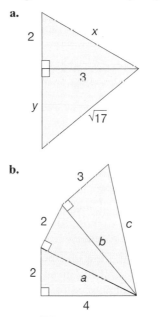

12. Find $\sqrt{13}$ using the following method: Make a guess, say r_1. Then find $13 \div r_1 = s_1$. Then find the average of r_1 and s_1 by computing $(r_1 + s_1)/2 = r_2$. Now find $13 \div r_2 = s_2$. Continue this procedure until r_n and s_n differ by less than 0.00001.

13. On your calculator, enter a positive number less than 1. Repeatedly press the square-root key. The displayed numbers should be increasing. Will they ever reach 1?

14. Using the square key on your calculator, find the squares of the following numbers. Then order the given number and its square in increasing order. What do you observe?
   a. 0.71   **b.** 0.98

15. Express the following values without exponents.

    a. $36^{1/2}$ **b.** $9^{3/2}$ **c.** $27^{2/3}$

    d. $(-32)^{3/5}$ **e.** $(81)^{3/4}$ **f.** $(-243)^{6/5}$

16. Write the following radicals in simplest form if they are real numbers.

    a. $\sqrt[5]{-32}$ **b.** $\sqrt[3]{-216}$ **c.** $\sqrt[6]{-64}$

17. Use a scientific calculator to calculate approximations of the following values. (They will require several steps and/or the use of the memory.)

    a. $(\sqrt{2})^{4/3}$ **b.** $\sqrt{3}^{\sqrt{2}}$ **c.** $\sqrt{17}^{\sqrt{17}}$ **d.** $391^{0.31}$

18. Determine the larger of each pair.

    a. $\sqrt[5]{7^2}, \sqrt[13]{7^5}$ **b.** $\pi^{\sqrt{2}}, (\sqrt{2})^{\pi}$

19. Solve the following equations.

    a. $3x + \sqrt{6} = 2x - 3\sqrt{6}$ **b.** $x - \sqrt{2} = 9\sqrt{3}$

    c. $5x - \sqrt{3} = 4\sqrt{3}$ **d.** $2\pi x - 6 = 5\pi x + 9$

20. Solve the following equations using three methods.

    a. $x + 9 = -5$ **b.** $x - (-\frac{3}{4}) = \frac{5}{6}$

    c. $3x - 4 = 9$ **d.** $\frac{1}{2}x + 1 = \frac{5}{7}$

    e. $6 = 3x - 9$ **f.** $-2 = (\frac{-5}{12})x + 3$

21. Solve the following inequalities.

    a. $x - \frac{2}{3} > \frac{5}{6}$ **b.** $-2x + 4 \leq 11$

    c. $3x + 5 \geq 6x - 7$ **d.** $\frac{3}{2}x - 2 < \frac{5}{6}x + \frac{1}{3}$

PROBLEMS

22. True or false? $\sqrt{p}$ is irrational for any prime p. If true, prove. If false, give a counterexample.

23. Prove that $\sqrt{6}$ is irrational. (*Hint*: You should use an indirect proof as we did for $\sqrt{2}$; however, this case requires a little additional reasoning.)

24. Prove that $\sqrt{p^7 q^5}$ is not rational where p and q are primes.

25. Prove or disprove: $\sqrt[n]{2}$ is irrational for any whole number $n \geq 2$.

26. Let p represent any prime. Determine whether the following are rational or irrational, and prove your assertion.

    a. $\sqrt[3]{p}$ **b.** $\sqrt[3]{p^2}$

27. **a.** Let r be a nonzero rational number and p and q be two irrational numbers. Determine whether the following expressions are rational or irrational. Prove your assertion in each case.

    (i) $r + p$ **(ii)** $r \cdot p$ **(iii)** $p + q$ **(iv)** $p \cdot q$

    b. What if $r = 0$? Would this change your answers in part (a)? Explain.

28. Give an example that shows that each of the following can occur.

    a. The sum of two irrational numbers may be an irrational number.

    b. The sum of two irrational numbers may be a rational number.

    c. The product of two irrational numbers may be an irrational number.

    d. The product of two irrational numbers may be a rational number.

29. Is the set of irrational numbers

    a. closed under addition?

    b. closed under subtraction?

    c. closed under multiplication?

    d. closed under division?

30. Take *any* two real numbers whose sum is 1 (fractions, decimals, integers, etc. are appropriate). Square the larger and add the smaller. Then square the smaller and add the larger.

    a. What will be true?

    b. Prove your assertion.

31. The tempered musical scale, first employed by Johann Sebastian Bach, divides the octave into 12 equally spaced intervals:

$$C\ C^{\#}\ D\ D^{\#}\ E\ F\ F^{\#}\ G\ G^{\#}\ A\ A^{\#}\ B\ C^{oct}.$$

The fact that the intervals are equally spaced means that the ratios of the frequencies between any adjacent notes are the same. For example,

$$C^{\#}{:}C = k \qquad \text{and} \qquad D{:}C^{\#} = k.$$

From this we see that $C^{\#} = k \cdot C$ and $D = k \cdot C^{\#} = k(k \cdot C) = k^2 C$. Continuing this pattern, we can show that $C^{oct} = k^{12} \cdot C$ (verify this). It is also true that two notes are an octave apart if the frequency of one is double the other. Thus $C^{oct} = 2 \cdot C$. Therefore, $k^{12} = 2$ or $k = \sqrt[12]{2}$. In tuning instruments, the frequency of A above middle C is 440 cycles per second. From this we can find the other frequencies of the octave:

$$A^{\#} = \sqrt[12]{2} \cdot 440 = 466.16$$
$$G^{\#} = 440/(\sqrt[12]{2}) = 415.31.$$

a. Find the remaining frequencies to the nearest hundredth of a cycle.

b. In the Greek scale, a fifth (C to G, F to C) had a ratio of $\frac{3}{2}$. How does the tempered scale compare?

c. Also in the Greek scale, a fourth (C to F, D to G) had a ratio of $\frac{4}{3}$. How close is the tempered scale to this ratio?

32. Two towns A and B are 3 miles apart. It is proposed to build a new school to serve 200 students in town A and 100 students in town B. How far from A should the school be built if the total distance traveled by all 300 students is to be as small as possible?

33. *Calendar calculus*:

a. Mark any 4 × 4 array of dates on a calendar.

		1	2	3	4	5
6	7	8	9	10	11	12
13	14	15	16	17	18	19
20	21	22	23	24	25	26
27	28	29	30	31		

b. Circle any numeral in the 4 × 4 array, say 15. Then cross out all other numerals in the same row and column as 15.

c. Circle any numeral not crossed out, say 21. Then cross out all other numerals in the same row and column as 21.

d. Continue until there are four circled numbers. Their sum should be 76 (this is true for this particular 4 × 4 array).

Try this with another 4 × 4 calendar array. Are all such sums the same there? Does this work for 3 × 3 calendar arrays? How about $n \times n$ arrays if we make bigger calendars?

34. Two numbers are reciprocals of each other. One number is 9 times as large as the other. Find the two numbers.

35. The following problem was given as a challenge to Fibonacci: Three men are to share a pile of money in the fractions $\frac{1}{2}, \frac{1}{3}, \frac{1}{6}$. Each man takes some money from the pile until there is nothing left. The first man returns one-half of what he took, the second returns one-third, and the third one-sixth. When the returned amount is divided equally among the men, it is found that they each have what they are entitled to. How much money was in the original pile, and how much did each man take from the original pile?

36. Chad was the same age as Shelly, and Holly was 4 years older than both of them. Chad's dad was 20 when Chad was born, and the average age of the four of them is 39. How old is Chad?

PROBLEMS FOR WRITING/DISCUSSION

1. Gerny says that 5 and −5 are both square roots of 25. So $\sqrt{25} = \pm 5$. Do you agree with Gerny? Explain.

2. A student who is trying to graph $\sqrt{4}, \sqrt{5}, \sqrt{6}, \sqrt{7}$, and $\sqrt{8}$ on the number line reasons that since $\sqrt{4} = 2$, the other numbers must go up by ones. So $\sqrt{5} = 3$, $\sqrt{6} = 4, \sqrt{7} = 5$, and $\sqrt{8} = 6$. What might be the student's mistake in thinking?

3. Suppose you have assigned your students the task of writing some problems that can be solved using the Pythagorean theorem. One of your students comes up to you and says she does not like decimals, so could you please give her a list of all the possible answers that would be only whole numbers. How would you respond?

9.3 FUNCTIONS AND THEIR GRAPHS

STARTING POINT Tanika and Marcelle each went for a bike ride down a different road. The graphs below represent each girl's bicycle speed as she traveled along her respective road. Describe the possible roads and/or bike-riding scenarios that would correspond to these graphs.

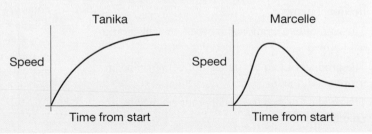

The Cartesian Coordinate System

The concept of a function was introduced in Section 2.4. Here we see how functions can be displayed using graphs on a coordinate system. This section has several goals: to emphasize the importance of functions by showing how they represent many types of physical situations, to help develop skills in graphing functions, and to help you learn how to use a graph to develop a better understanding of the corresponding function.

Suppose that we choose two perpendicular real number lines l and m in the plane and use their point of intersection, O, as a reference point called the **origin** [Figure 9.12(a)]. To locate a point P relative to point O, we use the directed real-number distances x and y that indicate the position of P left/right of and above/below the origin O, respectively. If P is to the right of line m, then x is positive [Figure 9.12(b)].

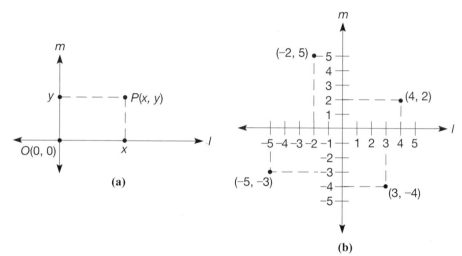

Figure 9.12

If P is to the left of line m, then x is negative. If P is on line m, then x is zero. Similarly, y is positive, negative, or zero, respectively, according to whether P is above, below, or on line l. The pair of real numbers x and y are called the **coordinates** of point P. We identify a point simply by giving its coordinates in an ordered pair (x, y). That is, by "the point (x, y)" we mean the point whose coordinates are x and y, respectively. In an ordered pair of coordinates, the first number is called the ***x*-coordinate,** and the second is the ***y*-coordinate.** Figure 9.13 shows the various possible cases for the coordinates of points in the plane.

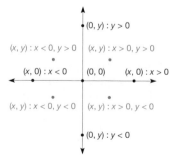

Figure 9.13

We say that lines l and m determine a **coordinate system** for the plane. Customarily, the horizontal line l is called the ***x*-axis,** and the vertical line m is called the ***y*-axis** for the coordinate system. Observe in Figure 9.14 that l and m have been relabeled as the *x*-axis and *y*-axis and that they divide the plane into four dis-

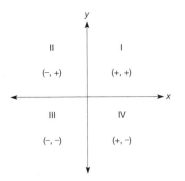

Figure 9.14

joint regions, called **quadrants.** (The axes are not part of any of the quadrants.) The points in quadrants I and IV have positive x-coordinates, while the points in quadrants II and III have negative x-coordinates. Similarly, the points in quadrants I and II have positive y-coordinates, while the points in quadrants III and IV have negative y-coordinates (Figure 9.14).

The following example provides a simple application of coordinates in mapmaking.

Example 9.15 Plot the points with the following coordinates.

$P_1 (-7, 5), P_2 (-5, 5), P_3 (-4, 3), P_4 (0, 3), P_5 (3, 4), P_6 (6, 4), P_7 (7, 3),$
$P_8 (5, -1), P_9 (6, -2), P_{10} (6, -7), P_{11} (-8, -7), P_{12} (-8, -3)$

Connect the points, in succession, P_1 to P_2, P_2 to P_3, . . . , P_{12} to P_1 with line segments to form a polygon (Figure 9.15).

Solution

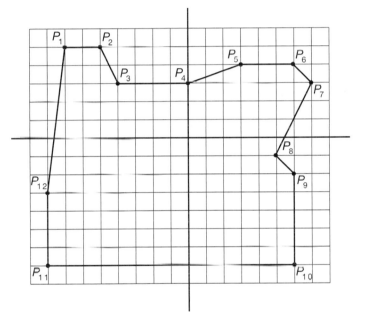

Figure 9.15

NCTM Standards 2000
Algebra
Grades 6–8
All students should use symbolic algebra to represent situations and to solve problems, especially those that involve linear relationships.

Notice that the polygon in Figure 9.15 is a simplified map of Oregon. Cartographers use computers to store maps of regions in coordinate form. They can then print maps in a variety of sizes. In the Problem Set we will investigate altering the size of a two-dimensional figure using coordinates.

Graphs of Linear Functions

As the name suggests, **linear functions** are functions whose graphs are lines. The next example involves a linear function and its graph.

Table 9.1

SALES, s	Earnings, $E(s)$
1000	1250
2000	1300
3000	1350
4000	1400
5000	1450

Example 9.16 A salesperson is given a monthly salary of $1200 plus a 5% commission on sales. Graph the salesperson's total earnings as a function of sales.

Solution Let s represent the dollar amount of the salesperson's monthly sales. The total earnings can be represented as a function of sales, s, as follows: $E(s) = 1200 + (0.05)s$. Several values of this function are shown in Table 9.1. Using these values, we can plot the function $E(s)$ (Figure 9.16). The mark on the vertical axis below 1200 is used to indicate that this portion of the graph is not the same scale as on the rest of the axis.

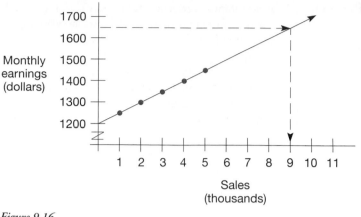

Figure 9.16

Notice that the points representing the pairs of values lie on a line. Thus, by extending the line, which is the graph of the function, we can see what salaries will result from various sales. For example, to earn $1650, Figure 9.17 shows that the salesperson must have sales of $9000.

A *linear function* has the algebraic form $f(x) = ax + b$, where a and b are constants. In the function $E(s) = (0.05)s + 1200$, the value of a is 0.05 and of b is 1200.

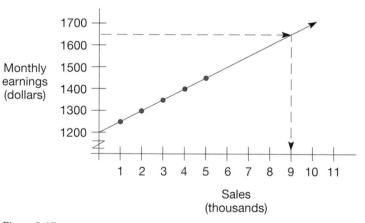

Figure 9.17

Graphs of Quadratic Functions

A **quadratic function** is a function of the form $f(x) = ax^2 + bx + c$, where a, b, and c are constants and $a \neq 0$. The next example presents a problem involving a quadratic function.

Example 9.17 A ball is tossed up vertically at a velocity of 50 feet per second from a point 5 feet above the ground. It is known from physics that the height of the ball above the ground, in feet, is given by the position function $p(t) = -16t^2 + 50t + 5$, where t is the time in seconds. At what time, t, is the ball at its highest point?

Table 9.2

t	$p(t)$
0	5
1	39
2	41
3	11

Solution Table 9.2 lists several values for t with the corresponding function values from $p(t) = -16t^2 + 50t + 5$. Figure 9.18 shows a graph of the points in the table. Unfortunately, it is unclear from the graph of these four points what the highest point will be. One way of getting a better view of this situation would be to plot several

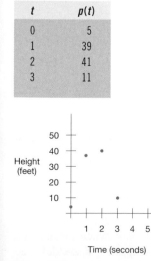

Figure 9.18

Reflection from Research

The emergence of the graphing calculator has caused an emphasis to be placed on the graphical representation of functions (Adams, 1993).

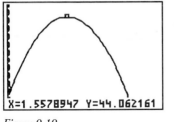

X=1.5578947 Y=44.062161

Figure 9.19

more points between 1 and 2, say $t = 1.1, 1.2, 1.3, \ldots, 1.9$. However, this can be tedious. Instead, Figure 9.19 shows how a graphics calculator can be used to get an estimate of this point.

By moving the cursor (the "□") to what appears to be the highest point on the graph, the calculator's display screen shows that the value $t = 1.5578947$ corresponds to that point. It can be shown *mathematically* that $t = \frac{25}{16} = 1.5625$ seconds is the exact time when the ball is at its highest point, 44.0625 feet. ■

www.wiley.com/ college/musser

Spotlight on Technology Quadratic functions can be further explored by using the Chapter 9 eManipulative activity, *Function Grapher*. Enter the general function $f(x) = ax^2 + bx + c$ by typing the following key strokes:

Once the function has been entered, click the graph button and the graph of the quadratic equation will appear. By selecting the Parameters and either a, b, or c, you will be able to change the values of a, b, and c by moving the slider. What role do a and c play in the shape of the graph of $f(x) = ax^2 + bx + c$?

Graphs of Exponential Functions

Amoebas have the interesting property that they split in two over time intervals. Therefore, the number of amoebas is a function of the number of splits. Table 9.3 lists the first several ordered pairs of this function, and Figure 9.20 shows the corresponding graph.

Table 9.3

NUMBER OF SPLITS	NUMBER OF AMOEBAS
0	1
1	2 $(= 2^1)$
2	4 $(= 2^2)$
3	8 $(= 2^3)$
4	16 $(= 2^4)$
5	32 $(= 2^5)$

NCTM Standards 2000
Algebra
Grades 6–8
All students should model and solve contextualized problems using various representations, such as graphs and equations.

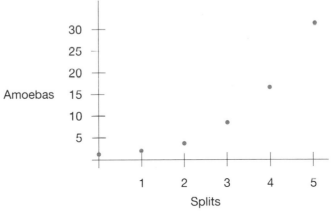

Figure 9.20

This functional relationship can be represented as the formula $f(x) = 2^x$, where $x = 0, 1, 2, \ldots$. This is an example of an **exponential function,** since, in the function rule, the variable appears as the exponent.

Exponential growth also appears in the study of compound interest. In Section 8.3 it was shown that for an initial principal of P_0, an interest rate of r, compounded annually, and time t, in years, the amount of principal is given by the equation $P(t) = P_0(1 + r)^t$. In particular, if $100 is deposited at 6% interest, the value of the investment after t years is given by $P(t) = 100 (1.06)^t$. Figure 9.21 shows a portion of the graph of this function.

Example 9.18 How long does it take to double your money when the interest rate is 6% compounded annually? (Assume that your money is in a tax-deferred account so that you don't have to pay taxes until the money is withdrawn.)

Solution If a horizontal line is drawn through $200 in Figure 9.21, it will intersect the graph of the function approximately above the 12. Thus it takes about 12 years to double the $100 investment. (A more precise estimate that can be obtained from the formula is 11.9 years.)

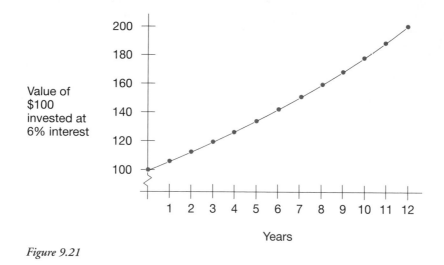

Figure 9.21

Interestingly, it takes only seven more years to add another $100 to the account and five more to add the next $100. This acceleration in accumulating principal illustrates the power of compounding, in particular, and of exponential growth, in general.

A similar phenomenon, decay, occurs in nature. Radioactive materials decay at an exponential rate. For example, the half-life of uranium-238 is 4.5 billion years. The formula for calculating the amount of ^{238}U after t billion years is $U(t) = (0.86)^t$. Figure 9.22 shows part of the graph of this function.

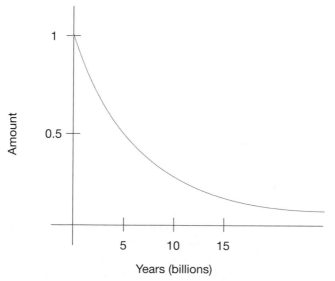

Figure 9.22

This graph shows that although uranium decays rapidly at first, relatively speaking, it lingers around a long time.

Graphs of Other Common Functions

Cubic Functions The following example illustrates a cubic function.

Example 9.19 A box is to be constructed from a piece of cardboard 20 cm-by-20 cm square by cutting out square corners and folding up the resulting sides (Figure 9.23). Estimate the maximum volume of a box that can be formed in this way.

Solution When a corner of dimensions 1 cm-by-1 cm is cut out, a box of dimensions 1 cm-by-18 cm by 18 cm is formed. Its volume is $1 \times 18 \times 18 = 324$. In general, if the corner is c by c, the volume of the resulting box is given by $V(c) = c(20 - 2c)(20 - 2c)$. Table 9.4 shows several sizes of corners together with the resulting box volumes. Using these values, we can sketch the graph of the function $V(c)$ (Figure 9.24).

The five points in the table are shown in the graph in Figure 9.24. From the graph it appears that when the corner measures about 3.5 by 3.5, the maximum volume is achieved, $V(3.5) = (3.5)(13)(13) \approx 592$ cm^3. It can be shown mathematically that the value $c = 3\frac{1}{3}$ actually leads to the maximum volume of about 593.

Figure 9.23

Table 9.4

CORNERS	VOLUME
1 cm by 1 cm	324 cm^3
2 cm by 2 cm	512 cm^3
3 cm by 3 cm	588 cm^3
4 cm by 4 cm	576 cm^3
5 cm by 5 cm	500 cm^3

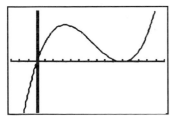

Volume (cm^3)

Length of corner (cm)

Figure 9.24

The function $V(c) = c(20 - 2c)(20 - 2c)$ can be rewritten as $V(c) = 4c^3 - 80c^2 + 400c$, a **cubic function.** Actually, the graph in Figure 9.24 looks similar to the quadratic function pictured earlier in this section. However, if the function $V(c) = 4c^3 - 80c^2 + 400c$ were allowed to take on all real-number values, its graph would take the shape as shown from a graphics calculator in Figure 9.25. (This shape is characteristic of all cubic functions.)

However, in Example 9.19, only a portion of this graph is shown, since the values of c are limited to $0 < c < 10$, the only lengths that produce corners that lead to a box.

Figure 9.25

www.wiley.com/
college/musser

Spotlight on Technology Spreadsheets can be used to graph a wide variety of functions, including those discussed in this section. One advantage of using a spreadsheet for graphing is that the table of function values is displayed right next to the graph itself, which makes it easier to see the connections between the two different representations. Refer to the dynamic spreadsheet, *Cubic*, in the spreadsheet webmodule. Use the spreadsheet to graph $f(x) = ax^3 + bx^2 + cx + d$. Set $a = c = d = 1$ and enter different values for b. What is the impact of the coefficient b on the shape of the graph of $f(x)$?

Table 9.5

AMOUNT (CENTS)	TAX (CENTS)
0–15	0
16–35	1
36–55	2
56–75	3
76–95	4
96–115	5

Step Functions The sales tax or the amount of postage are examples of step functions. Table 9.5 shows a typical sales tax, in cents, for sales up to $1.15. The graph in Figure 9.26 displays this information.

The open circles indicate that those points are *not* part of the graph. Otherwise, the endpoints are included in a segment. Notice that although the steps in this function are pictured as line segments, they could actually be pictured as a series of dots, one for each cent in the amount. A similar graph, which can be drawn for postage stamp rates, must use a line segment, since the weights of envelopes vary continuously. A function such as the one pictured in Figure 9.26 is called a **step function,** since its values are pictured in a series of line segments, or steps.

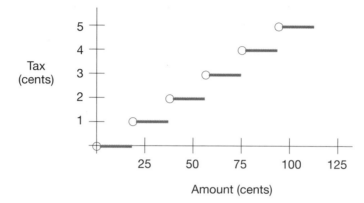

Figure 9.26

Graphs and Their Functions Thus far we have studied several special types of functions: linear, quadratic, exponential, cubic, and step. Rather than starting with a function and constructing the graph, this subsection will develop your graphical sense by first displaying a graph and then analyzing it to predict what type of function would produce the graph.

Example 9.20 Water is poured at a constant rate into the three containers shown in Figure 9.27. Which graph corresponds to which container?

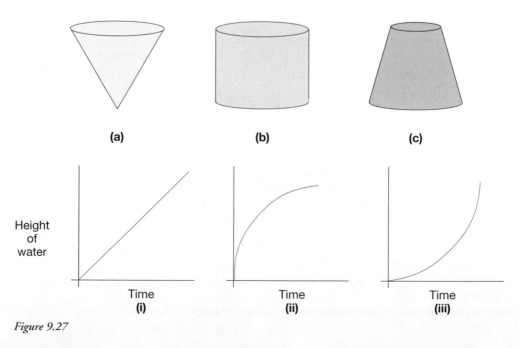

Figure 9.27

Solution Since the bottom of the figure in (a) is the narrowest, if water is poured into it at a constant rate, its height will rise faster initially and will slow in time. Graph (ii) is steeper initially to indicate that water is rising faster. Then it levels off slowly as the container is being filled. Thus graph (ii) best represents the height of water in container (a) as it is being filled. Container (b) should fill at a constant rate; thus graph (i) best represents its situation. Since the bottom of (c) is larger than its top, the water's height will rise more slowly at first, as in (iii). ■

Finally, since a function assigns to each element in its domain only one element in its codomain, there is a simple visual test to see whether a graph represents a function. The **vertical line test** states that a graph can represent a function if every vertical line that can be drawn intersects the graph in at most one point. Review the graphs of functions in this section to see that they pass this test by moving a vertical pencil across the graph as suggested in Figure 9.28.

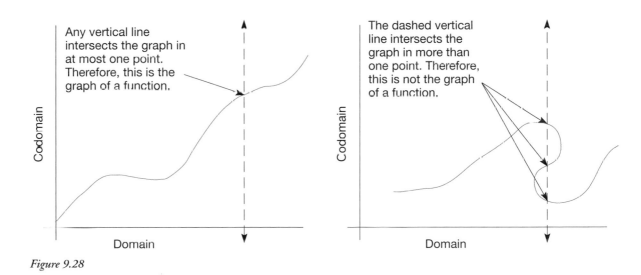

Figure 9.28

MATHEMATICAL MORSEL

Functions are used to try to predict the price action of the stock market. Since the action is the result of the psychological frame of mind of millions of individuals, price movements do not seem to conform to a nice smooth curve. One stock market theory, the Elliott wave theory, postulates that prices move in waves, 5 up and 3 down. Interestingly, when these waves are broken into smaller subdivisions, numbers of the Fibonacci sequence, such as 3, 5, 8, 13, 21, 34, and 55, arise naturally. Another interesting mathematical relationship associated with this theory is the concept of self-similarity. That is, when a smaller wave is enlarged, its structure is supposed to look exactly like the larger wave containing it. If the stock market behaved exactly as Elliott had postulated it should, everyone would become rich by playing the market. Unfortunately, it is not that easy.

Section 9.3 EXERCISE / PROBLEM SET A

EXERCISES

1. Plot the following points on graph paper.
   a. $(3, 2), (-3, 2), (-3, -2), (3, -2)$
   b. $(0, 5), (5, 0), (3, -6), (-2, 1)$
   c. $(-1, -3), (-2, -3), (-3, -4), (-5, -2)$
   d. $(2, -4), (-2, 5), (-2, -3), (1, -2)$

2. In which of the four quadrants will a point have the following characteristics?
   a. Negative y-coordinate
   b. Positive x-coordinate and negative y-coordinate
   c. Negative x-coordinate and negative y-coordinate

3. On a coordinate system, shade the region consisting of all points that satisfy both of the following conditions:
   $$-3 \le x \le 2 \quad \text{and} \quad 2 \le y \le 4.$$

4. Determine which of the following graphs represent functions. (*Hint*: Use the vertical line test.) For those that are functions, specify the domain and range.

   a.
   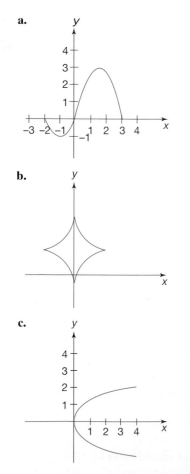

   b.

   c.

d.
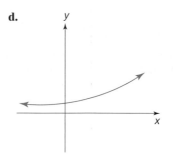

5. Consider the function f whose graph is shown next

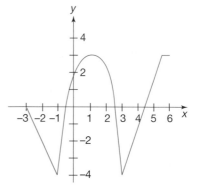

   a. Find the following: (i) $f(1)$, (ii) $f(-1)$, and (iii) $f(4.5)$.
   b. Specify the domain and range of the function.
   c. For which value(s) of x is $f(x) = 2$?

6. As you stand on a beach and look out toward the ocean, the distance that you can see is a function of the height of your eyes above sea level. The following formula and graph represent this relationship, where h is the height of your eyes in *feet* and d is the distance you can see *in miles*.

   $$d(h) = 1.2\sqrt{h}$$

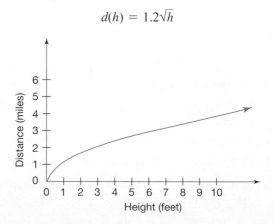

a. Use the formula to calculate the approximate values of $d(4)$ and $d(5.5)$. Use the graph to check your answers.

b. A child's eyes are about 3 feet 3 inches from the ground. How far can she see out to the horizon?

c. Specify the domain and range of the function.

7. Make a table of at least five values for each of the following linear functions, and sketch the graph of each function. How does the coefficient of the x affect the graph? How does the constant term affect the graph?

a. $f(x) = 2x + 3$ **b.** $m(x) = 40 - 5x$

c. $g(x) = 7.2x - 4.5$

8. Make a table of at least five values for each of the following functions and sketch their graphs.

a. $h(x) = \frac{1}{2}x^2 + x$ **b.** $r(x) = 3^x$

c. $s(x) = 2 - x^3$

9. The **greatest integer function** of x, denoted $f(x) = \llbracket x \rrbracket$, is defined to be the greatest integer that is less than or equal to x. For example, $\llbracket 3.5 \rrbracket = 3$, $\llbracket -3.9 \rrbracket = -4$, and $\llbracket 17 \rrbracket = 17$.

a. Evaluate the following.

　i. $\llbracket 2.4 \rrbracket$　　**ii.** $\llbracket 7.98 \rrbracket$

　iii. $\llbracket -4.2 \rrbracket$　　**iv.** $\llbracket 0.3 \rrbracket$

b. Sketch the graph of $f(x) = \llbracket x \rrbracket$ for $-3 \le x \le 3$.

10. a. Sketch the graph of each of the following linear functions. Compare your graphs. A graphics calculator would be helpful.

　i. $f(x) = 2x - 3$　　**ii.** $f(x) = \frac{1}{2}x - 3$

　iii. $f(x) = 4x - 3$　　**iv.** $f(x) = \frac{2}{3}x - 3$

b. How is the graph of the line affected by the coefficient of x?

c. How would a negative coefficient of x affect the graph of the line? Try graphing the following functions to test your conjecture.

　i. $f(x) = (-2)x - 3$　　**ii.** $f(x) = (-\frac{3}{4})x - 3$

11. Use the Chapter 9 eManipulative activity, *Function Grapher*, to graph the function $f(x) = ax + 2$ (enter ax as $a * x$). Move the slider for a back and forth to answer the following questions.

a. What happens to the shape of the graph as a gets larger?

b. What does the graph look like when $a = 0$?

c. How does the graph change when a is negative?

12. a. Sketch the graph of each function. Use a graphics calculator if available.

　i. $f(x) = x^2$　　　**ii.** $f(x) = x^2 + 2$

iii. $f(x) = x^2 - 2$　　**iv.** $f(x) = (x - 2)^2$

v. $f(x) = (x + 2)^2$

b. Taking the graph in part (i) as a standard, what effect does the constant 2 have on the graph in each of the other parts of part (a)?

c. Use the pattern you observed in part (a) to sketch graphs of $f(x) = x^2 + 4$ and $f(x) = (x - 3)^2$. Use a graphics calculator to check your prediction.

13. Use the Chapter 9 eManipulative activity, *Function Grapher*, to graph the function $f(x) = (x - b)^2 + c$. Move the slider for b and c back and forth to answer the following questions.

a. How does b affect the position of the graph?

b. How does c affect the position of the graph?

14. a. Sketch the graph of each of the following exponential functions. Use a graphics calculator if available. Compare your graphs.

　i. $f(x) = 2^x$　　**ii.** $f(x) = 5^x$

　iii. $f(x) = (\frac{1}{2})^x$　　**iv.** $f(x) = (\frac{3}{4})^x$

b. How is the shape of the graph of each function affected by the value of the base of the function?

c. Use the pattern you observed in part (a) to predict the shapes of the graphs of $f(x) = 10^x$ and $f(x) = (0.95)^x$. Check your prediction by sketching their graphs.

15. Use the Chapter 9 eManipulative activity, *Function Grapher*, to graph the function $f(x) = a^x$. Move the slider for a back and forth to answer the following questions.

a. What happens to the shape of the graph as a gets larger?

b. What does the graph look like when $a = 1$?

c. How does the graph look different when $0 < a < 1$?

16. On July 1, 2001, the first-class postal rates changed to the following:

34 cents for the first ounce or less
57 cents for over 1 oz and up to 2 oz
80 cents for over 2 oz and up to 3 oz
$1.03 for over 3 oz and up to 4 oz
$1.26 for over 4 oz and up to 5 oz
$1.49 for over 5 oz and up to 6 oz
$1.72 for over 6 oz and up to 7 oz
$1.95 for over 7 oz and up to 8 oz
$2.18 for over 8 oz and up to 9 oz
$2.41 for over 9 oz and up to 10 oz
$2.64 for over 10 oz and up to 11 oz
$2.87 for over 11 oz and up to 12 oz
$3.10 for over 12 oz and up to 13 oz

a. If $P(w)$ gives the rate for a parcel weighing w ounces, find each of the following.

   i. $P(0.5)$ **ii.** $P(5.5)$

   iii. $P(11.9)$ **iv.** $P(12.1)$

b. Specify the domain and range for P based on the previous list.

c. Sketch the graph of the first-class rates as a function of weight.

d. Suppose that you have 15 pieces weighing $\frac{3}{4}$ oz each that you wish to mail first class to the same destination. Explain why it is cheaper to package them together in one bundle than to mail them separately.

17. Sketch the graph of each of the following step functions.

  a. $f(x) = [\![x + 1]\!]$ for $0 \le x \le 4$

  b. $f(x) = [\![2 - x]\!]$ for $- \le x \le 3$

  c. $f(x) = 5 - [\![x]\!]$ for $0 \le x \le 5$

  d. $f(x) = 6 \left[\!\!\left[\dfrac{x}{2}\right]\!\!\right]$ for $2 \le x \le 6$

18. Which type of function best fits each of the following graphs: linear, quadratic, cubic, exponential, or step?

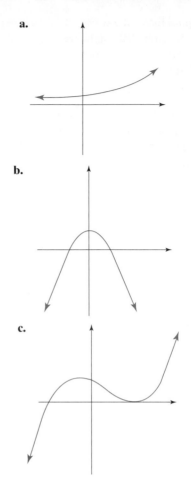

a.

b.

c.

PROBLEMS

19. The following graph shows the relationship between the length of the shadow of a 100-meter-tall building and the number of hours that have passed since noon.

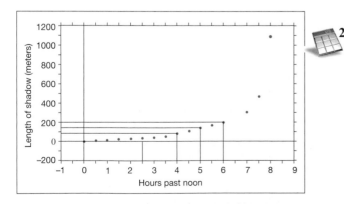

Hours past noon

a. If L represents the length of the shadow and n represents the number of hours since noon, why is L a function of n? What type of function does the graph appear to represent?

b. Use the graph to approximate $L(5)$, $L(8)$, and $L(2.5)$ to the nearest 50.

c. After how many hours is the shadow 100 meters long? When is it twice as long?

d. Why do you think the graph stops at $n = 8$?

20. A man standing at a window 55 feet above the ground leans out and throws a ball straight up into the air with a speed of 70 feet per second. The height, s, of the ball above the ground, as a function of the number of seconds elapsed, t, is given as

$$s(t) = -16t^2 + 70t + 55.$$

a. Sketch a graph of the function for $0 \le t \le 6$. If available, use a graphics calculator.

b. Use your graph to determine when the ball is about 90 feet above the ground. (NOTE: There are two times when this occurs. Use the formula as a check.)

c. About when does the ball hit the ground?

d. About how high does the ball go before it starts back down?

21. The population of the world is growing exponentially. A formula that can be used to make rough predictions of world population based on the population in 1990 and 2001 is given as

$$P(t) = 5.284e^{.0139t},$$

where $P(t)$ is the world population in billions, t is the number of years since 1990, and e is an irrational number approximately equal to 2.718. (NOTE: Scientific calculators have a key to calculate e.)

   a. Sketch the graph of the function P. A graphics calculator will be helpful.

   b. Use the formula to predict the world population in 2006.

   c. Use your graph to predict when the world population will reach 8 billion.

   d. Use your graph to estimate the current doubling time for the world population. That is, about how many years are required for the 1990 population to double?

22. A bicyclist pedals at a constant rate along a route that is essentially flat but has one hill, as shown in the next figure.

Which of the following graphs best describes what happens to the speed of the cyclist as she travels along the route?

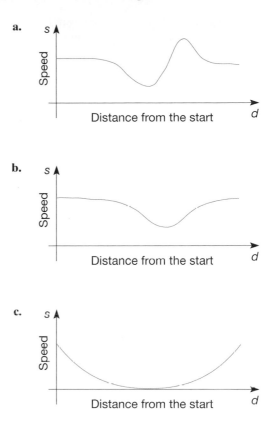

a.

b.

c.

23. Three people on the first floor of a building wish to take the elevator up to the top floor. The maximum weight that the elevator can carry is 300 pounds. Also, one of the three people must be in the elevator to operate it. If the people weigh 130, 160, and 210 pounds, how can they get to the top floor?

Section 9.3 EXERCISE / PROBLEM SET B

EXERCISES

1. Plot the following points on graph paper. Indicate in which quadrant or on which axis the point lies.

   a. $(-3, 0)$ b. $(6, 4)$ c. $(-2, 3)$
   d. $(0, 5)$ e. $(-1, -4)$ f. $(3, -2)$

2. In which of the four quadrants will a point have the following characteristics?

   a. Negative x-coordinate and positive y-coordinate

   b. Positive x-coordinate and positive y-coordinate

   c. Positive x-coordinate

3. A region in the coordinate plane is shaded where each mark on the axes represents one unit. Describe this region algebraically. That is, describe the values of the coordinates of the region using equations and/or inequalities.

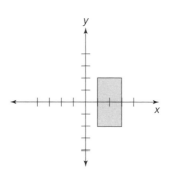

4. Determine which of the following graphs represent functions. That is, in which cases is y a function of x? For those that are functions, specify the domain and range.

a.

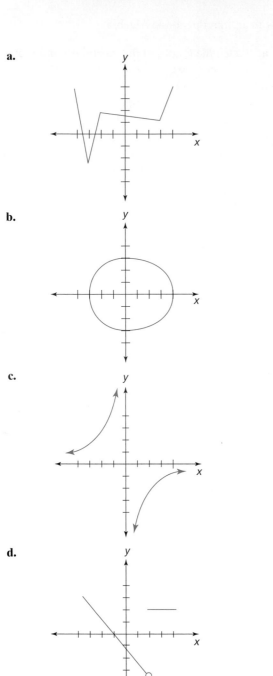

b.

c.

d.

5. Consider the function *f* whose graph follows.

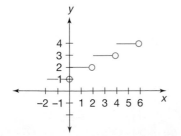

a. Use the graph to find the following: (i) $f(-1)$. (ii) $f(2)$, and (iii) $f(3.75)$.

b. Specify the domain and range of *f*.

c. For what value(s) of *x* is $f(x) = 3$? For what value(s) of *x* is $f(x) = 1.5$?

d. What type of function is *f*?

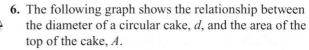

6. The following graph shows the relationship between the diameter of a circular cake, *d*, and the area of the top of the cake, *A*.

$$A(d) \approx 0.7854d^2$$

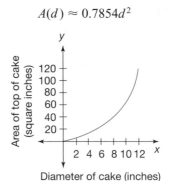

Diameter of cake (inches)

a. Which type of function is *A*?

b. Find $A(4)$ and $A(12)$ from the graph. Check your estimate using the formula.

c. Sketch the graph of $A(d) = 0.7854d^2$ for values of *d* between -5 and 5. A graphics calculator would be helpful.

d. Why are no points in the second quadrant included in the original graph?

7. Make a table of at least five values for each of the following linear functions and sketch their graphs.

a. $f(x) = 3x - 2$ **b.** $g(x) = -\frac{3}{4}x + 9$

c. $h(x) = 120x + 25$

8. Make a table of at least five values for each of the following functions and sketch their graphs.

a. $f(x) = x^2 - 4x$ **b.** $f(x) = \left(\frac{1}{2}\right)^x$

c. $f(x) = \frac{2}{3}x^3 - 4$

9. a. Evaluate the following.

     i. $[\![3.999]\!]$ **ii.** $[\![-17.1]\!]$

     iii. $[\![-4]\!]$ **iv.** $[\![-0.0001]\!]$

b. Sketch the graph of $f(x) = [\![-2x]\!]$ for $-3 \leq x \leq 3$.

10. a. Sketch the graph of each of the following linear equations. Use a graphics calculator if available. Compare your graphs.

     i. $f(x) = x + 2$ **ii.** $f(x) = x - 4$

     iii. $f(x) = x + 6.5$ **iv.** $f(x) = x$

b. How is the graph of the line affected by the value of the constant term of the function?

11. Use the Chapter 9 eManipulative activity, *Function Grapher*, to graph the function $f(x) = x + b$. Move

the slider for *b* back and forth to answer the following questions.

a. What does the graph look like when $b = 0$?

b. How does the value of *b* affect the graph of $f(x) = x + b$?

12. a. Sketch a graph of each of the following quadratic equations. Use a graphics calculator if available.

    i. $f(x) = x^2$ **ii.** $f(x) = 2x^2$

    iii. $f(x) = \frac{1}{2}x^2$ **iv.** $f(x) = -3x^2$

b. What role does the coefficient of x^2 play in determining the shape of the graph?

c. Use the pattern you observed in part (a) and in Exercise 10 to predict the shape of the graphs of $f(x) = 5x^2$ and $f(x) = \frac{1}{3}x^2 + 2$.

13. Use the Chapter 9 eManipulative activity, *Function Grapher*, to graph the function $f(x) = ax^2$ (enter *ax* as $a * x$). Move the slider for *a* back and forth to answer the following questions.

a. What happens to the shape of the graph as *a* gets larger?

b. What does the graph look like when $a = 0$?

c. How does the graph change when *a* is negative?

14. a. Draw graphs of each of the following pairs of exponential functions. Compare the graphs you obtain. Use a graphics calculator if available.

    i. $f(x) = (\frac{1}{3})^x$ and $f(x) = 3^{-x}$

    ii. $f(x) = (\frac{2}{5})^x$ and $f(x) = 2.5^{-x}$

    iii. $f(x) = 10^x$ and $f(x) = (0.1)^{-x}$

b. What interesting observation can be made about the pairs in part (a)?

15. Use the Chapter 9 eManipulative activity, *Function Grapher*, graph the function $f(x) = 2^{(cx)}$ (enter *cx* as $c \times x$). Move the slider for *c* back and forth to answer the following questions.

a. What happens to the shape of the graph as *c* gets larger?

b. What does the graph look like when $c = 0$?

c. How does the graph change when *c* is negative?

16. The Institute for Aerobics Research recommends an optimal heart rate for exercisers who want to get the maximum benefit from their workouts. The rate is a function of the age of the exerciser and should be between 65% and 80% of the difference between 220 and the person's age. That is, if *a* is the age in years, then the minimum heart rate for 1 minute is

$$r(a) = 0.65(220 - a)$$

and the maximum is

$$R(a) = 0.8(220 - a).$$

a. Sketch the graphs of the functions *r* and *R* on the same set of axes.

b. A woman 30 years old begins a new exercise program. To benefit from the program, into what range should her heart rate fall?

c. How are the recommended heart rates affected as the age of the exerciser increases? How does your graph display this information?

17. Sketch the graph of each of the following step functions.

a. $f(x) = [\![x + 3]\!]$ for $0 \le x \le 5$

b. $f(x) = [\![4 - x]\!]$ for $-2 \le x \le 2$

c. $f(x) = 4 - [\![2 - x]\!]$ for $0 \le x \le 4$

d. $f(x) = 10 \left[\!\left[\dfrac{x}{4}\right]\!\right]$ for $-4 \le x \le 8$

18. Which type of function best fits each of the following graphs: linear, quadratic, cubic, exponential, or step?

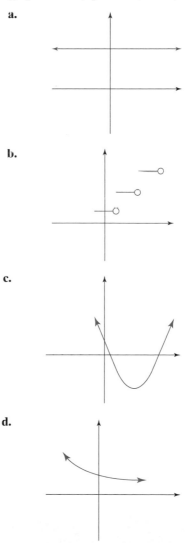

a.

b.

c.

d.

PROBLEMS

19. The length of time that passes between the time you see a flash of lightning and the time you hear the clap of thunder is related directly to your distance from the lightning. The following graph displays this relationship.

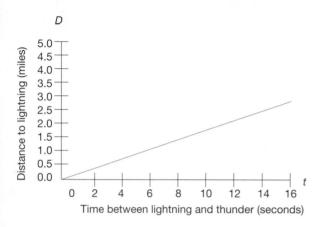

D

Distance to lightning (miles)

5.0
4.5
4.0
3.5
3.0
2.5
2.0
1.5
1.0
0.5
0.0

0   2   4   6   8   10   12   14   16   *t*

Time between lightning and thunder (seconds)

a. If D represents your distance from the lightning and t represents the elapsed time between the lightning and thunder, is D a function of t? Explain.

b. Use the graph to determine the approximate value of $D(8)$. Describe in words what this $D(8)$ means.

c. Write a formula for $D(t)$.

20. If interest is compounded, the value of an investment increases exponentially. The following formula gives the value, V, of an investment of $250 after t years, where the interest rate is 6.25% and interest is compounded continuously:

$$V(t) = 250e^{0.0625t}.$$

a. Sketch the graph of V. A graphics calculator will be helpful here.

b. Use the formula and your calculator to calculate the value of the $250 investment after 5 years.

c. Use your graph and your calculator to predict when the investment will be worth $700.

d. Use your graph to estimate the doubling time for this investment. That is, how long does it take to accumulate a total of $500?

21. A man is inflating a spherical balloon by blowing air into the balloon at a constant rate. Which of the following graphs best represents the radius of the balloon as a function of time?

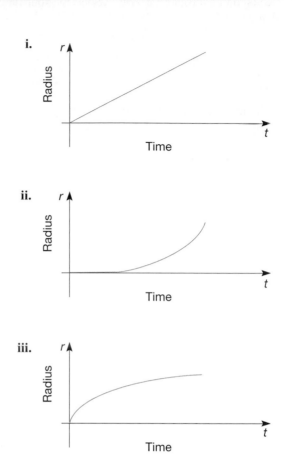

i.
Radius
r
Time
t

ii.
Radius
r
Time
t

iii.
Radius
r
Time
t

22. In an effort to boost sales, an employer offers each sales associate a $20 bonus for every $500 of sales. However, no credit is given for amounts less than a multiple of $500.

a. Two sales associates have sales totaling $758 and $1625. Calculate the amount of bonus each earned.

b. One sales associate was paid a bonus of $80. Give a range for the dollar amount of merchandise that he or she sold.

c. Make a table of values, and sketch the graph of the bonus paid by the employer as a function of the dollar value of the merchandise.

d. Write a function $B(n)$ that gives the bonus earned by an employee in terms of n, the number of dollars of merchandise sold. (*Hint*: Use the greatest integer function.)

23. The following table displays the number of cricket chirps per minute at various temperatures. Show how cricket chirps can thus be used to measure the temperature by expressing T as a function of n;

that is, find a formula for $T(n)$. Also graph your function.

cricket chirps per minute, n	20	40	60	80	100
temperature, $T(°F)$		45	50	55	60	65

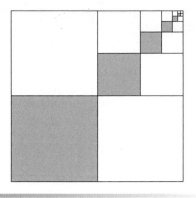

24. What fraction of the square region is shaded? Assume that the pattern of shading continues forever.

PROBLEMS FOR WRITING/DISCUSSION

1. Millicent was making a table of values to graph a function. The table looked like this:

x	1	2	3	4	5
y	3	7	11	15	19

She noticed that the y values formed an arithmetic sequence and her graph was a straight line. She wondered if every arithmetic sequence made a straight line graph. How would you respond?

2. Millicent's next table of values showed y's that seemed to form a geometric sequence.

x	1	2	3	4	5
y	2	6	18	54	162

Millicent wondered what kind of graph this would make. How would you respond to this question?

3. Millicent graphed the functions she had been working on in Problems 1 and 2. She noticed that both of the graphs seemed to be moving upward as she looked from left to right. She wondered what changes in the sequences would make the graphs go downward instead. How would you explain?

END OF CHAPTER MATERIAL

Solution of Initial Problem

A man's boyhood lasted for $\frac{1}{6}$ of his life, he played soccer for the next $\frac{1}{12}$ of his life, and he married after $\frac{1}{7}$ more of his life. A daughter was born 5 years after his marriage, and the daughter lived $\frac{1}{2}$ as many years as her father did. If the man died 4 years after his daughter did, how old was the man when he died?

Strategy: Solve an Equation

Let a represent the age of the father when he died. Then his boyhood was $\frac{1}{6}a$, he played soccer $\frac{1}{12}a$, and he married $\frac{1}{7}a$ years later. His daughter was born 5 years after his marriage. She lived $\frac{1}{2}$ as many years as her father, and he died 4 years after her, as shown in the following diagram.

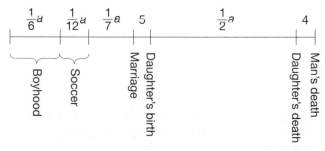

The diagram leads to the following equation.

$$\frac{1}{6}a + \frac{1}{12}a + \frac{1}{7}a + 5 + \frac{1}{2}a + 4 = a$$

Solving this equation, we obtain

$$\frac{25}{28}a + 9 = a$$
$$9 = \frac{3}{28}a$$
$$84 = a.$$

Therefore, the father lived to be 84 years old. Check this solution back in the story to convince yourself that it is correct.

Additional Problems Where the Strategy "Solve an Equation" Is Useful

1. A saver opened a savings account and increased the account by one-third at the beginning of each year. At the end of the third year, she buys a $10,000 car and still has $54,000. If interest earned is not considered, how much did she have at the end of the first year?

2. Albert Einstein was once asked how many students he had had. He replied, "One-half of them study only

arithmetic, one-third of them study only geometry, one-seventh of them study only chemistry, and there are 20 who study nothing at all." How many students did he have?

3. In an insect collection, centipedes had 100 legs and spiders had 8 legs. There were 824 legs altogether and 49 more spiders than centipedes. How many centipedes were there?

People in Mathematics

Paul Cohen (1934–) Paul Cohen has won two of the most prestigious awards in mathematics: the Fields medal and the Bocher Prize. In 1963, he solved the so-called continuum hypothesis, the first problem in David Hilbert's famous list of 23 unsolved problems. As a youngster in Brooklyn, Cohen was intensely curious about math and science. Children were not allowed in the main section of the public library, but he would sneak in to browse the math section. At age 9 he proved the converse of the Pythagorean theorem, and by age 11 his older sister was bringing him math books from the college library. A major influence was his attendance at Stuyvesant High School, a competitive math-science school in Manhattan. "When my proof [of the continuum hypothesis] was first presented, some people thought it was wrong. Then it was thought to be extremely complicated. Then it was thought to be easy. But of course it is easy in the sense that there is a clear philosophical idea."

Rozsa Peter (1905–1977) Rozsa Peter was a pioneer in the field of mathematical logic, writing two books and more than 50 papers on the subject. She was also known as a consummate teacher who engaged her students in the joint discovery of mathematics. She served for 10 years at a teacher's college in Budapest, where she wrote mathematics textbooks and proposed reforms in mathematics education. She fought against elitism and urged mathematicians to visit primary schools to communicate the spirit of their work. Her popularized account of mathematics, *Playing with Infinity*, was published in 1945 and has been translated into 12 languages. Peter wrote that she would like others to see that "mathematics and the arts are not so different from each other. I love mathematics not only for its technical applications, but principally because it is beautiful."

CHAPTER REVIEW

Review the following terms and exercises to determine which require learning or relearning—page numbers are provided for easy reference.

SECTION 9.1: The Rational Numbers

VOCABULARY/NOTATION

Rational number   356
Equality of rational numbers   356
Simplest form (lowest terms)   357
Addition of rational numbers   358

Positive rational number   359
Negative rational number   359
Subtraction of rational numbers   361

Multiplication of rational numbers   362
Reciprocal   363
Division of rational numbers   364

EXERCISES

1. Explain what the statement "the set of rational numbers is an extension of the fractions and integers" means.

2. Explain how the definition of the rational numbers differs from the definition of fractions.

3. Explain how the simplest form of a rational number differs from the simplest form of a fraction.

4. Explain the difference between $-\dfrac{3}{4}$ and $\dfrac{-3}{4}$.

5. True or false?

   a. $\dfrac{3}{-4} = \dfrac{-6}{8}$

   b. $\dfrac{12}{18} = \dfrac{-16}{-24}$

   c. $\dfrac{-3}{5} + \dfrac{2}{7} = \dfrac{31}{35}$

   d. $\dfrac{5}{9} - \dfrac{-1}{6} = \dfrac{13}{18}$

   e. $\dfrac{-5}{7} = \dfrac{5}{-7}$

   f. $\dfrac{2}{-5} \times \dfrac{-3}{7} = \dfrac{6}{35}$

   g. $-\left(\dfrac{-2}{3}\right) = \dfrac{2}{3}$

   h. $\dfrac{8}{90} \div \dfrac{2}{9} = \dfrac{8}{2}$

   i. $\dfrac{5}{7} \div \dfrac{4}{3} = \dfrac{7}{5} \times \dfrac{4}{3}$

   j. $\dfrac{-3}{4} \times \dfrac{-4}{3} = 1$

   k. $\dfrac{-2}{3} < \dfrac{-3}{7}$

   l. $\dfrac{15}{-9} > \dfrac{-13}{4}$

6. Name the property that is used to justify each of the following equations.

   a. $\dfrac{2}{7} + \dfrac{5}{8} = \dfrac{5}{8} + \dfrac{2}{7}$

   b. $\dfrac{3}{4} \times \left(\dfrac{-5}{7} \times \dfrac{6}{11}\right) = \left(\dfrac{3}{4} \times \dfrac{-5}{7}\right) \times \dfrac{6}{11}$

   c. $\dfrac{4}{13} \times 1 = \dfrac{4}{13}$

   d. $\dfrac{-5}{6}\left(\dfrac{4}{7} + \dfrac{3}{8}\right) = \dfrac{-5}{6}\left(\dfrac{4}{7}\right) + \dfrac{-5}{6}\left(\dfrac{3}{8}\right)$

   e. $\dfrac{2}{3} + \left(\dfrac{-2}{3} + \dfrac{5}{7}\right) = \left(\dfrac{2}{3} + \dfrac{-2}{3}\right) + \dfrac{5}{7}$

f. $\dfrac{5}{-8} \times \dfrac{8}{-5} = 1$

g. $\dfrac{-2}{3} + \dfrac{5}{-7}$ is a rational number.

h. $\dfrac{10}{12} + \dfrac{-5}{6} = 0$

i. $\dfrac{2}{7} + 0 = \dfrac{2}{7}$

j. $\dfrac{-4}{-5} \times \dfrac{-2}{7}$ is a rational number.

k. $\dfrac{2}{-3} \times \dfrac{-5}{7} = \dfrac{-5}{7} \times \dfrac{2}{-3}$

l. If $\dfrac{1}{2} + \dfrac{-2}{3} = x + \dfrac{-2}{3}$, then $\dfrac{1}{2} = x$.

7. Show how to determine if $\dfrac{-3}{7} < \dfrac{-5}{11}$ using

   a. the rational number line.

   b. common positive denominators.

   c. addition.

   d. cross-multiplication.

8. Complete the following, and name the property that is used as a justification.

   a. If $\dfrac{-2}{3} < \dfrac{3}{4}$ and $\dfrac{3}{4} < \dfrac{7}{5}$, then _____ < _____.

   b. If $\dfrac{-3}{5} < \dfrac{-6}{11}$, then $\left(\dfrac{-3}{5}\right)\dfrac{2}{3}$ _____ $\left(\dfrac{-6}{11}\right)\dfrac{2}{3}$.

   c. If $\dfrac{-4}{7} < \dfrac{7}{4}$, then $\dfrac{-4}{7} + \dfrac{5}{8} < \dfrac{7}{4} +$ _____.

   d. If $\dfrac{-3}{4} > \dfrac{11}{3}$, then $\left(\dfrac{-3}{4}\right)\left(\dfrac{-5}{7}\right)$ _____ $\dfrac{11}{3}\left(\dfrac{-5}{7}\right)$.

   e. There is a rational number _____ any two (unequal) rational numbers.

SECTION 9.2: The Real Numbers

VOCABULARY/NOTATION

EXERCISES

1. Explain how the set of real numbers extends the set of rational numbers.

2. Explain how the rational numbers and irrational numbers differ.

3. Which new property for addition and multiplication, if any, holds for real numbers that doesn't hold for the rational numbers?

4. Which new property for ordering holds for the real numbers that doesn't hold for the rational numbers?

5. True or false?
   a. $\sqrt{144} = 12$ b. $\sqrt{27} = 3\sqrt{3}$
   c. $\sqrt[4]{16} = 2$ d. $\sqrt[3]{27} = 3$

   e. $25^{1/2} = 5$ f. $36^{3/2} = 54$
   g. $(-8)^{5/3} = -32$ h. $4^{-3/2} = -\dfrac{1}{8}$

6. State four properties of rational-number exponents.

7. Solve the equation $-3x + 4 = 17$ using each of the following methods.
   a. Guess and Test   b. Cover-up
   c. Work Backward   d. Balancing

8. Solve.
   a. $\dfrac{-1}{6}x + \dfrac{2}{7} = \dfrac{4}{3}x - \dfrac{5}{14}$ b. $\dfrac{1}{3}x - \dfrac{4}{5} < \dfrac{-2}{5}x + \dfrac{1}{6}$

SECTION 9.3: Functions and Their Graphs

VOCABULARY/NOTATION

Origin 391	*x*-axis 391	Exponential function 394
Coordinates 391	*y*-axis 391	Cubic function 396
x-coordinate 391	Quadrants 392	Step function 397
y-coordinate 391	Linear function 392	Vertical line test 398
Coordinate system 391	Quadratic function 393	

EXERCISES

1. Sketch graphs of the following functions for the given values of *x* and identify their type from the following choices: linear, quadratic, exponential, and cubic.
   a. $x^3 + 5x + 7$ for $x = 1, 2, 3, 4$
   b. $2000(1.05)^x$ for $x = 1, 2, 3, 4, 5$
   c. $(x - 2)(x + 3)$ for $x = -4, -3, -2, -1, 0, 1, 2, 3, 4$

   d. $\dfrac{3}{4}x - \dfrac{5}{3}$ for $x = -2, -1, 0, 1, 2$

2. Sketch a portion of a step function.

3. Sketch a graph that does not represent a function and show how you can use the vertical line test to verify your assertion.

PROBLEMS FOR WRITING/DISCUSSION

1. Show why the problem $\dfrac{6}{7} \div \dfrac{3}{14}$ gives the same answer as $\dfrac{6}{3} \div \dfrac{7}{14}$. Is one problem easier than the other?

2. Miranda says, "You say I can't do $\sqrt{-4}$, but my last year's teacher said I couldn't subtract $3 - 5$, and then you showed us negative numbers. Will my next year's teacher let me do $\sqrt{-4}$?" What would you say?

3. Juan is trying to find $32^{(3/5)}$. He says it can be done in two ways, but he gets two different answers. If he takes the fifth root first, then he gets $2^3 = 8$. But if he

raises 32 to the third power first, then he gets $(32768)^5$, which his calculator says is $3.778 \cdot 10^{22}$. How would you discuss this with Juan?

4. Claudia says that when you see $3^4 \times 5^6$ or $7^9 \times 2^9$, there is nothing you can do because the bases of the exponents are unequal. Do you agree? How would you explain your reasoning?

5. Erik says that $3.25 > 3.5$ because $25 > 5$, and $6.2 < 6.04$ because $2 < 4$. Discuss.

6. Chuck asks you how it could be that $0.99999999\ldots$ would equal 1 as it says in his book. Doesn't 0.9 equal $\dfrac{9}{10}$? And $\dfrac{9}{10}$ is not equal to 1, right? Discuss.

7. Fatima wants you to show her some numbers other than π that are real but not rational. What would you show her?

8. Carol Ann was using the Pythagorean theorem to find one leg of a right triangle with hypotenuse 7 and leg 4. She came to the equation $x^2 + 4^2 = 7^2$, and she said, "Oh, I can make it $x + 4 = 7$, so $x = 3$." How would you explain her error?

9. Consider the problem $125^{-4/3}$. This problem can be done in six different ways. Try to find all six ways.

10. Glending tells you that if the bases of exponents are the same, then the exponents can be added, so $3^4 + 3^7 = 3^{11}$. Discuss.

CHAPTER TEST

Knowledge

1. True or false?
   a. The fractions together with the integers comprise the rational numbers.
   b. Every rational number is a real number.
   c. The square root of any positive rational number is irrational.
   d. 7^{-3} means $(-7)(-7)(-7)$.
   e. $25^{5/2}$ means $(\sqrt{25})^5$.
   f. If a, b, and c are real numbers and $a < b$, then $ac < bc$.
   g. If $(-3)x + 7 = 13$, then $x = -2$.
   h. If F is a function, the graph of F can be intersected at most once by any horizontal line.

2. Which of the following properties holds for (i) rational numbers, (ii) irrational numbers, (iii) real numbers?
   a. Associative property of multiplication
   b. Commutative property of addition
   c. Closure property of subtraction
   d. Closure property of multiplication
   e. Additive inverse

Skill

3. Compute the following problems and express the answers in simplest form.
   a. $\dfrac{-5}{3} + \dfrac{4}{7}$ b. $\dfrac{-3}{11} \div \dfrac{5}{2}$ c. $\dfrac{3}{(-4)} - \dfrac{(-5)}{7}$

4. Which properties can be used to simplify these computations?
   a. $\dfrac{2}{3} + \left(\dfrac{5}{7} + \dfrac{-2}{3}\right)$ b. $\dfrac{3}{4} \cdot \dfrac{5}{11} + \dfrac{5}{11} \cdot \dfrac{1}{4}$

5. Solve for x.
   a. $\left(\dfrac{-3}{5}\right)x + \dfrac{4}{7} < \dfrac{8}{5}$ b. $\dfrac{5}{4}x - \dfrac{3}{7} = \dfrac{2}{3}x + \dfrac{5}{8}$

6. Express the following values without using exponents.
   a. $(3^{10})^{3/5}$ b. $8^{7/3}$ c. $81^{-5/4}$

7. Sketch the graph of each of the following functions.
   a. $f(x) = 3x + 4$ b. $g(x) = x^2 - 3$
   c. $h(x) = 1.5^x$

8. List the following numbers in increasing order and underline the numbers that are irrational.
   $$\sqrt{2}, \frac{7}{5}, 1.\overline{41}, 1.41411411\ldots, 14.1\%, 1.41\overline{42}$$

9. Simplify
   a. $(-32)^{\frac{4}{5}}$ b. $\sqrt{108}$ c. $\sqrt{245}$
   d. $\dfrac{3 - (3 - 7) + -4}{3 + -2(5 + -2)}$

Understanding

10. Using the fact that $\dfrac{a}{b} \cdot \dfrac{c}{d} = \dfrac{ac}{bd}$, show that $\dfrac{3}{7} - \dfrac{3}{-7}$. (*Hint*: Make a clever choice for $\dfrac{c}{d}$.)

11. Cross-multiplication of inequality states: If $b > 0$ and $d > 0$, then $\dfrac{a}{b} < \dfrac{c}{d}$ if and only if $ad < bc$. Would this property still hold if $b < 0$ and $d > 0$? Why or why not?

12. By definition $a^{-m} = \dfrac{1}{a^m}$, where m is a positive integer. Using this definition, carefully explain why $\dfrac{1}{5^{-7}} = 5^7$.

13. Sketch pictures of a balancing scale that would represent the solution of the equation $2x + 3 = 9$.

14. Determine if $\sqrt{17} = 4.12310\overline{562}$. Explain.

15. Identify the following graphs as either linear, quadratic, exponential, cubic, step, or other.

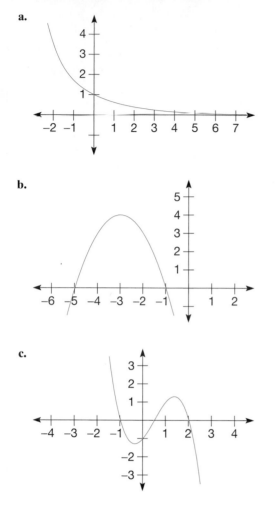

a.

b.

c.

Problem Solving/Application

16. Extending the argument used to show that $\sqrt{2}$ is not rational, show that $\sqrt{8}$ is not rational.

17. Four-sevenths of a school's faculty are women. Four-fifths of the male faculty members are married, and 9 of the male faculty members are unmarried. How many faculty members are there?

18. Some students *incorrectly* simplify fractions as follows: $\dfrac{3+4}{5+4} = \dfrac{3}{5}$. Determine all possible values for x such that $\dfrac{a+x}{b+x} = \dfrac{a}{b}$, that is, find all values for x for which this *incorrect* process works.

19. For the function $f(t) = (0.5)^t$, its value when $t = 0$ is $f(0) = (0.5)^0 = 1$. For what value of t is $f(t) = 0.125$?

20. Find an irrational number between $.\overline{45}$ and $.\overline{46}$.

21. Find three examples where the following mathematical statement is false.

$$\sqrt{a^2 + b^2} = a + b$$

22. Some corresponding temperatures in Celsius and Fahrenheit are given in the following table. Find an equation for the Fahrenheit temperature as a function of the Celsius temperature.

Celsuis	0	5	15	25	35	100
Fahrenheit	32	41	59	77	95	212

References for Reflections from Research

ADAMS, T. L. (1993). *The effects of graphing calculators and a model for conceptual change on community college students' concept of function*. Unpublished doctoral dissertation. University of Florida.

MOSS, J., & CASE, R. (1999). Developing children's understanding of the rational numbers: A new model and an experimental curriculum. *Journal for Research in Mathematics Education, 30*, 122–147.

NARODE, R. (1986). *Qualitative graphing: A construction in mathematics*. (ERIC Document Reproduction Service No. 289 745.)

QUINLAN, C. (1995). Analyzing teaching/learning strategies for algebra. In B. Atweh & S. Flavel (Eds.), MERGA 18: GALTHA, *Proceedings of the 18th annual conference* (pp. 459–464). Darwin, Australia: Northern Territory University.

SWAFFORD, J. O., & LANGRALL, C. W. (2000). Grade 6 students' preinstructional use of equations to describe and represent problem situations. *Journal for Research in Mathematics Education, 31*, 89–110.

FOCUS ON *Statistics in the Everyday World*

Statistics influence our daily lives in many ways: in presidential elections, weather forecasting, television programming, and advertising, to name a few. H. G. Wells once said, "Statistical thinking will one day be as necessary as the ability to read and write." The accompanying graphs from *USA Today* are testimony to Wells's statement.

One of the real challenges in interpreting everyday statistically based information is to keep alert to "misinformation" derived through the judicious misuse of statistics. Several examples of such misinformation follow.

1. An advertisement stated that "over 95% of our cars registered in the past 11 years are still on the road." This is an interesting statistic, but what if most of these cars were sold within the past two or three years? The implication in the ad was that the cars were durable. However, no additional statistics were provided from which the readers could draw conclusions.

2. The advertisement of another company claimed that only 1% of the more than half million people who used their product were unsatisfied and applied for their double-your-money-back guarantee. The implication is that 99% of their customers are happy, when it could be that many customers were unhappy, but only 1% chose to apply for the refund.

3. In an effort to boost its image, a company claimed that its sales had increased by 50% while its competitor's had increased by only 20%. No mention was made of earnings or of the absolute magnitude of the increases. After all, if one's sales are $100, it is easier to push them to $150 than it is to increase, say, $1 billion of sales by 20%.

4. A stockbroker who lets an account balance drop by 25% says to a client, "We'll easily be able to make a 25% recovery in your account." Unfortunately, a $33\frac{1}{3}$% increase is required to reach the break-even point.

Additional creative ways to influence you through the misuse of statistics via graphs are presented in this chapter.

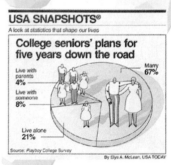

Four graphs from USA Today

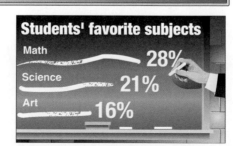

Source: Peter D. Hart Research Associates for the National Science Foundation and Bayer

Strategy
Look for a Formula

The strategy Look for a Formula is especially appropriate in problems involving number patterns. Often it extends and refines the strategy Look for a Pattern and gives more general information. For example, in the number sequence 1, 4, 7, 10, 13, . . . we observe many patterns. If we wanted to know the 100th term in the sequence, we could eventually generate it by using patterns. However, with some additional investigation, we can establish that the formula $T = 3n - 2$ gives the value of the nth term in the sequence, for $n = 1, 2, 3$, and so on. Hence the 100th term can be found directly to be $3 \cdot 100 - 2 = 298$. We will make use of the Look for a Formula strategy in this chapter and subsequent chapters. For example, in Chapter 13 we look for formulas for various measurement aspects of geometrical figures.

Initial Problem

A servant was asked to perform a job that would take 30 days. The servant would be paid 1000 gold coins. The servant replied, "I will happily complete the job, but I would rather be paid 1 copper coin on the first day, 2 copper coins on the second day, 4 on the third day, and so on, with the payment of copper coins doubling each day." The king agreed to the servant's method of payment. If a gold coin is worth 1000 copper coins, did the king make the right decision? How much was the servant paid?

Clues

The Look for a Formula strategy may be appropriate when

- A problem suggests a pattern that can be generalized.
- Ideas such as percent, rate, distance, area, volume, or other measurable attributes are involved.
- Applications in science, business, and so on are involved.
- Solving problems involving such topics as statistics, probability, and so on.

A solution of the Initial Problem appears on page 476.

INTRODUCTION

NCTM Standards 2000
Data Analysis and
Probability
Grades 6–8
All students should select, create,
and use appropriate graphical
representations of data including
histograms, box plots, and
scatterplots.

After World War II, W. Edwards Deming, an American statistician, was sent to Japan to aid in its reconstruction. Deming worked with the Japanese to establish quality control in their manufacturing system. If a problem arose, they would (1) formulate questions, (2) design a study, (3) collect data, (4) organize and analyze the data, (5) present the data, and finally (6) interpret the data to identify the cause of the problem. It is interesting to note that the most prestigious award given for quality manufacturing in Japan is the Deming Award. In the past several years, many of his techniques have also been adapted by American manufacturers. In Section 10.1, ways of organizing and presenting data are studied. Then, in Section 10.2, data are analyzed and interpreted. Finally in Section 10.3, misuses of statistics are presented.

10.1   ORGANIZING AND PICTURING INFORMATION

STARTING POINT

A survey was conducted at two major universities where 10 randomly selected students were asked how far their parents lived from campus. Looking at this data, what conclusions can you draw about the differences and similarities of the student populations at the two universities? How could you represent or organize the data to make those differences and/or similarities clearer?

UNIVERSITY A	UNIVERSITY B
600	80
50	200
710	10
320	70
10	1500
750	30
520	310
2000	40
640	90
60	740

Organizing Information

Line Plots Suppose that 30 fourth graders took a science test and made the following scores: 22, 23, 14, 45, 39, 11, 9, 46, 22, 25, 6, 28, 33, 36, 16, 39, 49, 17, 22, 32, 34, 22, 18, 21, 27, 34, 26, 41, 28, 25. What can we conclude about the students' performance? At the outset, we can say very little, since the data are so disorganized. First, let us put them in increasing order (Table 10.1).

Table 10.1   Science Test Scores

6, 9, 11, 14, 16, 17, 18, 21, 22, 22, 22, 22, 23, 25, 25, 26, 27, 28, 28, 32, 33, 34, 34, 36, 39, 39, 41, 45, 46, 49

Reflection from Research
Graphing provides students opportunities to use their sorting and classifying skills (Shaw, 1984).

From the table we can make the general observation that the scores range from 6 to 49 and seem rather spread out. With the **line plot** or **dot plot** in Figure 10.1, we can graph the scores and obtain a more visual representation of the data.

NCTM Standards 2000
Data Analysis and
Probability
Grades 3 – 5
All students should represent data
using tables and graphs such as
line plots, bar graphs, and line
graphs.

Reflection from Research
Stem and leaf plots maintain the
data so that individual elements
can be identified and are useful
for ordering data. These characteristics may make stem and leaf
plots preferable over bar or line
graphs (Landwehr, Swift, &
Watkins, 1987).

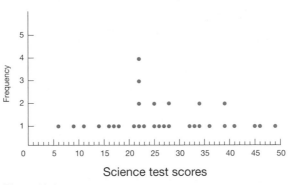

Figure 10.1

Each dot corresponds to one score. The **frequency** of a number is the number of times it occurs in a collection of data. From the line plot, we see that five scores occurred more than once and that the score 22 had the greatest frequency.

Stem and Leaf Plots One popular method of organizing data is to use a **stem and leaf plot.** To illustrate this method, refer to the list of the science test scores:

22, 23, 14, 45, 39, 11, 9, 46, 22, 25, 6, 28, 33, 36, 16,
39, 49, 17, 22, 32, 34, 22, 18, 21, 27, 34, 26, 41, 28, 25

A stem and leaf plot for the scores appears in Table 10.2. The stems are the tens digits of the science test scores, and the leaves are the ones digits. For example, 0 | 6 represents a score of 6, and 1|4 represents a score of 14.

Notice that the leaves are recorded in the order in which they appear in the list of science test scores, not in increasing order. We can refine the stem and leaf plot by listing the leaves in increasing order, as in Table 10.3.

Table 10.2

STEMS	LEAVES
0	9 6
1	4 1 6 7 8
2	2 3 2 5 8 2 2 1 7 6 8 5
3	9 3 6 9 2 4 4
4	5 6 9 1

Table 10.3

STEMS	LEAVES
0	6 9
1	1 4 6 7 8
2	1 2 2 2 2 3 5 5 6 7 8 8
3	2 3 4 4 6 9 9
4	1 5 6 9

Example 10.1 Make a stem and leaf plot for the following children's heights, in centimeters: 94, 105, 107, 108, 108, 120, 121, 122, 122, 123

Solution Use the numbers in the hundreds and tens places as the stems and the ones digits as the leaves (Table 10.4). For example, 10 | 5 represents 105 cm. ■

From the stem and leaf plot in Table 10.4, we see that no data occur between 108 and 120. A large empty interval such as this is called a **gap** in the data. We also see that several values of the data lie close together—namely, those with stems "10" and "12." Several values of the data that lie in close proximity form a **cluster.** Thus one gap and two clusters are evident in Table 10.4. The presence or absence of gaps and clusters is often revealed in stem and leaf plots as well as in line plots. *Gap* and *cluster* are imprecise terms describing general breaks or groupings in data and may be interpreted differently by different people. However, such phenomena often reveal useful information. For example, clusters of data separated by gaps in reading test scores for a class can help in the formation of reading groups.

Table 10.4

STEMS	LEAVES
9	4
10	5 7 8 8
11	
12	0 1 2 2 3

Suppose that a second class of fourth graders took the same science test as the class represented in Table 10.3 and had the following scores:

5, 7, 12, 13, 14, 22, 25, 26, 27, 28, 28, 29, 31, 32, 33,
34, 34, 35, 36, 37, 38, 39, 42, 43, 45, 46, 47, 48, 49, 49

Using a **back-to-back stem and leaf plot,** we can compare the two classes by listing the leaves for the classes on either side of the stem (Table 10.5). Notice that the

Table 10.5

CLASS 1		CLASS 2
9 6	0	5 7
8 7 6 4 1	1	2 3 4
8 8 7 6 5 5 3 2 2 2 2 1	2	2 5 6 7 8 8 9
9 9 6 4 4 3 2	3	1 2 3 4 4 5 6 7 8 9
9 6 5 1	4	2 3 5 6 7 8 9 9

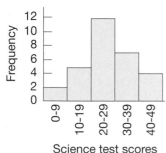

Figure 10.2

leaves increase as they move away from the stems. By comparing the corresponding leaves for the two classes in Table 10.5, we see that class 2 seems to have performed better than class 1. For example, there are fewer scores in the 10s and 20s in class 2 and more scores in the 30s and 40s.

Histograms Another common method of representing data is to group it in intervals and plot the frequencies of the data in each interval. For example, in Table 10.3, we see that the interval from 20 to 29 had more scores than any other, and that relatively few scores fell in the extreme intervals 0–9 and 40–49. To make this visually apparent, we can make a **histogram,** which shows the number of scores that occur in each interval (Figure 10.2). We determine the height of each rectangular bar of the histogram by using the frequency of the scores in the intervals. Bars are centered above the midpoints of the intervals. The vertical axis of the histogram shows the frequency of the scores in each of the intervals on the horizontal axis. Here we see that a cluster of scores occurs in the interval from 20 to 29 and that there are relatively few extremely high or low scores.

Notice that if we turn the stem and leaf plot in Table 10.3 counterclockwise through one-quarter of a turn, we will have a diagram resembling the histogram in Figure 10.2. An advantage of a stem and leaf plot is that each value of the data can be retrieved. With a histogram, only approximate data can be retrieved.

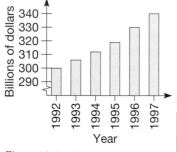

Figure 10.3   Source: U.S. National
Center for Educational Statistics.

www.wiley.com/
college/musser

Spotlight on Technology The Chapter 10 eManipulative activity, *Histogram*, makes constructing and adjusting histograms much simpler than doing it by hand. Enter the data from Table 10.5 for class 2 into the *Histogram* eManipulative activity. Once the data are entered, you can move the slider to change the cell width of the histogram. As the cell width gets smaller, what happens to the number of bars? Why? When the cell width gets smaller, there are also some gaps between some of the bars. Why are those gaps present for some cell widths and not for others?

Charts and Graphs

Bar Graphs A bar graph is useful for making direct visual comparisons over a period of time. The **bar graph** in Figure 10.3 shows the total school expenditures in the United States over a six-year period. The entries along the horizontal axis are years and the vertical axis represents billions of dollars, so the label of 300 on that axis actually means $300,000,000,000. The mark on the vertical axis is used to indicate that this part of the scale is not consistent with the rest of the scale. This is a common practice to conserve space.

Multiple-bar graphs can be used to show comparisons of data. In Figure 10.4 the nationwide enrollments in grades 9–12 and college are shown for the years 1980, 1985, 1990, and 1995. We see that there was a larger enrollment in grades 9–12 for the years 1980 and 1985 but the college enrollment surpassed it in 1990 and 1995.

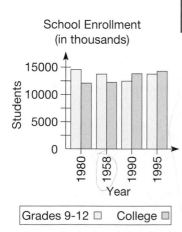

Figure 10.4   Source: U.S. National
Center for Educational Statistics.

A histogram and a bar graph are very similar and yet are different in subtle ways. Both types of graphs use rectangles or bars to illustrate the frequency or magnitude of some type of category. Histograms are typically drawn with the categories along the horizontal or *x*-axis and the frequency or magnitude along the vertical or *y*-axis. This orientation will result with the bars being drawn vertically. Bar graphs, on the other hand, can be drawn either with the bars vertical (categories on the *x*-axis) or horizontal (categories on the *y*-axis). The major distinction between a histogram and a bar graph is the type of data used for the categories. If the categories represent numbers that are continuous and could be regrouped in different intervals, then a histogram should be used. If, however, the categories represent discrete values, then a bar graph should be used. Because the intervals on the categories of a histogram cover all possible values of data, the bars on the graph are drawn with no spaces between them.

The graph in Figure 10.2 is a histogram because the categories on the *x*-axis represent a continuous set of numbers that cover all possible values and could be regrouped into different intervals, as shown in Figure 10.5. The graph in Figure 10.4 is a bar graph because there are gaps in the data used for categories along the *x*-axis. There are no data for the years between 1980 and 1985, between 1985 and 1990, and between 1990 and 1995. As a result, there must be a gap between the bars representing the enrollments for 1980, 1985, 1990, and 1995. The graph shown in Figure 10.3 is not as clear-cut as to whether it should be a histogram or a bar graph. Because every year from 1992 to 1997 is represented, a case could be made for using a histogram. However, because the nature of the data is more discrete, we chose to use a bar graph.

In Figure 10.4, high school and college enrollment were compared against each other using a double-bar graph. In that case, all the data were of the same type, but there are cases when two different types of data are of interest. In such cases, a double-bar graph with two different axes can be constructed. The graph in Figure 10.6 compares the per student expenditure against the average SAT scores for each state.

Notice that the vertical axis on the left represents the per-pupil expenditure and the vertical axis on the right has a very different scale because it represents the average SAT score for a given state. Based on this graph, one might conclude that spending more money on schools does not yield better student achievement. While this

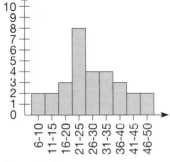

Figure 10.5

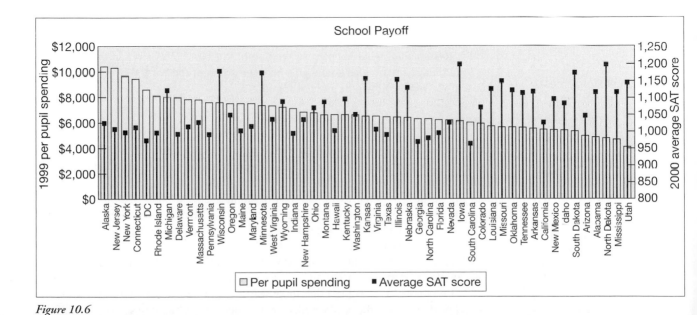

Figure 10.6

Name _____ Date _____

Ms. Carter's Class

Ms. Carter's class used the information in the data table to make a graph. Use the graph to answer questions on the following page.

Birth Months

From *Math Trailblazers*, Grade 2 Student Guide, p. 2, by the *TIMS PROJECT*. Copyright © 1997 by Kendall/Hunt Publishing Company. Reprinted with permission.

graph has been constructed correctly, there is a key piece of information that is missing. Do the same percentage of students take the test in all of the states? If only the best high school students take it in one state and all of the college-bound students take it in another state, then a comparison between those states' average SAT scores would be invalid. Such is the case with this data. For example, most of the universities in the state of Utah require incoming students to take the ACT college entrance exam instead of the SAT exam. Thus, only those top students who are intending to go to a school out of the state of Utah would take the SAT. In fact, a careful examination of the states with the top SAT scores reveals that most of them have a small percentage of students taking the exam, while most of those with lower average SAT score have two or three times the percentage of students taking the exam. Other examples of misleading statistics will be discussed further in Section 10.3.

Line Graphs A **line graph** is useful for plotting data over a period of time to indicate trends. Figure 10.7 gives an example.

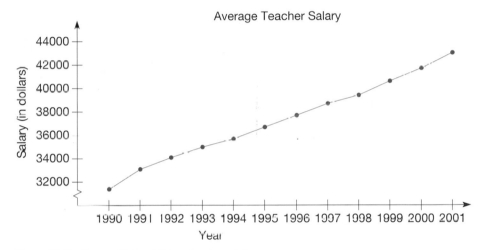

Figure 10.7 *Source*: National Education Association.

Once again the vertical scale has been compressed to conserve space and to help accentuate the trend. The convention of compressing the vertical axis is common and can have a significant influence on the appearance of the graph, even to the point of being deceptive. This issue will be discussed in further detail in Section 10.3.

Multiple-line graphs can be used to show trends and comparisons simultaneously. For example, Figure 10.8 shows the milk production each month for the years

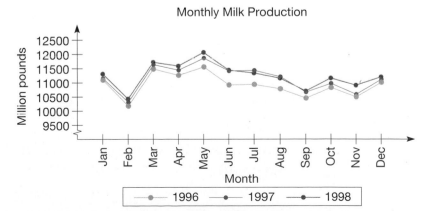

Figure 10.8 *Source*: Hoard's Dairyman Magazine.

1996–1998 (the December 1998 value is an approximation). Notice that the production falls off every February, builds to its peak every May, and then slows down for the remainder of the year. In 1997 and 1998 the production was consistently greater than that of 1996. Production in 1998 was greater than in 1997 except for the months of July and August, in which it was slightly less than the previous year. Notice that the break in the vertical axis does not affect the analysis of comparisons and trends.

Line graphs also can be used to display two different pieces of information simultaneously. For example, the graph in Figure 10.9 shows world fertilizer use and grain area per person from 1950 to 1985. By graphing this information together, it is noticeable that as fertilizer use was increased, the amount of area devoted to grain production was decreased.

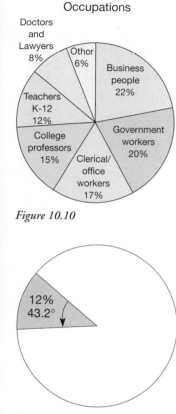

Figure 10.10

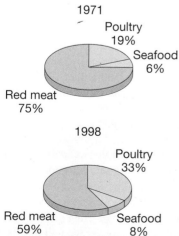

Figure 10.11

Changes in Meat Consumption per Person, 1971 and 1998 (in percentages)

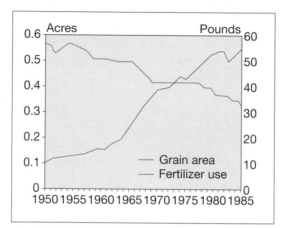

Figure 10.9 World fertilizer use and grain area per person, 1950–1986. *Source*: U.S. Department of Agriculture.

Circle Graphs The next type of graph we will consider is a **circle graph** or **pie chart.** Circle graphs are used for comparing parts of a whole. Figure 10.10 shows the percentages of people working in a certain community.

In making a circle graph, the area of a sector is proportional to the fraction or percentage that it represents. The central angle in the sector is equal to the given percentage of 360°. For example, in Figure 10.10 the central angle for the teachers' sector is 12% of 360°, or 43.2° (Figure 10.11).

Multiple-circle graphs can be used to show trends. For example, Figure 10.12 shows the changes in meat consumption between the two years 1971 and 1998. One can see that the relative amount of red meat consumed per person has declined and the relative amounts of both poultry and seafood have increased.

Example 10.2 In the 2000 Summer Olympics in Sydney, Australia, the highest medal count was held by the United States, as shown in the table below. Construct a circle graph to illustrate the different distribution of medals.

	GOLD	SILVER	BRONZE	TOTAL
UNITED STATES	39	25	33	97

Figure 10.12 *Source*: U.S. Department of Agriculture, 1999.

Solution Since 39 out of the 97 medals won by the United States were gold, the portion of the circle graph representing the gold medals should be determined by a $\frac{39}{97} \cdot 360° = 145°$ angle. Similarly, the regions for silver and bronze should be deter-

United States

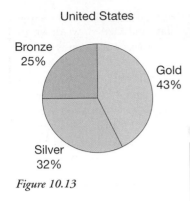

Bronze
25%

Gold
43%

Silver
32%

Figure 10.13

mined by a $\frac{25}{97} \cdot 360° = 93°$ angle and a $\frac{33}{97} \cdot 360° = 122°$ angle, respectively. Using these angles and a protractor, construct three sectors in a circle with these angle measures to represent gold, silver, and bronze as shown in Figure 10.13.

Notice that the sum of the percentages is exactly 100% and the sum of the angles determining the sectors of the circle is 360°. ■

www.wiley.com/
college/musser

Spotlight on Technology Circle graphs can be constructed very easily if the work is left to a spreadsheet. Refer to the dynamic spreadsheet, *Circle Graph Budget*, in the spreadsheet webmodule, which contains a monthly budget spreadsheet for you to work with. Enter the following values into the monthly budget categories: housing—$250, transportation—$200, food—$150, utilities—$125, entertainment—$50, savings—$75. Suppose the savings were increased by $100 a month. How does that change the appearance of the circle graph?

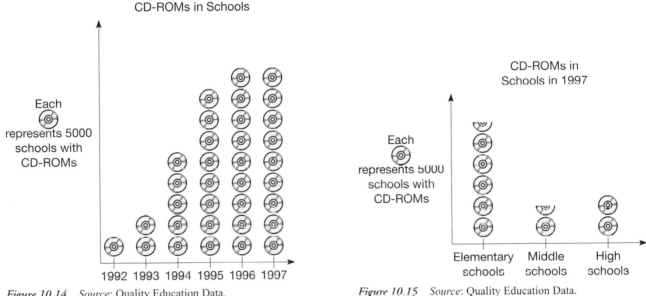

Figure 10.14 *Source*: Quality Education Data.

Figure 10.15 *Source*: Quality Education Data.

Pictographs Many common types of charts and graphs are used for picturing data. A **pictograph**, like the one in Figure 10.14, uses a picture, or icon, to symbolize the quantities being represented. From a pictograph we can observe the change in a quantity over time. We can also make comparisons between similar situations. For example, in Figure 10.15 we can compare the numbers of schools with CD-ROMs in their computers in American elementary, middle, and high schools in 1997. Notice that Figures 10.14 and 10.15 are equivalent to line plots, with pictures of CDs instead of dots.

Pictorial Embellishments With the continually increasing graphics capabilities of computers in a TV-intensive society, **pictorial embellishments** are commonly used with graphs in an attempt to make them more visually appealing. A pictorial embellishment is the addition of some type of picture or art to the basic graphs described thus far in this section. Although pictorial embellishments do make graphs more eye-catching, they also can have the effect of being visually deceptive, as we will discuss in Section 10.3.

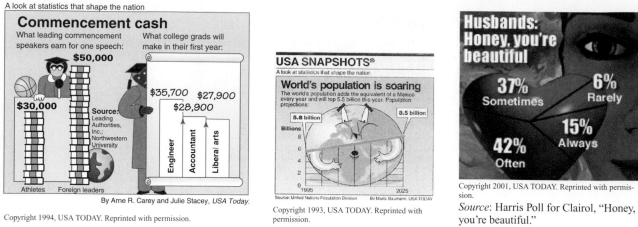

Figure 10.16

Figure 10.17

Source: Harris Poll for Clairol, "Honey, you're beautiful."

Figure 10.18

Figure 10.16 provides an example of a pictorial embellishment of a pictograph on the left and a bar graph on the right. Figures 10.17 and 10.18 show pictorial embellishments of a line graph and a circle graph, respectively. In all of these cases, the graphs could have easily been presented without the embellishments but, as most publishers have learned, you probably wouldn't look at it.

NCTM Standards 2000 Data Analysis and Probability Grades 6–8
All students should make conjectures about possible relationships between two characteristics of a sample on the basis of scatterplots of the data and approximate lines of fit.

Scatterplots Sometimes data are grouped into pairs of numbers that may or may not have a relation to each other. For example, data points might be records of dates and temperature, selling price of a house and its appraised value, employment and interest rates, or education and income. Such pairs of numbers can be plotted as points on a portion of the (x, y)-plane, forming what is called a **scatterplot.** For example, Table 10.6 lists significant earthquakes of the 1960s.

Table 10.6   Significant Earthquakes of the 1960s

DATE	PLACE	DEATHS	MAGNITUDES
Feb. 29, 1960	Morocco	12,000	5.8
May 21–30, 1960	Chile	5,000	8.3
Sept. 1, 1962	Iran	12,230	7.1
July 26, 1963	Yugoslavia	1,100	6.0
Mar. 27, 1964	Alaska	131	8.4
Aug. 19, 1966	Turkey	2,520	6.9
Aug. 31, 1968	Iran	12,000	7.4

To investigate the possible relationship between the magnitude of an earthquake and the number of deaths resulting from the trembler, we make a scatterplot of the data in the table.

Here the magnitude scale is placed along the horizontal axis and the number-of-deaths scale is placed along the vertical axis. For each earthquake we place a dot at the intersection of the appropriate horizontal and vertical lines. For instance, the dot representing the July 1963 earthquake in Yugoslavia is on the vertical line for magnitude 6 and is on an imagined horizontal line for 1100 deaths; that is, just a little above the horizontal line for 1000 deaths (Figure 10.19).

When we look at Figure 10.19, the scatterplot of the earthquake data, there does not appear to be any particular pattern other than that the magnitude of all the earthquakes is above 5. Can you explain why there does not seem to be a relationship between the magnitude of the earthquake and the number of deaths it causes? In the case of other

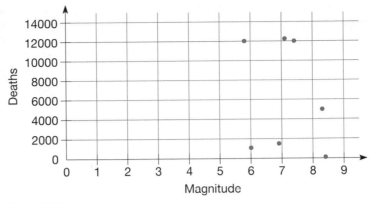

Figure 10.19

data, it often happens that you can see a pattern. Many times it seems that the data points are approximately on a line, as in the next example.

Example 10.3 Suppose that 10 people are interviewed and asked about their income level and educational attainments (Table 10.7).

Table 10.7 Educational Level vs. Income

PERSON	EDUCATIONAL LEVEL	INCOME (1000s)	DATA POINTS
1	12	22	(12, 22)
2	16	63	(16, 63)
3	18	48	(18, 48)
4	10	14	(10, 14)
5	14	2	(14, 2)
6	14	34	(14, 34)
7	13	31	(13, 31)
8	11	97	(11, 97)
9	21	92	(21, 92)
10	16	44	(16, 44)

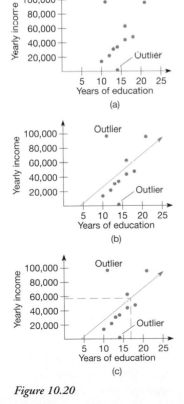

Figure 10.20

Plot this information in a scatterplot and draw a line that these data seem to approximate or fit.

Solution To visualize this information, we plot it on a graph with years of Education on the horizontal axis and yearly income on the vertical axis [Figure 10.20(a)].

There are two exceptional points in these data, called **outliers.** One is a person with an 11th-grade education who makes $97,000 a year. The interview revealed that this person owned his own successful tulip bulb import business. The other outlier was a person with two years of college (14 years of education) who made only $2000 annually. This unfortunate was an unemployed homeless person. Ignoring the outliers, we notice that these points lie roughly on the straight line. If there is a specific line that best fits some pairs of data, as shown in Figure 10.20(b), this line is called the **regression line.** The presence of a regression line indicates a possible relationship between educational level and yearly income, in which higher income levels correspond to higher educational levels. We call such a mutual relationship a **correlation.** This does not imply that one is the cause of the other, only that they are related. In many problems, you can use a straightedge and "eyeball" a best-fitting line, as we did in this example.

A regression line is very useful. If you know the value of one of the variables, say the educational level, then you can use the regression line to estimate a likely value for the other variable, the income level. For example, if we were to interview another person whose educational level was 17 years (one year of graduate school), then we could give an educated guess as to what this person's income level might be using the regression line. To make this estimate, you trace a vertical line from 17 on the horizontal axis up to the regression line; then you trace a horizontal line left until it intersects the income axis. The process is shown by the dashed lines in Figure 10.20(c). In this case, we use the regression line to project that this person's income level is likely to be close to $58,000. ■

Spotlight on Technology Scatterplots can be easily constructed by using the Chapter 10 eManipulative activity, *Scatterplots*. The dynamic nature of the eManipulative activity allows you to see how www.wiley.com/ the regression line changes when a data point is added or moved. college/musser Enter the data for Example 10.3 on the eManipulative by first adjusting the scale to be $8 < x < 22$ and $0 < y < 100$. As the data points from Table 10.7 are entered into the scatterplot, the regression will automatically be plotted to fit the data. Predict what would happen to the regression line if the two outliers were removed. Check your prediction.

From the preceding examples, we see that there are many useful methods of organizing and picturing data but that each method has limitations and can be misleading. Table 10.8 gives a summary of our observations about charts and graphs. Notice that although *individual* circle graphs are not designed to show trends, multiple-circle graphs may be used for that purpose, as illustrated in Figure 10.12.

NCTM Standards 2000 Data Analysis and Probability Grades 3–5
All students should compare different representations of the same data and evaluate how well each representation shows important aspects of the data.

Table 10.8

GRAPHS	GOOD FOR PICTURING	NOT AS GOOD FOR PICTURING
Bar	Totals and trends	Relative amounts
Line	Trends and comparisons of several quantities simultaneously	Relative amounts
Circle	Relative amounts	Trends
Pictograph	Totals, trends, and comparisons	Relative amounts
Scatterplot	Ordered pairs, correlations, trends	Relative amounts

MATHEMATICAL MORSEL

There is statistical evidence to indicate that some people postpone death so that they can witness an important birthday or anniversary. For example, there is a dip in U.S. deaths before U.S. presidential elections. Also, Presidents Jefferson and Adams died on the 4th of July, 50 years after signing the Declaration of Independence. This extending-death phenomenon is further reinforced by Jefferson's doctor, who quoted Jefferson on his deathbed as asking, "Is it the Fourth?" The doctor replied, "It soon will be." These were the last words spoken by Thomas Jefferson.

Section 10.1 EXERCISE / PROBLEM SET A

EXERCISES

1. A class of 30 students made the following scores on a 100-point test:

    63, 76, 82, 85, 65, 95, 98, 92, 76,
    80, 72, 76, 80, 78, 72, 69, 92, 72,
    74, 85, 58, 86, 76, 74, 67, 78, 88,
    93, 80, 70

   a. Arrange the scores in increasing order.

   b. What is the lowest score? the highest score?

   c. What score occurs most often?

   d. Make a line plot to represent these data.

   e. Make a frequency table, grouping the data in increments of 10 (91–100, 81–90, etc.).

   f. From the information in the frequency table, make a histogram.

   g. Which interval has the most scores?

   h. Using the Chapter 10 eManipulative activity, *Histogram*, construct a histogram of the above data. By moving the slider, group the data in increments of 5 and 8. Sketch each histogram.

   i. For each grouping in part (h), which interval has the largest number of scores? How do the two intervals compare?

2. Make a stem and leaf plot for the following weights of children in kilograms. Use two-digit stems.

    17.0, 18.1, 19.2, 20.2, 21.1, 15.8, 22.0,
    16.1, 15.9, 18.2, 18.5, 22.0, 16.3, 20.3,
    20.9, 18.5, 22.1, 21.4, 17.5, 19.4, 21.8,
    16.4, 20.9, 18.5, 20.6

3. Consider the following stem and leaf plot, where the stems are the tens digits of the data.

2	0 0 1 1 7
3	1 3 5 5 5
4	2 3 3 3 5 8 9
5	4 7

   a. Construct the line plot for the data.

   b. Construct the histogram for the data grouped by tens.

4. a. Make a back-to-back stem and leaf plot for the following test scores.

   Class 1: 57, 62, 76, 80, 93, 87, 76, 86, 75, 60, 59, 86, 72, 80, 93, 79, 58, 86, 93, 81

   Class 2: 68, 79, 75, 87, 92, 90, 83, 77, 95, 67, 84, 92, 85, 77, 66, 87, 92, 82, 90, 85

   b. Which class seems to have performed better?

5. The following pictograph represents the mining production in a given state.

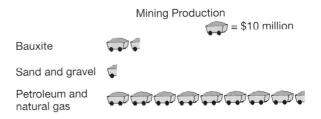

   a. About how many dollars worth of bauxite was mined?

   b. About how many dollars worth of sand and gravel was mined?

   c. About how many dollars worth of petroleum and natural gas were mined?

6. The following are data on public school enrollments during the twentieth century.

1900	15,503,110	1910	17,813,852
1920	21,578,316	1930	25,678,015
1940	25,433,542	1950	25,111,427
1960	36,086,771	1970	45,909,088
1980	40,984,093	1990	41,216,000

   a. Choose an appropriate icon, a reasonable amount for it to represent, and draw a pictograph.

   b. In which decades were there increases in enrollment?

   c. What other types of graphs could we use to represent these data?

7. The given bar graphs represent the average monthly precipitation in Portland, Oregon, and New York City.

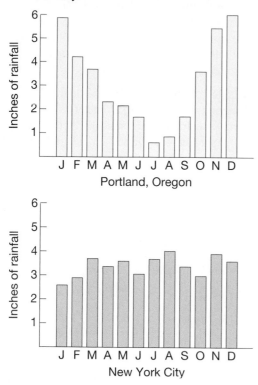

Portland, Oregon

New York City

a. Which city receives more precipitation, on the average, in January?

b. In how many months are there less than 2 inches precipitation in Portland? in New York City?

c. In which month does the greatest amount of precipitation occur in Portland? the least?

d. In which month does the greatest amount of precipitation occur in New York City? the least?

e. Which city has the greater annual precipitation?

8. Given are several gasoline vehicles and their fuel consumption averages.

Buick	27 mpg
BMW	28 mpg
Honda Civic	35 mpg
Geo	46 mpg
Neon	38 mpg
Land Rover	16 mpg

a. Draw a bar graph to represent these data.

b. Which model gets the least miles per gallon? the most?

c. _____ gets about three times as many miles per gallon as _____.

d. What is the cost of fuel for 80,000 miles of driving at $1.29 per gallon for each car?

e. Could a histogram be used in this case? Why or why not?

9. The populations of the world's nine largest urban areas in 1990 and their populations in 2000 are given in the following table.

World's Largest Urban Areas

	POPULATION (MILLIONS)	
	1990	**2000**
Tokyo/Yokohama	27.25	29.97
Mexico City	20.90	27.87
Sao Paulo	18.70	25.35
Seoul	16.80	21.98
New York	14.60	14.65
Bombay	12.10	15.46
Calcutta	11.90	14.09
Rio de Janeiro	11.70	14.17
Buenos Aires	11.70	12.91

Source: World Almanac, 1995.

a. Draw a double-bar graph of the data with two bars for each urban area.

b. Which urban area has the largest percentage growth?

c. Which area has the smallest percentage gain in population?

10. Public education expenditures in the United States, as a percentage of gross national product, are given in the following table.

YEAR	EXPENDITURE (%)
1940	3.6
1950	3.5
1960	4.8
1970	7.1
1980	6.7
1990	7.2

a. Make a line graph illustrating the data.

b. Make another line graph illustrating the data, but with a vertical scale unit interval twice as long as that of part (a) and the same otherwise.

c. Which of your graphs would be used to lobby for more funds for education? Which graph would be used to oppose budget increases?

11. The circle graphs here represent the revenues and expenditures of a state government. Use them to answer the following questions.

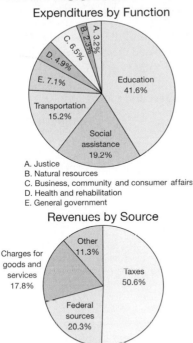

Expenditures by Function

A. 3.2%
B. 2.3%
C. 6.5%
D. 4.9%
E. 7.1%
Education 41.6%
Transportation 15.2%
Social assistance 19.2%

A. Justice
B. Natural resources
C. Business, community and consumer affairs
D. Health and rehabilitation
E. General government

Revenues by Source

Other 11.3%
Charges for goods and services 17.8%
Taxes 50.6%
Federal sources 20.3%

a. What is the largest source of revenue?

b. What percent of the revenue comes from federal sources?

c. Find the central angle of the sector "charges for goods and services."

d. What category of expenditures is smallest?

e. Which four categories, when combined, have the same expenditures as education?

f. Find the central angles of the sectors for "business, community, and consumer affairs" and "general government."

12. The following circle graph shows how a state spends its revenue of $4,500,000,000. Find out how much was spent on each category.

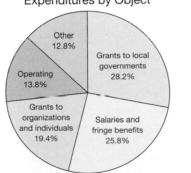

Expenditures by Object

Other 12.8%
Grants to local governments 28.2%
Operating 13.8%
Grants to organizations and individuals 19.4%
Salaries and fringe benefits 25.8%

Complete the following for Problems 13 and 14.

a. Make a scatterplot for the data.

b. Identify any outliers in the scatterplot.

c. Use the Chapter 10 eManipulative activity, *Scatterplot*, to construct a scatterplot and regression line. Sketch the regression line on the scatterplot constructed in part (a).

13. The college admissions office uses high school grade point average (GPA) as one of its selection criteria for admitting new students. At the end of the year, 10 students are selected at random from the freshman class and a comparison is made between their high school grade point averages and their grade point averages at the end of their freshman year in college.

HIGH SCHOOL GPA	FRESHMAN GPA
2.8	2.5
3.2	2.6
3.4	3.1
3.7	3.2
3.5	3.3
3.8	3.3
3.9	3.6
4.0	3.8
3.6	3.9
3.8	4.0

14. Students taking a speed reading course produced the following gains in their reading speeds:

WEEKS IN PROGRAM	SPEED GAIN (WORDS PER MINUTE)
2	50
4	100
4	140
5	130
6	170
6	140
7	180
8	230

Complete the following for Problems 15 and 16.

a. Make a scatterplot for the data.

b. Sketch the regression line. As a line that best fits this data, the line should have a balance of data points that are above it and below it.

c. Use the Chapter 10 eManipulative activity, *Scatterplot*, to construct a scatterplot and regression line. Describe how your regression line from part (b) compares to the one generated by the eManipulative.

15. A golf course professional collected the following data on the average scores for eight golfers and their average weekly practice time.

PRACTICE TIME (HOURS)	AVERAGE SCORE
6	79
3	83
4	92
6	78
3	84
2	94
5	80
6	82

16. A company that assembles electronic parts uses several methods for screening potential new employees. One of these is an aptitude test requiring good eye–hand coordination. The personnel director selects eight employees at random and compares their test results with their average weekly output.

APTITUDE TEST RESULTS	WEEKLY OUTPUT (DOZENS OF UNITS)
6	30
9	49
5	32
8	42
7	39
5	28
8	41
16	52

17. A doctor conducted a study to investigate the relationship between weight and diastolic blood pressure of males between 40 and 50 years of age. The scatterplot and regression line indicate the relationship.

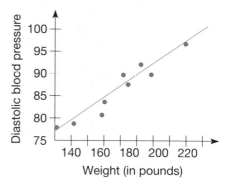

a. Predict the diastolic blood pressure of a 45-year-old man who weighs 160 pounds.

b. Predict the diastolic blood pressure of a 42-year-old man who weighs 180 pounds.

PROBLEMS

18. The projected enrollment (in thousands) of public and private schools in the United States in 2000 is given in the table.

TYPE OF SCHOOL	PUBLIC	PRIVATE
Elementary	33,903	4640
Secondary	13,537	1366
College	11,626	3263

Source: U.S. National Center for Educational Statistics.

a. What is an appropriate type of graph for displaying the data? Explain.

b. Make a graph of the data using your chosen type.

19. The federal budget is derived from several sources, as listed in the table.

Federal Budget Revenue, 1998

SOURCE	PERCENT
Individual income taxes	53
Social insurance receipts	31
Corporate taxes	12
Excise taxes	3
Estate and gift taxes	1
	100

Source: U.S. Internal Revenue Service.

a. What is an appropriate type of graph for displaying the data? Explain.

b. Make a graph of the data using your chosen type.

20. Given in the table is the average cost of tuition and fees at an American four-year college.

U.S. College Tuition and Fees

	PUBLIC	PRIVATE
1989	1846	9451
1990	2035	10,348
1991	2159	11,379
1992	2410	12,192
1993	2604	13,055
1994	2820	13,874
1995	2977	14,537
1996	3151	15,605
1997	3321	16,531

Source: U.S. National Center for Educational Statistics.

a. What is an appropriate type of graph for displaying the data? Explain.

b. Make a graph of the data using your chosen type.

c. For the nine-year period, which college costs increased at the greater rate—public or private?

21. The table below represents the percent of persons in each category who participated in television viewing or newspaper reading in the week prior to the survey in the spring of 2000.

Media Audiences, 2000

GROUP OF PEOPLE	TELEVISION VIEWING	NEWSPAPER READING
Not high school graduate	94.8	60
High school graduate	94.5	78.8
Attended college	93.6	83.7
College graduate	91.1	89.7

Source: Mediamark Research Inc.

a. What is an appropriate type of graph for displaying the data? Explain.

b. Make a graph of the data using your chosen type.

22. The table gives the number (in thousands) of cellular telephone subscribers.

a. What is an appropriate type of graph for displaying the data? Explain.

b. Make a graph of the data using your chosen type.

Cell Phone Subscibers

YEAR	NUMBER OF CELLULAR TELEPHONE SUBSCRIBERS (×1000)
1993	16,009
1994	24,134
1995	33,786
1996	44,043
1997	55,312
1998	69,209
1999	86,047

Source: Cellular Telecommunications Industry Association.

23. Given in the following table are revenues for public elementary and secondary schools from federal, state, and local sources.

Source of School Funds by Percent, 1920–1990

SCHOOL YEAR	FEDERAL	STATE	LOCAL
1920	0.3	16.5	83.2
1930	0.4	16.9	82.7
1940	1.8	30.3	68.0
1950	2.9	39.8	57.3
1960	4.4	39.1	56.5
1970	8.0	39.9	52.1
1980	9.8	46.8	43.4
1990	6.1	47.2	46.6

Source: National Center for Education Statistics.

a. What is an appropriate type of graph for displaying the data? Explain.

b. Make a graph of the data using your chosen type.

c. What trends does your graph display?

24. A company compared the commuting distance and number of absences for a group of employees, with the following data:

COMMUTING DISTANCE (MI.)	NUMBER OF ABSENCES (YR.)
8	4
21	5
8	5
8	3
2	2
15	5
17	7
11	4

a. Make a scatterplot of the data.

b. Estimate the regression line.

c. Predict the number of absences (per year) for an employee with a commute of 15 miles.

25. A report from the Bureau of Labor Statistics listed the 1993 median weekly earnings (for both men and women) of full-time workers in selected occupational categories. Predict the median weekly salary for a woman if the median weekly salary for a man is $450.

MEDIAN WEEKLY EARNINGS OCCUPATION	MEN	WOMEN
Managerial and prof. specialty	791	580
Technical, sales, admin. support	534	376
Service occupations	350	259
Precision production	511	344
Operators, fabricators, laborers	399	288
Transportation	456	358
Handlers, equip. cleaners	319	286
Farming, forestry, fishing	274	242

26. a. Check to see whether the first equation is true.

$$4^2 + 5^2 + 6^2 = 2^2 + 3^2 + 8^2$$
$$42^2 + 53^2 + 68^2 = 24^2 + 35^2 + 86^2$$

b. The numbers on each side of the first equation were rearranged to form the resulting second equation. Is the second equation true?

c. Determine whether similar equations always hold.

27. Find all four-digit squares whose digits are all even.

Section 10.1 EXERCISE / PROBLEM SET B

EXERCISES

1. The following are test scores out of 100 for one student throughout the school year in math class.

64, 73, 45, 74, 83, 71, 56, 82, 76, 85, 83, 87, 92, 84, 95, 92, 96, 92, 91

a. Express these scores in a line plot.

b. Express these scores in a histogram.

c. Use the Chapter 10 eManipulative activity, *Histogram*, to construct a histogram. By moving the slider, group the data in an increment of 3. Sketch the histogram.

2. Consider the following data, representing interest rates in percent.

12.50, 12.45, 12.25, 12.80, 12.50, 12.15, 12.80, 12.40, 12.50, 12.85

a. Make a stem and leaf plot using two-digit stems.

b. Make a stem and leaf plot using three-digit stems.

c. Which stem and leaf plot is more informative?

3. Consider the following stem and leaf plot, where the stems are the tens digits of the data.

4	0 1 1 1 2 7 9
5	2 4 5 6 7 8 8 8 9
6	3 3 3 3 3 4 5 7 9
7	9
8	1 1 2 7 8 9

a. Construct the line plot for the data.

b. Construct the histogram for the data grouped by tens.

4. a. Make a back-to-back stem and leaf plot for the following test scores.

Class 1: 65, 76, 78, 54, 86, 93, 45, 90, 86, 77, 65, 41, 77, 94, 56, 89, 76

Class 2: 74, 46, 87, 98, 43, 67, 78, 46, 75, 85, 84, 76, 65, 82, 79, 31, 92

b. Which class seems to have performed better?

5. Given are data for American automobile factory sales.

YEAR	NUMBER OF PASSENGER CARS (THOUSANDS)
1900	4
1910	181
1920	1,906
1930	2,787
1940	3,717
1950	6,666
1960	6,675
1970	6,547
1980	6,400
1990	6,050
1999	6,982

a. What problem would you encounter in trying to make a pictograph?

b. Construct a line graph representing these data.

6. Germany won 14 gold, 17 silver, and 26 bronze medals in the 2000 Summer Olympics. Using these data and the data from Example 10.2, construct a pictograph to show how the United States and Germany compared in each of the categories: gold, silver, and bronze.

7. The following bar graph represents the Dow-Jones Industrial Average for the month of September 2001. Use it to answer the following questions.

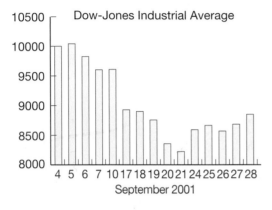

a. Does it appear that the average on September 5 was more than eight times the average on September 21? Is this true?

b. Does it appear that the average more than doubled from September 21 to September 24? Is this true?

c. Why is this graph misleading?

8. Given are several cars and some braking data.

MAKE OF CAR	BRAKING FROM 70 MPH TO 0 MPH (FT)
Chrysler	188
Lincoln	178
Cadillac	214
Oldsmobile	200
Buick	197
Ford	197

a. Draw a bar graph to represent these data.

b. Describe how one could read your graph to choose the safest car.

9. The following chart lists the four leading death rates per 100,000 population for three years in the United States.

a. Display these data in a triple-bar graph where each cause of death is represented by the three years.

b. Based on your graphs, in which causes are we making progress?

CAUSE OF DEATH	1970	1980	1990
Cardiovascular diseases	945	878	863
Cancer	163	184	203
Accidents	56	47	37
Pulmonary diseases	15	25	35

Source: Statistical Abstract of the United States.

c. Does your graph suggest where most of our research resources should be targeted? Explain.

10. Following is one tax table from a recent state income tax form.

IF YOUR TAXABLE INCOME IS:	YOUR TAX IS:
Not over $500	4.2% of taxable income
At or over $500 but not over $1000	$21.00 + 5.3% of excess over $500
Over $1000 but not over $2000	$47.50 + 6.5% of excess over $1000
Over $2000 but not over $3000	$112.50 + 7.6% of excess over $2000
Over $3000 but not over $4000	$188.50 + 8.7% of excess over $3000
Over $4000 but not over $5000	$275.50 + 9.8% of excess over $4000
Over $5000	$373.50 + 10.8% of excess over $5000

a. Compute the tax when taxable income is $0, $500, $1000, $2000, $3000, $4000, $5000, $6000.

b. Use these data to construct a line graph of tax versus income.

11. Roger has totaled his expenses for the last school year and represented his findings in a circle graph.

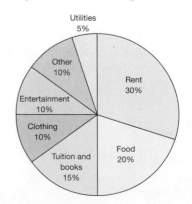

a. What is the central angle of the rent sector?

b. for the food sector?

c. for tuition and books?

d. If his total expenses were $6000, what amount was spent on rent? on entertainment? on clothing?

12. Of a total population of 135,525,000 people 25 years of age and over, 39,357,000 had completed less than four years of high school, 51,426,000 had completed four years of high school, 20,692,000 had completed one to three years of college, and 24,050,000 had completed four or more years of college.

a. To construct a circle graph, find the percentage (to nearest percent) and central angle (to nearest degree) for each of the following categories.

   i. Less than four years of high school

  ii. Four years of high school

 iii. One to three years of college

 iv. Four or more years of college

b. Construct the circle graph.

Complete the following for Problems 13 and 14.

a. Make a scatterplot for the data.

b. Identify any outliers in the scatterplot.

c. Use the Chapter 10 eManipulative activity, *Scatterplot*, to construct a scatterplot and regression line. Sketch the regression line on the scatterplot constructed in part (a).

d. Using the eManipulative, remove the outlier identified in part (b). Describe how the removal of the outlier affected the location of the regression line.

13. A female student thinks that people of similar heights tend to date each other. She measures herself, her roommates, and several others in the dormitory. Then she has them find out the heights of the last man each of the women dated. The heights are given in inches.

FEMALE	MALE
64	70
62	71
66	73
65	68
64	72
70	71
61	66
66	69

14. A high school career counselor does a 10-year follow-up study of graduates. Among the data she collects is a list of the number of years of education beyond high school and incomes earned by the graduates. The following table shows the data for 10 randomly selected graduates.

YEARS OF EDUCATION BEYOND HIGH SCHOOL	INCOME (1000S)
2	27
5	33
0	22
2	25
7	48
4	35
0	28
6	32
4	22
5	30

Complete the following for Problems 15 and 16.

a. Make a scatterplot for the data.

b. Sketch the regression line. As a line that best fits these data, the line should have a balance of data points that are above it and below it.

c. Use the Chapter 10 eManipulative activity, *Scatterplot*, to construct a scatterplot and regression line. Describe how your regression line from part (b) compares to the one generated by the eManipulative.

15. An Alaska naturalist made aerial surveys of a certain wooded area on 10 different days, noting the wind velocity and the number of black bears sighted.

WIND VELOCITY (MPH)	BLACK BEARS SIGHTED
2.1	93
16.7	60
21.1	30
15.9	63
4.9	82
11.8	76
23.6	43
4.0	89
21.5	49
24.4	36

16. A high school math teacher has students maintain records on their study time and then compares their average nightly study time to the scores received on an exam. A random sample of the students showed these comparisons:

STUDY TIME (NEAREST 5 MIN)	EXAM SCORE
15	58
25	72
50	85
20	75
25	68
30	88
40	80
15	74
25	78
30	70
45	94
35	75

17. In a study on obesity involving 12 women, the lean body mass (in kilograms) was compared to the resting metabolic rate. The scatterplot and regression line indicate the data and relationship.

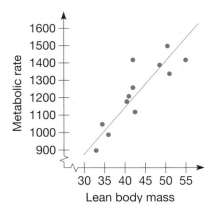

a. Predict the resting metabolic rate for a woman with a lean body mass of 40 kilograms.

b. Predict the resting metabolic rate for a woman with a lean body mass of 50 kilograms.

PROBLEMS

18. Given is the volume of all types of mail handled by the U.S. Postal Service in 1999.

Volume of Mail Handled 1999

TYPE	PIECES (MILLIONS)
First class	101.9
Priority	1.2
Periodicals (2nd Class)	10.3
Standard A (3rd Class)	85.7
Standard B (4th Class)	1.1
Other	0.5

Source: U.S. Postal Service.

a. What is an appropriate type of graph for displaying the data? Explain.

b. Make a graph of the data using your chosen type.

19. Projections of the population of the United States, by race and Hispanic origin, are given in the following table.

a. What is an appropriate type of graph for displaying the data? Explain.

b. Make a graph of the data using your chosen type.

U.S. Population Projections 2010–2020 (Millions)

	2010	2015	2020
White	242	249	257
Black	40	42	45
Hispanic	44	49	55
Other	18	20	23

Source: U.S. Census Bureau.

20. The federal budget is spent on several categories, as listed in the following table.

Federal Budget Expenses, 2000

EXPENSE CATEGORY	PERCENT
Human resources	65
National defense	17
Net interest	13
Physical resources	5
	100

Source: U.S. Office of Management and Budget.

a. What is an appropriate type of graph for displaying the data? Explain.

b. Make a graph of the data using your chosen type.

21. The growth of the U.S. population age 65 and over is given in the following table.

YEAR	PERCENT OF POPULATION AGE 65 AND OVER
1900	4.1
1910	4.3
1920	4.7
1930	5.5
1940	6.9
1950	8.1
1960	9.2
1970	9.8
1980	11.3
1990	12.5
2000	12.7*
2010	13.3*
2020	17.3*
2030	21.2*

Source: U.S. Bureau of the Census.
*Percentages from 2000 on are projections.

a. What is an appropriate type of graph for displaying the data? Explain.

b. Make a graph of the data using your chosen type.

22. The table gives the projected numbers of DVD player shipments worldwide for the years 2001–2004.

Worldwide DVD Player Shipments

YEAR	NUMBER OF DVD PLAYERS (MILLIONS)
2001	28
2002	39
2003	50
2004	61

Source: Cahners In-State Group.

a. What is an appropriate type of graph for displaying the data? Explain.

b. Make a graph of the data using your chosen type.

23. The following table gives the percentages of various types of solid waste in the United States in 1998.

TYPE	PERCENT OF TOTAL
Paper	38.2
Glass	5.7
Metals	7.6
Plastics	10.2
Rubber and leather	3.1
Textiles	3.9
Wood	5.4
Food wastes	10.0
Yard wastes	12.6
Other	3.3

Source: Franklin Associates, Ltd.

a. What is an appropriate type of graph for displaying the data?

b. Make a graph of the data using your chosen type.

24. A local bank compared the number of car loans and new home mortgages it processed each month for a year.

MONTH	CAR LOANS	MORTGAGES
Jan	45	6
Feb	36	6
Mar	48	10
Apr	62	14
May	60	15
Jun	72	18
Jul	76	14
Aug	84	15
Sep	67	12
Oct	60	10
Nov	53	9
Dec	68	11

a. Make a scatterplot of the data.

b. Estimate the regression line.

c. Predict the number of new home mortgages in a month that has 50 car loans.

25. During the last two decades corporations have invested in new plants and equipment as corporate profits have continued to increase. Predict the expenditures for new plants and equipment if corporate profits were $250 billion.

	CORPORATE PROFITS (BILLIONS)	EXPENDITURES FOR PLANTS AND EQUIPMENT (BILLIONS)
1970	69	106
1975	121	163
1980	192	318
1985	223	455
1990	293	592
1993	442	650

Source: 1995 *Information Please* almanac.

26. What is the 100th term in each sequence?

   a. 1, 4, 7, 10, 13, 16, . . .

   b. 1, 3, 6, 10, 15, 21, 28, . . .

   c. $\frac{1}{2} - \frac{1}{3}, \frac{1}{3} - \frac{1}{4}, \frac{1}{4} - \frac{1}{5}, \ldots$

27. What is the smallest number that ends in a 4 and is multiplied by 4 by moving the last digit (a 4) to be the first digit? (*Hint*: It is a six-digit number.)

PROBLEMS FOR WRITING/DISCUSSION

1. Your student, Rosa, asked everybody in the class how many pets they had (including dogs, cats, hamsters, guinea pigs, fish, etc.) and found the following statistics.

# PETS	# STUDENTS WITH THAT NUMBER OF PETS
0	6
1	7
2	3
3	5
4 or more	9

Rosa wanted to make a circle graph of the data, so she made the angles match the numbers in the chart by multiplying by 10. She got 60°, 70°, 30°, 50°, and 90°. There seemed to be some space left over, but Rosa said she just must have measured the angles wrong with her protractor. How could you help her?

2. Michael collected data on the favorite colors of everybody in the class. He then drew a line graph of the data, but Rosa said he should have drawn a circle graph. Which student was correct, and why?

3. Michael asked Rosa if he could have just drawn a bar graph or histogram to represent the data in Problem 2. Rosa said a bar graph would be OK, but not a histogram. Do you agree? Explain.

4. The following is a list of student midterm grades and their corresponding final exam grades.

(Midterm, Final Exam): (124, 250), (120, 176), (60, 148), (153, 283), (79, 240), (135, 241), (170, 255), (145, 281), (114, 210), (120, 272), (210, 299), (94, 220), (126, 233), (116, 249), (128, 285), (137, 272), (84, 207), (68, 202), (38, 209), (156, 213), (77, 270), (138, 275), (200, 275), (166, 266), (123, 260), (172, 263), (205, 292)

Suppose that a student has a midterm score of 180 points. What is our best guess for this student's final exam score? How sure are we that this is a good prediction?

10.2 ANALYZING DATA

STARTING POINT

Two girls are arguing over who is on the taller basketball team. The table lists the heights in inches of the players on the two teams. Identify ways that you could help these girls settle their disagreement about the heights of their respective teams. Some might say that the taller team is the team with the two tallest players on it. Describe another way to determine which team is the taller one by taking all players into account.

TEAM 1	TEAM 2
64	69
72	61
65	70
63	69
75	62
65	71
74	63
67	70
64	63
66	67

NCTM Standards 2000
Data Analysis and
Probability
Grades 6–8
All students should find, use, and
interpret measures of center and
spread, including mean and
interquartile range.

Measuring Central Tendency

Suppose that two fifth-grade classes take a reading test, yielding the following scores. Scores are given in year–month equivalent form. For example, a score of 5.3 means that the student is reading at the fifth-year, third-month level, where years mean years in school.

Class 1: 5.3, 4.9, 5.2, 5.4, 5.6, 5.1, 5.8, 5.3, 4.9, 6.1, 6.2, 5.7, 5.4, 6.9, 4.3, 5.2, 5.6, 5.9, 5.3, 5.8

Class 2: 4.7, 5.0, 5.5, 4.1, 6.8, 5.0, 4.7, 5.6, 4.9, 6.3, 7.8, 3.6, 8.4, 5.4, 4.7, 4.4, 5.6, 3.7, 6.2, 7.5

How did the two classes compare on the reading test? This question is complicated, since there are many ways to compare the classes. To answer it, we need several new concepts.

Since we wish to compare the classes as a whole, we need to take the overall performances into account rather than individual scores. Numbers that give some indication of the overall "average" of some data are called **measures of central tendency.** The three measures of central tendency that we study in this chapter are the mode, median, and mean.

Mode, Median, Mean To compare these two classes, we first begin by putting the scores from the two classes in increasing order.

Class 1: 4.3, 4.9, 4.9, 5.1, 5.2, 5.2, 5.3, 5.3, 5.3, 5.4, 5.4, 5.6, 5.6, 5.7, 5.8, 5.8, 5.9, 6.1, 6.2, 6.9

Class 2: 3.6, 3.7, 4.1, 4.4, 4.7, 4.7, 4.7, 4.9, 5.0, 5.0, 5.4, 5.5, 5.6, 5.6, 6.2, 6.3, 6.8, 7.5, 7.8, 8.4

The most frequently occurring score in class 1 is 5.3 (it occurs three times), while in class 2 it is 4.7 (it also occurs three times). Each of the numbers 5.3 and 4.7 is called the mode score for its respective list of scores.

DEFINITION

Mode

In a list of numbers, the number that occurs most frequently is called the **mode.** There can be more than one mode, for example, if several numbers occur most frequently. If each number appears equally often, there is no mode.

The mode for a class gives us some very rough information about the general performance of the class. It is unaffected by all the other scores. On the basis of the mode scores *only*, it appears that class 1 scored higher than class 2.

The median score for a class is the "middle score" or "halfway" point in a list of the scores that is arranged in increasing (or decreasing) order. The median of the data set 7, 11, 13, 17, 23 is 13. For the data set 7, 11, 13, 17, there is no middle score; thus the median is taken to be the average of 11 and 13 (the two middle scores), or 12. The following precise definition states how to find the median of any data set.

NCTM Standards 2000
Data Analysis and
Probability
Grades 3–5
All students should use measures
of center, focusing on the median,
and understand what each does or
does not indicate about the data
set.

DEFINITION

Median

Suppose that $x_1, x_2, x_3, \ldots, x_n$ is a collection of numbers in increasing order; that is, $x_1 \le x_2 \le x_3 \le \cdots \le x_n$. If n is odd, the **median** of the numbers is the middle score in the list; that is, the median is the number with subscript $\frac{n+1}{2}$. If n is even, the **median** is the arithmetic average of the two middle scores; that is, the median is one-half of the sum of the two numbers with subscripts $\frac{n}{2}$ and $\frac{n}{2} + 1$.

Since there is an even number of scores (20) in each class, we average the tenth and eleventh scores. The median for class 1 is 5.4. For class 2, the median is 5.2 (verify). On the basis of the median scores *only*, it appears that class 1 scored higher than class 2. Notice that the median does not take into account the magnitude of any scores except the score (or scores) in the middle. Hence it is not affected by extreme scores. Also, the median is not necessarily a member of the original set of scores if there are an even number of scores.

Example 10.4   Find the mode and median for each collection of numbers.
a. 1, 2, 3, 3, 4, 6, 9   **b.** 1, 1, 2, 3, 4, 5, 10
c. 0, 1, 2, 3, 4, 4, 5, 5   **d.** 1, 2, 3, 4

Solution

a. The mode is 3, since it occurs more often than any other number. The median is also 3, since it is the middle score in this ordered list of numbers.

b. The mode is 1 and the median is 3.

c. There are two modes, 4 and 5. Here we have an even number of scores. Hence we average the two middle scores to compute the median. The median is $\frac{3+4}{2} = 3.5$. Note that the median is not one of the scores in this case.

Reflection from Research
It is worthwhile to demonstrate the
need for other measures of central
tendency by pointing out the main
weakness of the mean—the extent
to which its value can be affected
by extreme scores (Brohan &
Moreland, 1981).

d. The median is $\frac{2+3}{2} = 2.5$. There is no mode, since each number occurs equally often.   ▮

From Example 10.4 we observe that the mode can be equal to, less than, or greater than the median [see parts (a), (b), and (c), respectively].

A third, and perhaps the most useful, measure of central tendency is the mean, also called the **arithmetic average.**

Reflection from Research
A difficult concept for students is
that the mean is not necessarily a
member of the data set (Brown &
Silver, 1989).

DEFINITION

Mean

Suppose that $x_1, x_2, \ldots, x_n$ is a collection of numbers. The **mean** of the collection is

$$\frac{x_1 + x_2 + \cdots + x_n}{n}.$$

The mean for each class is obtained by summing all the scores and dividing the sum by the total number of scores. For our two fifth-grade classes, we can compute the means as in Table 10.9.

Table 10.9

CLASS	SUM OF SCORES	MEAN
1	109.9	$\frac{109.9}{20} = 5.495$
2	109.9	$\frac{109.9}{20} = 5.495$

On the basis of the mean scores, the classes performed equivalently. That is, the "average student" in each class scored 5.495 on the reading test. This means that if all the students had equal scores (and the class total was the same), each student would have a score of 5.495. The mean takes every score into account and hence is affected by extremely high or low scores. Among the mean, median, and mode, any one of the three can be the largest or smallest measure of central tendency.

 Spotlight on Technology The mean of a data set can be found using the T1-34 II calculator. For example, to find the mean of 5, 5, 13, 15, and 17, first press [2nd] [STAT] [ENTER]. This will put the calculator in statistics mode with one variable. Both values of 5 can be entered separately or entered once with a frequency of 2. Enter the data as follows:

[DATA] 5 [▼] 2 [▼] 13 [▼] [▼] 15 [▼] [▼] 17 [ENTER]

Once the data is entered, the mean is computed by pressing [STATVAR] and then pressing the right arrow once so that $\bar{x}$ is underlined. Since $\bar{x}$ is the symbol commonly used to represent the mean, the second line of the display is [11], which is the mean of the five numbers above.

NCTM Standards 2000
Data Analysis and
Probability
Grades 6–8
All students should discuss and understand the correspondence between data sets and their graphical representations, especially histograms, stem-and-leaf plots, box plots, and scatterplots.

Box and Whisker Plots A popular application of the median is a **box and whisker plot** or simply a **box plot.** To construct a box and whisker plot, we first find the lowest score, the median, the highest score, and two additional statistics, namely the lower and upper quartiles. We define the lower and upper quartiles using the median. To find the lower and upper quartiles, arrange the scores in increasing order. With an even number of scores, say $2n$, the **lower quartile** is the median of the n smallest scores. The **upper quartile** is the median of the n largest scores. With an odd number of scores, say $2n + 1$, the lower quartile is the median of the n smallest scores, and the upper quartile is the median of the n largest scores.

We will use the reading test scores from class 1 as an illustration:

4.3, 4.9, 4.9, 5.1, 5.2, 5.2, 5.3, 5.3, 5.3, 5.4,
5.4, 5.6, 5.6, 5.7, 5.8, 5.8, 5.9, 6.1, 6.2, 6.9

Lowest score = 4.3
Lower quartile = median of 10 lowest scores = 5.2
Median = 5.4
Upper quartile = median of 10 highest scores = 5.8
Highest score = 6.9

Next, we plot these five statistics on a number line, then make a box from the lower quartile to the upper quartile, indicating the median with a line crossing the box. Finally, we connect the lowest score to the lower quartile with a line segment, one "whisker," and the upper quartile to the highest score with another line segment, the other whisker (Figure 10.21). The box represents about 50% of the scores, and each whisker represents about 25%.

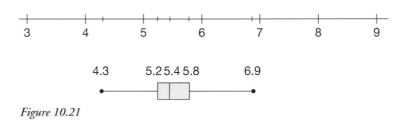

Figure 10.21

The difference between the upper and lower quartiles is called the **interquartile range (IQR).** This statistic is useful for identifying extremely small or large values of the data, called outliers. An **outlier** is commonly defined as any value of the data that lies more than 1.5 IQR units below the lower quartile or more than 1.5 IQR units above the upper quartile. For the class scores, IQR $= 5.8 - 5.2 = 0.6$, so that 1.5 IQR units $= (1.5)(0.6) = 0.9$. Hence any score below $5.2 - 0.9 = 4.3$ or above $5.8 + 0.9 = 6.7$ is an outlier. Thus 6.9 is an outlier for these data; that is, it is an unusually large value given the relative closeness of the rest of the data. Later in this section, we will see an explanation of outliers using z-scores. Often outliers are indicated using an asterisk. In the case of the earlier reading test scores, 6.9 was identified to be an outlier. This is indicated in Figure 10.22. When there are outliers, the whiskers end at the value farthest away from the box that is still within 1.5 IQR units from the end.

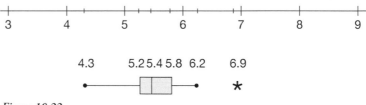

Figure 10.22

We can visually compare the performances of class 1 and class 2 on the reading test by comparing their box and whisker plots. The reading scores from class 2 are 3.6, 3.7, 4.1, 4.4, 4.7, 4.7, 4.7, 4.9, 5.0, 5.0, 5.4, 5.5, 5.6, 5.6, 6.2, 6.3, 6.8, 7.5, 7.8, and 8.4. Thus we have

Lowest score $= 3.6$
Lower quartile $= 4.7$
Median $= 5.2$
Upper quartile $= 6.25$
Highest score $= 8.4$
1.5 IQR $= 2.325$.

The box and whisker plots for both classes appear with outliers in Figure 10.23.

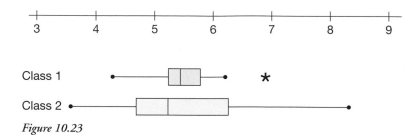

Figure 10.23

From the two box and whisker plots, we see that the scores for class 2 are considerably more widely spread; the box is wider, and the distances to the extreme scores are greater.

Example 10.5 Teacher salary averages for 1997 are given in Table 10.10. Construct a stem and leaf plot as well as box and whisker plots for the data. How do the salaries compare?

Table 10.10 Teacher Salary Averages in 1997 ($\times$ $1000)

STATE	ELEMENTARY TEACHERS	SECONDARY TEACHERS	STATE	ELEMENTARY TEACHERS	SECONDARY TEACHERS
AL	32.5	32.5	MT	29.6	30.7
AK	50.6	50.6	NE	31.8	31.8
AZ	33.3	33.3	NV	37.0	37.8
AR	29.5	31.3	NH	36.0	36.0
CA	42.5	44.5	NJ	48.7	51.6
CO	36.1	36.5	NM	29.4	30.4
CT	50.0	51.6	NY	47.0	49.3
DE	41.3	41.6	NC	31.0	31.4
DC	45.5	46.3	ND	27.9	27.4
FL	33.9	33.9	OH	38.3	39.4
GA	35.1	36.3	OK	30.1	30.6
HI	35.8	35.8	OR	40.6	41.5
ID	31.8	31.9	PA	46.6	47.7
IL	40.4	46.2	RI	43.0	43.1
IN	39.0	38.7	SC	32.6	33.4
IA	32.3	34.1	SD	26.9	26.6
KS	35.7	35.7	TN	33.9	35.2
KY	33.5	35.1	TX	32.3	33.8
LA	29.0	29.0	UT	32.0	32.0
ME	33.3	34.5	VT	37.9	36.5
MD	40.3	42.3	VA	34.7	37.3
MA	42.7	42.7	WA	37.8	37.9
MI	48.2	48.2	WV	32.9	33.7
MN	38.5	38.0	WI	38.7	39.9
MS	28.1	27.3	WY	31.8	31.6
MO	32.5	33.9			

Source: National Education Association.

Solution The stem and leaf plot is given in Table 10.11, where the statistics for constructing the box and whisker plots are shown in boldface type.

Table 10.11

ELEMENTARY TEACHERS		SECONDARY TEACHERS
9	26.	**6**
9	27.	3 4
1	28.	
6 5 4 0	29.	0
1	30.	4 6 7
8 8 8 0	31.	3 4 6 8 9
9 6 5 5 3 3 **0**	32.	**0** 5
9 9 5 3 3	33.	3 4 7 8 9 9
7	34.	1 5
8 7 **1**	35.	1 2 7 **8**
1 0	36.	0 3 5 5
9 8 0	37.	3 8 9
7 5 3	38.	0 7
0	39.	4 9
6 **4** 3	40.	
3	41.	5 **6**
7 5	42.	3 7
0	43.	1
	44.	5
5	45.	
6	46.	2 3
0	47.	7
7 2	48.	2
	49.	3
6 0	50.	6
	51.	6 **6**

Thus we have the following quartile statistics for constructing the box and whisker plots (Table 10.12). Using the statistics in Table 10.12, we can construct the box and whisker plots (Figure 10.24).

Since the box and whisker plot for the secondary teachers lies to the right of that of the elementary teachers, we see that secondary teachers were generally paid more.

Table 10.12

	ELEMENTARY TEACHERS	SECONDARY TEACHERS
Lowest data value	26.9	26.6
Lower quartile	32	32
Median	35.1	35.8
Upper quartile	40.4	41.6
Highest data value	50.6	51.6
Interquartile range	8.4	9.6
1.5 IQR	12.6	14.4
Outliers	$< 32 - 12.6 = 19.4$	$< 32 - 14.4 = 17.6$
	$> 40.4 + 12.6 = 53.0$	$> 41.6 + 14.4 = 56.0$

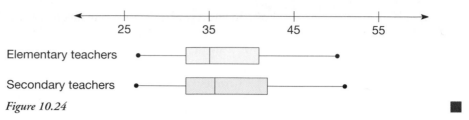

Figure 10.24

Notice how the box and whisker plots of Figure 10.24 give us a *direct visual comparison* of the statistics in Table 10.12. In the next section we will investigate methods of actually measuring the spread of data.

Percentiles When constructing box and whisker plots, we used medians and quartiles. Medians essentially divide the data so that 50% of the data are equal to or below the median. Similarly, quartiles divide the data into fourths. In other words, one-fourth of the data points are equal to or below the lower quartile and the other three-fourths of the data points are above it. The upper quartile is equal to or above three-fourths of the data and below the remaining one-fourth of the data. If we were to divide the data into 100 equal parts, **percentiles** could be used to mark the dividing points in the data. For example, the first percentile would separate the bottom 1% of the data from the top 99% and the 37th percentile would separate the bottom 37% of the data from the upper 63%. Formally, a number is in the ***n*th percentile** of some data if it is greater than or equal to *n*% of the data.

Percentiles are frequently used in connection with scores on large standardized tests like the ACT and SAT or when talking about the height and weight of babies. The doctor may say that your baby is in the 70th percentile for height and the 45th percentile for weight. This would mean that the baby is taller than 70% and heavier than 45% of the babies of the same age. Percentiles will be discussed later in this section.

Measuring Dispersion

Statistics that give an indication of how the data are "spread out" or distributed are called **measures of dispersion.** The **range** of the scores is simply the difference of the largest and smallest scores. For the class 1 scores at the beginning of this section, the range is $6.9 - 4.3 = 2.6$. For class 2, the range of the scores is $8.4 - 3.6 = 4.8$. The range gives us limited information about the distribution of scores, since it takes only the extremes into account, ignoring the intervening scores.

Variance and Standard Deviation Perhaps the most common measures of dispersion are the variance and the standard deviation.

⬢ DEFINITION

Variance

The **variance** of a collection of numbers is the arithmetic average of the squared differences between each number and the mean of the collection of numbers. Symbolically, for the numbers, $x_1, x_2, \ldots, x_n$, with mean $\bar{x}$, the variance is

$$\frac{(x - \bar{x})^2 + (x_2 - \bar{x})^2 + \cdots + (x_n - \bar{x})^2}{n}.$$

To find the variance of a set of numbers, use the following procedure.

1. Find the mean, $\bar{x}$.
2. For each number x, find the difference between the number and the mean, namely $x - \bar{x}$.
3. Square all the differences in step 2, namely $(x - \bar{x})^2$.
4. Find the arithmetic average of all the squares in step 3. This average is the variance.

Example 10.6   Find the variance for the numbers 5, 7, 7, 8, 10, 11.

Solution

The mean, $\bar{x} = \dfrac{5 + 7 + 7 + 8 + 10 + 11}{6} = 8.$

	STEP 1 $\bar{x}$	STEP 2 $x - \bar{x}$	STEP 3 $(x - \bar{x})^2$
5	8	−3	9
7	8	−1	1
7	8	−1	1
8	8	0	0
10	8	2	4
11	8	3	9

Step 4: $\dfrac{9 + 1 + 1 + 0 + 4 + 9}{6} = 4$, the variance.   ▪

● DEFINITION

Standard Deviation

The **standard deviation** is the square root of the variance.

Example 10.7   Find the standard deviation for the data in Example 10.6.

Solution The standard deviation is the square root of the variance, 4. Hence the standard deviation is 2.   ▪

In general, the greater the standard deviation, the more the scores are spread out.

Spotlight on Technology Finding the standard deviation for a collection of data is a straightforward task when using a calculator that possesses the appropriate statistical keys. Usually, a calculator must be set in its statistics or standard deviation mode. Then, after the data are entered one at a time, the mean and standard deviation can be found simply by pressing appropriate keys. For example, assuming that the calculator is in its statistics mode, enter the data 3, 4, 7, 8, 9 using the $\boxed{\Sigma+}$ key as follows:

$$3 \; \boxed{\Sigma+} \; 4 \; \boxed{\Sigma+} \; 7 \; \boxed{\Sigma+} \; 8 \; \boxed{\Sigma+} \; 9 \; \boxed{\Sigma+}$$

Pressing the $\boxed{n}$ key yields the number 5, which is the number of data entered. Pressing $\boxed{\bar{x}}$ yields 6.2, the mean of our data. Pressing $\boxed{\sigma_n}$ yields 2.315167381, the standard deviation. Squaring this result yields the variance, 5.36.

NOTE: When the key representing standard deviation is pressed in the preceding example, a number greater than 2.315167381 appears on some calculators. This difference is due to two different interpretations of standard deviation. If *all n* of the data for some experiment are used in calculating the standard deviation, then $\boxed{\sigma_n}$ is the correct choice. However, if only *n* pieces of data from a large collection of numbers (more than *n*) are used, the variance is calculated with an $n-1$ in the denominator. Some calculators have a $\boxed{\sigma_{n-1}}$ key to distinguish this case. Computing the standard deviation on the TI-34 II is identical to computing the mean described earlier in this section except in the final step we select *Sx* or *σx*.

www.wiley.com/
college/musser

Spotlight on Technology When computing the standard deviation of a set of data, changing one number can dramatically impact the standard deviation. To see how this occurs, a spreadsheet can be constructed that does all of the computation for each set of data. Refer to the dynamic spreadsheet, *Standard Deviation*, in the spreadsheet webmodule to work with. Using this spreadsheet, find two sets of data where the standard deviation of one set is twice the standard deviation of the other. What process did you use to find these sets of data?

Let us return to our comparison of the two fifth-grade classes on their reading test. Table 10.13 gives the variance and standard deviation for each class, rounded to two decimal places.

Table 10.13

CLASS	VARIANCE	STANDARD DEVIATION
1	0.29	0.54
2	1.67	1.29

Comparing the classes on the basis of the standard deviation shows that the scores in class 2 were more widely distributed than were the scores in class 1, since the greater the standard deviation, the larger the spread of scores. Hence class 2 is more heterogeneous in reading ability than is class 1. This finding may mean that more reading groups are needed in class 2 than in class 1 if students are grouped by ability. Although it is difficult to give a general rule of thumb about interpreting the standard deviation, it does allow us to compare several sets of data to see which set is more homogeneous. In summary, comparing the two classes on the basis of the mean scores, the classes performed equivalently on the reading. However, on the basis of the standard deviation, class 2 is more heterogeneous than class 1.

In addition to obtaining information about the entire class, we can use the mean and standard deviation to compare an individual student's performances on different tests relative to the class as a whole. Example 10.8 illustrates how we might do this.

Example 10.8   Adrienne made the following scores on two achievement tests. On which test did she perform better relative to the class?

	TEST 1	TEST 2
Adrienne	45	40
Mean	30	25
Standard deviation	10	15

Solution Comparing Adrienne's scores only to the means seems to suggest that she performed equally well on both tests, since her score is 15 points higher than the mean

in each case. However, using the standard deviation as a unit of distance, we see that she was 1.5 (15 divided by 10) standard deviations above the mean on test 1 and only 1 (15 divided by 15) standard deviation above the mean on test 2. Hence she performed better on test 1, relative to the whole class. ■

We are able to make comparisons as in Example 10.8 more easily if we use z-scores.

DEFINITION

z-score

The **z-score**, z, for a particular score, x, is $z = \dfrac{x - \bar{x}}{s}$,

where $\bar{x}$ is the mean of all the scores and s is the standard deviation.

The z-score of a number indicates how many standard deviations the number is away from the mean. Numbers above the mean have positive z-scores, and numbers below the mean have negative z-scores.

Example 10.9 Compute Adrienne's z-score for tests 1 and 2 in Example 10.8.

Solution For test 1, her z-score is $\dfrac{45 - 30}{10} = 1.5$, and for test 2, her z-score is $\dfrac{40 - 25}{15} = 1$. ■

Notice that Adrienne's z-score tells us how far her score was above the mean, measured in multiples of the standard deviation. Example 10.10 illustrates several other features of z-scores.

Example 10.10 Find the z-scores for the data 1, 1, 2, 3, 4, 9, 12, 18.

Solution We first find the mean, $\bar{x}$, and the standard deviation, s.

$$\bar{x} = \frac{1 + 1 + 2 + 3 + 4 + 9 + 12 + 18}{8} = \frac{50}{8} = 6.25$$

$$s = 5.78 \text{ to two places (verify)}$$

Hence we can find the z-scores for each number in the set of data (Table 10.14). ■

Table 10.14

SCORE	z-SCORE
1	$\dfrac{1 - 6.25}{5.78} = -0.91$
2	$\dfrac{2 - 6.25}{5.78} = -0.74$
3	$\dfrac{3 - 6.25}{5.78} = -0.56$
4	$\dfrac{4 - 6.25}{5.78} = -0.39$
9	$\dfrac{9 - 6.25}{5.78} = 0.48$
12	$\dfrac{12 - 6.25}{5.78} = 0.99$
18	$\dfrac{18 - 6.25}{5.78} = 2.03$

The computations in Table 10.14 suggest the following observations.

CASE 1: If $x > \bar{x}$, then $x - \bar{x} > 0$, so $z = \dfrac{x - \bar{x}}{s} > 0$.

Conclusion: x is greater than the mean if and only if the z-score of x is positive.

CASE 2: If $x = \bar{x}$, then $z = \dfrac{x - \bar{x}}{s} = \dfrac{\bar{x} - \bar{x}}{s} = 0$.

Conclusion: The z-score of the mean is 0.

CASE 3: If $x < \bar{x}$, then $x - \bar{x} < 0$, so $z = \dfrac{x - \bar{x}}{s} < 0$.

Conclusion: x is less than the mean if and only if the z-score of x is negative.

We will use z-scores to provide even more defined information later in this section.

Distributions

Large amounts of data are commonly organized in increasing order and pictured in relative frequency form in a histogram. The **relative frequency** that a number occurs is the percentage of the total amount of data that the number represents. For example, in a collection of 100 numbers, if the number 14 appears 6 times, the relative frequency of 14 is 6%. A graph of the data versus the relative frequency of each number in the data is called a **distribution.** Two hypothetical distributions are discussed in Example 10.11.

Example 10.11   For the data in Figures 10.25 and 10.26, identify the mode and describe any observable symmetry of the data.

Solution The distribution in Figure 10.25 has two modes, 34 and 36 kilograms. The modes are indicated by the "peaks" of the histogram. The distribution is also symmetrical, since there is a vertical line that would serve as a "mirror" line of symmetry, namely a line through 35 on the horizontal axis. The distribution in Figure 10.26 has only one mode (4 hours) and is not symmetrical.

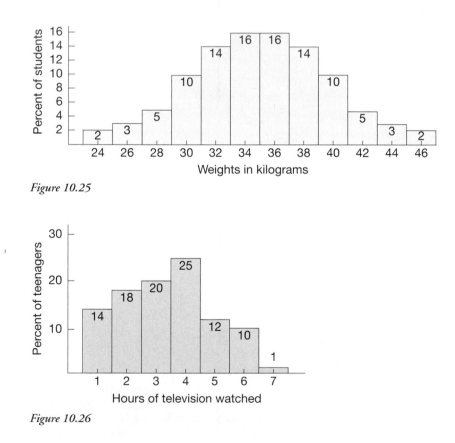

Figure 10.25

Figure 10.26   ■

In Figure 10.25 students' weights were rounded to the nearest 2 kilograms, producing 12 possible values from 24 to 46. Suppose, instead, that very accurate weights were obtained for the students, say to the nearest gram (one one-thousandth of a kilogram). Suppose, also, that a smooth curve was used to connect the midpoints of the "steps" of the histogram. One possibility is shown in Figure 10.27. The curve shows a symmetrical "bell-shaped" distribution with one mode.

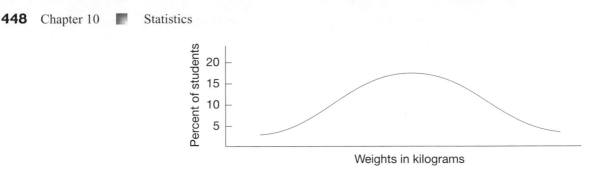

Figure 10.27

Distributions of physical measurements such as heights and weights for one sex, for large groups of data, frequently are smooth bell-shaped curves, such as the curve in Figure 10.27. There is a geometrical, or visual, way to interpret the median, mean, and mode for such smooth distributions. The vertical line through the median cuts the region between the curve and the horizontal axis into two regions of equal area (Figure 10.28). (NOTE: This characterization of the median does not always hold for histograms because they are not "smooth.")

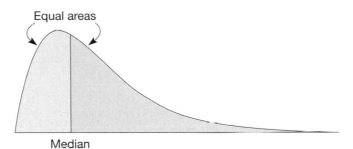

Figure 10.28

The mean is the point on the horizontal axis where the distribution would balance (Figure 10.29). This characterization of the mean holds for all distributions, histograms as well as smooth curves. Since the mode is the most frequently occurring value of the data, the highest point or points of the graph occur above the mode(s).

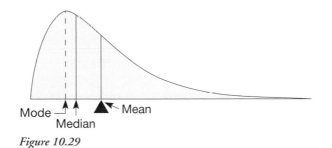

Figure 10.29

A special type of smooth, bell-shaped distribution is the **normal distribution.** The normal distribution is symmetrical, with the mean, median, and mode all being equal. Figure 10.30 shows the general shape of the normal distribution. (The technical definition of the normal distribution is more complicated than we can go into here.) An interesting feature of the normal distribution is that it is completely determined by the mean, $\bar{x}$, and the standard deviation, s. The "peak" is always directly above the mean. The standard deviation determines the shape, in the following way. The larger the standard deviation, the lower and flatter is the curve. That is, if two normal distributions are represented using the same horizontal and vertical scales, the one with the larger standard deviation will be lower and flatter (Figure 10.31).

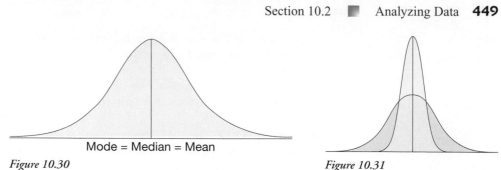

Mode = Median = Mean

Figure 10.30

Figure 10.31

The distribution of the weights in Figure 10.25 is essentially normal, so we could determine everything about the curve from the mean and the standard deviation as follows:

1. About 68% of the data are between $\bar{x} - s$ and $\bar{x} + s$.
2. About 95% of the data are between $\bar{x} - 2s$ and $\bar{x} + 2s$.
3. About 99.7% of the data are between $\bar{x} - 3s$ and $\bar{x} + 3s$ (Figure 10.32).

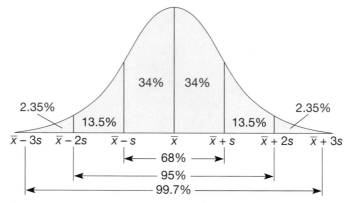

Figure 10.32

We can picture our results about z-scores for normal distributions in Figure 10.33. From Figures 10.32 and 10.33, we see the following:

1. About 68% of the scores are within one z-score of the mean.
2. About 95% of the scores are within two z-scores of the mean.
3. About 99.7% of the scores are within three z-scores of the mean.

z-scores of 2 or more in a normal distribution are very high (higher than 97.5% of all other scores—50% below the mean plus 47.5% up to $z = 2$). Also, z-scores of 3 or more are extremely high. On the other hand, z-scores of -2 or less from a normal distribution are lower than 97.5% of all scores.

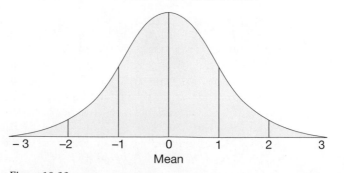

Figure 10.33

A z-score of 2 in a normal distribution is very high; in fact, it is about the 97.5 percentile. By comparing the graphs in Figures 10.32 and 10.33, it can be seen that a z-score of 2 is above 97.5% of the scores. On the other hand, a z-score of -1 is between the 15th and 16th percentiles. Now that we see this connection between z-scores and percentile, we could compute what percentile a score on the SAT would be in.

Example 10.12 In 1998, the mean and standard deviation for the math portion of the SAT were 512 and 112 respectively. If Quinn scored 686 on the math portion, what percentile was he in?

Solution Since Quinn scored a 686, his z-score would be computed using the mean of 512 and standard deviation of 112 for that year. This would give him a z-score of

$$z = \frac{686 - 512}{112} \approx 1.55357.$$

We can now refer to the percentiles and z-scores in Table 10.15 to see that Quinn's score on the math SAT in 1998 was about the 94th percentile and, therefore, it was higher than 94% of the other scores.

Table 10.15

PERCENTILE	z-SCORE	PERCENTILE	z-SCORE	PERCENTILE	z-SCORE
1	−2.326	34	−0.412	67	0.44
2	−2.054	35	−0.385	68	0.468
3	−1.881	36	−0.358	69	0.496
4	−1.751	37	−0.332	70	0.524
5	−1.645	38	−0.305	71	0.553
6	−1.555	39	−0.279	72	0.583
7	−1.476	40	−0.253	73	0.613
8	−1.405	41	−0.228	74	0.643
9	−1.341	42	−0.202	75	0.674
10	−1.282	43	−0.176	76	0.706
11	−1.227	44	−0.151	77	0.739
12	1.175	45	−0.126	78	0.772
13	−1.126	46	−0.1	79	0.806
14	−1.08	47	−0.075	80	0.842
15	−1.036	48	−0.05	81	0.878
16	−0.994	49	−0.025	82	0.915
17	−0.954	50	0	83	0.954
18	−0.915	51	0.025	84	0.994
19	−0.878	52	0.05	85	1.036
20	−0.842	53	0.075	86	1.08
21	−0.806	54	0.1	87	1.126
22	−0.772	55	0.126	88	1.175
23	−0.739	56	0.151	89	1.227
24	−0.706	57	0.176	90	1.282
25	−0.674	58	0.202	91	1.341
26	−0.643	59	0.228	92	1.405
27	−0.613	60	0.253	93	1.476
28	−0.583	61	0.279	94	1.555
29	−0.553	62	0.305	95	1.645
30	−0.524	63	0.332	96	1.751
31	−0.496	64	0.358	97	1.881
32	−0.468	65	0.385	98	2.054
33	−0.44	66	0.412	99	2.326

Tabulated values of z-scores for a normal distribution can be used to explain the relatively unlikely occurrence of outliers. For example, for data from a normal distribution, small outliers have z-scores less than -2.6 and are smaller than 99.5% of the data. Similarly, large outliers from a normal distribution have z-scores greater than 2.6 and are larger than 99.5% of the data. Thus outliers represent very rare observations. The normal distribution is a very commonly occurring distribution for many large collections of data. Hence the mean, standard deviation, and z-scores are especially important statistics.

MATHEMATICAL MORSEL

Did it rain a lot or didn't it? Sometimes the answer to that question depends on how you want to measure it. For example, during October 1994 in Portland, Oregon, the most commonly occurring daily precipitation total (the mode) was 0 inches. In the same month the median daily precipitation total was 0 inches. These measures would seem to indicate that it was a dry month. But was it? The mean daily precipitation in October of 1994 was 0.27 inches. By most standards, this measure would indicate that it did rain a lot. How could this happen? How could two measures say it was dry and another measure indicate that it was wet? Here's how. On 21 of the days in that October, there was no measurable rain and yet on three of the 10 days that it did rain, it rained 2.33, 2.44, and 2.44 inches.

OCTOBER 1994

DAY OF MONTH	1	2	3	4	5	6	7	8	9	10	
DAILY PRECIPITATION	0	0	0	0	0	0	0	0	0	0	
DAY OF MONTH	11	12	13	14	15	16	17	18	19	20	
DAILY PRECIPITATION	0	0	.12	.13	0	0	T	0	T	.03	
DAY OF MONTH	21	22	23	24	25	26	27	28	29	30	31
DAILY PRECIPITATION	.13	0	T	0	.09	2.33	2.44	.24	0	.46	2.44

Section 10.2   EXERCISE / PROBLEM SET A

EXERCISES

1. Calculate the mean, median, and mode for each collection of data.

  a. 8, 9, 9, 10, 11, 12

  b. 17, 2, 10, 29, 14, 13

  c. 4.2, 3.8, 9.7, -4.8, 0, -10.0

  d. 29, 42, -65, -73, 48, 17, 0, 0, -36

2. Calculate the mean, median, and mode for each collection of data.

  a. 1, 2, 3, 4, 5, 5

  b. 2, 4, 6, 8, 10

  c. 12, 14, 10, 9, 7, 13, 16, 19, 15, 10, 2

  d. -20, 9, 5, -8, 5, -1, 0

3. Scores for Mrs. McClellan's class on mathematics and reading tests are given in the following table. Which student is the "average" student for the group?

STUDENT	MATHEMATICS TEST SCORE	READING TEST SCORE
Rob	73	87
Doug	83	58
Myron	62	90
Alan	89	70
Ed	96	98

4. All the students in a school were weighed. Their average weight was 31.4 kilograms, and their total weight was 18,337.6 kilograms. How many students are in the school?

5. Which of the following situations are possible regarding the mean, median, and mode for a set of data? Give examples.

   a. Mean = median = mode

   b. Mean < median = mode

6. Make a box and whisker plot for the following heights of children, in centimeters.

   120,   121,   121,   124,   126,   128,   132,
   134,   140,   142,   147,   150,   152,   160

7. a.   Make box and whisker plots on the same number line for the following test scores.

   Class 1: 57,   58,   59,   60,   62,   72,   75,
              76,   76,   79,   80,   80,   81,   86,
              86,   86,   87,   93,   93,   93
   Class 2: 66,   67,   68,   75,   77,   77,   79,
              82,   83,   84,   85,   85,   87,   87,
              90,   90,   92,   92,   92,   95

   b. Which class performed better on the test? Explain.

8. Compute the variance and standard deviation for each collection of data.

   a. 4, 4, 4, 4, 4

   b. −4, −3, −2, −1, 0, 1, 2, 3, 4

   c. 14.6, −18.7, 29.3, 15.4, −17.5

9. Compute the variance and standard deviation for each collection of data. What do you observe?

   a. 1, 2, 3, 4, 5

   b. 3, 6, 9, 12, 15

   c. 5, 10, 15, 20, 25

   d. −6, −12, −18, −24, −30

   e. Use the spreadsheet, *Standard Deviation*, from the spreadsheet webmodule to find the standard deviation for the sets of data 3, 8, 13, 18, 23 and 31, 36, 41, 46, 51. Describe how the data and results in part (c) compare to these sets of data and their standard deviations.

10. Compute the mean, median, mode, variance, and standard deviation for the distribution represented by this histogram.

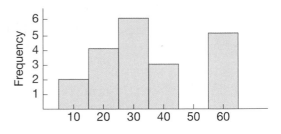

11. Compute the z-scores for the following test scores.

STUDENT	SCORE	STUDENT	SCORE
Larry	59	Lou	62
Curly	43	Jerry	65
Moe	71	Dean	75
Bud	89		

12. Given in the table are projected changes in the U.S. population for the period 1986–2010. For example, the population of Alaska is expected to increase 38.7%. Make a box and whisker plot for states east of the Mississippi River (in boldface) and beneath it a box and whisker plot for states west of the Mississippi River. What trends, if any, do your box and whisker plots reveal?

Projected Population Changes (1986–2010)

STATE	PERCENT CHANGE	STATE	PERCENT CHANGE	STATE	PERCENT CHANGE
AK	38.7	LA	1.0	**OH**	−3.3
AL	13.2	**MA**	7.1	OK	6.2
AR	10.3	**MD**	25.2	OR	10.5
AZ	51.4	**ME**	11.1	**PA**	−6.4
CA	34.4	**MI**	−0.6	**RI**	10.9
CO	23.6	MN	8.4	**SC**	22.9
CT	10.4	MO	8.6	SD	1.9
DE	23.3	**MS**	14.6	**TN**	13.8
FL	43.8	MT	−3.1	TX	30.3
GA	42.3	**NC**	26.5	UT	27.8
HI	41.2	ND	−10.4	**VA**	25.9
IA	−17.4	NE	−4.3	**VT**	12.0
ID	7.4	**NH**	37.5	WA	17.4
IL	−0.5	**NJ**	16.0	**WI**	−4.1
IN	−1.8	NM	45.0	**WV**	−16.5
KS	4.2	NV	46.7	WY	−4.1
KY	−0.5	**NY**	2.1		

Source: U.S. Bureau of the Census.

13. Twenty-seven major league baseball players have hit more than 400 home runs in their careers as of 1998.

PLAYER	HOME RUNS
Hank Aaron	755
Babe Ruth	714
Willie Mays	660
Frank Robinson	586
Harmon Killebrew	573
Reggie Jackson	563
Mike Schmidt	548
Mickey Mantle	536
Jimmie Foxx	534
Willie McCovey	521
Ted Williams	521
Ernie Banks	512
Eddie Mathews	512
Mel Ott	511
Eddie Murray	504
Lou Gehrig	493
Stan Musial	475
Willie Stargell	475
Dave Winfield	465
Mark McGwire	457
Carl Yastrzemski	452
Dave Kingman	442
Andre Dawson	438
Billy Williams	426
Darrell Evans	414
Barry Bonds	411
Duke Snider	407

Source: The Baseball Encyclopedia.

a. Make a stem and leaf plot and a box and whisker plot of the data.

b. Outliers between 1.5 and 3.0 IQR are called **mild outliers,** and those greater than 3.0 IQR are called **extreme outliers.** What outliers, mild or extreme, occur?

14. a. What percentile is the median score?

b. In a normal distribution, what percentile has a z-score of 1? 2? -1? -2?

15. On the verbal portion of the SAT in 1998 the mean was 505 and the standard deviation was 111. If Marcella had a score of 630 on the exam, what percent of all of the students who took the exam had a score lower than hers?

16. Vince's 1998 ACT reading score was below 33% of all of the scores. If the mean and standard deviation for all ACT reading scores in 1998 were 21.3 and 6.1 respectively, what was Vince's score?

17. If the average (mean) mid-twenties male weighs 169 pounds and a weight of 150 is in the 31st percentile, what is the standard deviation of the weights in this age group?

PROBLEMS

18. The class average on a reading test was 27.5 out of 40 possible points. The 19 girls in the class scored 532 points. How many total points did the 11 boys score?

19. When 100 students took a test, the average score was 77.1. Two more students took the test. The sum of their scores was 125. What is the new average?

20. The mean score for a set of 35 mathematics tests was 41.6, with a standard deviation of 4.2. What was the sum of all the scores?

21. Here are Mr. Emery's class scores for two tests. On which test did Lora do better relative to the entire class?

STUDENT	TEST 1 SCORE	TEST 2 SCORE
Lora	85	89
Verne	72	93
Harvey	89	96
Lorna	75	65
Jim	79	79
Betty	86	60

22. At a shoe store, which statistic would be most helpful to the manager when reordering shoes: mean, median, or mode? Explain.

23. a. On the same axes, draw a graph of two normal distributions with the same means but different variances. Which graph has a higher "peak"?

b. On the same axes, draw a graph of two normal distributions with different means but equal variances. Which graph is farther to the right?

24. Reading test scores for Smithville had an average of 69.2. Nationally, the average was 60.3 with a standard deviation of 7.82. In Miss Brown's class, the average was 75.9.

a. What is the z-score for Smithville's average score?

b. What is the z-score for Miss Brown's class average?

c. Assume that the distribution of all scores was a normal distribution. Approximately what percent of students in the country scored lower than Miss Brown's average?

25. A dirt biker must circle a 5-mile track twice. His average speed must be 60 mph. On his first lap, he averaged 30 mph. How fast must he travel on his second lap in order to qualify?

26. A $3 \times 3 \times 3$ cube was painted on all faces, then cut apart into 27 little $1 \times 1 \times 1$ cubes.

a. How many $1 \times 1 \times 1$ cubes had no faces painted? one face painted? two faces painted? three faces painted? four or more faces painted?

b. Answer the same questions for a $4 \times 4 \times 4$ and a $5 \times 5 \times 5$ cube.

c. Answer the same questions for an $n \times n \times n$ cube, where n is any whole number greater than 1.

Section 10.2 EXERCISE / PROBLEM SET B

EXERCISES

1. Calculate the mean, median, and mode for each collection of data. Give exact answers.

a. $-10, -9, -8, -7, 0, 0, 7, 8, 9, 10$

b. $-5, -3, -1, 0, 3, 6$

c. $-6.5, -6.3, -6.1, 6.0, 6.3, 6.6$

d. $3 + \sqrt{2}, 4 + \sqrt{2}, 5 + \sqrt{2}, 6 + \sqrt{2}, 7 + \sqrt{2}$

2. Calculate the mean, median, and mode for each collection of data. Give exact answers.

a. $\sqrt{2}, 3\sqrt{2}, -8\sqrt{2}, 4\sqrt{2}, 3\sqrt{2}, 0$

b. $-2\pi, 4\pi, 0, 6\pi, 10\pi, 4\pi$

c. $-3 + \pi, -8 + \pi, -15 + \pi, \pi, 4 + \pi, 4 + \pi, 18 + \pi$

d. $\sqrt{2} + \pi, 2\sqrt{2} + \pi, \pi, -3\sqrt{2} + \pi, \sqrt{3} + \pi, \sqrt{3} + \pi$

3. Jamie made the following grades during fall term at State University. What was his grade point average? (A = 4 points, B = 3 points, C = 2, D = 1, F = 0.)

COURSE	CREDITS	GRADE
English	2	B
Chemistry	3	C
Mathematics	4	A
History	3	B
French	3	C

4. Twenty-seven students averaged 70 on their midterm. Could 21 of them have scored above 90? Explain.

5. Which of the following situations are possible regarding the mean, median, and mode for a set of data? Give examples.

a. Mean < median < mode

b. Mean = median < mode

6. a. From the box and whisker plot for 80 test scores, find the lowest score, the highest score, the lower quartile, the upper quartile, and the median.

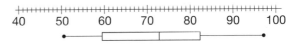

b. Approximately how many scores are between the lowest score and the lower quartile? between the lower quartile and the upper quartile? between the lower quartile and the highest score?

7. a. Consider the following double stem and leaf plot (Table 10.5).

CLASS 1		CLASS 2
9 6	0	5 7
8 7 6 4 1	1	2 3 4
8 8 7 6 5 5 3 2 2 2 2 2 1	2	2 5 6 7 8 8 9
9 9 6 4 4 3 2	3	1 2 3 4 4 5 6 7
9 6 5 1	4	2 3 5 6 7 8 9

Construct a box and whisker plot for each class on the same number line for the test scores.

b. Which class performed better? Explain.

c. From the following box and whisker plots, which class performed the best? Explain.

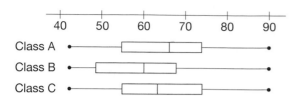

8. Compute the variance and standard deviation for each collection of data.

a. 5, 5, 5, 5, 5, 5, 5

b. 8.7, 3.8, 9.2, 14.7, 26.3

c. 1, 3, 5, 7, 9, 11

d. $-13.8, -12.3, -9.7, -15.4, -19.7$

9. Use the spreadsheet, *Standard Deviation*, from the spreadsheet webmodule to compute the standard deviations described below.

a. Compute the variance and standard deviation for the data 2, 4, 6, 8, and 10.

b. Add 0.7 to each element of the data in part (a) and compute the variance and standard deviation.

c. Subtract 0.5 from each data value in part (a) and compute the variance and standard deviation.

d. Given that the variance and standard deviation of the set of data a, b, c, and d is 16 and 4, respectively, what are the variance and standard deviation of the set $a + x$, $b + x$, $c + x$, $d + x$, where x is any real number?

10. Compute the mean, median, mode, variance, and standard deviation for the data in the following table.

NUMBER	FREQUENCY
15	2
18	3
19	4
20	1

11. Compute the z-scores for the following data.

8, 10, 4, 3, 6, 9, 2, 1, 15, 20

12. Given in the table are school expenditures per student by state in 1997.

School Expenditures, 1997 (×100)

STATE	EXPENDITURES PER STUDENT	STATE	EXPENDITURES PER STUDENT
AL	55	MT	60
AK	104	NE	56
AZ	48	NV	54
AR	45	NH	66
CA	53	NJ	103
CO	56	NM	55
CT	88	NT	96
DE	81	NC	56
DC	82	ND	50
FL	60	OH	61
GA	65	OK	45
HI	61	OR	66
ID	48	PA	77
IL	60	RI	80
IN	64	SC	54
IA	55	SD	50
KS	66	TN	53
KY	60	TX	60
LA	61	UT	38
ME	68	VT	76
MD	71	VA	64
MA	76	WA	61
MI	73	WV	68
MN	65	WI	70
MS	44	WY	65
MO	54		

Source: National Education Association.

a. Make a stem and leaf plot of the data, using one-digit stems.

b. What gaps or clusters occur?

c. Which, if any, data values are outliers (using IQR units)? What explanation is there for the occurrence of outliers in these data?

d. Make a box and whisker plot for states east of the Mississippi River (see Exercise 12 in Part A), and beneath it a box and whisker plot for states west of the Mississippi River. What trends, if any, do your box and whisker plots reveal?

13. Twenty baseball pitchers have won 300 or more games in their careers, as of 1998.

PITCHER	VICTORIES	PITCHER	VICTORIES
Cy Young	511	John Clarkson	326
Walter Johnson	416	Don Sutton	324
Grover Alexander	373	Nolan Ryan	324
Christy Mathewson	373	Phil Niekro	318
Warren Spahn	363	Gaylord Perry	314
James Galvin	361	Tom Seaver	311
Charles Nichols	361	Charles Radbourne	311
Tim Keefe	342	Mickey Welch	308
Steve Carlton	329	"Lefty" Grove	300
Eddie Plank	327	Early Wynn	300

Source: The Baseball Encyclopedia.

   a. Make a stem and leaf plot and a box and whisker plot of the data.

   b. What outliers, mild or extreme, occur?

14. Assume a certain distribution with mean 65 and standard deviation 10. Find the 50th percentile score. Find the 16th percentile and the 84th percentile scores.

15. Sabino took the ACT in 1997 and received a composite score of 22. If the mean and standard deviation for that year were, respectively, 21.0 and 4.7, what percent of all of the students who took the exam scored better than him?

16. Dorian's score of 572 on the verbal portion of the 1996 SAT exam placed him in the 73rd percentile. If the mean on this exam was 505, what was the standard deviation?

17. Using the information from Part A, Exercise 17, determine what percent of the males age 20–29 weigh less than 200 pounds.

PROBLEMS

18. The average height of a class of students is 134.7 cm. The sum of all the heights is 3771.6 cm. There are 17 boys in the class. How many girls are in the class?

19. The average score on a reading test for 58 students was 87.3. Twelve more students took the test. The average of the 12 students was 90.7. What was the average for all students?

20. Suppose that the variance for a set of data is zero. What can you say about the data?

21. a. Give two sets of data with the same means but different variances.

   b. Give two sets of data with the same variances but different means.

22. Amy's z-score on her reading test was 1.27. The class average was 60, the median was 58.5, and the variance was 6.2. What was Amy's "raw" score (i.e., her score before converting to z-scores)?

23. a. Can two different numbers in a distribution have the same z-score?

   b. Can all of the z-scores for a distribution be equal?

24. a. For the distribution given here by the histogram, find the median according to the following definition: The median is the number through which a vertical line divides the area under the graph into two equal areas. (Recall that the area of a rectangle is the product of the length of the base and the height.)

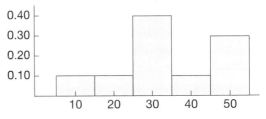

   b. Find the median according to the definition in Section 10.1. Are the two "medians" equal?

25. The **unbiased standard deviation,** s_{n-1}, is computed in exactly the same way as the standard deviation, s, except that instead of dividing by n, we divide by $n - 1$. That is, s_{n-1} is equal to

$$\sqrt{\frac{(x_1 - x)^2 + (x_2 - x)^2 + \cdots + (x_n - x)^2}{n - 1}}$$

where $x_1, \ldots, x_n$ are the data and $\bar{x}$ is the mean. The unbiased standard deviation of a sample is a better estimate of the true standard deviation for a normal distribution.

   a. Compute s_{n-1} and s for the following data: 1, 2, 3, 4, 5.

   b. True or false? $s_{n-1} \geq s$ for all sets of data. Explain.

26. Amy deposited $1000 in the bank at 8% annual interest. If she leaves her money on deposit for 10 years, how much will she have at the end of 10 years?

27. Prove or disprove: If a three-digit number whose digits are all the same is divided by the sum of its digits, the result is 37.

PROBLEMS FOR WRITING/DISCUSSION

1. Spike looks at the data 5, 6, 7, 5, 8, 8, 9, 4, 9 and tells you that the median is 8. Do you agree? If not, how can you explain his misconception?

2. Chris gathered data about how tall the students were in grades 3, 4, and 5 in her school. She made a stem and leaf chart for each grade level and found that in each grade there was a cluster that occurred in the forties (inches). She decided that fourth, fifth, and sixth graders in her school were all about the same height. What would you say to Chris?

3. Over the summer the third-grade classroom was painted lavender. Amber took a poll of her third-grade classmates in September to see how they liked the new color. They were asked to respond on a five-point scale with 1 meaning they really did not like the new color, 3 being neutral, and 5 meaning they really liked it. Amber announced the results as follows: The median was 5, but the mean was 3.9, so it seemed people were pretty neutral about it. How would you respond?

10.3   MISLEADING GRAPHS AND STATISTICS

STARTING POINT Mayor Marcus is running for a second term as mayor against the challenger, Councilwoman Claudia. One of the hot topics is crime prevention. Each of the graphs displays crime statistics for the four years of Mayor Marcus's current term. What are the differences between the two graphs? Depending on which candidate you are, which graph would you chose to make your point?

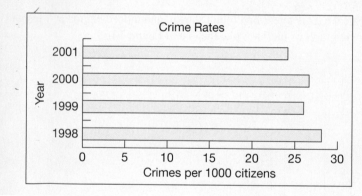

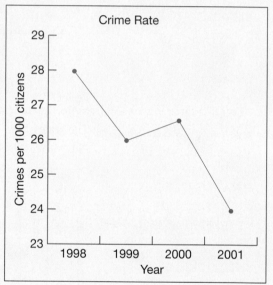

Reflection from Research
Graphing gives the child an opportunity to compare, count, add, subtract, sequence, and classify data. A tactile and visual representation of amounts facilitates children's understanding of comparative values (Choate & Okey, 1981).

Clearly presenting statistical data is a challenging task. When presenting quantitative information in a graphical form, determining what to emphasize from the data and how to construct the actual graphs must both be considered. If some aspect of the graph is distorted, a misleading graph can easily result. Distortion may be benign and unintentional, but at other times it is intentional with the purpose to deceive or misdirect the reader. In this section we will look at ways in which the elements of a graph can be manipulated to create different impressions of the data. We will also look at how sampling can affect the quality of the data.

First we consider variations on the basic kinds of graphs. We particularly wish to consider ways that the graph may subtly mislead so that you can determine when you are being misled. This knowledge can point out honest ways to put your viewpoint in the most favorable light. We will also consider graphs that have been enhanced with pictorial embellishments. These graphs are more interesting and can reinforce your message, but they also can be misleading. Finally, we will look at how data are gathered through sampling and how bias can be introduced by the size and type of samples used.

Scaling and Axis Manipulation

If someone wants the differences among the bars of a histogram or bar chart to look more dramatic, a chart is often displayed with part of the vertical axis missing. Puffed Oats, a children's cereal, is advertised as wholesome since it has less sugar than the other children's cereals even though it has 9 grams of sugar. The high-sugar-content cereals chosen to be compared to Puffed Oats had the following grams of sugar per serving: 15, 14, 13, 11. The bar graph in Figure 10.34 shows the grams of sugar in each variety of cereal.

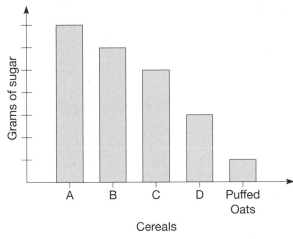

Figure 10.34

The scale of the vertical axis is intentionally not shown, and indeed begins at 8 instead of 0. A less misleading graph would look like the one in Figure 10.35

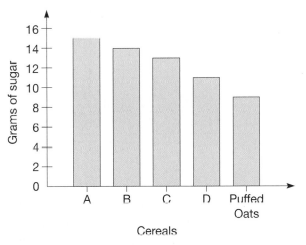

Figure 10.35

Notice that the Puffed Oats company did not choose to compare the sugar content of their cereal with either cornflakes (2 grams per serving) or shredded wheat (0 grams per serving).

Example 10.13 The prices of three brands of baked beans are as follows:

Brand X—79¢, Brand Y—89¢, Brand Z—99¢

Draw a bar graph so the Brand X looks like a much better buy than the other two brands.

Solution Brand X can be made to look much cheaper than the other two brands by starting the price scale at 75¢, as shown in Figure 10.36.

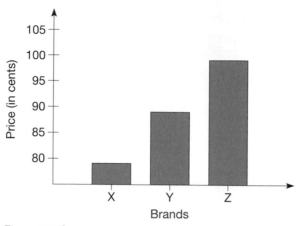

Figure 10.36

Notice that although the values from 0 to 75 have been left off the *y*-axis, there is no marking on the axis indicating the removal of these numbers, making it more difficult to notice the scaling of the vertical axis. ■

Another technique to distort the nature of some data is to reverse the axes and reverse the orientation of an axis. Figure 10.37 is a bar graph that shows declining profits of a company.

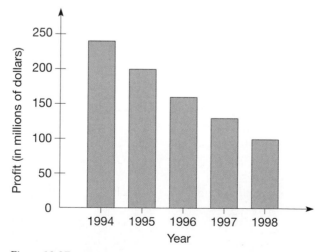

Figure 10.37

In Figure 10.38 the same data are displayed in a horizontal bar graph in which the years are in the reverse order.

The graph in Figure 10.38 displays the same information but has less of a negative connotation because it does not have the "feel" of a decreasing trend.

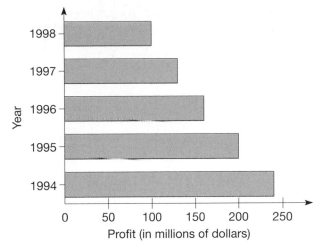

Figure 10.38

Table 10.16

YEAR	PERCENT OF THE LABOR FORCE THAT IS UNEMPLOYED
1992	7.5
1993	6.9
1994	6.1
1995	5.6
1996	5.4
1997	4.9
1998	4.5
1999	4.2
2000	4.0

Source: U.S. Bureau of Labor Statistics.

Example 10.14 The unemployment rates for the United States from 1992 to 2000 are displayed in Table 10.16.

If a political candidate wanted to mislead the voters into believing that the incumbent senator or member of Congress had not been successful in reducing the unemployment rate, how could he construct a bar graph to mislead readers intentionally?

Solution Since the categories along the *x*-axis of a bar graph do not necessarily need to be in any specific order, the years can be shown in reverse chronological order. By showing the years in decreasing order, the graph in Figure 10.39 can be used to lead citizens to think that the unemployment rate is increasing. This reverse trend is further accentuated by (i) starting the graph at 4.5, and (ii) making the graph narrow.

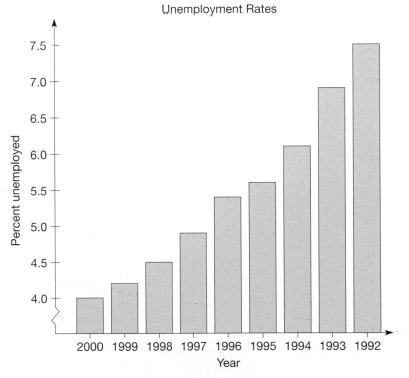

Figure 10.39 *Source*: U.S. Bureau of Labor Statistics.

Line Graphs and Cropping

What we have seen regarding bar graphs also applies to line graphs. Recall the data of average teacher salaries displayed in the line graph in Figure 10.7. That graph makes it appear as if the increase was fairly significant. Suppose, however, that the teachers' union wants to make a case for better teacher pay. This increase may be made less dramatic by extending the scale of the vertical axis and using larger increments, as in Figure 10.40.

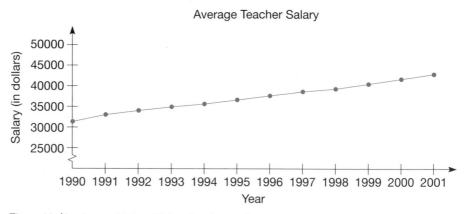

Figure 10.40   *Source*: National Education Association.

Example 10.15   Draw two line graphs of the unemployment data (see Table 10.16) from Example 10.14 that give different impressions of the situation.

Solution

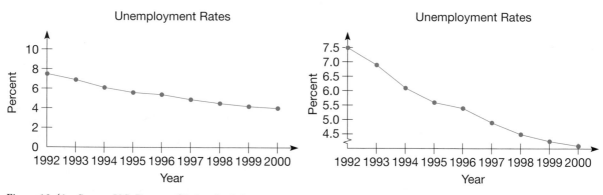

Figure 10.41   *Source*: U.S. Bureau of Labor Statistics.

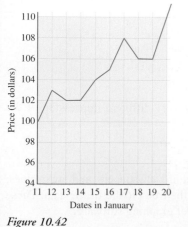

Figure 10.42

The graph on the left in Figure 10.41 suggests that the rate of unemployment is decreasing slowly, whereas the graph on the right gives the impression that unemployment is decreasing more rapidly. ■

Figure 10.42 shows the values of a stock from January 11 through January 20.

The stock appears to be a good buy because it is on an upward trend. Notice that the graph is rising above the edge of the vertical scale. Graphs that do this or even go to the edge of the scale make the trend appear more dramatic.

This kind of scale manipulation is part of a larger phenomenon called cropping. **Cropping** refers to the choice of the window that the graph uses to view the data. Suppose we wish to present the price of a certain company's stock. We may choose which time period and vertical axis to display. In other words, when we

show a picture we have to choose a window in which to frame it. Figure 10.43 shows the value of the stock over the previous five months; the stock price is plotted every 10 days.

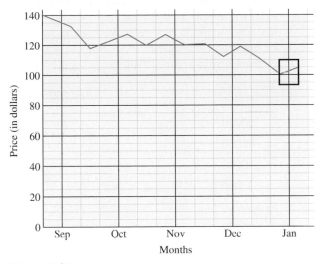

Figure 10.43

The data from Figure 10.42 are now contained in the box of Figure 10.43. Thus, this graph gives a very different perception regarding the value of the stock. This different perception is caused by the change in the vertical scale as well as the horizontal scale.

The downward trend in Figure 10.43 would be more apparent if we choose the vertical scale to be between 100 and 140. The data from Figure 10.43 are shown in Figure 10.44.

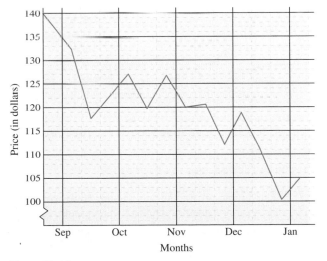

Figure 10.44

Notice how by changing the vertical axis, we get a very different impression of the price trend of the company's stock.

Three-Dimensional Effects

Three-dimensional effects, which are often found in newspapers and magazines, make a graph more attractive but can also obscure the true picture of the data. These graphs are difficult to draw unless you have computer graphing software.

The data for average teacher salary shown in Figure 10.40 are shown using a bar graph with three-dimensional effects in Figure 10.45.

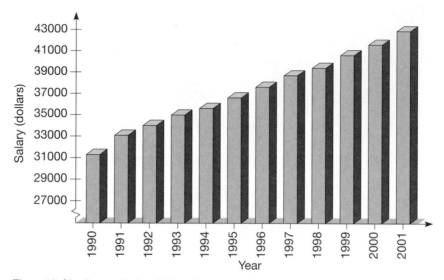

Figure 10.45   *Source*: National Education Association.

The perspective of the graph makes it difficult to see exact values. For example, the average salary in 1997 was $38,700, but to glance at the graph it could be estimated to be as much as $40,000.

Line charts with three-dimensional effects may also reduce the amount of visible information, as shown in Figure 10.46.

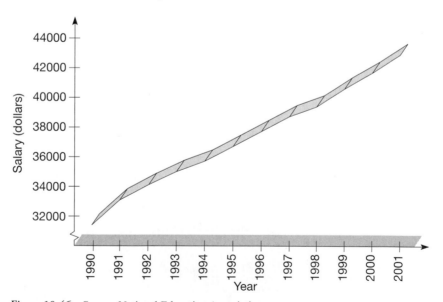

Figure 10.46   *Source*: National Education Association.

The upward trend is still apparent, but the exact values are very difficult to read. This is a graph of the same data as shown in Figures 10.45 and 10.40.

Objects, either two dimensional or three dimensional, that are used to represent quantities in pictographs can also be a point of deception. Consider the pictographs of milk cartons showing the increased consumption of skim milk from 1980 to 1995 [Figure 10.47(a)]

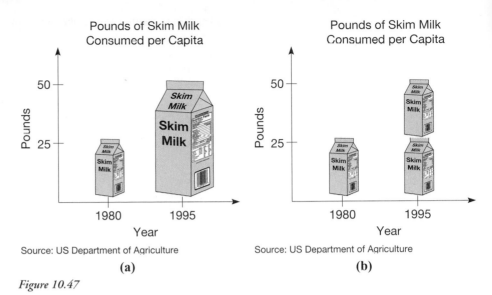

Figure 10.47

The amount of skim milk consumed per capita in 1995 (53.8 pounds per year) is twice as much as that consumed in 1980 (26.9 pounds per year). At first glance, it might seem appropriate to make one carton twice as tall as the other. However, looking at the pictures of the two cartons in Figure 10.47(a), we get the impression that the taller one is much more than twice the volume of the other. In addition to making the height of the larger twice the height of the smaller, the larger carton's width and depth have been doubled. Thus, the carton on the right in Figure 10.47(a) represents a volume that is $2 \times 2 \times 2 = 8$ times as large as the one on the left. The pictograph in Figure 10.47(b) shows how a 3-D pictograph could be constructed without deception.

Circle Graphs

Circle graphs allow for visual comparisons of the relative sizes of fractional parts. The graph in Figure 10.48 shows the relative sizes of the vitamin content in a serving of cornflakes and milk. Four vitamins are present—B_1, B_2, A, and C. We can conclude that most of the vitamin content is B_1 and B_2, that less vitamin A is present, and that the vitamin C content is the least. However, the graph is deceptive, in that it gives no indication whatsoever of the actual amount of these four vitamins, either by weight (say in grams) or by percentage of minimum daily requirement. Thus, although the

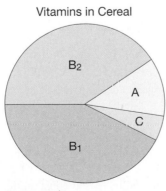

Figure 10.48

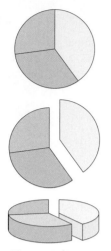

Figure 10.49

NCTM Standard
Draw inferences from charts, tables, and graphs that summarize data from real-world situations.

circle graph is excellent for picturing relative amounts, it does not necessarily indicate absolute amounts.

Circle graphs or pie charts can also be manipulated to reinforce a particular message or even to mislead. It is very common to take a sector of the "pie" and **explode** it (that is, move it slightly away from the center; Figure 10.49).

This gives the sector more emphasis and may make it seem larger than it is. Making it three-dimensional and exploding the sector makes the largest sector seem even larger still. The graph in Figure 10.50 is a good example of the dominant effect of the exploded sector representing the share of stocks owned by individuals.

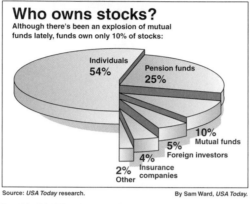

A look at statistics that shape your finances

Who owns stocks?
Although there's been an explosion of mutual funds lately, funds own only 10% of stocks:

Individuals 54%
Pension funds 25%
10% Mutual funds
5% Foreign investors
4% Insurance companies
2% Other

Source: *USA Today* research.   By Sam Ward, *USA Today.*

Copyright 1994, USA TODAY. Reprinted with permission.

Figure 10.50

A third way in which circle graphs can be deceptive is illustrated in the following example.

Example 10.16   Figure 10.51 shows what looks like a circle graph embedded in a picture of a hamburger. It conceals a misleading piece of distortion. Can you spot it?

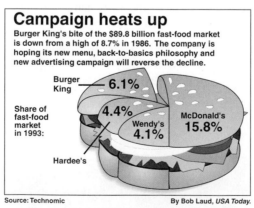

Campaign heats up
Burger King's bite of the $89.8 billion fast-food market is down from a high of 8.7% in 1986. The company is hoping its new menu, back-to-basics philosophy and new advertising campaign will reverse the decline.

Burger King 6.1%
4.4%
Wendy's 4.1%
McDonald's 15.8%

Share of fast-food market in 1993:

Hardee's

Source: Technomic   By Bob Laud, *USA Today.*

Copyright 1994, USA TODAY. Reprinted with permission.

Figure 10.51

Solution The percentages do not add up to 100%. There are only a total of 30.4%. The impression is given that McDonald's and the other chains have a much larger share of the market than they actually do. This graph also provides an example of a pictorial embellishment, which we will now discuss as another source of misleading graphs. ■

Deceptive Pictorial Embellishments

Pictorial embellishments in both two-dimensional and three-dimensional situations can also lead to confusion and be deceptive. Figure 10.52 displays a bar chart, embedded into a gasoline pump nozzle, which compares the price of gas in Tokyo, Japan; Caracas, Venezuela; and the average price in the United States.

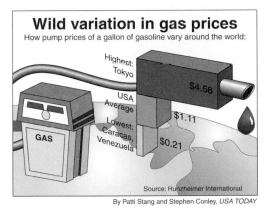

Copyright 1994, USA TODAY. Reprinted with permission.

Figure 10.52

The chart has a visual appeal but is drawn in a misleading way. The length of the bar corresponding to Tokyo is 1 inch in the original graph, which is to represent a price of $4.58 per gallon. Thus 1 inch of bar represents $4.58. The length of the bar for the United States was 1/4 inch in the original graph so that an inch represents only $1.11 × 4 = $4.44. The length for Caracas was 1/16 inch in the original graph, giving a scale of $0.21 × 16 = $3.36 per inch. These discrepancies, while slight, make the differences appear more pronounced.

Figure 10.53 gives a variation on a bar chart by curving the bars. The point of the graphic is that Barbie dolls may be considered to be as much ambassadors of the United States as the representatives of the government. Curving the bars makes them appear to be closer to the same length because the lower edge of the "U.S. embassies" bar is compared to the upper edge of the "Barbie doll sales" bar.

Source: Mattel Inc.   By Patti Stang and Elys A. McLean, *USA Today.*

Copyright 1993, USA TODAY. Reprinted with permission.

Figure 10.53

Example 10.17   The three-dimensional bar chart in Figure 10.54 compares the average size of a city in the National Football Conference with the average size of a city in the American Football Conference. What is misleading about it?

A look at statistics that shape the sports world

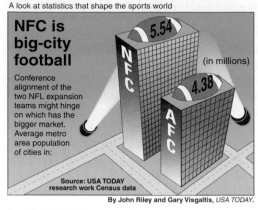

Copyright 1993, USA TODAY. Reprinted with permission.

Figure 10.54

Solution The population sizes are labeled at the top of the skyscrapers and the skyscrapers appear as bars in a bar chart. However, they are not drawn to scale. Since the NFC skyscraper is $1\frac{5}{16}$ inch tall in the original graph, a vertical inch represents 4.22 million people ($5.54/1\frac{5}{16} = 4.22$). However, a vertical inch on the AFC skyscraper in the original graph represents 5.19 million people since it is 27/32 inches tall [$4.38/(27/32) = 5.19$]. There is more deception afoot in this pictorial embellishment. The NFC building is wider than the AFC building, and the perspective gives the larger building a more imposing presence. ■

Any graph may be embedded in a picture to make it more eyecatching and provide emphasis so that you interpret the graph in a desired way. Figure 10.55 shows a line graph of the number of babies delivered by midwives. This shows a strong increasing trend.

A look at statistics that shape our lives

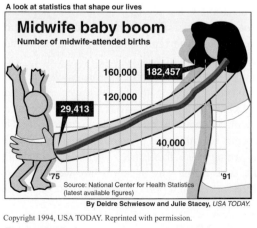

Copyright 1994, USA TODAY. Reprinted with permission.

Figure 10.55

By making the line of the graph the arm of the midwife, the eye is directed upward from the infant at the left of the graph up the arm to the midwife. This exaggerates the increasing nature of the graph.

NCTM Standards 2000
Data Analysis and
Probability
Grades 6–8
All students should use
observations about differences
between two or more samples
to make conjectures about the
populations from which the
samples were taken.

Samples and Bias

All of the examples of misleading statistics that we have looked at thus far have dealt with the way in which the data were presented. However, this assumes that the data were accurate to begin with, which may not be the case, depending on how the data were gathered. One of the most common uses of statistics is gathering and analyzing information about specific groups of people or objects. In the following, we will look at how this information is gathered and analyzed and how bias can enter this process.

As President William Jefferson Clinton was facing the possibility of impeachment during the summer and fall of 1998, one of the interesting controversies of the process was conflict between public opinion polls and the opinions of the members of the House of Representatives. A question that naturally arises regarding the public opinion polls is, "How is such information gathered?" Do the pollsters contact *every* voter in the United States? If they only contact a subset of the voters, how is that subset selected? Is the information collected from voters in the East or in the West, Republicans or Democrats, young voters or older voters? How all of these questions are addressed will determine the quality of the data collected.

The entire group in question is called the **population,** and the subset of the population that is actually observed, questioned, or analyzed is called a **sample.** If a sample is carefully chosen, we may assume that it is representative of the population and shares the main characteristics of the group. The results we obtain from the sample, such as means or percentages, can then be used as estimates for values we would find in the population. However, a great deal of care should be taken in selecting a sample.

Reflection from Research
Students need help as they
transition from understanding
the colloquial term, *sample*, as a
piece of cheese on a toothpick in
a supermarket to the statistical
meaning of *sample* where
variation and representation
are important (Watson &
Moritz, 2000).

Example 10.18   Suppose you wish to determine voter opinion regarding the ballot measure to fund the proposed new library. To determine this, you survey potential voters among the pedestrians on Main Street during the lunch hour. What is the population and what is the sample?

Solution The population consists of people who are going to vote in the upcoming election. The sample consists of those interviewed on the street who say they will be voting in the election.   ■

If a sample is not representative of the population, we will draw an erroneous conclusion. A **bias** is a flaw in the sampling procedure that makes it more likely that the sample will not be representative of the population. As an example, suppose a late-night news program wished to have a call-in telephone poll on a gun control issue with a 50-cent cost of participation. Such a telephone poll has many sources of bias. An important source is the fact that it takes an effort and some expense to participate. This means that people who have strong opinions about gun control and are willing to part with 50 cents are more likely to participate. Other sources of bias include the fact that there is nothing to prevent nonresidents from participating or to prevent people from voting more than once. There are other forms of bias that can also affect the result, such as the way questions are worded. In this section, we will discuss how to analyze surveys and polls and how to choose samples that are free of bias.

Example 10.19   Suppose you wish to determine voter opinion regarding the elimination of the capital gains tax (a profit made on an investment is called a capital gain). To determine this, you survey potential voters near Wall Street in New York City. Identify a source of bias in this poll.

Solution One source of bias in choosing this sample is that many people involved in trading stocks work on Wall Street and their income could be enhanced by the elimina-

tion of the capital gains tax. The percentage of people in this sample that favor elimination is likely to be much higher than that of the population as a whole. ∎

The population and sample need not always consist of people, as we see in the next example.

Example 10.20   To test the reliability of a lot (a unit of production) of automobile components produced at a certain factory, the first 30 components of a lot of 1000 are tested for defects. Describe the population, the sample, and any potential sources of bias.

Solution The population is the lot of 1000 automobile components that are produced at the factory. The sample is the set of the first 30 produced from the lot. Bias results from the fact that the first 30 are chosen. It is possible that these 30 were made with special care or that they were made at the start of the process when defects are more likely. ∎

A summary of the common errors that occur when surveys are conducted is provided in Table 10.17.

Table 10.17   Common Sources of Bias Surveys

TYPE OF ERROR	DESCRIPTION
Faulty sampling	The chosen sample is not representative.
Faulty questions	Questions worded so as to influence the answers.
Faulty interviewing	Failure to interview all of the chosen sample. Misreading the questions. Misinterpreting the answers.
Lack of understanding or knowledge	The person being interviewed does not understand what is being asked or does not have the information needed.
False answers	The person being interviewed intentionally gives incorrect information.

MATHEMATICAL MORSEL

Several presidential election polls went statistically awry in this century. A spectacular failure was the 1935 *Literary Digest* poll predicting that Alfred Landon would defeat Franklin Roosevelt in the 1936 election. So devastated was the *Literary Digest* by its false prediction that it subsequently ceased publication. The *Literary Digest* poll used voluntary responses from a preselected sample—but only 23% of the people in the sample responded. Evidently, the majority of those who did were more enthusiastic about their candidate (Landon) than were the majority of the entire sample. Thus the sampling error was so large that a false prediction resulted. A study by J. H. Powell showed that if the data were analyzed and weighted according to how the respondents represented the general population, they would have picked Roosevelt.

The Dewey–Truman 1948 Gallup poll also used a biased sample. Interviewers were allowed to select individuals based on certain quotas (e.g., sex, race, and age). However, the people selected tended to be more prosperous than average, which produced a sample biased toward Republican candidates. Also, the poll was conducted three weeks before the election, when Truman was gaining support and Dewey was slipping.

Nowadays, sampling procedures are done with extreme care to produce representative samples of public opinion.

Section 10.3 EXERCISE / PROBLEM SET A

EXERCISES

1. The world record time for the mile run is given in the following table:

    a. Draw a line graph of this data using 3:30.0 as the baseline for the graph.

    b. What effect does having 3:30.0 as the baseline have on the impression made by the graph?

YEAR	WORLD RECORD FOR MILE RUN	
1950	4:01.4	(4 min 1.4 sec)
1955	3:58.0	
1960	3:54.5	
1965	3:53.6	
1970	3:51.1	
1975	3:49.4	
1980	3:48.8	
1985	3:46.3	
1990	3:46.3	
1995	3:44.4	
2000	3:43.1	

2. Since 1900, the death rate related to certain causes (other than old age) in the United States has fallen, while it has risen for several other causes. For major cardiovascular disease, the death rate per 100,000 population was as follows:

1950	1980	1990	1998
510.8	434.5	368.3	347.6

Source: National Center for Health Statistics.

    a. Draw a bar graph for this data using the same distance between each of the bars.

    b. Draw a line graph for the data having the years as the baseline with the usual spacing.

    c. Which graphing approach do you prefer? Why?

Use the following for Problems 3 and 4.

The following pictorial embellishment of a circle graph was taken from the May 17, 1993, issue of *Fortune* magazine. In it, the ovals that represent the "nest eggs" have lengths that are in proportion to the total amounts in the pension accounts. This tends to exaggerate the amounts they represent. That is, the area of the third oval is actually *four* times the area of the first oval although the amount it represents is only *two* times as great.

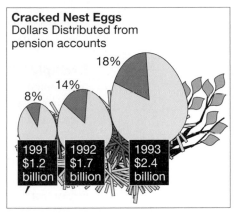

Cracked Nest Eggs
Dollars Distributed from pension accounts

Credit: *Keehan for Fortune*
Source: Fidelity Investments © 1993 Time Inc. All rights reserved.

3. Create a set of three pie charts based on the data from the pictograph. Make all the circles the same size. How does making the circles the same size affect the impression about the amounts involved?

4. Create a segmented bar chart based on the data from the pictograph. Make each of the bars proportional in height to the amounts in the pension accounts.

5. The following graphs represent the average wages of employees in a given company.

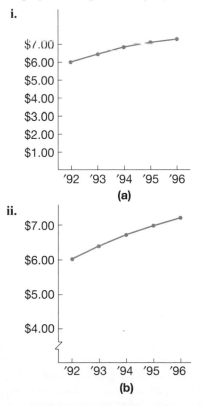

a. Do these graphs represent the same data?

b. What is the difference between these graphs?

c. Which graph would you use if you were the leader of a labor union seeking increased wages?

d. Which graph would you use if you were seeking to impress prospective employees with wages?

6. Health-care costs became a major issue in the last decade for both employers and employees. The following graph shows changes that occurred during this period.

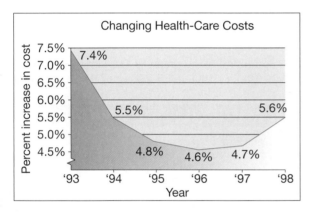

Changing Health-Care Costs

Redo the graph, showing percentage of change without shortening the vertical scale.

7. Create a 3-D bar chart for the following data.

YEAR	NEW CAR SALES (× 1000)
1992	8,213
1994	8,991
1996	8,527
1998	8,142

8. Use the following pie chart for Meat Consumption per Person, 1998, to create an "exploded" 3-D pie chart to emphasize the amount of red meat consumed per person.

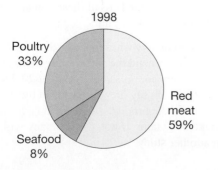

1998

Poultry 33%

Red meat 59%

Seafood 8%

9. Using perspective with pie charts can be deceiving.

52 weeks ending June 13, 1992, in millions of units

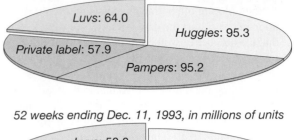

Luvs: 64.0

Huggies: 95.3

Private label: 57.9

Pampers: 95.2

52 weeks ending Dec. 11, 1993, in millions of units

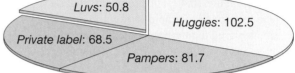

Luvs: 50.8

Huggies: 102.5

Private label: 68.5

Pampers: 81.7

Source: Company reports, Nielson Marketing Research, *Investors Business Daily*.

a. Use the data from these two pie charts to draw two new pie charts in the usual manner.

b. How do the pie charts you drew compare to the original ones?

c. Do the comparative pieces seem the same as before?

10. Identify three ways in which bar graphs can be deceptive.

11. a. Which of the following pictographs would be correct to show that sales have doubled from the left figure to the right figure?

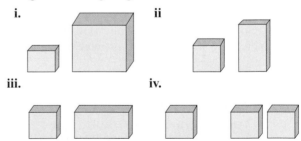

i.

ii

iii.

iv.

b. What is misleading about the other(s)?

In Problems 12 and 13 identify the population being studied and the sample that is actually observed.

12. A light bulb company says that its light bulbs last 2000 hours. To test this, a package of 8 bulbs is purchased and the bulbs are kept lit until they burn out. Five of the bulbs burn out before 2000 hours.

13. The registrar's office is interested in the percentage of full-time students who commute on a regular basis. One hundred students are randomly selected and briefly interviewed; 75 of these students commute on a regular basis.

PROBLEMS

14. Pictographs are often drawn incorrectly even if there is no intent to distort the data. Suppose we want to show that the number of women in the work force today is twice what it was at some time in the past. One way this could be done is to have two pictures of women representing the number of women in the work force and draw the one for today twice as tall as the one for the past, similar to what was done with the milk cartons in Figure 10.47. The problem is that most people tend to respond to graphics by comparing areas; we are also used to interpreting depth and perspective in drawings depicting three-dimensional objects.

Suppose we want to compare the revenue of two companies. Suppose company A had revenues of $5,000,000 last year and company B had $10,000,000.

a. If we want to use the area of circles to represent the revenues of the companies, what should be the radius of the circle for company B if the radius of the circle for company A is 1 inch? Explain.

b. If we want to use the volume of spheres to represent the revenues of the companies, what should be the radius of the sphere for company B if the radius of the sphere for company A is 1 inch? Explain.

15. One indicator of how well the economy is doing is the number of "Help Wanted" ads that appear in the newspapers. Redo the following graph so that the increase in 1994 appears even more dramatic than it is.

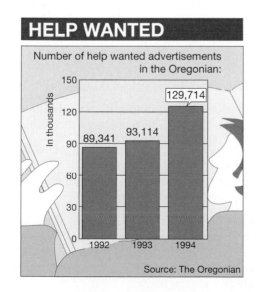

HELP WANTED

Number of help wanted advertisements in the Oregonian:

89,341 — 1992
93,114 — 1993
129,714 — 1994

In thousands

Source: The Oregonian

16. Prepare a vertical bar chart for the data on the federal tax burden per capita in such a way that the amount actually appears to be decreasing.

The Federal Tax Burden per Capita

FISCAL YEARS 1990–1995					
1990	1991	1992	1993	1994	1995
$4,026	$4,064	$4,153	$4,382	$4,701	$5,049 (est)

17. Redraw the graph on the increases in the federal tax burden per capita, 1990–1995, to emphasize the changes and make the increases appear more dramatic.

18. Redo the following graph so that agriculture prices from 1988 to 1996 don't appear to change so much.

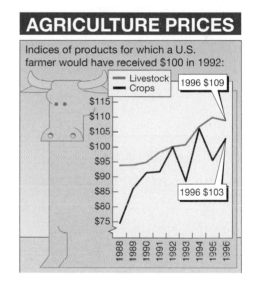

AGRICULTURE PRICES

Indices of products for which a U.S. farmer would have received $100 in 1992:

— Livestock
— Crops

1996 $109
1996 $103

$115
$110
$105
$100
$95
$90
$85
$80
$75

1988 1989 1990 1991 1992 1993 1994 1995 1996

In Problems 19 and 20 identify the population being studied, the sample actually observed, and discuss any sources of bias.

19. A biologist wants to estimate the number of fish in a lake. As part of the study, 250 fish are caught, tagged, and released back into the lake. Later, 500 fish are caught and examined; 18 of these fish are found to be tagged and the rest are untagged.

20. A drug company wishes to claim that 9 out of 10 doctors recommend the active ingredients in their product. They commission a study of 20 doctors. If at least 18 doctors say they recommend the active ingredients in the product, the company will feel free to make this claim. If not, the company will commission another study.

Section 10.3 EXERCISE / PROBLEM SET B

EXERCISES

1. Harness Racing Records for the Mile

TROTTERS		PACERS	
1921	1:57.8	1904	1:56
1922	1:57	1938	1:55
1922	1:56.8	1955	1:54.8
1937	1:56.6	1960	1:54.6
1937	1:56	1966	1:54
1938	1:55.2	1966	1:53.6
1969	1:54.8	1971	1:52
1980	1:54.6	1980	1:49.2
1982	1:54	1989	1:48.4
1987	1:52.2	1993	1:46.2

Source: 1995 *Information Please* almanac.

a. Draw a line graph of the data on Trotters using 1:40.0 as the baseline for the graph.

b. What effect does having 1:40.0 as the baseline have on the impression made by the graph?

2. Redraw the bar graph from Figure 10.37 with horizontal bars, but this time reverse the order of the bars from how they appear in Figure 10.38.

a. What is the visual impression regarding profits in this graph?

b. Which graph would you use? Why?

For Problems 3 and 4 refer to the graph used for Exercise 3 in Part A.

3. Create a proportional bar graph based on the data from the pictograph. In a proportional bar chart, all bars are the same height. How does making the bars all the same height affect the impression about the amount of funds distributed?

4. Create a set of three pie charts based on the data in the pictograph. Make the area of each circle proportional to the amount in the pension fund. That is, the area of the circle for 1993 should be twice the area of the circle for 1991.

5. A circle graph with equal-sized sectors is shown in (i). The same graph is shown in (ii), but drawn as if three-dimensional and in perspective.

i.

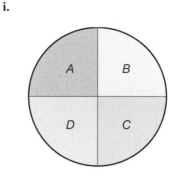

ii.

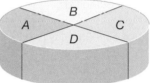

Explain how the perspective version is deceptive.

6. From 1985 to 1998, the minimum wages based on 1998 dollars is shown in the following graph. Redo the graph with a full vertical scale.

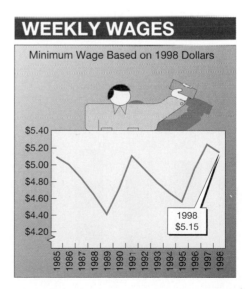

7. Create a 3-D line chart for the following data on the projected number of landfills in the United States.

YEARS	LANDFILLS
1985	6000
1990	3300
1995	2600
2000	1500
2005	1100

8. Use the pie chart from Exercise 8, Part A, to create an "exploded" 3-D pie chart to emphasize the amount of poultry consumed per person. Rotate the pie chart further to emphasize the poultry.

9. The following graphs appeared together in an environmental publication. Estimate values from each graph, combine them into a single set of numbers, and produce a single bar graph.

Smog Levels Above Standards, Selected U.S. Cities
Average Number of Days

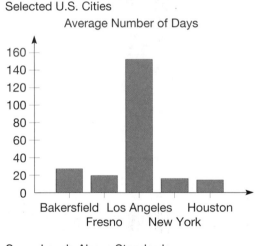

Smog Levels Above Standards, Selected Canadian Cities
Average Number of Days

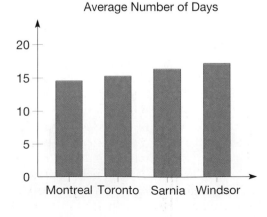

10. Identify three ways in which circle graphs can be deceptive.

11. Record sales of a certain singing group tripled from March to June. Is the following graph an accurate representation of the increase in sales? Why or why not?

Record Sales

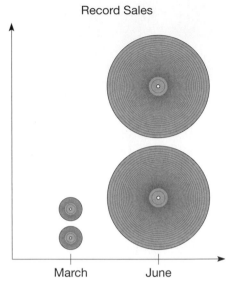

In Problems 12 and 13 identify the population being studied and the sample that is actually observed.

12. A chest of 1000 gold coins is to be presented to the king. The royal minter believes the king will not notice if only one of the coins is counterfeit. The king is suspicious and has 20 coins taken from the top of the chest and tested to see if they are pure gold.

13. The mathematics department is concerned about the amount of time students regularly set aside for studying. A questionnaire is distributed in three classes having a total of 82 students.

PROBLEMS

Use the following graph for Problems 14 and 15.

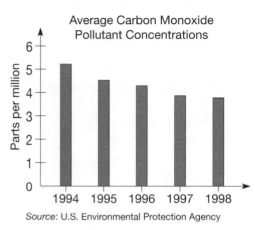

Average Carbon Monoxide Pollutant Concentrations

Source: U.S. Environmental Protection Agency

14. Redraw the graph on Average Carbon Monoxide Pollutant Concentration to emphasize the changes and make the decreases less dramatic.

15. Redraw the graph on Average Carbon Monoxide Pollutant Concentration to emphasize the changes and make the increases more dramatic.

16. Gun control has been a major political issue for many years. The following graph shows the number of robberies committed with firearms from 1992 to 1998.

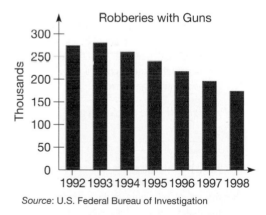

Robberies with Guns

Source: U.S. Federal Bureau of Investigation

a. Redo the graph so the decrease appears even greater.

b. Redo the graph so the decrease is not so obvious.

17. During the 1980s and early 1990s, many changes occurred with respect to the work force, including downsizing and hiring of temporary employees. As a result, job security became a significant concern. The following graph shows the changes in attitude among workers.

HOW SECURE THEY FEEL

Percent of employees reporting their job security was "good" or "very good"

Period	Management	Non-management
1980-82	79%	75%
1983-85	71%	72%
1986-88	65%	58%
1989-91	64%	61%
1992-94	55%	51%

Redo the graph so that

a. the downward trend is obvious.

b. the trend is apparently even worse than it is.

In Problems 18 and 19 identify the population being studied, the sample actually observed, and discuss any sources of bias.

18. A college professor is up for promotion. Teaching performance, as judged through student evaluations, is a significant factor in the decision. The professor is asked to choose one of his classes for student evaluations. The day of the evaluations he passes out questionnaires and then remains in the room to answer any questions about the form and filling it out.

19. There are two candidates for student body president of a college. Candidate Johnson believes that the student body resources should be used to enhance the social atmosphere of the college and that the number one priority should be dances, concerts, and other social events. Candidate Jackson believes that sports should be the number one priority and wants to subsidize student sporting events and enlarge the recreation facility. A poll is taken by the student newspaper. One interviewer goes to a coffeehouse near the college one evening and asks students which candidate they prefer. Another interviewer goes to the gym and asks students which candidate they prefer.

PROBLEMS FOR WRITING/DISCUSSION

1. Discuss the misleading attributes of the following graph and what could be done to the graph to make it more mathematically accurate.

2. If only part of a vertical axis on a graph is shown (see Figures 10.36, 10.39, and 10.40), does it necessarily mean

that the graph was constructed with the intent to deceive? Discuss some legitimate reasons for cropping a graph.

3. Identify any misleading features of the following graph and discuss what could be done to correct them.

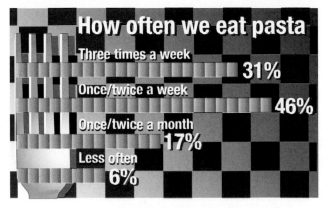

END OF CHAPTER MATERIAL

Solution of Initial Problem

A servant was asked to perform a job that would take 30 days. The servant would be paid 1000 gold coins. The servant replied, "I will happily complete the job, but I would rather be paid 1 copper coin on the first day, 2 copper coins on the second day, 4 on the third day, and so on, with the payment of copper coins doubling each day." The king agreed to the servant's method of payment. If a gold coin is worth 1000 copper coins, did the king make the right decision? How much was the servant paid?

Strategy: Look for a Formula

Make a table.

DAY	PAYMENT (COPPER COINS)	TOTAL PAYMENT TO DATE
1	$1 = 2^0$	1
2	$2 = 2^1$	$1 + 2 = 3$
3	$4 = 2^2$	$1 + 2 + 4 = 7$
4	$8 = 2^3$	$1 + 2 + 4 + 8 = 15$
5	$16 = 2^4$	$1 + 2 + 4 + 8 + 16 = 31$
.	.	.
.	.	.
.	.	.
n	2^{n-1}	$1 + 2 + 4 + 8 + \cdots + 2^{n-1} = S$

From our table we see on the nth day, where n is a whole number from 1 to 30, the servant is paid 2^{n-1} copper coins. His total payment through n days is $1 + 2 + 4 + \cdots + 2^{n-1}$ copper coins. Hence we wish to find a formula for $1 + 2 + \cdots + 2^{n-1}$. From the table it appears that this sum is $2^n - 1$. (Check this for $n = 1, 2, 3, 4, 5$.) Notice that this formula allows us to make a quick calculation of the value of S for any whole number n. In particular, for $n = 30$, $S = 2^{30} - 1$, so the servant would be paid $2^{30} - 1$ copper coins altogether. Using a calculator, $2^{30} - 1 = 1,073,741,823$. Hence the servant is paid the equivalent of 1,073,741.823 gold coins. The king made a very costly error!

Additional Problems Where the Strategy "Look for a Formula" Is Useful

1. Hector's parents suggest the following allowance arrangements for a 30-week period: a penny a day for the first week, 3 cents a day for the second week, 5 cents a day for the third week, and so on, or $2 a week. Which deal should he take?

2. Jack's beanstalk increases its height by $\frac{1}{2}$ the first day, $\frac{1}{3}$ the second day, $\frac{1}{4}$ the third day, and so on. What is the smallest number of days it would take to become at least 100 times as tall as its original height?

3. How many different (nonzero) angles are formed in a fan of rays like the one pictured on the left, but one having 100 rays?

People in Mathematics

Mina Rees (1902–1997) Mina Rees graduated from Hunter College, a women's school where mathematics was one of the most popular majors. "I wanted to be in the mathematics department, not because of its practical uses at all; it was because it was such fun!" Ironically, much of her recognition in mathematics has been for practical results. During World War II, she served on the National Defense Research Committee, working on wartime applications of mathematics. Later, she was director of mathematical sciences in the Office of Naval Research. Rees also taught for many years at Hunter College and the City College of New York, where she served as president. After her retirement, she was active in the applications of research to social problems. "I have always found that mathematics was an advantage when I was dean or president of a college. If your habit is to organize things a certain way, the way a mathematician does, then you are apt to have an organization that is easier to present and explain."

Andrew Gleason (1921–) Andrew Gleason says that he has always had a knack for solving problems. As a young man, he worked in cryptanalysis during World War II. The work involved problems in statistics and probability, and Gleason—despite having only a bachelor's degree—found that he understood the problems better than many experienced mathematicians. After the war, he made his mark in the mathematical world when he contributed to the solution of Hilbert's famous Fifth Problem. Today, Gleason is a longtime professor of mathematics at Harvard. "[As part of the School Mathematics Project] I worked with a group of kids who had just finished the first grade. One day I produced some squared paper and said, 'Here's how you multiply.' I drew a 3 × 4 rectangle and said, 'This is 3 times 4; we count the squares and get 12. So 3 × 4 is 12.' Then I did another, 4 × 5. Then I gave each kid some paper and said, 'You do some.' They were very soon doing two-digit problems."

CHAPTER REVIEW

Review the following terms and exercises to determine which require learning or relearning—page numbers are provided for easy reference.

SECTION 10.1: Organizing and Picturing Information

VOCABULARY/NOTATION

EXERCISES

1. Construct a back-to-back stem and leaf plot for the following two data sets:

Class 1: 72, 74, 76, 74, 23, 78, 37, 79, 80, 23, 81, 90, 82, 39, 94, 96, 41, 94, 94

Class 2: 17, 99, 25, 97, 29, 40, 39, 97, 40, 95, 92, 89, 40, 49, 40, 85, 52, 80, 52, 51

2. Construct a histogram for the data for class 1 in Exercise 1 using intervals 0–9, 10–19, ... , 90–100.

3. Draw a multiple-bar graph to represent the following two data sets.

YEAR	1988	1990	1992	1994	1996
SALARIES OF BEGINNING ELEMENTARY TEACHERS (IN THOUSANDS OF DOLLARS)	18.9	19.1	19.4	19.7	20.6
SALARIES OF BEGINNING SECONDARY TEACHERS (IN THOUSANDS OF DOLLARS)	19.6	20.3	20.9	21.8	22.5

4. Draw a double-line graph representing the data sets in Exercise 3.

5. Draw a circle graph to display the following data: Fruit, 30%; Vegetable, 40%; Meat, 10%; Milk, 10%; Others, 10%.

6. The manager of a sporting goods store notes that high levels of rainfall have a negative effect on sales of beach equipment and apparel. Sales in thousands of dollars and summer rainfall in inches measured for various years are recorded in the following table.

RAIN (IN INCHES)	SALES (IN THOUSANDS OF DOLLARS)
10	300
22	120
20	160
2	360
21	180
5	320
18	340

Make a scatterplot of these data. Identify any outliers. Sketch a regression line. If the predicted rainfall for the coming summer is 15 inches, what is the best prediction for sales? If the sales in one year were $260,000, what is the best guess for rainfall that summer?

SECTION 10.2: Analyzing Data

VOCABULARY/NOTATION

Measures of central tendency 437
Mode 437
Median 438
Arithmetic average 438
Mean 438
Box and whisker plot 439
Lower quartile 439
Upper quartile 439
Interquartile range (IQR) 440
Outlier 440
Percentile 443
nth percentile 443
Measures of dispersion 443
Range 443
Variance 443
Standard deviation 444
z-score 446
Relative frequency 447
Distribution 447
Normal distribution 449

EXERCISES

1. Determine the mode, median, and mean of the data set: 1, 2, 3, 5, 9, 9, 13, 14, 14, 14.

2. Construct the box and whisker plot for the data in Exercise 1.

3. Find the range, variance, and standard deviation of the data set in Exercise 1.

4. Find the z-scores for 2, 5, and 14 for the data set in Exercise 1.

5. What is the usefulness of the z-score of a number?

6. In a normal distribution, approximately what percent of the data are within 1 standard deviation of the mean?

7. On a test whose scores form a normal distribution, approximately how many of the scores have a z-score between −2 and 2?

8. Find the percentile of 2, 5, and 14 for the data set in Exercise 1.

SECTION 10.3: Misleading Graphs and Statistics

VOCABULARY/NOTATION

Scaling   458
Cropping   461
Three-dimensional effects   462

Explode   465
Deceptive pictorial
    embellishments   466

Population   468
Sample   468
Bias   468

EXERCISES

1. From April 1993 to April 1994, the average weekly wages in manufacturing in Oregon went through many changes, as shown in the following graph. Redo the graph with a full vertical scale.

WEEKLY WAGES

Average weekly manufacturing earnings in Oregon

April
$483.94

A M J J A S O N D J F M A
1993   1994

2. Health-care reform has become a major political issue. The following graph shows health-care spending as a percentage of the gross domestic product (GDP). The GDP is the value of all goods and services produced in the national economy.

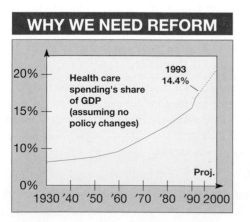

WHY WE NEED REFORM

20%   Health care   1993
      spending's share   14.4%
      of GDP
15%   (assuming no
      policy changes)

10%

0%
   1930 '40 '50 '60 '70 '80 '90 2000
                                    Proj.

a. Redo the graph so the increase appears even greater.

b. Redo the graph so the increase is not so dramatic.

3. Use the data in Problem 1 of Section 10.3 Problems for Writing/Discussion to construct a circle graph. Construct a second circle graph of this same data with the sector representing "the kids" exploded.

4. On the first page of this chapter evaluate the graph about "college seniors' plans." Discuss what aspects of the pictorial embellishment might be misleading.

5. We wish to determine the opinion of the voters in a certain town with regard to allowing in-line skating in the town square. A survey is taken of adult passersby near the local high school one late afternoon. What is the population in this case? What is the sample? What sources of bias might there be in the sampling procedure?

6. In the following scenario, identify and discuss any sources of bias in the sampling method.

A Minnesota-based toothpaste company claims that 90% of dentists prefer the formula in its toothpaste to any other. To prove this, they conduct a study. They send questionnaires to 100 dentists in the Minneapolis–St. Paul area asking if they prefer this formula to others.

PROBLEMS FOR WRITING/DISCUSSION

1. Five houses sold for $90,000, $100,000, $105,000, $120,000, and $224,000. Would the mean or the median be the better representative of house prices in this neighborhood? Explain.

2. Could the mode ever be the most representative average of a set of data? Explain your reasoning and give an example.

3. If you want to compare two sets of data, would you use two box and whisker plots or a double stem and leaf? What are the advantages of each?

4. Suppose you need to find out how many miles per day are driven by the typical 30-year-old driver in your state. How would you go about compiling these statistics? What information would you need, and how would you go about finding it? Discuss.

5. In a normal distribution of test scores are the median and mean equal? What does it mean if the median is greater than the mean?

6. Statistics are used for keeping track of trends. We try to explain/rationalize these trends and, from inferences, predict future events. Suppose you learned that the number of births to teenage mothers in the United States had been tabulated in 1990, 1995, and 2000, and each time the number had increased dramatically. You wish to predict the number of births to teen mothers in the year 2005. What would you need to know?

7. One of the students in your class was absent the day of the test. The teacher announced that the class average for the 24 students who took the test was 75%. After the other student returned and took the test, the teacher announced that the class average had increased to 76%. Explain how you can calculate what the absentee student got on her test.

8. Sketch two pictographs, one of which accurately illustrates that Miata sales tripled in 1999, and the other of which inaccurately represents that information. Explain the difference.

9. A nineteenth-century British prime minister, Benjamin Disraeli, is said to have exclaimed, "There are lies, damned lies, and statistics." Can you explain what he meant by this? Do you agree? Why or why not?

10. In a college course in which students could accumulate a maximum of 750 points per quarter, a student complained to the professor that he really deserved a B− even though his grade was a 79. After all, he only missed an 80 by one little point. If you were the professor, how would you explain the student's error?

CHAPTER TEST

Knowledge

1. True or false?

   a. The mode of a collection of data is the middle score.

   b. The range is the last number minus the first number in a collection of data.

   c. A z-score is the number of standard deviations away from the median.

   d. The median is always greater than the mean.

   e. A circle graph is effective in displaying relative amounts.

   f. Pictographs can be used to mislead by displaying two dimensions when only one of the dimensions represents the data.

   g. Every large group of data has a normal distribution.

   h. In a normal distribution, more than half of the data are contained within 1 standard deviation from the mean.

   i. When determining the opinion of a voting population, the larger the sample the better.

   j. A score in the 37th percentile is greater than 63% of all of the scores.

   k. When the vertical axis of a bar graph is cropped or compressed, it is done to mislead the reader.

2. Identify three measures of central tendency and two measures of dispersion.

3. Identify the kinds of information that bar graphs and line graphs are good for picturing and circle graphs are not. Conversely, identify the kinds of information that circle graphs are good for picturing but bar and line graphs are not.

Skill

4. If a portion of a circle graph is to represent 30%, what will be the measure of the corresponding central angle?

5. Find the mean, median, mode, and range of the following data: 5, 7, 3, 8, 10, 3.

6. If a collection of data has a mean of 17 and a standard deviation of 3, what numbers would have z-scores of -2, -1, 1, and 2?

7. Calculate the standard deviation for the following data: 15, 1, 9, 13, 17, 8, 3.

8. On a football team with a mean weight of 220 pounds and a standard deviation of the weights being 35 pounds, what percentile is a 170-pound receiver or a 290-pound lineman?

9. Using the following scores, construct a box and whisker plot.

    97, 54, 81, 80, 69, 94, 86, 79, 82, 64, 84, 72, 78

10. Use the data in the following golf ball advertisement to produce a new bar graph in which the length of each bar is proportional to the combined distances it represents.

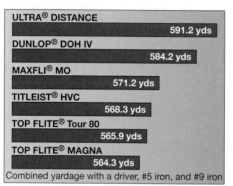

ULTRA® DISTANCE — 591.2 yds
DUNLOP® DOH IV — 584.2 yds
MAXFLI® MO — 571.2 yds
TITLEIST® HVC — 568.3 yds
TOP FLITE® Tour 80 — 565.9 yds
TOP FLITE® MAGNA — 564.3 yds
Combined yardage with a driver, #5 iron, and #9 iron

11. A statistics professor gives an 80-point test to his class, with the following scores:

    35, 44, 48, 55, 56, 57, 60, 61, 62, 62, 63, 64, 67, 70, 71, 71, 75

    To provide an example of how histograms might be constructed, she is considering two options.
    a. Grouping the data into subintervals of length 10, beginning with 71–80, 61–70, etc.
    b. Grouping the data into subintervals of length 8, beginning with 73–80, 65–72, etc.

    Draw the histogram for each option.

12. A sociologist working for a large school system is interested in demographic information on the families having children in the schools served by the system. Two hundred students are randomly selected from the school system's database and a questionnaire is sent to the home address in care of the parents or guardian. Identify the population being studied and the sample that was actually observed.

Understanding

13. If possible, give a single list of data such that the mean equals the mode and the mode is less than the median. If impossible, explain why.

14. If possible, give a collection of data for which the standard deviation is zero and the mean is nonzero. If impossible, explain why.

15. Give a reason justifying the use of each histogram constructed in Problem 11. Why might the professor use the first one? Why might she use the second one?

16. Explain how pictographs can be deceptive.

17. Give an example of two sets of data with the same means and different standard deviations.

18. Explain how line graphs can be deceptive.

19. What type of graph would be best for displaying the data in the following table? Justify your answer and construct the graph.

High School Graduates Enrolled in College

YEAR	MALE	FEMALE
1990	57.8	62.0
1991	57.6	67.1
1992	59.6	63.8
1993	59.7	65.4
1994	60.6	63.2
1995	62.6	61.4
1996	60.1	69.7

Source: U.S. National Center for Educational Statistics.

20. Redraw the following graph of the increases in the federal tax burden per capita, 1990–1995, to deemphasize the changes. Manipulate the horizontal and/or vertical axes so that the increases appear less dramatic.

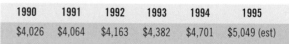

The Federal Tax Burden per Capita, Fiscal Years 1990–1995

1990	1991	1992	1993	1994	1995
$4,026	$4,064	$4,163	$4,382	$4,701	$5,049 (est)

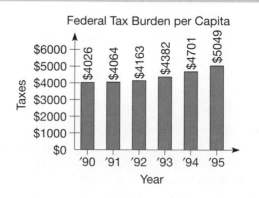

Federal Tax Burden per Capita

Problem-Solving/Application

21. In a distribution, the number 7 has a *z*-score of -2 and the number 19 has a *z*-score of 1. What is the mean of the distribution?

22. If the mean of the numbers 1, 3, *x*, 7, 11 is 9, what is *x*?

23. On which test did Ms. Brown's students perform the best compared to the national averages? Explain.

	MS. BROWN'S CLASS AVERAGE	NATIONAL AVERAGE	AVERAGE DEVIATION
Reading	77.9	75.2	12.3
Mathematics	75.2	74.1	14.2
Science	74.3	70.3	13.6
Social studies	71.7	69.3	10.9

24. Identify any possible sources of bias in the sampling procedure in the following scenario.

A soft-drink company produces a lemon-lime drink that it says people prefer by a margin of two-to-one over its main competitor, a cola. To prove this claim, it sets up a booth in a large shopping mall where customers are allowed to try both drinks. The customers are filmed for a possible television commercial. They are asked which drink they prefer.

25. On the first page of this chapter evaluate the graph about "dominating college lacrosse." Discuss what aspects of the graph might be misleading.

References for Reflections from Research

BOHAN, H., & MORELAND, M. J. (1981). Developing some statistical concepts in the elementary school. In A. P. Shulte & J. R. Smart (Eds.), *Teaching Statistics and Probability* (pp. 60–63). Reston, VA: National Council of Teachers of Mathematics.

BROWN, C. A., & SILVER, E. A. (1989). Data organization and interpretation. In M. M. Lindquist (Ed.), *Results from the fourth mathematics assessment of the National Assessment of Education Progress*. Reston, VA: National Council of Teachers of Mathematics.

CHOATE, L. D., & OKEY, J. K. (1981). Graphically speaking: Primary level graphing experiences. In A. P. Shulte & J. R. Smart (Eds.), *Teaching statistics and probability* (pp. 33–40). Reston, VA: National Council of Teachers of Mathematics.

LANDWEHR, J. M., SWIFT, J., & WATKINS, A. E. (1987). *Exploring surveys and information from samples: Quantitative literacy series*. Palo Alto, CA: Dale Seymour.

SHAW, J. M. (1984). Making graphs. *Arithmetic Teacher*, *31*(5), 7–11.

WATSON, J. M., & MORITZ, J. B. (2000). Developing concepts of sampling. *Journal for Research in Mathematics Education*, *31*, 44–70.

FOCUS ON *Probability in the Everyday World*

t is generally agreed that the science of probability began in the sixteenth century from the so-called *problem of the points*. The problem is to determine the division of the stakes of two equally skilled players when a game of chance is interrupted before either player has obtained the required number of points in order to win. However, real progress on this subject began in 1654 when Chevalier de Mere, an experienced gambler whose theoretical understanding of the problem did not match his observations, approached the mathematician Blaise Pascal for assistance. Pascal communicated with Fermat about the problem and, remarkably, each solved the problem by different means. Thus, in this correspondence, Pascal and Fermat laid the foundations of probability.

Blaise Pascal

Now, probability is recognized in many aspects of our lives. For example, when you were conceived, you could have had any of 8,388,608 different sets of characteristics based on 23 pairs of chromosomes. In school, if you guess at random on a 10-item true/false test, there is only about a 17% probability that you will answer 7 or more questions correctly. In the manufacturing process, quality control is becoming the buzzword. Thus it is important to know the probability that certain parts will fail when deciding to revamp a production process or offer a warranty. In investments, advisers assign probabilities to future prices in an effort to decide among various investment opportunities. Another important use of probability is in actuarial science, which is used to determine insurance premiums. Probability also continues to play a role in games of chance such as dice and cards.

One very popular application of probability is the famous "birthday problem." Simply stated, in a group of people, what is the probability of two people having the same month and day of birth? Surprisingly, the probability of such matching birth dates is about 0.5 when there are 23 people and almost 0.9 when there are 40 people. An interesting application of this problem is the birthdays of the 39 American presidents through Reagan. Presidents Polk and Harding were both born on November 2 and Presidents Andrew Johnson and Wilson were both born on December 29. The surprising solution of this problem will be possible using the concepts developed in this chapter.

Strategy
Do A Simulation

A simulation is a representation of an experiment using some appropriate objects (slips of paper, dice, etc.) or perhaps a computer program. The purpose of a simulation is to run many replications of an experiment that may be difficult or impossible to perform. As you will see, to solve the following Initial Problem, it is easier to simulate the problem than to perform the actual experiment many times by questioning five strangers repeatedly.

Initial Problem

At a party, a friend bets you that at least two people in a group of five strangers will have the same astrological sign. Should you take the bet? Why or why not?

Clues

The Do a Simulation strategy may be appropriate when

- A problem involves a complicated probability experiment.
- An actual experiment is too difficult or impossible to perform.
- A problem has a repeatable process that can be done experimentally.
- Finding the actual answer requires techniques not previously developed.

A solution of the Initial Problem appears on page 540.

INTRODUCTION

In this chapter we discuss the fundamental concepts and principles of probability. Probability is the branch of mathematics that enables us to predict the likelihood of uncertain occurrences. There are many applications and uses of probability in the sciences (meteorology and medicine, for example), in sports and games, and in business, to name a few areas. Because of its widespread usefulness, the study of probability is an essential component of a comprehensive mathematics curriculum. In the first section of this chapter we develop the main concepts of probability. In the second section some counting procedures are introduced that lead to more sophisticated methods for computing probabilities. In the third section, simulations are developed and several applications of probability are presented. Finally, in the last section, additional counting methods referred to as permutations and combinations are discussed. These methods are used to determine probabilities on large sets.

11.1   PROBABILITY AND SIMPLE EXPERIMENTS

STARTING POINT

A red cube, a white cube, and a blue cube are placed in a box. One cube is randomly drawn, its color is recorded, and it is returned to the box. A second cube is drawn and its color recorded. What are the chances (probability) of drawing a red cube? (*Hint:* Drawing a red cube could be done on the first draw, the second draw, or both draws.)

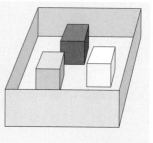

Simple Experiments

Probability is the mathematics of chance. Example 11.1 illustrates how probability is commonly used and reported.

Reflection from Research
When teachers use contexts (e.g., a lottery) for teaching probability concepts, many elementary students have difficulty learning the mathematical concepts because their personal experiences interfere (e.g., "It's impossible to win the lottery because no one in my family has ever won.") (Taylor & Biddulph, 1994).

Example 11.1
a. The probability of precipitation today is 80%.
Interpretation: On days in the past with atmospheric conditions like today's, it rained at some time on 80% of the days.

b. The odds that a patient improves using drug X are 60 : 40.
Interpretation: In a group of 100 patients who have had the same symptoms as the patient being treated, 60 of them improved when administered drug X, and 40 did not.

c. The chances of winning the lottery game "Find the Winning Ticket" are 1 in 150,000.
Interpretation: If 150,000 lottery tickets are printed, only one of the tickets is the winning ticket. If more tickets are printed, the fraction of winning tickets is approximately $\frac{1}{150,000}$.   ■

Probability tells us the relative frequency with which we expect an event to occur. Thus it can be reported as a fraction, decimal, percent, or ratio. The greater the probability, the more likely the event is to occur. Conversely, the smaller the probability, the less likely the event is to occur.

To study probability in a mathematically precise way, we need special terminology and notation. An **experiment** is the act of making an observation or taking a measurement. An **outcome** is one of the possible things that can occur as a result of an experiment. The set of all the possible outcomes is called the **sample space.** Finally, an **event** is any subset of the sample space.

Since a sample space is a set, it is commonly represented in set notation with the letter S. Similarly, because an event is a subset, in set notation, it is frequently represented with letters like A, B, C, or the generic letter E for event. These concepts are illustrated in Example 11.2.

Example 11.2

a. Experiment: Toss a fair coin and record whether the top side is heads or tails.

Sample Space: There are two possible outcomes when tossing a coin, heads or tails. Hence the sample space is $S = \{H, T\}$, where H and T are abbreviations for heads and tails, respectively.

Event: Since an event is simply a subset of the sample space, we will first consider all the subsets of the sample space S. The subsets are $\{\}, \{H\}, \{T\}, \{H, T\}$. It is not always the case that we can describe in words an event associated with each subset, but in this case we can. The events are as follows:

A = getting a heads = $\{H\}$
B = getting a tails = $\{T\}$
C = getting either a heads or a tails = $\{H, T\}$
D = getting neither a heads nor a tails = $\{\}$

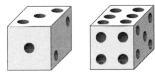

Figure 11.1

b. Experiment: Roll a standard six sided die with one, two, three, four, five, and six dots on the six faces (Figure 11.1). Record the number of dots showing on the top face.

Sample Space: There are six outcomes:—1, 2, 3, 4, 5, 6—where numerals represent the number of dots. Thus the sample space is $S = \{1, 2, 3, 4, 5, 6\}$.

Event: For this experiment, there are many more events than for the previous example of tossing a single coin. In fact, there are $2^6 = 64$ possible events. Each event is a subset of S. Some of the events are:

A = getting a prime number of dots = $\{2, 3, 5\}$
B = getting an even number of dots = $\{2, 4, 6\}$
C = getting more than 4 dots = $\{5, 6\}$

Reflection from Research
When presented with a regular, six-sided die or a bag with six identical balls numbered one to six, many children feel the die is "fairer" (Truran, 1995).

c. Experiment: Spin a spinner as shown in Figure 11.2 once and record the color of the indicated region.

Sample Space: There are 4 different colored regions (outcomes) on this spinner, so the sample space is $S = \{R, Y, G, B\}$. It is important to note that the regions on the spinner are the same size. If they were not the same size, we would have to approach the sample space differently.

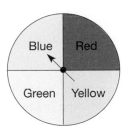

Figure 11.2

Event: Some of the possible events for this experiment are:

A = pointing to the red region = $\{R\}$
B = pointing to a blue or green region = $\{B, G\}$
C = pointing to a region with a primary color = $\{R, Y, B\}$

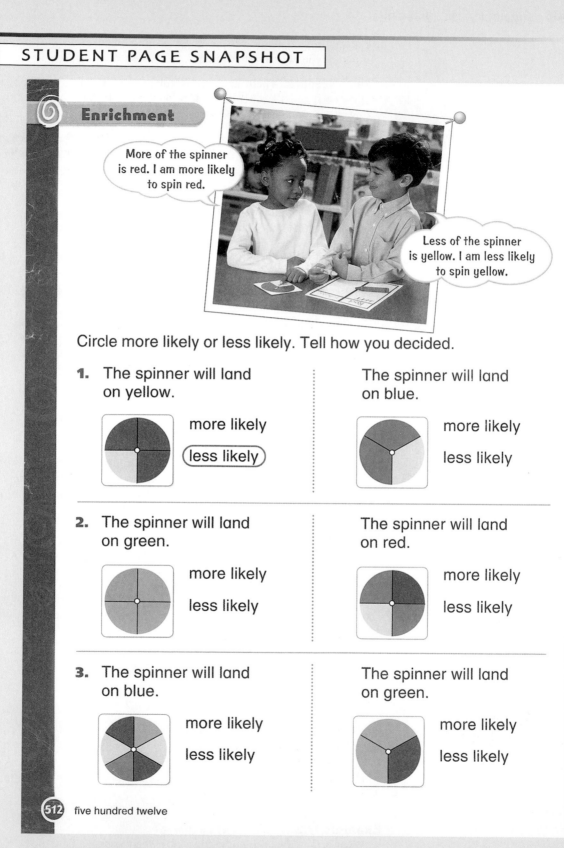

Enrichment

More of the spinner is red. I am more likely to spin red.

Less of the spinner is yellow. I am less likely to spin yellow.

Circle more likely or less likely. Tell how you decided.

1. The spinner will land on yellow.

more likely

(less likely)

The spinner will land on blue.

more likely

less likely

2. The spinner will land on green.

more likely

less likely

The spinner will land on red.

more likely

less likely

3. The spinner will land on blue.

more likely

less likely

The spinner will land on green.

more likely

less likely

d. Experiment: A single card is drawn from a standard deck of playing cards. The suit and type of card are recorded.

Sample Space: There are 4 suits [diamonds (◆), hearts (♥), spades (♠), and clubs (♣)] and 13 cards (2, 3, 4, 5, 6, 7, 8, 9, 10, jack, queen, king, and ace) in each suit for a total of 52 possible outcomes.

$$S = \{2◆, 3◆, 4◆, 5◆, 6◆, 7◆, 8◆, 9◆, 10◆, J◆, Q◆, K◆, A◆,$$
$$2♥, 3♥, 4♥, 5♥, 6♥, 7♥, 8♥, 9♥, 10♥, J♥, Q♥, K♥, A♥,$$
$$2♠, 3♠, 4♠, 5♠, 6♠, 7♠, 8♠, 9♠, 10♠, J♠, Q♠, K♠, A♠,$$
$$2♣, 3♣, 4♣, 5♣, 6♣, 7♣, 8♣, 9♣, 10♣, J♣, Q♣, K♣, A♣\}$$

Event: This sample space of 52 elements has $2^{52} = 4,503,599,627,370,496$ different subsets (events). Some of the events are:

$A =$ drawing a diamond $= \{2◆, \ 3◆, \ 4◆, \ 5◆, \ 6◆, \ 7◆, \ 8◆, \ 9◆,$
$\qquad 10◆, J◆, Q◆, K◆, A◆\}$

$B =$ drawing a face card $= \{J◆, \ Q◆, \ K◆, \ J♥, \ Q♥, \ K♥, \ J♠, \ Q♠, \ K♠,$
$\qquad J♣, Q♣, K♣\}$

$C =$ drawing a diamond or face card $= \{2◆, 3◆, 4◆, 5◆, 6◆, 7◆, 8◆,$
$\qquad 9◆, 10◆, J◆, Q◆, K◆, A◆, J♥, Q♥, K♥,$
$\qquad J♠, Q♠, K♠, J♣, Q♣, K♣\}$

$D =$ drawing a diamond face card $= \{J◆, Q◆, K◆\}$

Notice that $D = A \cap B$ and $C = A \cup B$.   ■

NCTM Standards 2000
Data Analysis and
Probability
Grades 3–5
All students should describe events as likely or unlikely and discuss the degree of likelihood using such words as *certain*, *equally likely*, and *impossible*.

Computing Probabilities in Simple Experiments

The probability of an event, E, is the fraction (decimal, percent, or ratio) indicating the relative frequency with which event E should occur in a given sample space S. Two events are **equally likely** if they occur with equal relative frequency (i.e., equally often).

● DEFINITION

Probability of an Event with Equally Likely Outcomes

Suppose that all of the outcomes in the nonempty sample space S of an experiment are equally likely to occur. Let E be an event, $n(E)$ be the number of outcomes in E, and $n(S)$ the number of outcomes in S. Then the **probability of event E**, denoted $P(E)$, is

$$P(E) = \frac{\text{number of elements in } E}{\text{number of elements in } S},$$

or in symbols

$$P(E) = \frac{n(E)}{n(S)}.$$

Using this definition, we can compute the probabilities of some of the events described in Example 11.2.

Example 11.3
a. What is the probability of getting tails when tossing a fair coin?

b. For the experiment of rolling a standard six-sided die and recording the number of dots on the top face, what is the probability of getting a prime number?

c. On the spinner found in Figure 11.2, what is the probability of pointing to a primary color?

d. For the experiment of drawing a card from a standard deck of playing cards, what is the probability of getting a diamond? What is the probability of getting a diamond face card?

Solution

a. While the probability of getting tails might seem like common sense, we will discuss it in terms of the definition in order to lay the groundwork for more complicated probabilities. The sample space for this experiment is $S = \{H, T\}$, where each of the outcomes is equally likely. The event of getting tails corresponds to the subset $B = \{T\}$. Thus the probability of getting tails is

$$P(B) = \frac{n(B)}{n(S)} = \frac{1}{2}.$$

b. Since all of the outcomes in the sample space $S = \{1, 2, 3, 4, 5, 6\}$ are equally likely and the event of getting a prime number is subset $A = \{2, 3, 5\}$, the probability of getting a prime is

$$P(A) = \frac{n(A)}{n(S)} = \frac{3}{6} = \frac{1}{2}.$$

c. Since each region is exactly the same size, each color has an equally likely chance of being selected. The event of pointing to a primary color is subset $C = \{R, Y, B\}$ and $S = \{R, Y, G, B\}$, so the probability of pointing to a primary color is

$$P(C) = \frac{n(C)}{n(S)} = \frac{3}{4}.$$

d. Since each card in the deck has an equally likely chance of being drawn, we can again use the previous definition. The event of getting a diamond is represented by subset A, which consists of 13 cards, and the event of getting a diamond face card is subset $D = \{J\blacklozenge, Q\blacklozenge, K\blacklozenge\}$. Thus the probability of drawing a diamond is

$$P(A) = \frac{n(A)}{n(S)} = \frac{13}{52} = \frac{1}{4}$$

and the probability of a diamond face card is

$$P(D) = \frac{n(D)}{n(S)} = \frac{3}{52}. \qquad ■$$

These examples provide a sense of the types of numbers that probabilities can take on. By using the fact that $\varnothing \subseteq E \subseteq S$, we can determine the range for $P(E)$. In particular, $\varnothing \subseteq E \subseteq S$, so

$$0 = n(\varnothing) \le n(E) \le n(S);$$

hence

$$\frac{0}{n(S)} \le \frac{n(E)}{n(S)} \le \frac{n(S)}{n(S)}$$

so that

$$0 \le P(E) \le 1.$$

The last inequality tells us that the probability of an event must be between 0 and 1, inclusive. If $P(E) = 0$, the event E contains no outcomes (hence E is an **impossible**

event); if $P(E) = 1$, the event E equals the entire sample space S (hence E is a **certain event**).

For each of the examples considered thus far, we see that the probability is simply a ratio of the number of objects or outcomes of interest compared to the total number of objects or outcomes under consideration. The objects or outcomes of interest make up the event. Thus, a more general description of probability is

$$P(\text{event}) = \frac{\text{the number of objects or outcomes of interest}}{\text{the total number of objects or outcomes under consideration}}.$$

The primary use of a sample space is to make sure that you have accounted for all possible outcomes. The examples done thus far could likely be done without listing a sample space, but they prepare us for using a sample space to compute the probabilities in the next few examples.

Each of the experiments that we have investigated thus far involve doing an action with one object once: tossing a coin, rolling a die, spinning a spinner, drawing a card. Computing probabilities becomes more difficult when multiple actions or objects are involved. Examples of using multiple objects such as tossing three coins and rolling two dice follow.

T   H   H

Figure 11.3

Example 11.4 When tossing three coins—a penny, a nickel, and a dime—what is the probability of getting exactly two heads (Figure 11.3)?

Solution While it may seem that since there are three coins and two of them need to be heads, we might simply say that it is the probability of two out of three. This reasoning, however, does not take into consideration all of the possible outcomes. To do this, we will fall back on the idea of a sample space and event. The sample space for this experiment is

$$S = \{\overbrace{\text{HHH}}^{3\text{ heads}}, \overbrace{\text{HHT, HTH, THH}}^{2\text{ heads}}, \underbrace{\text{HTT, THT, TTH}}_{1\text{ head}}, \underbrace{\text{TTT}}_{0\text{ heads}}\}$$

where the first letter in each three-letter sequence represents the outcome of the penny, the second letter is the nickel, and the last letter is the dime. The event of getting exactly two heads is $A = \{\text{HHT, HTH, THH}\}$. Thus the probability of getting exactly two heads is

$$P(A) = \frac{n(A)}{n(S)} = \frac{3}{8}.$$ ■

Table 11.1

OUTCOME	FREQUENCY
HHH	71
HHT	67
HTH	56
THH	64
TTH	53
THT	61
HTT	66
TTT	62
Total	500

This probability is based on *ideal* occurrences and is referred to as a **theoretical probability**. Another way to approach this problem is by actually tossing three coins many times and recording the results. Computing probability in this way by determining the ratio of the frequency of an event to the total number of repetitions is called **experimental probability**. Table 11.1 gives the observed results of tossing a penny, nickel, and dime 500 times.

From Table 11.1, the outcomes of the event of getting exactly two heads occurred as follows: HHT, 67 times; HTH, 56 times; and THH, 64 times. Thus the experimental probability of getting exactly two heads is

$$\frac{67 + 56 + 64}{500} = \frac{187}{500} = .374,$$

which is comparable to the theoretical probability of

$$P(E) = \frac{n(E)}{n(S)} = \frac{3}{8} = .375.$$

Experimental probability has the advantage of being established via observations. The obvious disadvantage is that it depends on a particular set of repetitions of an experiment and may not generalize to other repetitions of the same type of experiment. In either case, however, the probability was found by determining a ratio. From this point on, all probabilities will be computed theoretically unless otherwise indicated.

www.wiley.com/college/musser

Spotlight on Technology Tossing three coins 500 times would be a tedious task. Using a spreadsheet to accomplish this would only require the push of a button. Refer to the dynamic spreadsheet, *Coin Toss*, in the Spreadsheet webmodule, which contains a coin toss spreadsheet for you to work with. Using this spreadsheet, perform five different experiments of 100 tosses. In any case did the experimental probability match the theoretical? What was the closest match? What was the worst match?

Reflection from Research
A common error experienced by children considering probability with respect to sums of numbers from two dice is that they mistakenly believe that the sums are equally likely (Fischbein & Gazit, 1984).

Example 11.5 The experiment of tossing two fair, six-sided dice is performed and the sum of the dots on the two faces is recorded. Let A be the event of getting a total of 7 dots, B be the event of getting 8 dots, and C be the event of getting at least 4 dots. What is the probability of each of these events?

Solution In determining the sample space for this experiment, one might consider listing only the sums of 2, 3, 4, and so forth. However, since these outcomes are not equally likely, the definition for determining the probability of an event with equally likely outcomes cannot be used. As a result, we list all of the outcomes of tossing two dice and then determine which of those outcomes yield sums of 2, 3, 4, and so forth. The sample space, S, for this experiment is shown in Figure 11.4(a).

(1,1)	(1,2)	(1,3)	(1,4)	(1,5)	(1,6)
(2,1)	(2,2)	(2,3)	(2,4)	(2,5)	(2,6)
(3,1)	(3,2)	(3,3)	(3,4)	(3,5)	(3,6)
(4,1)	(4,2)	(4,3)	(4,4)	(4,5)	(4,6)
(5,1)	(5,2)	(5,3)	(5,4)	(5,5)	(5,6)
(6,1)	(6,2)	(6,3)	(6,4)	(6,5)	(6,6)

(a)

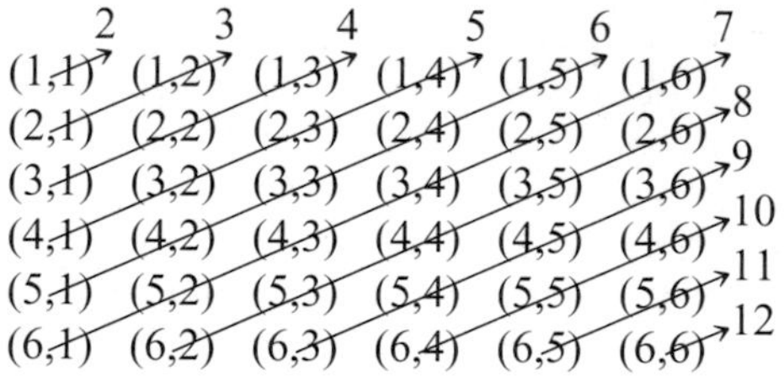

(b)

Figure 11.4

A question that often arises with this experiment is "why do you list both (1,2) and (2,1) when we are only interested in the sum of three?" To better understand this, imagine that the two dice are different colors, red and green. This would mean that 1 dot on the red die and 2 dots on the green die is a *different* outcome than 2 dots on the red die and 1 dot on the green die. Thus both outcomes are listed separately. By looking at the sample space in Figure 11.4(a) and the sums of dots (the numbers at the ends of the arrows) in Figure 11.4(b), the size of the sample space [$n(S) = 36$] and the size of the various subsets representing events can be determined. Using this information, $P(A)$, $P(B)$, and $P(C)$ are shown in Table 11.2.

Table 11.2

EVENT E	$N(E)$	$P(E)$
A	$n(A) = 6$	$P(A) = \frac{6}{36} = \frac{1}{6}$
B	$n(B) = 5$	$P(B) = \frac{5}{36}$
C	$n(C) = 33$	$P(C) = \frac{33}{36} = \frac{11}{12}$

Spotlight on Technology The rolling of two dice and recording the sum of the number of dots on their faces can be simulated using a spreadsheet. Refer to the dynamic spreadsheet, *Roll the* www.wiley.com/ college/musser *Dice*, in the Spreadsheet webmodule. Use the spreadsheet to simulate rolling two dice 200 times. How close are the results of this experiment to the theoretical probabilities in Table 11.2?

All of the examples discussed thus far have been experiments consisting of one action. In the case of tossing three coins or rolling two dice, it was still only one action, but performed on more than one object. We now want to consider experiments that consist of doing two or more actions in succession. For example, consider the experiment of tossing one coin three times. Would this experiment have a different sample space than the experiment of tossing three different coins once as in Example 11.4? No. In fact, it is often helpful in listing a sample space for experiments of this type to be aware of this connection. The next example is an illustration of an experiment of two actions done in succession.

Figure 11.5

Example 11.6 A jar contains four marbles: one red, one green, one yellow, and one white (Figure 11.5). If we draw two marbles from the jar, one after the other, without replacing the first one drawn, what is the probability of each of the following events?

A: One of the marbles is red.
B: The first marble is red or yellow.
C: The marbles are the same color.
D: The first marble is not white.
E: Neither marble is blue.

Solution The sample space consists of the following outcomes. ("RG," for example, means that the first marble is red and the second marble is green.)

RG	GR	YR	WR
RY	GY	YG	WG
RW	GW	YW	WY

Thus $n(S) = 12$. Since there is exactly one marble of each color and all marbles are physically identical to the touch, we assume that all the outcomes are equally likely. Then

$A = \{RG, RY, RW, GR, YR, WR\}$, so $P(A) = \frac{6}{12} = \frac{1}{2}$.
$B = \{RG, RY, RW, YR, YG, YW\}$, so $P(B) = \frac{6}{12} = \frac{1}{2}$.
$C = \emptyset$, the empty event. That is, C is impossible, so $P(C) = \frac{0}{12} = 0$.
$D = \{RG, RY, RW, GR, GY, GW, YR, YG, YW\}$, so $P(D) = \frac{9}{12} = \frac{3}{4}$.
$E = $ the entire sample space, S. So $P(E) = \frac{12}{12} = 1$.

Notice that event B in Example 11.6 can be represented as the union of two events corresponding to drawing red on the first marble or yellow on the first marble. That is, if we let $L = \{RG, RY, RW\}$ and $M = \{YR, YG, YW\}$, then $B = L \cup M$. Observe that $L \cap M = \emptyset$. If we compute $P(L \cup M)$, $P(L)$, and $P(M)$, we find $P(L \cup M) = P(B) = \frac{1}{2}$, while $P(L) + P(M) = \frac{3}{12} + \frac{3}{12} = \frac{1}{2}$. Hence $P(L \cup M) = P(L) + P(M)$. Thus the probability of B can be found by adding the probabilities of two *disjoint* events whose union is event B, that is, $P(B) = P(L) + P(M)$.

The set of outcomes in the sample space S but not in event D is called the **complement of the event** D, written $\overline{D}$. Because $S = D \cup \overline{D}$ and $D \cap \overline{D} = \emptyset$, we see that $n(D) + n(\overline{D}) = n(S)$ or $n(\overline{D}) = n(S) - n(D)$. Therefore,

$$P(\overline{D}) = \frac{n(\overline{D})}{n(S)} = \frac{n(S) - n(D)}{n(S)} = \frac{n(S)}{n(S)} - \frac{n(D)}{n(S)} = 1 - P(D).$$

Similarly, $P(D) = 1 - P(\overline{D})$. Thus $P(\overline{D})$ in Example 11.6 is the probability that the first marble is white, namely $\frac{3}{12}$ or $\frac{1}{4}$. So $P(D) = 1 - P(\overline{D}) = 1 - \frac{1}{4} = \frac{3}{4}$, as we found directly.

Problem-Solving Strategy
Draw a Diagram

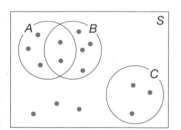

Figure 11.6

Example 11.7   Figure 11.6 shows a diagram of a sample space S of an experiment with equally likely outcomes. Events A, B, and C are indicated, their outcomes represented by points. Find the probability of each of the following events: S, $\emptyset$, A, B, C, $A \cup B$, $A \cap B$, $A \cup C$, $\overline{C}$.

Solution   In Table 11.3, we tabulate the number of outcomes in each event and their probabilities. For example, $n(A) = 5$ and $n(S) = 15$, so $P(A) = \frac{5}{15} = \frac{1}{3}$.

Table 11.3

EVENT, E	$n(E)$	$P(E) = \dfrac{n(E)}{n(S)}$
S	15	$\frac{15}{15} = 1$
$\emptyset$	0	$\frac{0}{15} = 0$
A	5	$\frac{5}{15} = \frac{1}{3}$
B	6	$\frac{6}{15} = \frac{2}{5}$
C	3	$\frac{3}{15} = \frac{1}{5}$
$A \cup B$	9	$\frac{9}{15} = \frac{3}{5}$
$A \cap B$	2	$\frac{2}{15}$
$A \cup C$	8	$\frac{8}{15}$
$\overline{C}$	12	$\frac{12}{15} = \frac{4}{5}$

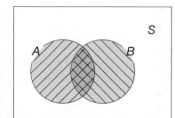

Figure 11.7

In Example 11.7, $P(A \cup B) = \frac{9}{15}$, while $P(A) + P(B) - P(A \cap B) = \frac{5}{15} + \frac{6}{15} - \frac{2}{15} = \frac{9}{15} = P(A \cup B)$. So $P(A \cup B) = P(A) + P(B) - P(A \cap B)$. This result is true for *all* events A and B. In Figure 11.7, observe how the region $A \cap B$ is shaded *twice*, once from A and once from B. Thus to find the number of elements in $A \cup B$, we can calculate $n(A) + n(B)$. *But* we have to subtract $n(A \cap B)$ so that we do not count the elements in $A \cap B$ twice. Hence $n(A \cup B) = n(A) + n(B) - n(A \cap B)$ for sets A and B.

In Example 11.7, events A and C are disjoint, or **mutually exclusive.** That is, they have no outcomes in common. In such cases, $P(A \cup C) = P(A) + P(C)$, since $A \cap C = \emptyset$. Verify this in Example 11.7. Also, observe that $P(C) + P(\overline{C}) = 1$. Occasionally, it is simpler to compute the probability of an event indirectly, using the complement. That is, $P(C) = 1 - P(\overline{C})$.

NCTM Standards 2000
Data Analysis and
Probability
Grades 6–8
All students should understand
and use appropriate terminology
to describe complementary and
mutually exclusive events.

We can summarize our observations about probabilities as follows.

PROPERTY

Properties of Probability

1. For any event A, $0 \le P(A) \le 1$.

2. $P(\varnothing) = 0$.

3. $P(S) = 1$, where S is the sample space.

4. For all events A and B, $P(A \cup B) = P(A) + P(B) - P(A \cap B)$.

5. If $\overline{A}$ denotes the complement of event A, then $P(\overline{A}) = 1 - P(A)$.

Observe in item 4, when $A \cap B = \varnothing$, that is, A and B are mutually exclusive, we have $P(A \cup B) - P(A) + P(B)$. The properties of probability apply to all experiments and sample spaces.

Finally, let's consider the case when the outcomes are *not* equally likely. For example, what if the regions on a spinner are not the same size.

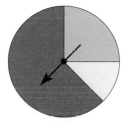

(a)

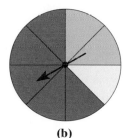

(b)

Figure 11.8

Example 11.8 For the spinner in Figure 11.8(a), what is the probability of pointing to the blue region?

Solution Since the regions are not the same size, it cannot be said that the probability of pointing to the blue region is one out of three. It is clear that the probability of pointing to the blue is greater than half, but how much greater? Because each of the outcomes red, green, and blue are not equally likely, we cannot use the sample space $S = \{R, G, B\}$ to compute the probability. We can, however, determine some type of ratio for the probability. In this case, the spinner can be divided into eight equally shaped and sized regions [see Figure 11.8(b)]. Since five of the eight equally sized regions are blue, we know that the probability of pointing to a blue is the ratio of blue regions to total regions which is $\frac{5}{8}$. ■

Example 11.9 A bag of candy contains 6 red gumballs, 3 green gumballs, and 2 blue gumballs. If one gumball is drawn from the bag, what is the probability that it will be red?

Solution If we try to approach this problem using the sample space $S = \{R, G, B\}$, difficulties arise because there are a different number of each color of gumball. While we could write the sample space in a different way, it is simpler to view this probability as a ratio of gumballs of interest (red) to total gumballs. Since there are 6 red gumballs and a total of 11 gumballs altogether, the probability of getting a red gumball is $\frac{6}{11}$. ■

In summary, probabilities are computed by determining a ratio of the number of objects of interest compared to total number of objects. In some cases this ratio can be determined directly. In other cases, we may list the sample space to ensure that we have accounted for all possible outcomes.

MATHEMATICAL MORSEL

The following true story was reported in a newspaper article. A teacher was giving a standardized true/false achievement test when she noticed that Johnny was busily flipping a coin in the back of the room and then marking his answers. When asked what he was doing he replied, "I didn't have time to study, so instead I'm using a coin. If it comes up heads, I mark true, and if it comes up tails, I mark false." Half an hour later, when the rest of the students were done, the teacher saw Johnny still flipping away. She asked, "Johnny, what's taking you so long?" He replied, "It's like you always tell us. I'm just checking my answers."

Section 11.1 EXERCISE / PROBLEM SET A

EXERCISES

1. According to the weather report, there is a 20% chance of snow in the county tomorrow. Which of the following statements would be appropriate?

   a. Out of the next five days, it will snow one of those days.

   b. Of the 24 hours, snow will fall for 4.8 hours.

   c. Of past days when conditions were similar, one out of five had some snow.

   d. It will snow on 20% of the area of the county.

2. List the elements of the sample space for each of the following experiments.

   a. A quarter is tossed.

   b. A single die is rolled with faces labeled A, B, C, D, E, and F.

   c. A regular tetrahedron die (with four faces labeled 1, 2, 3, 4) is rolled and the number on the bottom face is recorded.

   d. The following "red-blue-yellow" spinner is spun once. (All sectors are equal in size and shape.)

   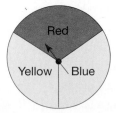

3. An experiment consists of tossing four coins. List each of the following.

   a. The sample space

   b. The event of a head on the first coin

   c. The event of three heads

   d. The event of a head or a tail on the fourth coin

   e. The event of a head on the second coin and a tail on the third coin

4. An experiment consists of tossing a regular dodecahedron die (with 12 congruent faces). List the following.

   a. The sample space

   b. The event of an even number

   c. The event of a number less than 8

   d. The event of a number divisible by 2 and 3

   e. The event of a number greater than 12

5. Identify which of the following events are certain (C), possible (P), or impossible (I).

   a. You throw a 2 on a die.

   b. A student in this class is less than 2 years old.

   c. Next week has only 5 days.

6. One way to find the sample space of an experiment involving two parts is to use the Cartesian product. For example, an experiment consists of tossing a dime and a quarter.

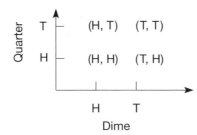

Sample space for dime $D = \{H, T\}$
Sample space for quarter $Q = \{H, T\}$

The sample space of the experiment is

$$D \times Q = \{(H, H), (H, T), (T, H), (T, T)\}.$$

Using this method, construct the sample space of the following experiment.

Toss a coin and roll a tetrahedron die (four faces).

7. A die is rolled 60 times with the following results recorded.

OUTCOME	1	2	3	4	5	6
FREQUENCY	10	9	10	12	8	11

Find the experimental probability of the following events.

a. Getting a 4

b. Getting an odd number

c. Getting a number greater than 3

8. Refer to Example 11.5 which gives the sample space for the experiment of rolling two dice, and give the probabilities of the following events.

a. A 4 on the second die

b. An even number on each die

c. At least 7 dots in total

d. A total of 15 dots

e. A total greater than 1

9. A dropped thumbtack will land point up or point down.

a. Do you think one outcome will happen more often than the other? Which one?

b. The results for tossing a thumbtack 60 times are as follows.

Point up: 42 times
Point down: 18 times

What is the experimental probability that it lands point up? point down?

c. If the thumbtack was tossed 100 times, about how many times would you expect it to land point up? point down?

10. You have a key ring with five keys on it.

a. One of the keys is a car key. What is the probability of picking that one?

b. Two of the keys are for your apartment. What is the probability of selecting an apartment key?

c. What is the probability of selecting either the car key or an apartment key?

d. What is the probability of selecting neither the car key nor an apartment key?

11. Two dice are thrown. If each face is equally likely to turn up, find the following probabilities.

a. The sum is even.

b. The sum is not 10.

c. The sum is a prime.

d. The sum is less than 9.

e. The sum is not less than 9.

12. What is the probability of getting yellow on each of the following spinners?

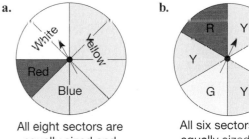

a. All eight sectors are equally sized and shaped.

b. All six sectors are equally sized and shaped.

13. A die is made that has two faces marked with 2s, three faces marked with 3s, and one face marked with a 5. If this die is thrown once, find the following probabilities.

a. Getting a 2

b. Not getting a 2

c. Getting an odd number

d. Not getting an odd number

14. A card is drawn from a standard deck of cards. Find $P(A \cup B)$ in each part.

a. $A = \{\text{getting a black card}\}, B = \{\text{getting a heart}\}$

b. $A = \{\text{getting a diamond}\}, \quad B = \{\text{getting an ace}\}$

c. $A = \{\text{getting a face card}\}, \quad B = \{\text{getting a spade}\}$

d. $A = \{\text{getting a face card}\}, \quad B = \{\text{getting a 7}\}$

15. With the spinner in Example 11.2(c), spin twice and record the color on each spin. For this experiment, consider the sample space and following events.

A: getting a green on the first spin
B: getting a yellow on the second spin
$A \cup B$: getting a green on the first spin or a yellow on the second spin

$$A$$

	RR	YR	GR	BR
B	RY	YY	GY	BY
	RG	YG	GG	BG
	RB	YB	GB	BB

Verify the following:

$$n(S) = 16, n(A) = 4, n(B) = 4$$
$$n(A \cup B) = 7, n(A \cap B) = 1$$
$$P(A) = \frac{4}{16}, P(B) = \frac{4}{16},$$
$$P(A \cup B) = \frac{7}{16}, \text{ and } P(A \cap B) = \frac{1}{16}.$$

Show that $P(A \cup B) = P(A) + P(B) - P(A \cap B)$. Apply this to find $P(A \cup B)$ in the following cases.

a. A: getting a red on first spin
B: getting same color on both spins

b. A: getting a yellow or blue on first spin
B: getting a red or green on second spin

16. For the experiment in Problem 15 where a spinner is spun twice, consider the following events:

A: getting a blue on the first spin
B: getting a yellow on one spin
C: getting the same color on both spins

Describe the following events and find their probabilities.

a. $A \cup B$ **b.** $B \cap C$ **c.** $\overline{B}$

17. A student is selected at random. Let A be the event that the selected student is a sophomore and B be the event that the selected student is taking English. Write in words what is meant by each of the following probabilities.

a. $P(A \cup B)$ **b.** $P(A \cap B)$ **c.** $1 - P(A)$

PROBLEMS

18. Two fair six-sided dice are rolled and the sum of the dots on the top faces is recorded.

a. Complete the table, showing the number of ways each sum can occur.

SUM	2	3	4	5	6	7	8	9	10	11	12
WAYS	1	2	3								

b. Use the table to find the probability of the following events.

A: The sum is prime.
B: The sum is a divisor of 12.
C: The sum is a power of 2.
D: The sum is greater than 3.

19. The probability of a "geometric" event involving the concept of measure (length, area, volume) is determined as follows. Let $m(A)$ and $m(S)$ represent the measures of the event A and the sample space S, respectively. Then

$$P(A) = \frac{m(A)}{m(S)}.$$

For example, in the first figure, if the length of S is 12 cm and the length of A is 4 cm, then $P(A) = \frac{4}{12} = \frac{1}{3}$. Similarly, in the second figure, if the area of region B is 10 cm² and the area of region S is 60 cm², then $P(B) = \frac{10}{60} = \frac{1}{6}$.

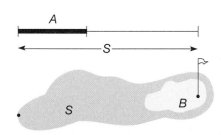

A bus travels between Albany and Binghamton, a distance of 100 miles. If the bus has broken down, we want to find the probability that it has broken down within 10 miles of either city.

a. The road from Albany to Binghamton is the sample space. What is $m(S)$?

b. Event A is that part of the road within 10 miles of either city. What is $m(A)$?

c. Find $P(A)$.

20. The dartboard illustrated is made up of circles with radii of 1, 2, 3, and 4 units. A dart hits the target randomly. What is the probability that the dart hits the bull's-eye? (*Hint*: The area of a circle with radius r is πr^2.)

Section 11.1 EXERCISE / PROBLEM SET B

EXERCISES

1. For visiting a resort area you will receive a special gift.

CATEGORY I	CATEGORY II	CATEGORY III
A. New car	D. 25-inch color TV	G. Meat smoker
B. Food processor	E. AM/FM stereo	H. Toaster oven
C. $2500 cash	F. $1000 cash	I. $25 cash

The probabilities are as follows: A, 1 in 52,000; B, 25,736 in 52,000; C, 1 in 52,000; D, 3 in 52,000; E, 25,736 in 52,000; F, 3 in 52,000; G, 180 in 52,000; H, 180 in 52,000; I, 160 in 52,000.

a. Which gifts are you most likely to receive?

b. Which gifts are you least likely to receive?

c. If 5000 people visit the resort, how many would be expected to receive a new car?

2. List the sample space for each experiment.

a. Tossing a dime and a penny

b. Tossing a nickel and rolling a die

c. Drawing a marble from a bag containing one red and one blue marble and drawing a second marble from a bag containing one green and one white marble

3. A bag contains one each of red, green, blue, yellow, and white marbles. Give the sample space of the following experiments.

a. One marble is drawn.

b. One marble is drawn, then replaced, and a second one is then drawn.

c. One marble is drawn, but not replaced, and a second one is drawn.

4. An experiment consists of tossing a coin and rolling a die. List each of the following.

a. The sample space

b. The event of getting a head

c. The event of getting a 3

d. The event of getting an even number

e. The event of getting a head and a number greater than 4

f. The event of getting a tail or a 5

5. Identify which of the following events are certain (C), possible (P), or impossible (I).

a. There are at least four Sundays this month.

b. It will rain today.

c. You throw a head on a die.

6. Use the Cartesian product to construct the sample space of the following experiment:

Toss a coin, and draw a marble from a bag containing purple, green, and yellow marbles.

7. A loaded die (one in which outcomes are not equally likely) is tossed 1000 times with the following results.

OUTCOME	1	2	3	4	5	6
NUMBER OF TIMES	125	75	350	250	150	50

Find the experimental probability of the following events.

a. Getting a 2   **b.** Getting a 5

c. Getting a 1 or a 5   **d.** Getting an even number

8. Refer to Example 11.4, in which three fair coins are tossed. Assign theoretical probabilities to the following events.

a. Getting a head on the first coin

b. Getting a head on the first coin and a tail on the second coin

c. Getting at least one tail

d. Getting exactly one tail

9. A snack pack of colored candies contained the following:

COLOR	Brown	Tan	Yellow	Green	Orange
NUMBER	7	3	5	3	4

One candy is selected at random. Find the probability that it is of the following color.

a. Brown   **b.** Tan

c. Yellow   **d.** Green

e. Not brown   **f.** Yellow or orange

10. An American roulette wheel has 38 slots around the rim. Two of them are numbered 0 and 00 and are green; the others are numbered from 1 to 36 and half are red, half are black. As the wheel is spun in one direction, a small ivory ball is rolled along the rim in the opposite direction. The ball has an equally likely chance of falling into any one of the 38 slots, assuming that the wheel is fair. Find the probability of each of the following.

a. The ball lands on 0 or 00.

b. The ball lands on 23.

c. The ball lands on a red number.

d. The ball does not land on 20–36.

e. The ball lands on an even number or a green slot.

11. A card is drawn at random from a deck of 52 playing cards. What is the probability of drawing each of the following?

a. A black card   **b.** A face card

c. Not a face card   **d.** A black face card

e. A black or a face card

f. An ace or a face card

g. Neither an ace nor a face card

h. Not an ace

12. A spinner with three equally sized and shaped sectors is spun once.

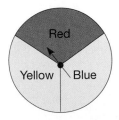

a. What is the probability of spinning red (R)?

b. What is the probability of spinning blue (B)?

c. What is the probability of spinning yellow (Y)?

d. Here the sample space is divided into three different events, R, B, and Y. Find the sum, $P(R) + P(B) + P(Y)$.

e. Repeat the preceding parts with the spinner with eight sectors of equal size and shape. Do you get the same result as in part (d)?

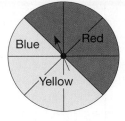

13. One die is thrown. If each face is equally likely to turn up, find the following probabilities.

a. Getting a 6   **b.** Not getting a 6

c. An even number turning up

d. An even number not turning up

e. The number dividing 6

f. The number not dividing 6

14. A bag contains six balls on which are the letters a, a, a, b, b, and c. One ball is drawn at random from the bag. Let A, B, and C be the events that balls a, b, or c are drawn, respectively.

a. What is $P(A)$?   **b.** What is $P(B)$?

c. What is $P(C)$?   **d.** Find $P(A) + P(B) + P(C)$.

e. An unknown number of balls, each lettered c, are added to the bag. It is known that now $P(A) = \frac{1}{4}$ and $P(B) = \frac{1}{6}$. What is $P(C)$?

15. Consider the experiment in Example 11.4 where three coins are tossed. Consider the following events:

> A: The number of heads is 3.
> B: The number of heads is 2.
> C: The second coin lands heads.

Describe the following events and find their probabilities.

a. $A \cup B$ **b.** $\overline{B}$ **c.** $\overline{C}$ **d.** $B \cap C$

16. A bag contains 2 red balls, 3 blue balls, and 1 yellow ball.

a. What is the probability of drawing a red ball?

b. How many red balls must be added to the bag so that the probability of drawing a red ball is $\frac{1}{2}$?

c. How many blue balls must be added to the bag so that the probability of drawing a red ball is $\frac{1}{5}$?

17. What is false about the following statements?

a. Since there are 50 states, the probability of being born in Pennsylvania is $\frac{1}{50}$.

b. The probability that I am taking math is 0.80 and the probability that I am taking English is 0.50, so the probability that I am taking math and/or English is 1.30.

c. The probability that the basketball team wins its next game is $\frac{1}{3}$; the probability that it loses is $\frac{1}{2}$.

d. The probability that I get an A in this course is 1.5.

PROBLEMS

18. A bag contains an unknown number of balls, some red, some blue, and some green. Find the smallest number of balls in the bag if the following probabilities are given. Give the P(green) for each situation.

   a. $P(\text{red}) = \frac{1}{6}$, $P(\text{blue}) = \frac{1}{3}$

   b. $P(\text{red}) = \frac{3}{5}$, $P(\text{blue}) - \frac{1}{6}$

   c. $P(\text{red}) = \frac{1}{5}$, $P(\text{blue}) = \frac{3}{4}$

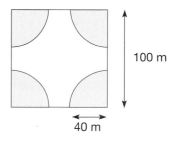

100 m

40 m

19. A paraglider wants to land in the unshaded region in the square field illustrated, since the shaded regions (four quarter circles) are briar patches. If he lost control and was going to hit the field randomly, what is the probability that he would miss the briar patch?

20. A microscopic worm is eating its way around the inside of a spherical apple of radius 6 cm. What is the probability that the worm is within 1 cm of the surface of the apple? (*Hint*: $V = \frac{4}{3}\pi r^3$, where r is the radius.)

PROBLEMS FOR WRITING/DISCUSSION

1. James says that if there are two children in a family, then there are two girls, two boys, or one of each. So each of the three possibilities must have a probability of 1/3. Do you agree with James? Explain.

2. Melissa was tossing a quarter to try to determine the odds of getting heads after a certain number of tosses. She got five tails in a row! Jennifer said, "You are sure to get heads on the next toss!" Karen said, "No, she's

definitely going to get tails!" Explain the reasoning of each of these students. Do you agree with either one? Explain.

3. Shirley's parents are taking her to New Orleans for a week. At the time of year they are going, the probability of rain on any given day is 40%. Shirley says that means there is a 60% chance it will not rain the whole week she is there. Do you agree? Explain.

11.2 PROBABILITY AND COMPLEX EXPERIMENTS

STARTING POINT

Two red cubes, one white cube, and one blue cube are placed in a box. One cube is randomly drawn, its color is recorded, and it is returned to the box. A second cube is drawn and its color recorded. What is the probability of drawing a blue and a red cube? (*Hint*: Since order is not specified, this could be a ßR or an Rß.)

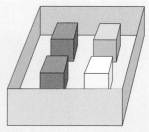

Tree Diagrams and Counting Techniques

In some experiments it is inefficient to list all the outcomes in the sample space. Therefore, we develop alternative procedures to compute probabilities.

    A **tree diagram** can be used to represent the outcomes of an experiment. The experiment of drawing two marbles, one at a time, from a jar of four marbles without replacement, which was illustrated in Example 11.6, can be conveniently represented by the outcome tree diagram shown in Figure 11.9.

    The diagram in Figure 11.9 shows that there are 12 outcomes in the sample space, since there are 12 right-hand endpoints on the tree. Those 12 outcomes are the same